Mervyn Ewart
O.A.C. -44.

Pro-Meds.

frontispiece

Journal of Chemical Education

JACOBUS HENRICUS VAN'T HOFF

Because of van't Hoff's important and fundamental contributions to the subject, he has often been referred to as "the father of physical chemistry."

(*For biographical note see page 267.*)

PHYSICAL CHEMISTRY

By

FRANK THOMSON GUCKER, JR.
Associate Professor of Chemistry
Northwestern University

And

WILLIAM BUELL MELDRUM
Professor of Chemistry
Haverford College

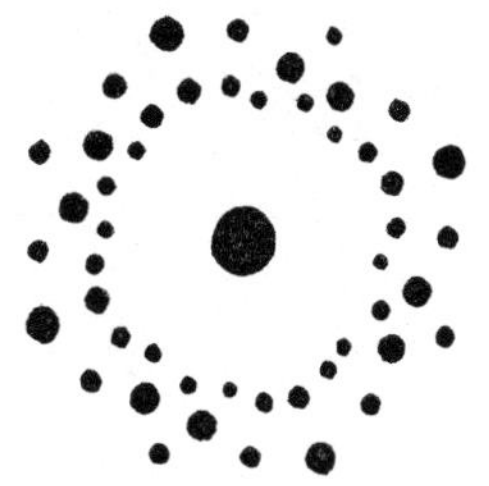

AMERICAN BOOK COMPANY

NEW YORK CINCINNATI CHICAGO
BOSTON ATLANTA DALLAS SAN FRANCISCO

E. P. 1
Gucker & Meldrum, Physical Chemistry
MADE IN U.S.A.

PREFACE

This book is designed as a text for the first course in physical chemistry. It is intended to acquaint the student with the experimental basis of the science, familiarize him with the modern theoretical explanation of these facts, show him some of the problems to which physicochemical principles have been applied in many fields of chemistry and related sciences, and give him a reasonable facility in handling similar problems. A satisfactory introductory text cannot be merely descriptive; it must include the application of mathematical logic to the experimental facts. A student with a good knowledge of the calculus will obtain a more complete mastery of physical chemistry than one without such knowledge, but the text is so arranged that, by making suitable omissions, reference to the calculus can be completely avoided in a course for students without the requisite mathematical background. The significance of differentials and the process of integration are explained briefly in chapter 1, since the use of differentials is essential to the clear presentation of certain topics and for the derivation of certain formulas which otherwise must be taken on faith by the student. Most of those derivations which require the use of integration and the solving of differential equations have been brought together in the final chapter on thermodynamics and mathematical derivations.

Students elect the study of physical chemistry for a variety of reasons. Some intend to become professional chemists or chemical engineers; others are interested in the application of physical chemistry in a career of botany, geology, physics, or some other related science; many take it as part of their preparation for the study of medicine or dentistry. The authors share the opinion expressed by teachers of chemistry in the colleges and of physiological chemistry in the medical schools, that all of these students of physical chemistry, whatever the field of their future specialization, should master the *basic principles of physical chemistry*, rather than seek to anticipate too much the application of these principles to the specific problems of their intended professions, of which they have, at present, too limited a knowledge. Consequently, this book is devoted to the discussion of the principles of physical chemistry and their development, with reference to topics in other fields only when they serve to illustrate physicochemical principles.

In order to give the student an adequate understanding of the methods of physical chemistry, emphasis is laid upon the experimental facts and the laboratory procedures by which they are obtained. Many drawings and a number of photographs of apparatus add to the clarity of the presentation. Graphs are used extensively to help the student understand the significance of physicochemical relationships and to familiarize him with this extremely valuable method of studying physicochemical data. Problems and exercises at the end of most of the chapters serve to test the student's mastery of the subject and enable him to obtain a better understanding of the principles than is possible by study of the text alone. Reading lists at the end of the chapters indicate where one may go for further information on particular topics; the scope of each of these references is indicated. A list of symbols will be found in the Appendix for the convenience of easy reference. Finally, the photographs of some of those physical chemists who have been most instrumental in developing the science, and biographical sketches of these men and a number of others, serve to make the student conscious of the historical background of physical chemistry.

The content of the book is sufficiently complete for a full year course or, by a proper selection of topics, it may readily be adapted to a one-semester course such as that frequently given to premedical students or to combined classes of premedical students and chemists. Discussion of the proposed text with friends in the medical schools and colleges convinced the authors that there is no definite set of topics generally recognized as "premedical physical chemistry." The choice of topics for a one-semester course remains largely an individual matter on the part of the instructor. Realizing this fact, the authors have sought to provide a wide range of choice so that certain topics could be omitted without serious impairment of continuity. The authors are of the opinion, also, that the student who can take only a one-semester course in physical chemistry will benefit by having a book somewhat more comprehensive than that required for the immediate needs of the course, since he will find it very useful later for reference in his graduate or professional training.

A one-semester course for premedical students should include as many as possible of the topics having direct application to physiological chemistry, physiology, and other subjects in the curriculum of the medical school. Such a course should include, for example, the study of osmotic pressure, *p*H, indicators, adsorption, colloids, and enzymes, which are covered in chapters 10, 16 to 19, and 21, of the text. Preparation for these topics would require the study of at least some sections of other chapters, such as chapter 3 on the structure of atoms and molecules, chapter 6 on liquids, chapter 8 on thermochemistry, chapter 9 on solutions of nonelectrolytes, chapter 11 on reaction kinetics, chapter 12 on the ionic theory, and chapter 13 on ionic equilibria, including hydrolysis and the behavior of ampholytes.

Where a one-semester course is given to a class including students majoring in chemistry or chemical engineering, as well as premedical students, most teachers would prefer to omit some of the topics suggested above, in order to include chapters 4 and 5 on gases, chapter 14 on electrolytic conductance, and chapter 15 on electromotive force.

The detailed table of contents will be found a useful aid in mapping out such a one-semester course. Also, the authors will be glad to furnish, upon request, a detailed outline for a one-semester course of any special type.

The authors wish to express their indebtedness to the many who have aided them in the preparation of the book. They wish particularly to express their appreciation to the following: Dr. D. Wright Wilson, of the Medical School, University of Pennsylvania, Dr. J. S. Hepburn, of Hahnemann Medical College, Dr. C. R. Hoover, of Wesleyan University, Dr. H. M. Chadwell, of Tufts College, and Drs. J. B. Zinn and C. A. Sloat, of Gettysburg College, for advice regarding the content of the proposed book; Drs. T. O. Jones and W. E. Cadbury, Jr., of Haverford College, and Drs. Arthur Frost, Robert Burwell, Malcolm Dole, and Irving M. Klotz, of Northwestern University, for reading and criticizing certain chapters; Mr. H. P. Thomas, formerly of Haverford College, for aid in collecting data on atomic weights; Dr. Ernst A. Hauser, of the Massachusetts Institute of Technology, for photographs of the formation of drops; Dr. John Swartout, formerly of Northwestern University, for the photograph of the du Noüy ring; Dr. Sterling B. Hendricks, of the Department of Agriculture, for the photograph of the Laue spots; Dr. George L. Clark, of the University of Illinois, for X-ray photographs; Dr. J. W. Williams, of the University of Wisconsin, for the photographs of the ultracentrifuge and the sedimentation of proteins; Dr. Arnold O. Beckman, of the National Technical Laboratories of Pasadena, for the picture of a *p*H meter; the Leeds and Northrup Company, of Philadelphia, for illustrations of the conductance and electromotive force apparatus; the Bausch and Lomb Optical Company, of Rochester, for the illustration of a colorimeter; Dr. N. W. Rakestraw, of Brown University, Editor of the *Journal of Chemical Education,* and Mr. Harvey J. Mack, of Easton, Pa., for the loan of cuts of portraits; Dr. Frederick G. Keyes, of the Massachusetts Institute of Technology, for the portrait of Arthur A. Noyes; Mr. Charles Eckert and Mr. Frank Lamb, of Northwestern University, for assistance in checking the problems; and Eléonore H. Gucker, for assistance in reading proof and preparing the index.

TABLE OF CONTENTS

CHAPTER 1

INTRODUCTION

A knowledge of the principles of *physical chemistry* is an important aid in the study of almost any field of natural science. It is essential to a real understanding of many of the problems of the worker in pure chemistry, the industrial chemist, the chemical engineer, and the physician. The subject cannot be regarded as a simple one, for it applies to many different properties and phenomena. The student should realize, however, that it deals primarily with *general principles*, and he should seek to study these general principles against the background of facts which he has acquired in earlier courses in chemistry.

The Scope of Physical Chemistry. ***Physical chemistry*** *may be defined as the systematic application of physical methods and physical concepts to the study of chemical systems.* It classifies and correlates the properties of substances and the phenomena observed in chemical processes and thus establishes the *laws* which describe in general terms the relations and behavior of substances. In addition to this integration of factual knowledge, physical chemistry develops *theories* which enable us to picture why substances have certain properties or why they behave as they do. Thus the factual generalizations are explained, and the logical prediction of hitherto unstudied properties or behavior is made possible. In this way, empiricism (the method of trial and error) has largely disappeared from chemistry.

Physical chemistry deals with such topics as the following: The composition and structure of matter; the states of matter and changes in state; relations between the properties and the composition of substances; the properties of solutions of nonelectrolytes and of electrolytes; homogeneous and heterogeneous equilibria; reaction kinetics; electrochemistry; thermal effects of changes and the applications of thermodynamics.

The study of chemical reactions and chemical reactivity has followed, mainly, two lines of attack: (1) The *kinetic* approach explains reactions by a mechanical picture which involves molecular motion in accordance with the kinetic theory. The kinetic theory, ignoring the complexities of nature, yields mathematical generalizations which are extremely useful even though they are only approximately valid. (2) The *thermodynamic*, or mathematical, approach, on the other hand, involves the precise measurement of energy changes and other phenomena and the discovery of mathematical equations which may accurately predict new relationships. Thus it aims to express chemical reactivity and other properties in terms of precise mathematics.

The Scientific Method. The progress of physical chemistry, like that of science in general, has been favored by the application of the **scientific method.** This involves usually the following steps: (1) By experience or by planned experiment, *facts* regarding the properties or behavior of matter are accumulated. (2) These isolated facts are correlated and *classified.* (3) When a number of facts have been correlated and placed within a single class, then a general statement covering the class may be made; this *generalization*, if it is of sufficient scope or importance, may be termed a *law.* (4) To explain the general behavior as expressed in the law, a possible mechanism or picture is imagined. If this mechanism or picture is merely an intelligent guess, it is termed a *hypothesis;* if it has reasonable substantiation in fact, it is termed a *theory. Deductions* are drawn from the postulates of the theory, mathematically or otherwise, and the correctness of these deductions is tested by experiment; if the deductions prove to be correct, the theory itself is verified.

The application of the scientific method as a guiding principle in chemistry is illustrated by the development of such laws and theories as the *periodic law*, the *kinetic theory of gases*, the *ionic theory*, the *law of mass action*, and the *laws of thermodynamics.* The growth of each of these extended over many years, and its detailed study, with the scientific method in mind, would well repay the student. In each case he would find that the accumulation of facts was followed by classification, generalization, and the statement of one or more laws; then the enunciation of a theory to explain the correlated facts; and finally the experimental testing of deductions from the theory. The testing of a theory not only clarifies and refines the postulates of the theory but also points the way for advancement in new directions. Every one of our important physicochemical theories has been altered as a result of such experimental testing.

Development of Physical Chemistry. *Physical chemistry* was not recognized as a separate branch of the science until late in the nineteenth century, although actually it began much earlier. During the past few decades it has extended so widely that it has been subdivided into several other branches, such as *colloid chemistry, reaction kinetics, electrochemistry,* and *chemical thermodynamics,* each of which has assumed the magnitude of a science in itself. We shall trace here, very briefly, the development of knowledge on certain topics and urge that the student supplement this by reading some more complete treatise.[1]

Gases. In 1662 Robert Boyle stated his famous law, and a few years later, in 1678, Robert Hooke suggested that a gas consists of molecules in motion, thus laying the foundation stone of the *kinetic theory.* The work of Charles in 1787, with that of Gay-Lussac in 1802, established the second of the gas laws, $V = kT$. Dalton's law of partial pressures was published in 1801. In 1808 Gay-Lussac summarized the studies of Humboldt, Davy, and Berthollet, as well as his own, on the reactions among gases, in his *law of reacting volumes.* In 1811 Avogadro enunciated his hypothesis, which later found important application. In 1829 Thomas Graham announced the *law of gaseous diffusion.* The further development of the *kinetic theory* by Clausius, Krönig, Clerk Maxwell, and others provided a clear picture of the constitution of a gas and of its behavior. From it the various *gas laws* could be deduced by mathematical reasoning, as could also *Avogadro's hypothesis.* This deduction, coupled with the successful application of the hypothesis by Cannizzaro in working out a consistent system of atomic and molecular weights in 1860, ensured its general acceptance as a *law.* In 1873 J. H. van der Waals derived his well-known equation to account for observed deviations of gases from the simple gas laws. In 1865 Loschmidt, at Vienna, made the first determination of the number of molecules in a given volume of gas, obtaining the value 2.7×10^{19} in 1 cc. under standard conditions. This agrees well with the results obtained more recently by many different methods. The *liquefaction* of various gases was accomplished by Faraday and others early in the nineteenth century. The study of *critical temperatures* and the *Joule-Thomson effect* has led to the liquefaction of even the most permanent gases, hydrogen and helium.

[1] See reading list at end of chapter, page 14.

The Elements. Lavoisier, adopting Boyle's concept of an element as a simple substance, made a clear distinction between *element* and *compound.* The study of the proportions in which elements combine led John Dalton to enunciate, in 1808, his *atomic theory,* which encouraged an active study of the known elements. This study, together with *Prout's hypothesis,* 1815, impelled an analytical examination of minerals by Berzelius, Dumas, and others, which resulted in the addition of 24 elements by 1830. In 1860 the invention of the *spectroscope,* by Bunsen and Kirchhoff, provided a new tool for analytical research, which soon brought to light a number of new elements. The *periodic table* and the *periodic law,* enunciated by Mendeléeff in 1867, correlated the properties of known elements and indicated the existence of others then undiscovered. Between 1890 and 1900 Ramsay added an entire new group to the periodic table by the discovery of the rare gases of the atmosphere, and during the same decade the first of the radioactive elements were identified. The study of characteristic X-ray spectra, begun by Moseley in 1913, has proved an extremely sensitive and absolutely reliable way of determining the existence of elements and their places in the periodic table.

Solutions. The study of *solutions,* especially aqueous ones, has been particularly important in the development of physical chemistry. *Electrolytic properties* were extensively examined early in the nineteenth century, but the systematic study of the colligative properties, *freezing-point depression, boiling-point elevation, vapor pressure lowering,* and *osmotic pressure,* was not undertaken until after 1870. This work culminated in the enunciation of the *ionic theory* by Arrhenius in 1887.

Since 1887, physical chemists have sought to test and to extend the ionic theory, and they are continuing intensive research on electrolytic properties of solutions today. The study of the ionization constants of weak electrolytes and *hydrogen-ion concentration,* the development of the concept of *activity,* and the theory of *interionic attraction* are a few of the important results of later research. References to these developments are made in appropriate places in the text.

Reaction Kinetics. As early as 1777 Wenzel, a foundry chemist at Freiberg, stated that the rate of solution of a metal was increased by increasing the amount of acid. However, there was no systematic investigation of the influence of the mass of a reagent on

facing page 4 *Journal of Chemical Education*

Plate I. FRANÇOIS MARIE RAOULT

(*For biographical note see page 233.*)

reaction rate until the middle of the nineteenth century. In 1850 Wilhelmy, at Heidelberg, showed that the rate of inversion of cane sugar in the presence of acid was proportional to the quantity of sugar in a given volume of solution. Berthelot and others studied the rates of esterification of alcohols and showed that Wilhelmy's mathematical expression applied to such reactions also.

In 1867 Guldberg and Waage stated their *law of mass action;* independently, van't Hoff in 1877 discovered the same generalization and demonstrated the applicability of the law to reactions of different *orders.* He emphasized the importance of the *velocity constant* as a measure of chemical affinity. In 1889 Arrhenius derived a mathematical expression for the effect of temperature on reaction velocity, introducing the concept of *energy of activation.* The proportions of reactants present at equilibrium in a reversible reaction were studied by Berthelot and St. Gilles in 1863; by Guldberg and Waage in 1867; and by van't Hoff in 1877. Van't Hoff clearly stated that in a reversible reaction a condition of equilibrium means equality of opposing velocities.

Thermodynamics. Coincident with the growth of the knowledge of chemical reactivity from the standpoint of *kinetics* there developed the science of *thermodynamics.* In 1824 Carnot, a French army officer, studied the extent to which heat could be transformed into useful work. This study was further advanced by Clapeyron, at Paris, and by Clausius, at Zurich. In 1842 the *first law of thermodynamics* (the *law of conservation of energy*) was announced. In the same year Clausius and William Thomson (Lord Kelvin), at Glasgow, deduced the *second law of thermodynamics.* Reasoning from the *second law,* J. Willard Gibbs in 1876 derived the extremely important generalization known as the *phase rule,* which was first applied to chemical systems by Roozeboom in 1888.

In 1884 Le Chatelier, Professor of Chemistry at Paris, pointed out the effects which alteration of pressure, concentration, or temperature, would have on a given reacting system, and thus introduced the generalization, important both in industrial chemistry and in pure science, known as the *principle of Le Chatelier.*

The genius of van't Hoff brought thermodynamics to bear on equilibria in chemical systems in general. Among numerous important contributions two deserve special mention: (1) the mathematical relation between the equilibrium constant and the heat of reaction which permits the calculation of the quantitative effect upon the equilibrium proportions in a system when the temperature is changed; (2) the principle that the *maximum external work* obtainable from a chemical reaction may be taken as a quantitative measure of *chemical affinity.* Since the time of van't Hoff the thermodynamic relations in systems involving differences of electrical potential, *i.e.*, galvanic cells, have been intensively studied.

The Use of Mathematics in Physical Chemistry. *Mathematics may be defined as the science which treats of the exact relations between magnitudes and operations, and of the methods by which other magnitudes are deduced from those known or assumed.* Mathematics, it might be said, is logic in its exact form. Mathematical deductions, however, are no more correct than the premises upon which they are based. Naturally the chemist, in developing chemistry according to the scientific method and in seeking to make chemistry *an exact science,* favors a mathematical treatment of data and generalizations whenever this is practicable. The development of new forms of apparatus and more refined technique has provided more numerous and more accurate experimental data for the more fruitful application of mathematics. Hence, the aim of the physical chemist to state the laws of chemistry in precise mathematical equations has been accomplished to a marked degree. Furthermore, such equations can be transformed or combined by the ordinary mathematical processes to deduce other relationships, which may be verified by subsequent experimentation, thus pointing the way to a more complete understanding of nature and her laws.

Three mathematical tools of especial usefulness in physical chemistry will be discussed briefly. They are logarithms, the calculus, and graphical representation.

(1) Logarithms. The use of logarithms is a time saver in calculations involving the multiplication or division of several large numbers, and a necessity in certain other calculations. Since *logarithms* are treated in courses in elementary mathematics, here we need only recall to the student the meaning of the terms and symbols used.

The **common logarithm** *of a number* A, designated by $\log A$, *is the power to which 10 must be raised in order to give the number.* Thus, if $A = 10^n$, then $\log A = n$. For example, $\log 1000 =$

$\log 10^3 = 3$; $\log 10 = 1$; $\log 1 = 0$; $\log 0.0001 = \log 10^{-4} = -4$. Similarly, the logarithm of 248.7 is 2.3957; this means that $248.7 = 10^{2.3957}$. In the logarithm last mentioned, 2.3957, the number to the left of the decimal point, 2, is called the *characteristic* of the logarithm, and the number to the right of the decimal point, 3957, is called the *mantissa*. The *characteristic* indicates the position of the decimal point in the number and is readily found by inspection. Thus, if the number is between 1 and 10, the characteristic is 0; if between 10 and 100, it is 1; if between 100 and 1000, it is 2; if between 0.0001 and 0.001, it is -4; and so on. The logarithm of a number less than 1 is usually written with a negative characteristic but a positive mantissa. Thus, $\log 0.001763 = \log (1.763 \times 10^{-3})$. This may be written $\bar{3}.2462$ or, better, $7.2462 - 10$. In tables of logarithms, such as that found on pages 654–655, only the mantissas are listed.

In using logarithms the following formulas find frequent application:

(1) The logarithm of a product:

$$\log AB = \log A + \log B$$

(2) The logarithm of a fraction:

$$\log \frac{A}{B} = \log A - \log B$$

(3) The logarithm of a number raised to a given power n:

$$\log A^n = n \log A$$

(4) The logarithm of a given root of a number:

$$\log \sqrt[n]{A} = \frac{1}{n} \log A$$

To illustrate the method of using logarithms in calculations, let us consider an example: What volume will 374.5 ml. of oxygen, measured at 395 mm. pressure and at 25° C., occupy at S.T.P.[1]? Using the formula,

$$V = V_1 \times \frac{P_1}{P} \times \frac{T}{T_1}$$

we have:

$$V = 374.5 \times \tfrac{395}{760} \times \tfrac{273}{298} \text{ ml.}$$

Then

$$\log V = \log 374.5 + \log 395 + \log 273 - \log 760 - \log 298$$

[1] Standard temperature and pressure, *i.e.*, 0° C. and 760 mm. of mercury.

Taking the logarithms from the table on pages 654–655 and tabulating them in orderly fashion, the positive ones to the left and the negative ones to the right, we have:

log 374.5 =	2.5735	log 760 =	2.8808
log 395 =	2.5966	log 298 =	2.4742
log 273 =	2.4362	Sum =	5.3550
Sum =	7.6063		
Minus	5.3550		
log V =	2.2513		

From the tables we find that this is the logarithm of 178.4, hence

$$V = 178.4 \text{ ml.}$$

The derivation of physicochemical equations leads, as a rule, to expressions involving not *common logarithms* but *natural logarithms.* These are logarithms referred not to the base 10 but rather to the base e, which has the value 2.7182818 · · · and is the summation of the exponential series, $1 + \frac{1}{\underline{|1}} + \frac{1}{\underline{|2}} + \frac{1}{\underline{|3}} + \cdots$. The logarithm of a number A to the base e is designated by $\log_e A$ or $\ln A$. It is the power to which e must be raised in order to give the number; thus, if $A = e^m$, then $\log_e A$ (or $\ln A$) $= m$.

To change a *common* logarithm to a *natural* logarithm multiply by 2.303; to change a *natural* logarithm to a *common* logarithm divide by 2.303 or multiply by 0.4343, which is equal to $\log_{10} e$.

(2) The calculus. The methods of *the calculus* are widely applied in physical chemistry. Physical chemistry deals not only with chemical systems which are in equilibrium but also with those that are undergoing change with some changing condition. The calculus deals with changes by *infinitesimal increments* and with methods of calculating from them the corresponding changes over *finite increments.* To understand just what this statement means, let us consider a specific example, that of the decomposition, or transmutation, of a radioactive element.

According to the *mass law*, the rate of decomposition is proportional to the amount of the radioactive element present at any instant. As the decomposition proceeds, the amount available and the rate of decomposition, *i.e.*, the amount decomposed in unit time, decrease continuously. We wish to develop an equation which will express the rate at any instant, *e.g.*, at the end of t minutes. The rate r is proportional to the amount of radioactive element x, thus:

$$r = kx$$

where k is the proportionality factor, or *velocity constant.* To calculate the rate by dividing the total change Δx, in Figure 1, by the total time Δt would give the *average* rate over the whole time;

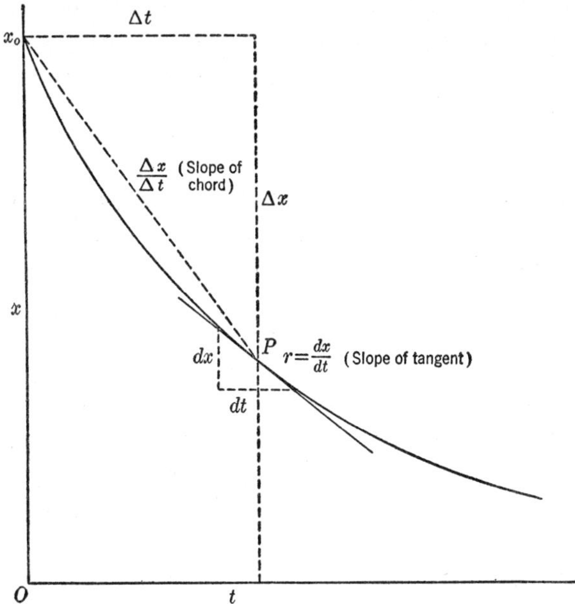

Fig. 1. Using the Calculus to Find the Slope of a Curve.

but this value, $\Delta x/\Delta t$, of the slope of the chord is *greater* than the rate at the time t, which corresponds to the slope of the tangent. If we take points along the curve nearer and nearer to a point P and draw lines parallel to the x and t axes, the ratio $\Delta x/\Delta t$ of the height to the base of the successive triangles (which is equal to the slope of the corresponding chord) will approach more and more closely to the actual rate, which is the slope of the tangent of the curve at P. If, as we approach P, we designate these limiting values of the sides as dx and dt, which are called *differentials,* we can write:

$$r = -\frac{dx}{dt} = kx$$

The negative sign is used because x is *decreasing* as t increases. This expression enables us to determine the rate of the reaction at any given instant if we know k and x, or can find dx/dt.

As already pointed out, dx and dt are too small to be measured, but we can convert this equation involving infinitesimals into another involving finite quantities which expresses the same relationship. This is accomplished by the process known as *integration*, which means finding the equation of a *curve* from that of its *slope* and is the reverse of *differentiation*. The integral sign $\int$ is derived from S for *sum* and means the sum of the differentials over any range. In this case the differential equation is written:

$$\int k dt = - \int \frac{dx}{x}$$

The process of integration consists in determining, largely from experience with differentiation, the functions corresponding to these differentials. Here, the integrated equation is

$$kt = - \ln x + C$$

where C is a constant determined from the fact that, when $t = 0$, $x = x_0$, the initial amount of radioactive material, which gives:

$$C = \ln x_0$$

and

$$\ln \frac{x_0}{x} = 2.303 \log \frac{x_0}{x} = kt$$

If, instead of considering the total change in amount during the first t minutes of the reaction, the change from x_1 to x_2 during the time interval t_1 to t_2 be considered, the differential equation is written:

$$\int_{t_1}^{t_2} k dt = - \int_{x_1}^{x_2} \frac{dx}{x}$$

which by integration and conversion to common logarithms becomes:

$$\log \frac{x_1}{x_2} = \frac{(t_2 - t_1)k}{2.303}$$

In this way, from a *differential equation* applying to a continuously changing system, we obtain an *integrated* expression which enables us to determine the amount of reactant at any given moment, or to determine the numerical value of k, which is characteristic of the given reaction at the given temperature.

In this book we do not make extensive use of the calculus. To avoid it completely, however, and at the same time offer an adequate discussion of such topics as reaction velocity and change of equilibrium constants with temperature, is quite impossible. This explanation is intended to give the student unfamiliar with the calculus some idea of the symbols, concepts, and methods involved. It is quite beyond his present knowledge to attempt to solve differential equations or even to gain a complete understanding of what the process of integration means.[1]

(3) Graphical methods. Graphical methods of illustrating the simultaneous variation of two interdependent magnitudes are extremely useful. They are commonly employed to show visually how a property or an effect varies with a condition. If two magnitudes only are involved, the simultaneous variation may be represented on a two-dimensional diagram. If, however, three magnitudes vary simultaneously, as in the ideal gas laws equation,

$$PV = RT$$

where P, the pressure, V, the volume, and T, the absolute temperature, are all interdependent variables, the representation requires a three-dimensional diagram. Because of the practical difficulty of constructing three-dimensional diagrams, it is customary to keep one of the factors constant and to plot the remaining two variables on a two-dimensional diagram. The actual plot of the simultaneous values of P, V, and T in the above expression would give as a result a curved *surface.* When only two variables are involved, we obtain a line curve. A series of these curves correspond to the contours of the surface.

For many of the graphs in physical chemistry no simple mathematical expressions can be written. For some, however, we see the applicability of equations for simple curves. For example, in the gas laws equation given in the foregoing paragraph, if T is constant, then $PV = k$, in which we recognize the equation for a rectangular hyperbola, Figure 2 (*a*). If P is constant, then $V = kT$, which would be the equation for a straight line passing through the origin, Figure 2 (*b*). Conversely, a graph consisting of a straight line through the origin always implies direct proportionality. If a direct proportionality equation is modified by the presence of an additive, or subtractive, constant term, as in the equation,

$$y = a + kx$$

[1] For further information on this subject the student is referred to F. Daniels, *Mathematical Preparation for Physical Chemistry.* McGraw-Hill Book Co., New York, 1928.

where x and y are variables and k and a are constants, then it represents a straight line parallel to a direct proportionality curve $y = kx$, Figure 2 (c). Either x or y would be a *linear function* of the other, but they would not be proportional since, obviously,

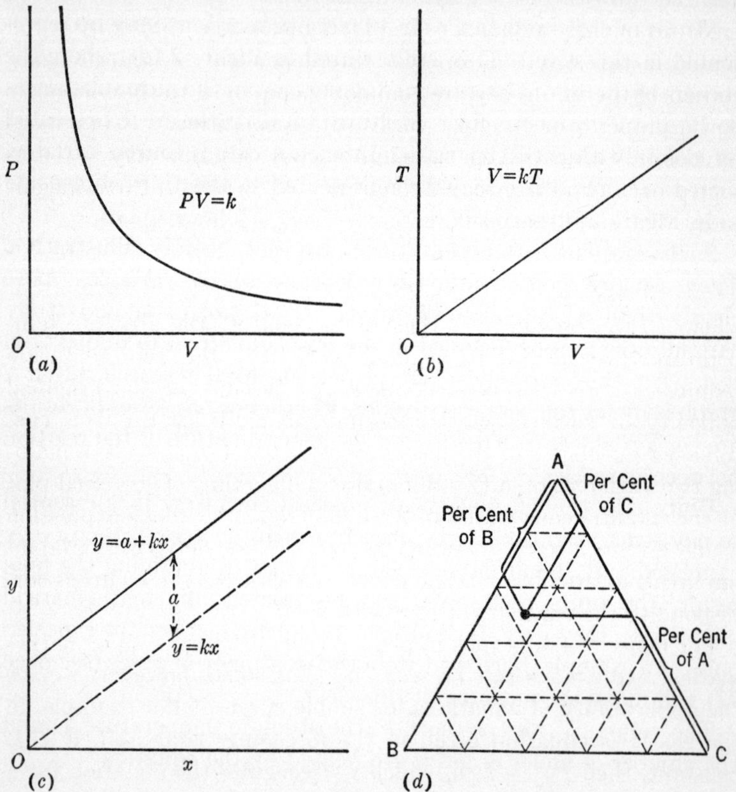

Fig. 2. Typical Graphs Used in Physical Chemistry.

the doubling of x would not double y. Examples of such a curve are found in Figure 138 on page 292. The equation there given for the variation of the velocity constant k for a given reaction with the temperature T has the form

$$\ln k = B - \frac{A}{RT}$$

in which R, B, and A are constants. As will be noted from Figure 138, plotting the experimental data gives a straight line. The velocity constant, k, is a *linear function* of the reciprocal of the absolute temperature; it is not directly proportional.

In certain cases, three variables may be represented by means of triangular co-ordinates, provided only *two* of them are *independent* and the third can be calculated from them. The compositions of mixtures of three substances in varying proportions may be represented in this way. This is illustrated in Figure 2 (*d*), where the corners of the triangle represent 100 per cent of the pure substances A, B, and C, respectively. Mixtures of all three are represented by points within the triangle. In such a case a fourth variable, such as temperature, may be represented in the third dimension as in Figure 254, page 617.

Such graphical representations are not merely illustrative. They usually portray the interdependence of variables more clearly than a statement in words. The student should study carefully the graphs included in the text, and strive to understand just what they represent. In physicochemical research, often a graph is by far the best way to show whether or not series of results are concordant and to determine the general nature of the relation between variables.

Units. In the calculations of physical chemistry it is essential to pay strict attention to the *units* in which the various factors are expressed. It should be realized, also, that in obtaining the final result, the units themselves can be treated like mathematical quantities; they may, for example, be squared, cubed, or canceled out. An example, borrowed from the treatment of gases (see page 77) will make the meaning of this clear.

The volume V, the pressure P, the absolute temperature T, and the number of moles of gas n are related by the equation

$$PV = nRT$$

Let us suppose that our task is to evaluate the constant R. We shall assume that we have 1 mole of gas at S.T.P. Then we may put P equal to 76×13.6 g. per sq. cm., V equal to 22,400 cc., and T equal to 273° A. Hence we may write:

$$R = \frac{76 \times 13.6 \text{ g./cm.}^2 \times 22{,}400 \text{ cm.}^3}{1 \text{ mole} \times 273 \text{ deg.}}$$

$$= \frac{76 \times 13.6 \times 22{,}400}{1 \times 273} \cdot \text{g. cm.}^{-2} \times \text{cm.}^3 \times \text{mole}^{-1} \times \text{deg.}^{-1}$$

$$= 84{,}808 \text{ g.} \times \text{cm.} \times \text{mole}^{-1} \times \text{deg.}^{-1}$$

Thus R has the *units* of *g. cm. per degree per mole.* Since the product of g. cm. corresponds to the unit of *work*, and work per degree represents *heat capacity*, we see that R can be expressed in units of *heat capacity per mole.*

READING LIST

The following books are recommended to students of physical chemistry who wish more extensive information than can be given in this elementary textbook.

A. Findlay, *A Hundred Years of Chemistry.* The Macmillan Company, New York, 1937. This extremely interesting and authoritative history traces the development of the various fields of chemistry from about the beginning of the nineteenth century. Pages 80–131 and 264–289 deal specifically with the development of physical chemistry.

F. J. Moore (rev. by W. T. Hall), *A History of Chemistry*, 3d ed. McGraw-Hill Book Company, New York, 1939. Much of Chapter XXX, "Inorganic Chemistry Since 1860," deals with the development of physical chemistry and this includes interesting biographical material.

S. Glasstone, *A Textbook of Physical Chemistry.* D. Van Nostrand Company, New York, 1940. This well-written text contains in its 1289 pages a very complete discussion of the field.

H. S. Taylor (Editor), *A Treatise on Physical Chemistry*, 2d ed. D. Van Nostrand Company, New York, 1930. Excellent for reference.

TABLES OF PHYSICOCHEMICAL DATA

International Critical Tables, published in 1930 by the McGraw-Hill Book Company, New York, for the National Research Council. Seven volumes and an index volume. The most authoritative source for such data published prior to 1930. The data were critically evaluated and only the best values given. In subsequent references to these tables, the title is abbreviated to *I. C. T.*

Landolt-Börnstein, *Physikalisch-Chemische Tabellen*, 5th ed. Julius Springer, Berlin, 1923. (2 vols.) 1695 pp. First Supplement, 1927. 919 pp. Second supplement (2 vols.), 1931. 1707 pp. Third supplement (3 vols.), 1935. 3039 pp. A very useful compilation of physicochemical data, which is kept well up to date by the publication of additional sections.

Handbook of Chemistry. N. A. Lange, Handbook Publishers, Inc., Sandusky, Ohio. New editions frequently.

Handbook of Chemistry and Physics. Chemical Rubber Co., Cleveland, Ohio. New editions frequently.

CHAPTER 2

COMPOSITION OF MATTER

The Elements. All the matter in the universe, as far as we know, is composed of about ninety elements. Spectroscopic analysis shows that even the most distant stars contain the same elements which are found on the earth and apparently no others. The combinations in which the elements occur in the earth's crust depend chiefly upon the reactivities of the elements and upon the stabilities and solubilities of their compounds. The most conspicuously inactive elements, like platinum, gold, and silver, occur mainly in the elementary state; those which are inactive at ordinary temperatures, like nitrogen, oxygen, and sulfur, *may* be found in the elementary state; the more active and most common elements, such as magnesium, phosphorus, chlorine, and zinc, occur only as compounds. In the course of geologic ages, each element, by interaction with contiguous elements, has been converted into that state of combination in which it is most stable in its environment. Thus, sodium, bromine, chlorine, and the other elements that form no insoluble compounds are found in water solution or in masses left by the evaporation of such solutions; whereas those that form insoluble compounds occur as solid minerals in the earth's crust.

From these naturally occurring substances nearly all of the elements have been isolated, and vast numbers of new substances have been prepared; such processes form the basis of modern chemical industry. The proportions in which the elements unite, the vigor and speed with which they react, and the changes in composition which are brought about by various methods, follow definite physicochemical laws, the study of which forms an important part of physical chemistry.

The Laws of Chemical Combination. The quantitative behavior of elements in forming compounds is described by five simple generalizations: the law of conservation of mass; the law of definite proportions; the law of multiple proportions; the law of chemical equivalence; and Gay-Lussac's law of reacting volumes.

(1) The law of the conservation of mass states that *the products of a chemical reaction have the same total mass as the reagents.* In other words, *mass is neither created nor destroyed during a chemical reaction.* The philosophical dogma of the indestructibility of matter was advanced as early as the fifth century B.C., but it often was challenged during the Middle Ages. No experimental test of the hypothesis was made until Lavoisier, in 1770, converted tin and other metals into their oxides in *sealed* flasks, so that no gas could enter or escape. He proved the correctness of the law within about 0.2 per cent, which was his experimental error.

Later work has verified the law within much smaller limits. Between 1893 and 1908 Hans Landolt, editor of the well-known *Physikalisch-Chemische Tabellen,* carried out a series of painstaking investigations at the University of Berlin on the basis of which he concluded that "the final result of the whole investigation shows that in all of the 15 reactions studied, a change in the total weight of the substances has not been detected" beyond about 0.00001 per cent. In 1913 J. J. Manley, at Oxford University, again verified the law with about the same degree of accuracy. We may therefore regard the law of conservation of mass in the case of chemical reactions as proved within *one part in ten million.*

There is more recent evidence that this law may not hold exactly for changes in which very large amounts of energy are liberated. Einstein and others have concluded from the theory of relativity that matter and energy are merely different aspects of the same thing and that they can be converted into each other. According to these calculations, one gram of mass corresponds to about 9×10^{20} ergs, or 2×10^{13} calories.[1] Even as vigorous a reaction as the combustion of carbon in oxygen, yielding 10,000 calories per gram of carbon, would show a decrease in mass of only about 4×10^{-9} g. per gram of carbon burned, which would escape detection by the best analytical balance. The losses of mass in radioactive changes, which involve much larger amounts of energy, might be detectable, but as yet they have not been measured. The relationship has, however, been used with complete success in calculating the isotopic weights of the light elements in transmutation experiments.

The other four laws of chemical combination are studied in every

[1] F. Soddy, *The Interpretation of the Atom.* G. P. Putnam's Sons, New York, 1932. Pp. 196–197.

course in elementary chemistry. They require no discussion here and need only be restated.

(2) **The law of definite proportions:** *When two elements form a compound, they unite in a certain definite proportion by weight.* In other words, *the composition by weight of a pure substance is always the same.*

(3) **The law of multiple proportions:** *When two elements unite to form more than one compound, a fixed weight of one is found to unite with weights of the other which are in the ratio of small whole numbers.*

(4) **The law of chemical equivalence:** *The weights of any two substances, whether elements or compounds, which are chemically equivalent to the same weight of a third substance are chemically equivalent to each other.* This law finds constant application, especially in analytical chemistry. One half of the atomic weight of oxygen, or 8.0000 on the atomic weight scale, is taken as the standard for equivalent weights. Since the weight in grams is most frequently used, we may define the term *gram-equivalent weight*, or *gram equivalent*, thus: *The* ***gram equivalent*** *of a substance, either compound or element, is that weight which is chemically equivalent to 8.0000 grams of oxygen.*

(5) **Gay-Lussac's law of reacting volumes:** *There is a simple integral ratio between the volumes of gaseous reagents and products in a chemical reaction, provided these volumes are measured at the same temperature and pressure.* This law holds *approximately* in the case of all gaseous reactions, but it does not hold *exactly* in any case. Recent accurate studies of the reacting volumes of gases yield results like the following:

In forming water:

$$\frac{\text{volume hydrogen}}{\text{volume oxygen}} = \frac{2.0025}{1.0000}$$

In forming nitric oxide:

$$\frac{\text{volume nitrogen}}{\text{volume oxygen}} = \frac{1.0026}{1.0000}$$

The reason for such deviations from the law is that *real gases* do not behave exactly like the *ideal gas* postulated by the kinetic theory (see page 101).

The Periodic Law and Periodic Table. The *periodic law* and the *periodic table* comprise the most comprehensive generalization in chemistry. The *table* may be regarded as a summary of the *law* upon which it is based. It classifies the elements in accordance with their physical and chemical properties. Probably more than any other physicochemical generalization, it impresses the thoughtful student with the essential unity of matter and its dependence upon some ultimate characteristic of structure. It provides the most logical basis for the study and correlation of the chemistry of the elements.

During the first half of the nineteenth century numerous attempts were made to classify the elements,[1] but it was not until 1869 that Mendeléeff[2] presented the first generally acceptable system. His second periodic table, published in 1871, is shown on page 19. His **periodic law** may be stated thus: *The physical and chemical properties of the elements are periodic functions of their atomic weights.*

Modifications in the Mendeléeff Table. If the periodic table of Mendeléeff given on page 19 is compared with the modern table on page 20, several important alterations will be apparent: (1) Cu, Ag, and Au have been placed definitely in Group I. (2) Spaces left blank by Mendeléeff have been filled by the discovery of the elements Sc, Ga, Ge, Hf, and Re, the first three of which were predicted by Mendeléeff and their properties described in 1869. (3) Eleven *rare earth* elements have been added, for which a separate "box" had to be inserted. (4) The discovery of the inert gases, He, Ne, A, Kr, Xe, and Rn, caused the addition of *Group 0* to the table. (5) Several blanks in the table of Mendeléeff have been filled by radioactive elements, notably, Rn, Ra, Ac, and Pa. (6) Most atomic weights are given to at least two decimal places as a result of increased accuracy in research methods.

Other important developments which are not shown in the table but which must be considered in its study are the following: (1) The existence of *isotopes* (the atomic weights of which are virtually whole numbers if the atomic weight of oxygen is taken as 16.0000) has been established. (2) The *atomic weights* of the elements are known to be the average of the various isotopic weights. (3) Radioactive disintegration and the nature of the radioactive

[1] See F. P. Venable, *The Periodic Law.* Chemical Publishing Co., Easton, Pa., 1896. Also, Meldrum and Gucker, *Introduction to Theoretical Chemistry.* American Book Company, New York, 1936. Pp. 5–12.

[2] Dmitri Ivanovitch Mendeléeff (1834–1907) was born in Tobolsk, Siberia, of enterprising pioneer parents. He was professor of chemistry at the University of St. Petersburg (Leningrad) and was noted for his services in developing the resources of Russia as well as for his work in pure chemistry.

TABLE 1

MENDELÉEFF'S SECOND TABLE (1871)

Series	I	II	III	IV	V	VI	VII	VIII
	—	—	—	RH_4	RH_3	RH_2	RH	—
	R_2O	RO	R_2O_3	RO_2	R_2O_5	RO_3	R_2O_7	RO_4
1	H = 1							
2	Li 7	Be 9.4	B 11	C 12	N 14	O 16	F 19	
3	Na 23	Mg 24	Al 27.3	Si 28	P 31	S 32	Cl 35.5	
4	K 39	Ca 40	— 44	Ti 48	V 51	Cr 52	Mn 55	Fe 56 Co 59 Ni 59 Cu 63
5	(Cu 63)	Zn 65	— 68	— 72	As 75	Se 78	Br 80	
6	Rb 85	Sr 87	(?)Yt 88	Zr 90	Nb 94	Mo 96	— 100	Ru 104 Rh 104 Pd 106 Ag 108
7	(Ag 108)	Cd 112	In 113	Sn 118	Sb 122	Te 125	I 127	
8	Cs 133	Ba 137	(?)Di 138	(?)Ce 140	—	—	—	— — — —
9	(—)	—	—	—	—	—	—	
10	—	—	(?)Er 178	(?) La 180	Ta 182	W 184	—	Os 195 Ir 197 Pt 198 Au 199
11	(Au 199)	Hg 200	Tl 204	Pb 207	Bi 208	—	—	
12	—	—	—	Th 231	—	U 240	—	

In modern tables Yt and Nb are replaced by Y and Cb respectively.

TABLE 2. A Modern Arrangement of the Mendeléeff Periodic Table

Group	0	I		II		III		IV		V		VI		VII		VIII		
Subgroup		A	B	A	B	A	B	A	B	A	B	A	B	A	B			
Type Formula		R_2O		RO		R_2O_3		RO_2		R_2O_5		RO_3		R_2O_7		(RO_4)		
Period 1		1 H 1.0080																
2	2 He 4.003	3 Li 6.940		4 Be 9.02		5 B 10.82		6 C 12.010			7 N 14.008		8 O 16.0000		9 F 19.00			
3	10 Ne 20.183	11 Na 22.997		12 Mg 24.32		13 Al 26.97		14 Si 28.06		15 P 30.98		16 S 32.06			17 Cl 35.457			
4	18 A 39.944	19 K 39.096		20 Ca 40.08		21 Sc 45.10		22 Ti 47.90		23 V 50.95		24 Cr 52.01		25 Mn 54.93		26 Fe 55.85	27 Co 58.94	28 Ni 58.69
			29 Cu 63.57		30 Zn 65.38		31 Ga 69.72		32 Ge 72.60		33 As 74.91		34 Se 78.96		35 Br 79.916			
5	36 Kr 83.7	37 Rb 85.48		38 Sr 87.63		39 Y 88.92		40 Zr 91.22		41 Cb 92.91		42 Mo 95.95		43		44 Ru 101.7	45 Rh 102.91	46 Pd 106.7
			47 Ag 107.880		48 Cd 112.41		49 In 114.76		50 Sn 118.70		51 Sb 121.76		52 Te 127.61		53 I 126.92			
6	54 Xe 131.3	55 Cs 132.91		56 Ba 137.36		Rare Earths 57 - 71		72 Hf 178.6		73 Ta 180.88		74 W 183.92		75 Re 186.31		76 Os 190.2	77 Ir 193.1	78 Pt 195.23
			79 Au 197.2		80 Hg 200.61		81 Tl 204.39		82 Pb 207.21		83 Bi 209.00		84 Po 210		85			
7	86 Rn 222	87		88 Ra 226.05		89 Ac 227		90 Th 232.12		91 Pa 231		92 U 238.07						

RARE EARTHS

	57 La 138.92	58 Ce 140.13	59 Pr 140.92	60 Nd 144.27	61	62 Sm 150.43	63 Eu 152.0
64 Gd 156.9	65 Tb 159.2	66 Dy 162.46	67 Ho 164.94	68 Er 167.2	69 Tm 169.4	70 Yb 173.04	71 Lu 174.99

change have been studied. About 40 radioactive elements have been placed in the periodic table, most of them as isotopes of familiar stable elements. (4) The physical properties of most of the elements and their compounds have been determined with a high degree of accuracy. (5) The establishment of the ***atomic number*** *of an element* as *the number of excess positive charges on the nucleus of an atom* has furnished a characteristic of an element more fundamental than *atomic weight* as a basis for the classification of the elements. (6) The chemical relations of the elements have become more clearly understood in the light of the modern theory of atomic and molecular structure.

The Modern Periodic Law. The modern periodic law is based, not upon the *atomic weight,* but upon the *atomic number.* The atomic weight differs for different isotopes of the same element, while the atomic number is the same for all and is quite characteristic of the element. The law is now stated: *The chemical and physical properties of the elements are periodic functions of their atomic numbers.* The periodicity in one *chemical* property, the valence, for the elements of lower atomic number, is shown in Figure 3.

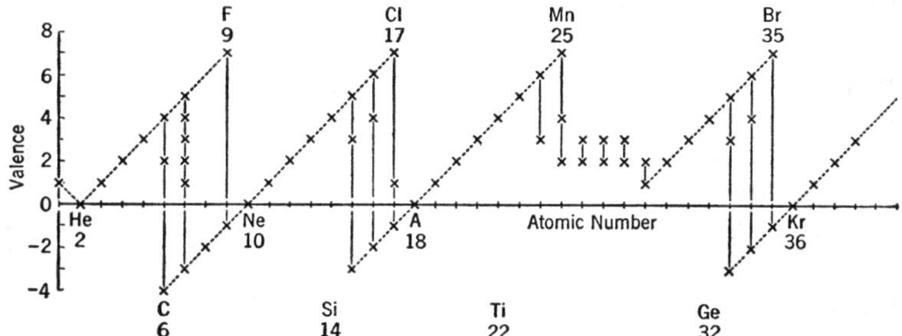

Fig. 3. Periodicity in Valence for the Lower Elements.

Atomic Volumes and Other Physical Properties of the Elements. The ***atomic volume*** *is the volume occupied by one gram atom of an element.* It is numerically equal to the atomic weight divided by the density. In 1870, while Mendeléeff was establishing the periodic law for the physical and chemical properties of the elements, the German chemist Lothar Meyer pointed out the periodicity of their atomic volumes. He plotted the atomic volumes of the elements against their atomic weights and showed that the lines connecting these points made up a series of waves, with chemically similar elements occurring at corresponding points on successive waves. In Figure 4 we have plotted the atomic volumes against the atomic numbers, which are more fundamental than the atomic weights. The curve consists of a series of waves, the crests of all but the first of which are occupied by the alkali metals. The height of each successive crest is greater than that of the one before it; thus the atomic volume of cesium is over twice that of sodium. The trough of each wave is occupied by the elements in the middle of a period — the nonmetals in the first two periods and the transition elements in the other longer periods. The elements on the descending (left hand) slope of each wave are metals of decreasingly basic nature, while those on the ascending slopes are nonmetals of increasingly acid properties.

Other physical properties of the elements are closely related to their atomic volumes. As T. W. Richards first pointed out, if the atomic volume is large, the atoms are spaced relatively far apart, and the elements should be easy to compress; if the atomic volume is small, the atoms are tightly packed together, and the element should be incompressible. Hence the coefficients of *compressibility* should parallel the atomic volumes. This is seen to be the case if we compare the two curves in Figure 4. The same considerations apply to the coefficients of *thermal expansibility*. If the atoms are crowded together in the solid, they must be subject to large forces, which will not readily be overcome by a rise in temperature. Such elements will have a small coefficient of thermal expansibility. Elements with a large atomic volume have their atoms widely spaced and will be influenced more by a rise in temperature. As Figure 4 shows, the coefficients of thermal expansibility parallel the atomic volume and compressibility curves.

Another property which depends upon the atomic volume is the *melting point* of an element, which represents the temperature at which the ordered arrangement of the crystal suddenly goes over to the more random arrangement of the liquid. If the crystal forces are small, the atomic volume will be large, and thermal motion will break down the crystalline structure at a low temperature. This is true of the alkali metals. If the crystal forces are large, the atomic volumes will be small and a high temperature is required to melt the crystal. Thus we find that the melting points of boron, carbon, and all the transition elements are extremely

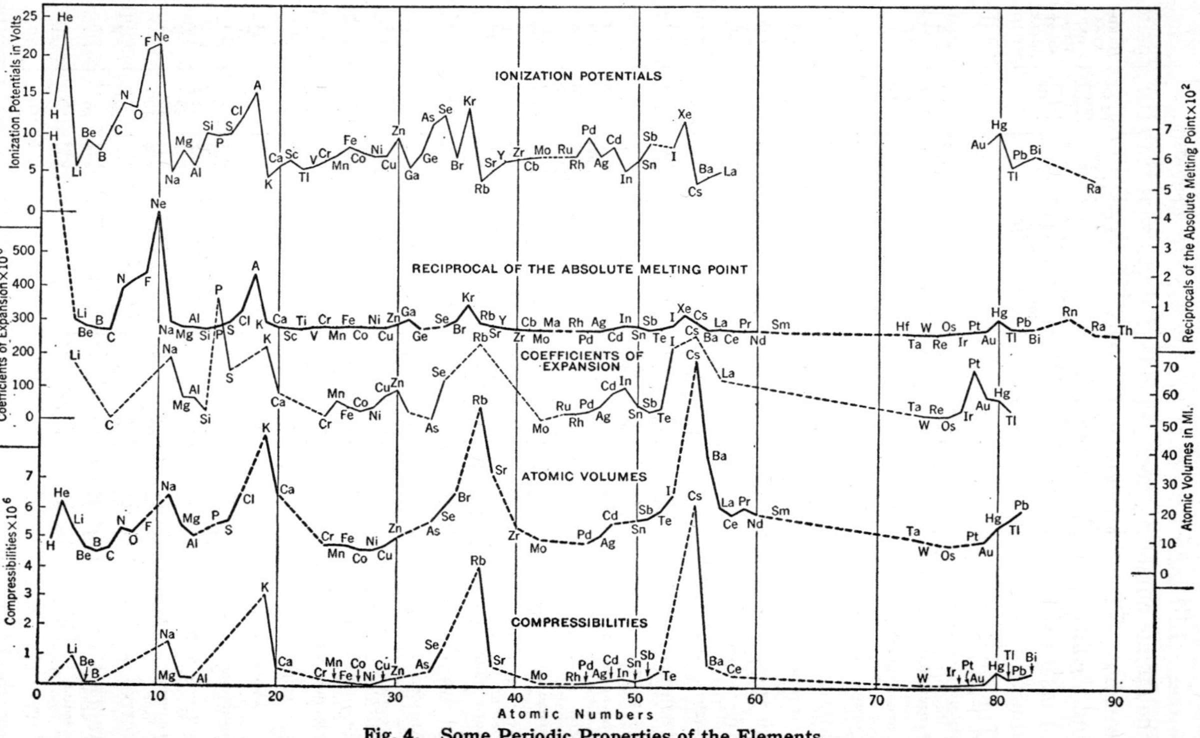

Fig. 4. Some Periodic Properties of the Elements.

TABLE 3

Some Physical Properties of the Elements

(In the solid state and, wherever possible, at room temperature)

Element	Atomic Number	Density	Atomic Volume	Cubical Coefficient of		Melting Point °C.	Electrical Resistivity $\times 10^6$	Hardness on Rydberg Scale
				Compressibility $\times 10^6$	Thermal Expansion $\times 10^6$			
Hydrogen	1	0.081	12.4	>29	—	− 259	—	—
Helium	2	0.188	21.3	—	—	− 272	—	—
Lithium	3	0.53	13.1	9.1	168	186	9.3	0.6
Beryllium	4	1.8	5.0	0.93	—	1350	18.5	—
Boron	5	(2)	5	0.3	(6)	2300	10^{12}	9.5
Carbon (graphite)	6	2.26	5.3	3.0	9	3500	1400	—
Nitrogen	7	1.03	13.6	—	—	− 210	—	—
Oxygen	8	1.43	11.2	—	—	− 218	—	—
Fluorine	9	(1.3)	15	—	—	− 223	—	—
Neon	10	(1.0)	20	—	—	− 249	—	—
Sodium	11	0.97	23.7	15.6	213	98	4.6	0.4
Magnesium	12	1.74	14.0	2.9	76.8	651	4.5	2.0
Aluminum	13	2.70	10.0	1.5	69.0	660	2.6	2.9
Silicon	14	2.4	11.7	0.3	(15)	1420	10^5	7.0
Phosphorus (yellow)	15	1.82	17.0	20.8	375	44	10^{17}	0.5
Sulfur (rhombic)	16	2.07	15.5	13.1	192	113	10^{23}	2.0
Chlorine	17	(1.9)	18.7	—	—	− 102	—	—
Argon	18	1.65	24.2	—	—	− 189	—	—
Potassium	19	0.86	45.3	32.1	249	62	7.0	0.5
Calcium	20	1.55	25.8	5.8	75	810	4.6	1.5
Scandium	21	(2.5)	18	—	—	1200	—	—
Titanium	22	4.5	10.6	—	—	1800	3	—
Vanadium	23	5.96	8.6	—	—	1710	—	—
Chromium	24	7.1	7.3	0.9	24.6	1615	2.6	9.0
Manganese	25	7.2	7.6	0.9	69	1260	5	5.0
Iron	26	7.86	7.1	0.6	35.1	1535	10.0	4.5
Cobalt	27	8.9	6.6	0.6	36.9	1480	9.7	—
Nickel	28	8.90	6.6	0.4	38.4	1452	6.9	—
Copper	29	8.92	7.1	0.8	49.8	1083	1.7	3.0
Zinc	30	7.14	9.2	1.7	99	419	6	2.5
Gallium	31	5.91	11.8	2.0	54	30	53	1.5
Germanium	32	5.36	13.6	1.4	—	959	10^5	—
Arsenic	33	5.7	13.1	4.5	14.1	814	35	3.5
Selenium	34	4.8	16.4	12.2	111	220	12	2.0
Bromine	35	(3.4)	23.5	—	—	− 7	10^{14}	—
Krypton	36	3.4	25	—	—	− 169	—	—
Rubidium	37	1.53	55.8	40.5	270	39	12.5	0.3
Strontium	38	2.6	34	7.2	—	800	23	1.8
Yttrium	39	5.51	16.1	—	—	1490	—	—
Zirconium	40	6.4	14.3	—	—	1700	170	—
Columbium	41	8.4	11.1	—	—	1950	—	—
Molybdenum	42	10.2	9.4	0.5	12	2620	4.8	—
—	43	—	—	—	—	—	—	—
Ruthenium	44	12.2	8.4	—	27.3	2450	10	6.5
Rhodium	45	12.5	8.3	0.4	25.2	1955	5.1	—
Palladium	46	12.0	8.9	0.6	35.4	1555	10.8	4.8
Silver	47	10.5	10.3	1.0	56.7	961	1.6	2.7
Cadmium	48	8.6	13.1	2.1	89.4	321	7.5	2.0
Indium	49	7.3	15.7	2.6	99	155	9	1.2
Tin	50	7.31	16.2	1.9	60	232	11.4	1.8
Antimony	51	6.68	18.2	2.4	34.2	631	39	3.0
Tellurium	52	6.24	20.4	—	50.4	452	10^4	2.3
Iodine	53	4.93	25.8	13.2	279	114	10^{15}	—
Xenon	54	(2.7)	49	—	—	− 140	—	—
Cesium	55	1.90	70	62	291	26	20	0.2
Barium	56	3.5	39	10.5	—	850	—	—
Lanthanum	57	6.15	22.6	5.8	—	826	59	—
Cerium	58	6.90	20.3	3.7	—	640	78	—
Praseodymium	59	6.5	21.6	3.4	—	940	88	—
Neodymium	60	6.9	20.9	—	—	840	79	—

(Sources: *International Critical Tables*, supplemented by Landolt-Börnstein *Tabellen*, and recent literature. Doubtful values in parentheses.)

high. We would expect the melting point curve for the elements to show a periodicity exactly opposite to the atomic volume curve, with a peak where the latter had a trough. In order to parallel the atomic volume curve, the *reciprocal* of the absolute melting point usually is plotted, as in Figure 4. This curve does not show such pronounced variations as the preceding ones but parallels them in a general way.

The same considerations may be applied to the *hardness* of solids. We would expect elements with small atomic volumes to be harder than those less tightly packed in the crystal. This is indeed the case, as can be seen from Table 3, which contains data for the first 60 elements. There are many gaps in our knowledge of the other 32 elements.

The properties of the elements do not show absolute regularity in their periodic relationships. Some of the elements exist in several crystal forms, which differ in their physical properties. At room temperature some are gases, some liquids, and some solids. Solid oxygen at − 220° C. cannot rightly be compared with solid iron at 20° C. Nonmetals and metals differ in their crystal structures, thus introducing an additional complication.

Fundamental Chemical Theory. Under this heading we will review briefly the basic principles from which atomic and molecular weights, formulas, and equations have been derived. *Our whole system of fundamental chemical theory rests squarely upon the atomic theory and the kinetic theory of gases.* If either one of these were removed, the whole structure would collapse. On the other hand, if the two theories are accepted as true, we can deduce logically all of the conclusions which are included in the scheme of fundamental theory. Since all of this material has been studied already in the elementary chemistry course or is discussed elsewhere in this book, we will only summarize it here. The student should seek to follow the logical sequence as the scheme develops rather than to study the details at this time. This will be facilitated by the chart given on page 26 which shows in a diagrammatic way how the various laws and theories are co-ordinated. In this chart *theory*, *fact* or *law*, and *arbitrarily chosen standard* are distinguished by the use of three kinds of types, namely, **boldface** for **theory,** lightface for experimental facts or laws, and *italics* for *arbitrarily chosen standards.* The essential steps in the scheme are treated briefly in the following paragraphs.

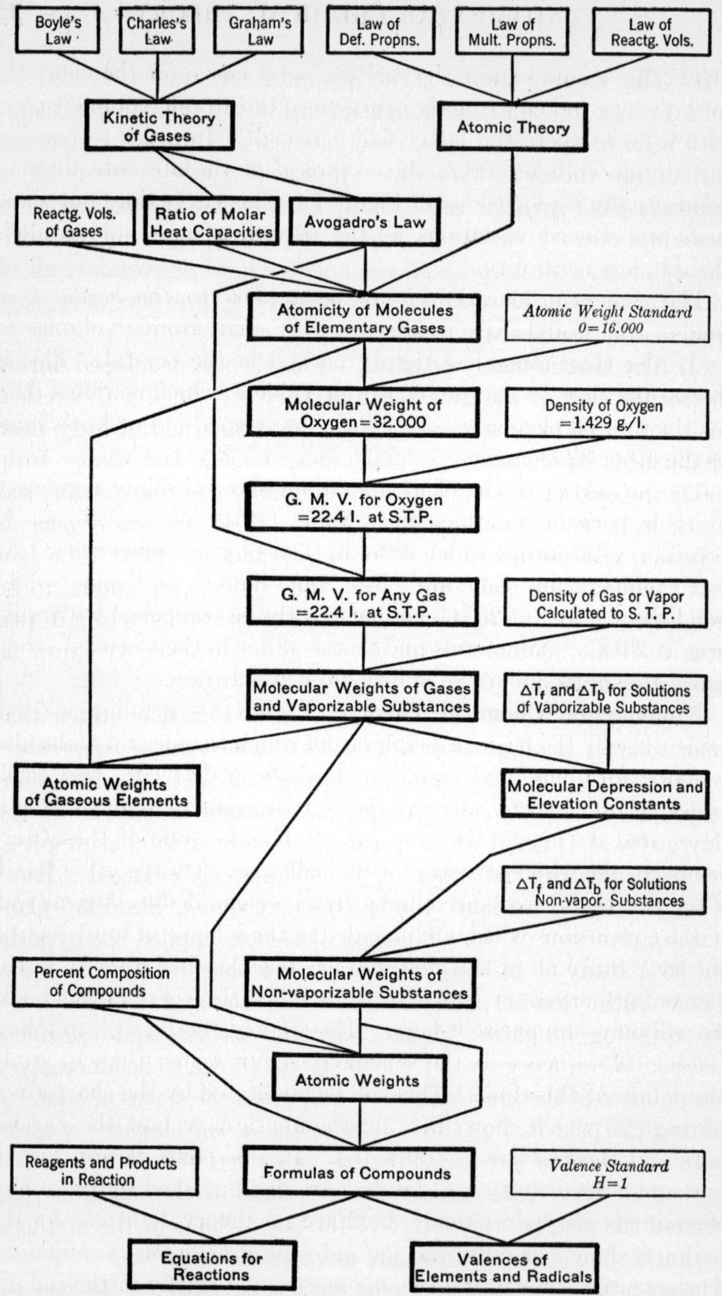

Fig. 5. Fundamental Chemical Theory.

(1) The atomic theory. The *atomic theory* was advanced by John Dalton in 1803. Although several of the original postulates have been proved erroneous, two remain which form the essential part of the theory. These are: First, *all matter is composed of extremely small particles called atoms;* and, second, *it is between these atoms that chemical combination takes place.*[1] The laws of *conservation of mass, definite proportions,* and *multiple proportions,* all of which have been established experimentally, are necessary consequences of the theory.

(2) The kinetic theory of gases. This theory, developed during the second half of the nineteenth century, provided a theoretical basis for three laws of gaseous behavior which had already been established experimentally. The first, *Boyle's law,* dates from 1662; the second, known as the *law of Charles and Gay-Lussac,* was stated in its complete form in 1802; the third, the *law of gaseous diffusion,* was published by Thomas Graham in 1829. The fact that these various deductions from the theory were known to be true, served to validate the theory and any other deduction drawn from it. One such deduction is the generalization we know as *Avogadro's law.*

(3) Avogadro's law. This familiar generalization states that *equal volumes of all gases under the same conditions of temperature and pressure contain the same number of molecules.* As first published in 1811 by Amadeo Avogadro, professor of physics at the University of Turin, it was a *hypothesis,* merely an intelligent guess. For half a century the status of the idea scarcely changed. However, in 1860, a brilliant young Italian chemist, Stanislao Cannizzaro, professor at the University of Genoa, applied the hypothesis to a study of gaseous reactions. For the first time, he drew a clear distinction between *atoms* and *molecules* and clearly defined the meaning of *atomic weight, molecular weight,* and *equivalent weight.* When Avogadro's hypothesis was shown to be a necessary consequence of the kinetic theory, it assumed the status of a *theory.* During the past two or three decades the *actual number*[2] *of molecules in 1 mole of gas at S.T.P.* has been determined by various methods. The close agreement of these determinations has ensured the general acceptance of the law. Some of the methods used and the values obtained are given in Table 4.

[1] For a fuller discussion of the present status of the theory see Meldrum and Gucker, *Introduction to Theoretical Chemistry.* Pp. 34–44.

[2] Known as **Avogadro's number** or *N*.

TABLE 4

AVOGADRO'S NUMBER

THE NUMBER OF MOLECULES IN A MOLE OF ANY SUBSTANCE

OBSERVER	DATE	METHOD	N
Sutherland	1893	Kinetic theory of gases	5.95 to 6.80×10^{23}
Fowler	1899	Scattering of solar radiation	6.04×10^{23}
Planck	1900	Radiation laws	6.05×10^{23}
Einstein	1905	Brownian movement	6.03×10^{23}
Regener	1908	Charge on alpha particle	6.04×10^{23}
Perrin	1909	Brownian movement	6.09×10^{23}
Millikan	1910	Charge of electron	6.06×10^{23}
Sommerfeld	1916	Fine structure of spectral lines	6.08×10^{23}
Millikan	1939	Charge of electron (recalculated *)	6.02×10^{23}
Miller and DuMond . . .	1940	X-ray study of crystal structure	6.023×10^{23}

* Recalculated on the basis of most recent values of the viscosity of air, through which the charged oil drop moves in these experiments.

The most probable value of N is 6.023×10^{23}, the average value obtained from X-ray studies (page 179) and other methods. Accordingly, 22.414 liters of the *ideal gas* at S.T.P. contains 6.023×10^{23} molecules. By extension, 1 mole of any substance is composed of 6.023×10^{23} molecules or, if ionized, of $6.023 \times 10^{23}\ \nu$ ions, where ν (nu) is the number of ions into which 1 molecule dissociates. *Real gases* show the same deviations from Avogadro's law that they do from the gas laws.

(4) The atomicity of an elementary gas. The number of atoms in the molecule of an elementary gas, like chlorine, is readily deduced by the application of the atomic theory and Avogadro's law to the volume relations in a reaction in which the gaseous element forms a gaseous compound.

Experiment shows that a given volume of hydrogen reacts with an equal volume of chlorine to form twice the volume of hydrogen chloride, thus:

1 liter hydrogen + 1 liter chlorine ⟶ 2 liters hydrogen chloride

If we assume that 1 liter of chlorine contains n molecules, then, according to Avogadro's law, 1 liter of hydrogen also contains n molecules and 2 liters of hydrogen chloride contain 2 n molecules. Thus, we may write:

n molecules hydrogen + n molecules chlorine ⟶
2 n molecules hydrogen chloride

Simplifying, by dividing through by 2 n, we obtain:

$\frac{1}{2}$ molecule hydrogen + $\frac{1}{2}$ molecule chlorine ⟶
1 molecule hydrogen chloride

According to the atomic theory, each molecule of hydrogen chloride must contain *at least one atom* of chlorine. Therefore, one-half a molecule of chlorine, which produces one molecule of hydrogen chloride, must consist of at least one atom and, hence, one molecule of chlorine must contain at least two atoms. Likewise, it could be shown that hydrogen, oxygen, and nitrogen must also have at least two atoms in their molecules. Heat capacity studies, interpreted on the basis of the kinetic theory (see page 93), furnish additional evidence that these gases are actually *diatomic*. Such studies indicate, also, that helium, neon, and the other gases of the zero group are *monatomic*.

(5) The atomic weight of oxygen. Ordinary oxygen consists of three isotopes (see page 49). The average weight of the oxygen atom is taken as the standard for atomic weights of the elements. To it is given, by arbitrary choice, the value 16.0000. Thus the *unit* of atomic weights, which as yet has received no special name, is $\frac{1}{16.0000}$ of the average mass of the oxygen atom. Most of the elements consist of two or more isotopes, hence *the* ***atomic weight*** *of any element may be defined as the average weight of an atom of the element relative to the average weight of the oxygen atom taken as 16.0000.* Thus, when we say that the atomic weight of sulfur is 32.06 we mean that:

$$\frac{\text{the average weight of the sulfur atom}}{\text{the average weight of the oxygen atom}} = \frac{32.06}{16.0000}$$

(6) The molecular weight of oxygen. Since the atomic weight of oxygen is 16.0000 and the molecule is diatomic, the *molecular weight* is 32.0000. *The* ***molecular weight*** *of a substance may be defined as the average weight of a molecule of the substance relative to the average weight of the oxygen atom taken as 16.0000.* The *mole*, or *gram molecular weight*, of oxygen is 32.0000 grams.

(7) The molar volume of a gas. The *molar*, or *gram molecular*, *volume of a gas is the volume which 1 mole of gas will occupy under specified conditions of temperature and pressure* (*usually S.T.P.*). At S.T.P. the experimental value of the density of oxygen is 1.4290 grams per liter. Thus 1.4290 g. of oxygen occupy 1 liter at S.T.P., and hence 32.0000 g. of oxygen occupy 32.0000/1.4290 liters, or 22.393 liters at S.T.P. When this volume is corrected for deviations from Boyle's law, it becomes 22.414 liters (see page

110). For approximate work this molar volume is rounded off to 22.4 liters at S.T.P.

Assuming Avogadro's law, the molar volume of any gas at S.T.P. is 22.4 liters. Thus if M is the molecular weight of any gaseous substance X, and if N is the number of molecules at S.T.P. in 22.4 liters of X or of oxygen, then we have:

$$\frac{\text{Wt. of 22.4 liters of } X}{\text{Wt. of 22.4 liters of oxygen}} = \frac{M \times N}{32 \times N} = \frac{M}{32}$$

But 22.4 liters of oxygen, as shown above, weigh 32.0000 grams; hence, 22.4 liters of X weigh M grams, and the mole of gas occupies 22.4 liters at S.T.P.

(8) Molecular weights of gases and vaporizable substances. Once the molar volume has been established as 22.4 liters at S.T.P., we can determine the molecular weights of gases or of substances which vaporize without decomposition at temperatures which can readily be controlled. The molecular weight of a gàs may be found from the weight of a known volume under known conditions. From this the density of the gas at S.T.P. is calculated and the molecular weight found by multiplying by 22.4.

In the case of a liquid or a solid, a known weight of the substance is vaporized and its volume determined at a known temperature and pressure. From this its density under these conditions is calculated. The gas laws are then applied to find the molar volume under the same conditions. The product of the molar volume and the density once more gives the molecular weight. The Dumas method and the Victor Meyer method are the best known applications of this method (see pages 112 and 113).

(9) The atomic weights of gaseous elements. When the molecular weight of a gas has been found from the density, as described above, it may be divided by the atomicity of the gas, *i.e.*, by the number of atoms in the molecule, to obtain the atomic weight. By applying the *method of limiting density*, the molecular weight and hence the atomic weight may be determined with great accuracy (see page 109). This method has been used to determine the atomic weights of the diatomic gases, hydrogen, nitrogen, and chlorine, and of the *noble gases*, like helium and neon, which are all monatomic.

(10) The molecular weights of nonvaporizable substances. The molecular weights of substances which decompose or do not vaporize readily are determined by one of several methods which depend upon the colligative properties of solutions. The *freezing point depression method* and the *boiling point elevation method* are most used. These are discussed in detail on pages 252 and 254.

The former method depends upon the fact that the freezing point depression of a fairly dilute solution in a given solvent is proportional to the molal concentration:

$$\Delta T_f = K_f m$$

where ΔT_f is the observed freezing point depression, m is the molal concentration, and K_f is the *molal depression constant.* The numerical values of K_f were found by using solutes of which the molecular weights had already been determined by the *vapor density method.* For water it is 1.86. Since $m = \frac{g}{M}$, where g is the number of grams of solute in 1000 g. of water and M is the molecular weight, the above expression may be written:

$$\Delta T_f = K_f \frac{g}{M} \qquad \text{or} \qquad M = K_f \frac{g}{\Delta T_f}$$

The *boiling point elevation method* depends upon the fact that the elevation of the boiling point of a given solvent by a nonvolatile solute is proportional to the molal concentration:

$$\Delta T_b = K_b m$$

where ΔT_b is the observed boiling point elevation, m is the molal concentration, and K_b is the *molal elevation constant.* By using solutes of which the molecular weights had been found by the *freezing point depression method,* the numerical values for K_b were determined. For water it is 0.52. Substituting $\frac{g}{M}$ for m, as before, we find:

$$\Delta T_b = K_b \frac{g}{M} \qquad \text{or} \qquad M = K_b \frac{g}{\Delta T_b}$$

(11) Cannizzaro's method for finding atomic weights. The method outlined here, like that given on page 30, is a *fundamental* method, which has been most used in fixing the atomic weights *approximately.* Methods for determining atomic weights *accurately* are discussed on pages 34–41.

The reasoning involved in this method is as follows: A molecule of a compound must contain *at least one* atom of each constituent element. Hence, one mole of the substance may contain 1, 2, 3,

. . . *n* gram atoms of each element. If a large number of compounds of a given element are studied to determine the weight of the element present in one mole of each, the smallest such weight may be taken as the *gram atom* of the element. In other words, *the* ***gram atom*** *of the element is the smallest weight of the element contained in a mole of any of its compounds.*

We may illustrate the application of Cannizzaro's method in the case of *carbon.* First, it is necessary to determine the molecular weights of a large number of carbon compounds and to analyze each for its carbon content. The weight of carbon in 1 mole of each substance is then computed, yielding results like those given in Table 5.

TABLE 5

DETERMINATION OF ATOMIC WEIGHTS BY CANNIZZARO'S METHOD

COMPOUND	MOLECULAR WEIGHT	PER CENT CARBON	GRAMS CARBON PER MOLE
Sucrose	342	42.0	144
Glucose	180	40.0	72
Diethyl ether	74	64.9	48
Glycerol	92	38.9	36
Acetic acid	60	40.0	24
Ethanol	46	52.7	24
Carbon monoxide . . .	28	42.8	12
Methanol	32	37.5	12

The smallest weight of carbon found in 1 mole of any of the thousands of carbon compounds so examined is 12 grams, which is accepted as the approximate atomic weight of carbon.

(12) Formulas, equations, and the valences of the elements. A detailed discussion of the derivation of *chemical formulas, chemical equations,* and the *valences of the elements* will be found in every elementary chemistry text and need not be repeated here. Note, however, that each of these is based directly upon the preceding scheme of development and hence depends ultimately upon the atomic theory and the kinetic theory of gases. It will suffice to remind the student that:

(*a*) The determination of the *formula* of a compound with certainty requires its *molecular weight,* the *percentage composition,* and the *atomic weights of the constituent elements.* If the molecular weight cannot be determined, as in the case of many mineral substances, the simplest *empirical formula* is taken to represent the compound.

(*b*) When the formulas for the reagents and products in a reaction are known, they are written in the familiar *equation* form. The equation is balanced in order to conform with the law of conservation of mass.

(*c*) The *valences of the elements* are deduced from the formulas of the compounds in which they occur. Hydrogen is taken as standard and its valence given the value *1*, by arbitrary choice. *The* ***valence*** *of any other element is the number of hydrogen atoms, or atoms equivalent to hydrogen, one atom of the given element will hold.*

Approximate Determination of Atomic Weights. We shall now summarize some of the methods used to determine the atomic weights of the elements. These fall into two categories — methods for fixing the *approximate values,* and methods for determining the *atomic weights accurately.* Approximate methods include the following:

(1) Cannizzaro's method. As described on page 31, this method involves the determination of the smallest weight of the given element in the mole of any of its compounds.

(2) Method applied to gaseous elements. The molecular weight of an elementary gas may be found from its density, and the atomicity deduced from reacting volumes. Dividing the molecular weight by the atomicity gives us the atomic weight.

(3) From isomorphism. Two substances are isomorphous when they form similar crystals and crystallize together as *mixed crystals,* which are homogeneous solids containing the components in varying proportions. Mitscherlich summarized the *law of isomorphism* in 1819: "The same number of atoms combined in the same manner produce the same crystalline form; the crystalline form is independent of the chemical nature of the atoms, and is only determined solely by their number and mode of combination."[1] As an example of the application of this law we may cite his determination of the atomic weight of *selenium.* He showed that potassium sulfate and potassium selenate are isomorphous and found their compositions to be:

Potassium Sulfate		*Potassium Selenate*	
Potassium . .	44.83 per cent	Potassium . .	35.29 per cent
Oxygen . . .	36.78	Oxygen . . .	28.96
Sulfur	18.39	Selenium . . .	35.75

[1] From Freund, *The Study of Chemical Composition.* Cambridge University Press, London, 1904. P. 413.

The ratio of the weights of sulfur and selenium combined with a given weight of potassium, *e.g.*, 44.83 grams, in the two compounds will be the ratio of the atomic weights of the two elements. Hence:

$$\frac{45.40 \text{ g. selenium}}{18.39 \text{ g. sulfur}} = \frac{\text{at. wt. selenium}}{\text{at. wt. sulfur}} = \frac{\text{at. wt. selenium}}{32.0}$$

Thus the atomic weight of selenium was found to be 79.0.

(4) From the atomic heat capacity of a solid element. According to the ***rule of Dulong and Petit,*** enunciated in 1819, *the specific heat, s, of a solid element multiplied by its atomic weight A is approximately equal to a constant, 6.2 calories per degree per gram atom:*

$$s \times A = 6.2 \text{ cal.} \times \text{deg.}^{-1} \times \text{g.a.}^{-1}$$

The method was successfully applied to find the atomic weights of sodium, potassium, lithium, barium, and various other elements (see also page 160).

(5) From the periodic law. Even as late as 1869, when Mendeléeff published his periodic law, the atomic weights of some of the elements were uncertain. Mendeléeff used the periodic table to deduce the approximate values of several of these. For example, the atomic weight of *uranium* was thought to be 116 and Mendeléeff placed it between *tin* and *antimony* in his first table. After an examination of its physical and chemical properties, he decided in 1871 that it belonged in Group VI as a higher analog of *molybdenum* and *tungsten,* with an atomic weight a little over twice as great, 240. Twelve years later this was confirmed by Zimmermann's study of the vapor densities of uranium chloride and bromide.

Mendeléeff also correctly deduced the atomic weight of *indium,* which had been discovered by means of the spectroscope in 1863. Its equivalent weight was found to be 37.7. Like iron and chromium, it forms alums; hence its oxide, with a density midway between those of SnO_2 and CdO, was probably In_2O_3. Accordingly, Mendeléeff gave it the atomic weight of 37.7×3, or 113.1, which filled an available place in the table.

Accurate Determination of Atomic Weights. "Atomic weight accuracy" calls for a purity of material and a precision of experimentation that will yield results significant to four or five figures. Most of the atomic weights are now known to at least the second decimal place. The methods which are most used are three in number.

(1) From molecular weights of gases. We have seen on page 30 that the atomic weight of a gaseous element may be determined from accurate measurements of the molecular weight, using the *method of limiting densities* (page 108) to correct for deviations from Boyle's law. In this way Baxter and Starkweather [1] found 20.183 for the atomic weight of *neon* and 39.944 for the atomic weight of *argon.* In both these cases the molecular weight was also the atomic weight, since the inert gases are monatomic. The method can be applied, also, to any element forming gaseous compounds. As an illustration we may take the determination of the atomic weight of nitrogen by Dietrichson, O'Brien, and Bircher.[2] They found the molecular weight of ammonia to be 17.0300. Assuming the atomic weight of hydrogen to be 1.0080, the atomic weight of *nitrogen* must be $17.0300 - 3 \times 1.0080$, or 14.0060.

(2) By accurate determination of the equivalent weight. This is the oldest method; by it over 70 of the present values have been determined. The equivalent weight of the element is found by determining accurately the weight which combines with a known weight of oxygen or of some other element of known atomic weight. The method was first employed successfully by J. J. Berzelius, over a century ago. It was improved by J. S. Stas, professor at Brussels, who was noted for his very careful and accurate work. T. W. Richards of Harvard University and two of his students, G. P. Baxter of Harvard and O. Hönigschmid of Munich, have applied still finer technique. Of the atomic weights listed in the 1941 table, over half were determined in the laboratories of these three men, 56 of them by the *equivalent weight method.* As an example of this method we may take the determination by Baxter and Thomas [3] of the atomic weight of *cesium* (see Table 6, pages 38–40).

Determination of the atomic weight of cesium. The cesium salt used was prepared from the mineral *pollucite,* a hydrated cesium aluminum silicate, $H_2Cs_4Al_4Si_9O_{29}$, found in Maine. The mineral was treated with hot concentrated nitric acid to yield about 3600 g. of cesium nitrate. This was repeatedly recrystallized to remove as nitrates such elements as sodium, lithium, potassium, rubidium, and thallium. The cesium nitrate was treated with hot perchloric acid solution, and the resulting cesium perchlorate was recrystal-

[1] *J. Am. Chem. Soc.*, **50**, 605 (1928); *ibid.*, **55**, 1 (1933); *Proc. Nat. Acad. Sci.*, **14**, 50 (1928).
[2] *J. Am. Chem. Soc.*, **55**, 1 (1933).
[3] *J. Am. Chem. Soc.*, **56**, 1108 (1934).

lized in platinum vessels. This salt was then decomposed by heating to form cesium chloride, which was further recrystallized in quartz vessels by saturating the solution with pure hydrogen chloride. Finally, the cesium chloride was fused in platinum.

The cesium chloride samples, weighing about 10 g., were removed in a quartz bottling apparatus, weighed, and dissolved to give approximately an 0.08 *N* solution. A nearly equivalent weight, about 5 g., of pure silver, dissolved in nitric acid, was slowly added to the cesium chloride solution. After standing, with slight agitation, for one week, the excess chloride or silver ion was determined with the nephelometer. The atomic weight of cesium was found from the ratio:

$$\frac{\text{Cs} + 35.457}{107.880} = \frac{\text{weight of CsCl}}{\text{weight of Ag}}$$

All weights were corrected to the vacuum basis.

Thirteen independent determinations gave values for the atomic weight ranging from 132.888 to 132.916, averaging 132.906. The value accepted for the atomic weight was 132.91.

(3) From isotopic mass and abundance data. This is the newest method and is the one used to determine the present accepted atomic weight of hydrogen. It is dependent upon three measurements. The first is the determination, by the mass spectrograph (or by nuclear disintegration reactions) of the masses of the various isotopes of the element relative to the mass of the oxygen isotope O^{16} taken as 16.00000. On this basis, the accepted values for the two hydrogen isotopes, H and D, are 1.00813 and 2.01472, respectively.

The second measurement involves the determination of the ratio of the isotopes in the naturally occurring element. This may be found from a comparison of the intensities of the mass spectral lines on the photographic plate or of the ion beams by means of an ionization chamber. The value for hydrogen was determined by Swartout and Dole[1] by comparing the density of "ordinary" water (from Lake Michigan) with that of water freed from deuterium, D, and with that of heavy water D_2O. Light and heavy water form nearly ideal solutions (see page 232), with no appreciable change in volume on mixing, hence in mixtures containing small amounts of deuterium oxide, the increase in density is proportional

[1] *J. Am. Chem. Soc.*, **61**, 2027 (1939).

to the concentration, and the relative concentrations of the isotopes are given by the equation:

$$\frac{\text{concentration of H}}{\text{concentration of D}} = \frac{0.1080}{0.0000155} = 6970$$

The average of the values obtained by eight different investigators [1] during the past five years is H : D = 6400 : 1. Using this value, the atomic weight of hydrogen on the physical scale, *i.e.*, referred to $O^{16} = 16.00000$, may be found thus:

$$\text{at. wt.} = \frac{(6400 \times 1.00813) + 2.01472}{(6400 + 1)} = 1.00829$$

Finally, it is necessary to determine the constant by which the atomic weights on the physical scale may be converted to those on the chemical scale. Using the isotopic masses and the abundance ratios determined with the mass spectrograph for the three oxygen isotopes, the physical atomic weight of oxygen from fresh lake water has been calculated to be 16.0043. In order to convert atomic weights from the physical scale to the chemical scale, the physical atomic weight is multiplied by $\frac{16.00000}{16.0043}$, or 0.99973. Thus the atomic weight of hydrogen is $1.00829 \times 0.99973 = 1.00801$, which has been rounded off to 1.0080 in the 1941 atomic weight table.

It is essential to specify the source of the element and its treatment prior to the final determination since the abundance ratio of the isotopes may alter during the treatment.[2] The source of the oxygen taken for the determination of the conversion factor must also be specified; it has been found that the atomic weight of atmospheric oxygen is slightly higher than that of oxygen from fresh lake water.

Methods by Which Accepted Atomic Weights Were Determined. Table 6 summarizes the determinations of the atomic weights of the elements which have been accepted by the International Committee on Atomic Weights and as they appear in the 1941 table. The references in the last column are to the annual reports of the Committee in the *Journal of the American Chemical Society*. These reports contain references to the original papers. Column

[1] "Tenth Report of the Committee on Atomic Weights of the International Union of Chemistry," *J. Am. Chem. Soc.*, **62**, 669 (1940).

[2] Urey and Greiff, *J. Am. Chem. Soc.*, **57**, 321 (1935).

TABLE 6

Atomic Weights and Their Determination

Element	At. Wt.	Determined By	Year	Method	Reference *J. Am. Chem. Soc.*
Aluminum	26.97	Krepelka	1925	C. E. $AlCl_3 : 3\ Ag$	**47,** 603 (1925)
Antimony	121.76	Willard & McAlpine	1922	C. E. $SbBr_3 : 3\ Ag$	**44,** 432 (1922)
Argon	39.944	Baxter and Starkweather	1928	Limiting density	**50,** 609 (1928)
Arsenic	74.91	Baxter et al.	1933	C. E. $AsBr_3 : 3\ Ag$	**56,** 757 (1934)
Barium	137.36	Hönigschmid & Sachtleben	1929	C. E. $Ba(ClO_4)_2 : 2\ Ag$	**51,** 649 (1929)
Beryllium	9.02	Hönigschmid & Birckenbach	1922	C. E. $BeCl_2 : 2\ Ag : 2\ AgCl$	**47,** 598 (1925)
Bismuth	209.00	Hönigschmid & Birckenbach	1921	C. E. $BiCl_3 : 3\ Ag$	**47,** 598 (1925)
Boron	10.82	Baxter et al.	1923	C. E. $BCl_3 : 3\ Ag$	**47,** 598 (1925)
Bromine	79.916	Baxter	1905	C. E. Ag : AgBr	**47,** 598 (1925)
Cadmium	112.41	Baxter et al.	1916	C. E. Cd : $CdBr_2$	**39,** 336 (1917)
Calcium	40.08	Hönigschmid & Kempter	1930	C. E. $CaCl_2 : 2\ AgCl$	**53,** 1631 (1931)
Carbon	12.010	Baxter et al.	1937	C. E. Combustion; $C_6H_5COCl : Ag$	**60,** 737 (1938)
Cerium	140.13	Hönigschmid & Holch	1928	C. E. $CeCl_3 : 3\ Ag$	**51,** 649 (1929)
Cesium	132.91	Baxter & Thomas	1933	C. E. CsCl : Ag	**56,** 759 (1934)
Chlorine	35.457	Richards & Wells	1905	C. E. Ag : AgCl	**47,** 598 (1925)
Chromium	52.01	Baxter et al.	1909	C. E. $Ag_2CrO_4 : 2\ Ag$	**47,** 598 (1925)
Cobalt	58.94	Baxter & Dorcas	1924	C. E. $CoCl_2 : 2\ Ag$	**47,** 599 (1925)
Columbium	92.91	Hönigschmid & Wintersberger	1934	C. E. $CbCl_5 : 5\ Ag$	**57,** 790 (1935)
Copper	63.57	Richards	1887	C. E. Cu : 2 Ag	**31,** 5 (1909)
Dysprosium	162.46	Hönigschmid & Welsbach	1925	C. E. $DyCl_3 : 3\ Ag : 3\ AgCl$	**50,** 613 (1928)
Erbium	167.2	Hönigschmid & Wittner	1937	C. E. $ErCl_3 : 3\ Ag : 3\ AgCl$	**60,** 743 (1938)
Europium	152.0	Jantsch	1908	C. E. $Eu_2O_3 : Eu_2(SO_4)_3 8\ H_2O$	**30,** 3 (1908)
Fluorine	19.00	Moles & Batuecas	1919	Limiting density of CH_3F	**42,** 1761 (1920)
Gadolinium	156.9	Naeser & Hopkins	1935	C. E. $GdCl_3 : 3\ Ag$	**59,** 223 (1937)
Gallium	69.72	Richards & Craig	1922	C. E. $GaCl_3 : 3\ Ag$	**47,** 599 (1925)
Germanium	72.60	Baxter & Cooper	1924	C. E. $GeCl_4 : 4\ Ag$	**47,** 599 (1925)
Gold	197.2	Mallet	1889	C. E. Au : 3 Ag	**31,** 5 (1909)
Hafnium	178.6	Hönigschmid & Zintl	1925	C. E. $HfBr_4 : 4\ AgBr$	**48,** 551 (1928)
Helium	4.003	Aston, Bainbridge & Jordan	1937	Mass spectroscope	**60,** 737 (1938)
Holmium	164.94	Hönigschmid & Wittner	1940	C. E. $HoCl_3 : 3\ Ag$	**63,** 849 (1941)
Hydrogen	1.0080	Swartout & Dole; Hall & Jones	1940	Mass spectroscope	**62,** 669 (1940)

Element	At. Wt.	Determined By	Year	Method	Reference *J. Am. Chem. Soc.*
Indium	114.76	Baxter & Alter	1933	C. E. $InCl_3 : 3\ Ag$	**56,** 758 (1934)
Iodine	126.92	Hönigschmid & Striebel	1932	C. E. $AgI : AgCl$	**55,** 445 (1933)
Iridium	193.1	A. Joly	1890	C. E. $3\ KCl : K_3\ Ir\ Cl_6$	**31,** 5 (1909)
Iron	55.85	Baxter & Hoover	1912	C. E. $Fe_2O_3 : 2\ Fe$	**62,** 669 (1940)
Krypton	83.7	Watson	1931	Limiting pressure	**54,** 1272 (1932)
Lanthanum	138.92	Baxter & Behrens	1932	C. E. $LaBr_3 : 3\ Ag : 3\ AgBr$	**55,** 446 (1933)
Lead	207.21	Hecht & Kroupa	1937	C. E. $PbCl_2 : 2\ AgCl$	**59,** 224 (1937)
Lithium	6.940	Richards & Willard	1910	C. E. $LiCl : AgCl : Ag$	**47,** 599 (1925)
Lutecium	174.99	Hönigschmid & Wittner	1939	C. E. $LuCl_3 : 3\ AgCl$	
Magnesium	24.32	Richards & Parker	1896	C. E. $MgCl_2 : 2\ Ag$	**31,** 1 (1909)
Manganese	54.93	Baxter & Hines	1906	$MnBr_2 : 2\ AgBr$	**31,** 5 (1909)
Mercury	200.61	Hönigschmid & Birckenbach	1923	$HgCl_2 : 2\ Ag$	**47,** 599 (1925)
Molybdenum	95.95	Hönigschmid & Wittman	1936	C. E. $MoCl_5 : 5\ Ag$	**60,** 741 (1937)
Neodynium	144.27	Baxter & Chapin	1911	C. E. $NdCl_3 : 3\ Ag : 3\ AgCl$	**33,** 1 (1911)
Neon	20.183	Baxter & Starkweather	1928	Limiting density	**50,** 605 (1928)
Nickel	58.69	Baxter & Parsons	1921	C. E. $Ni : O$	**44,** 430 (1922)
Nitrogen	14.008	Scheuer	1912	Limiting densities of oxides	**35,** 1807 (1913)
Osmium	190.2	Nier	1937	Mass spectroscope	**60,** 743 (1928)
Oxygen	**16.0000**	**(Standard)**			
Palladium	106.7	Amberg	1906	C. E. $Pd : PdCl_2(NH_3)_2$	**29,** 108 (1907)
Phosphorus	30.98	Hönigschmid & Wenn	1937	C. E. $POCl_3 : 3\ Ag : 3\ AgCl$	**61,** 223 (1939)
Platinum	195.23	Archibald et al.	1909	C. E. $Pt : K_2PtCl_6$	**32,** 1115 (1910)
Potassium	39.096	Baxter & MacNevin	1933	C. E. $KCl : Ag$	**56,** 755 (1934)
Praseodymium	140.92	Baxter & Stewart	1915	C. E. $PrCl_3 : 3\ Ag : 3\ AgCl$	**37,** 516 (1915)
Protactinium	231	von Grosse	1935	C. E. $2\ K_2PaF_7 : Pa_2O_3$	**58,** 545 (1936)
Radium	226.05	Hönigschmid & Sachtleben	1934	C. E. $RaBr_2 : RaCl_2$	**58,** 545 (1936)
Radon	222	Gray & Ramsay	1911	Limiting pressure	**33,** 1641 (1911)
Rhenium	186.31	Hönigschmid & Sachtleben	1930	C. E. $AgReO_4 : AgBr$	**53,** 1635 (1931)
Rhodium	102.91	Renz	1911	C. E. $Rh : Rh(NH_3)_5Br_3$	**32,** 1115 (1910)
Rubidium	85.48	Archibald et al.	1936	C. E. $RbCl : Ag$	**59,** 222 (1937)
Ruthenium	101.7		1900		**31,** 5 (1909)
Samarium	150.43	Stewart & James	1917	C. E. $SmCl_3 : 3\ Ag$	**39,** 2605 (1917)
Scandium	45.10	Hönigschmid	1920	C. E. $ScBr : 3\ Ag$	**43,** 386 (1931)

TABLE 6

ATOMIC WEIGHTS AND THEIR DETERMINATION (*Continued*)

ELEMENT	AT. WT.	DETERMINED BY	YEAR	METHOD	REFERENCE *J. Am. Chem. Soc.*
Selenium	78.96	Hönigschmid & Kapfenberger	1933	C. E. 2 Ag : Ag_2Se	**56,** 759 (1934)
Silicon	28.06	Baxter et al.	1923	C. E. $SiCl_4$: 4 Ag	**47,** 599 (1925)
Silver	107.880	Richards & Forbes	1907	C. E. Ag : $AgNO_3$	**30,** 310 (1908)
Sodium	22.997	Goldbaum	1912	C. E. Na : NaCl	**34,** 226 (1912)
Strontium	87.63	Richards, Thorpe & Francis	1909	C. E. 2 Ag : $SrCl_2$ 2 Ag : $SrBr_2$: $SrSO_4$	**32,** 1114 (1910)
Sulfur	32.06	Richards & Jones	1907	C. E. 2 AgCl : Ag_2SO_4	**53,** 1630 (1931)
Tantalum	180.88	Hönigschmid & Schlee	1934	C. E. $TaBr_5$: 5 Ag	**58,** 545 (1934)
Tellurium	127.61	Hönigschmid et al.	1933	C. E. $TeBr_4$: 4 Ag	**56,** 759 (1934)
Terbium	159.2	Urbain	1907	C. E. $Tb_2(SO_4)_3$: 8 H_2O	**29,** 109 (1907)
Thallium	204.39	Hönigschmid et al.	1922	C. E. TlCl : Ag : AgCl	**47,** 599 (1925)
Thorium	232.12	Hönigschmid	1916		**51,** 654 (1929)
Thulium	169.4	James & Stewart	1920	C. E. $TmCl_3$: 3 Ag	**42,** 2022 (1920)
Tin	118.70	Briscoe	1915	C. E. $SnCl_4$: 4 Ag	**38,** 490 (1916)
Titanium	47.90	Baxter & Butler	1923	C. E. $TiCl_4$: 4 Ag	**49,** 586 (1927)
Tungsten	183.92	Hönigschmid & Wenn	1936	C. E. WCl_6 : 6 Ag	**60,** 743 (1938)
Uranium	238.07	Hönigschmid & Wittner	1935	C. E. UCl_4 : 4 Ag : 4 AgCl UBr_4 : 4 Ag : 4 AgBr	**59,** 224 (1937)
Vanadium	50.95	Scott & Johnson	1929	C. E. $VOCl_3$: 3 Ag : 3 AgCl	**53,** 1632 (1931)
Xenon	131.3	Whytlaw-Gray et al.	1931	Limiting pressure	**54,** 1272 (1932)
Ytterbium	173.04	Hönigschmid & Striebel	1933	C. E. $YbCl_3$: 3 Ag : 3 AgCl	**56,** 753 (1934)
Yttrium	88.92	Hönigschmid & Welsbach	1927	C. E. YCl_3 : 3 Ag : 3 AgCl	**50,** 611 (1928)
Zinc	65.38	Richards & Rogers	1895	C. E. $ZnCl_2$: 2 Ag	**18,** 203 (1896)
Zirconium	91.22	Hönigschmid	1925	C. E. $ZrBr_4$: 4 Ag : 4 AgBr	**47,** 608 (1925)

5 shows the method by which the atomic weight was determined; the chemical equivalent weight method is indicated by "C.E." followed by one analytical ratio employed. Certain of the older values have been recalculated several times because of changes in the values for Ag, Cl, and other atomic weights frequently used in analytical ratios. The *limiting density method* and *limiting pressure method* are described briefly on page 108 *et seq.*

PROBLEMS AND EXERCISES

1. Assuming Avogadro's number, calculate the number of molecules in:
(*a*) 1.600 l. of chlorine at S.T.P.
(*b*) 1.600 l. of chlorine at 70° C. and 780 mm. pressure.
(*c*) 6.000 g. of dextrose, $C_6H_{12}O_6$.
(*d*) 0.0001000 g. of sucrose, $C_{12}H_{22}O_{11}$.
(*e*) 1.000 ml. of water at 4° C. (density = 1.000 g./ml.).
(*f*) 1.000 ml. of water at 20° C. (density = 0.9982 g./ml.).

2. Assuming that the gas laws are obeyed, find the molar volume of a gas at:
(*a*) 100° C. and 20 mm. pressure.
(*b*) − 100° C. and 20 atmospheres pressure.

3. Calculate the density of each of the following gases (1) at S.T.P. and (2) at 50° C. and 5 atmospheres pressure:
(*a*) hydrogen bromide; (*b*) ammonia; (*c*) helium.

4. Compute the following atomic weights from the data given:
(*a*) *Tin:* Wt. stannic chloride = 9.39855 g.; wt. silver = 15.5666 g.; at. wt. Cl = 35.457; at. wt. Ag = 107.880.
(*b*) *Cadmium:* Wt. cadmium carbonate = 0.6600 g.; wt. cadmium = 0.4302 g.; at. wt. C. = 12.010.
(*c*) *Lead:* Wt. lead bromide = 6.28465 g.; wt. silver bromide = 6.43124 g.; at. wt. Br = 79.916; at. wt. Ag = 107.880.

5. Plot the coefficients of compressibility of the elements given in Table 3 against their atomic numbers and predict the coefficients of compressibility of vanadium and tellurium.

6. Make a similar plot of the coefficients of thermal expansibility and predict the coefficient for germanium, scandium, and titanium.

7. Plot the densities and melting points of the elements given in Table 3 against their atomic numbers, using such a scale that both curves can be put on the same graph paper. Do these curves show a periodic variation? How do they compare with the atomic volume curve and the other curves of Figure 4?

READING LIST

Alembic Club Reprints, No. 2, "Foundations of the Atomic Theory." Papers by Dalton and others. No. 4 "Foundations of the Molecular Theory." Papers by Dalton, Gay-Lussac, and Avogadro.

Alexander Findlay, *A Hundred Years of Chemistry*. The Macmillan Company, New York, 1937. A historical sketch of exceptional interest. See especially pp. 46–63.

Ida Freund, *The Study of Chemical Composition*. Cambridge Univ. Press, London, 1904. Excellent historical and critical discussion of fundamental laws and theories.

Joshua C. Gregory, *A Short History of Atomism*. A. & C. Black, London, 1931. A discussion of atoms from the times of the Greek philosophers to the "coming of the electron."

W. B. Meldrum and F. T. Gucker, Jr., *Introduction to Theoretical Chemistry*, American Book Company, New York, 1936. See especially pp. 1–45.

W. M. Travers, *The Discovery of the Rare Gases*. E. Arnold & Co., London, 1928. A well-told story by one who was in daily contact with the work.

Mary Elvira Weeks, *The Discovery of the Elements*, 4th ed. Published by the *Journal of Chemical Education*, Easton, Pa., 1939. A valuable source of information on the elements.

F. P. Venable, *The Periodic Law*. Chemical Publishing Company, Easton, Pa., 1896. Includes charts of various suggested arrangements of the elements.

CHAPTER 3

THE STRUCTURE OF ATOMS AND MOLECULES

A knowledge of the structure of atoms and molecules is essential to the understanding of many concepts in physical chemistry, such as the difference between an electrolyte and a nonelectrolyte, the mechanism of ionic dissociation and of electrolytic decomposition, and the behavior of galvanic cells. We cannot give here a complete presentation of the properties of the atom and of the theories of atomic structure; for this one must consult books devoted more exclusively to this large and important physicochemical field (see page 73). We can only review those features of the subject essential to the understanding of the behavior of substances in solution and other phenomena in elementary physical and physiological chemistry.

In the development of the theories of atomic structure, as has frequently been the case in advancing science, investigation in several apparently unrelated fields played a part. We shall deal with these very briefly.

Prout's Hypothesis. The idea of thc unity of matter, founded on something more than abstract philosophical speculation, was introduced by Dr. William Prout, an English physician, in 1815, eleven years after John Dalton had enunciated his atomic theory. Prout concluded that the atomic weights of the elements were integral multiples of the atomic weight of hydrogen and, therefore, that hydrogen must be the "primordial substance" of which all matter is composed. More accurate determinations of atomic weights, especially by Berzelius, Dumas, and Stas, definitely proved that certain atomic weights, notably those of chlorine, copper, and zinc, were not integral multiples of that of hydrogen. Since the premise was false, the conclusion probably was also, and Prout's hypothesis was completely discredited. Stas, whose painstaking atomic weight determinations were inspired by the desire to test Prout's hypothesis, wrote: "I have arrived at the absolute conviction, the complete certainty, as far as it is possible for a human being to attain to certainty in such matters, that the law of Prout is nothing but an illusion, a mere speculation definitely contradicted by experience." The determination of a larger number of atomic weights showed, however, that they were not scattered at random, but that more of them than the laws of probability predicted were approximately multiples of the atomic weight of hydrogen. Mendeléeff's discovery, in 1869, that the properties of the elements were repeated periodically when they were arranged in the order of their atomic weights, suggested that there must be some characteristic, other than the mere weights of the atoms, which determines the properties of the elements.

Radiations in Evacuated Tubes. At atmospheric pressure, air or any other gas is a poor conductor of electricity. The discharge between the terminals of an induction coil passes as a violent spark at a potential drop of about 35,000 volts per cm. However, when the pressure is diminished, the discharge passes more readily, the conductance apparently reaching a maximum at a pressure of about 0.1 mm.

If the discharge is passed through a tube of the form shown in Figure 6, evacuated to about 0.1 mm. pressure, in which C is the cathode and A the anode, radiations of three types are produced:

(1) Cathode rays. These consist of electrons which are shot off perpendicularly from the cathode with a speed of 10,000 to 90,000 miles per second, depending upon the voltage. They are negatively charged particles since they are bent towards the positive plate in an electrical field. Like light, they mark the photographic plate. When they impinge on glass or other material, they cause it to fluoresce.

(2) Positive rays. These are dimly luminous and consist of positively charged particles of atomic or molecular mass. They are, in fact, gas ions, such as N_2^+, N^+, O_2^+, and O^+, depending upon the gas present in the tube. They are formed by collision of the cathode rays with the gas molecules in the evacuated tube. Their positive charge is indicated by their deflection towards the negative electrode in an electrical field. Their mass may be computed from the extent of deflection, the strength of the field, and the charge on the particle.

(3) X rays. X rays are produced when cathode rays strike matter, *e.g.*, the glass at the end of the tube shown in Figure 6. They consist not of matter but of electromagnetic waves which are unaffected by electric and magnetic fields and travel with the velocity of light. The wave lengths of visible light lie between

4000 and 8000 Å (1 Å = 10^{-8} cm.), but those of X rays are very much shorter, between 0.1 and 100 Å. Because of their short wave lengths they are highly penetrating. X rays produced at high voltages have shorter wave lengths and are more penetrating

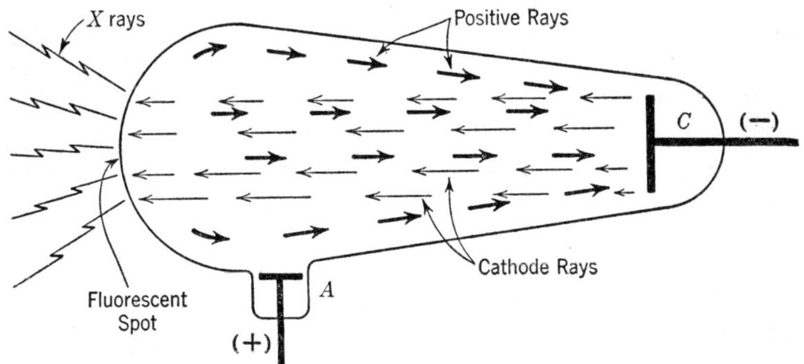

Fig. 6. Cathode-Ray Tube, Showing Types of Radiations.

than those produced at low voltages; the shorter waves compose the *hard X rays* and the longer waves, the *soft X rays.* X rays affect the photographic plate just as light does.

Radioactivity. Henri Becquerel, in 1895, discovered the radioactivity of *uranium* compounds and showed that it was an atomic property and not dependent upon the state of combination of the active element. In 1898 Pierre and Marie Curie discovered the strongly radioactive elements *polonium* and *radium,* the chemical properties of which placed them in the same groups in the periodic table as bismuth and barium, respectively. The discovery of the radioactivity of *thorium* and of the radioactive elements *actinium* and *ionium* followed.

The radiations from radium were systematically studied and identified as belonging to three types, designated by Rutherford as *alpha, beta,* and *gamma* rays, respectively, all of which affect the photographic plate, ionize the air and so render it conducting, and cause fluorescence in certain substances upon which they impinge. The *alpha* and *beta* rays were shown to consist of charged particles; the *gamma* rays of waves. In order to determine the nature of the rays the experiment illustrated in Figure 7 was performed. Some radioactive material was placed in a hole bored in a lead block *B.* Suitably placed lead screens and slits *S* selected a narrow beam of radiations which passed perpendicularly through a strong electrical field applied between the plates C and fell on the photographic plate P. As shown in the diagram, the electrical field separated the beam into three kinds of rays having the following characteristics:

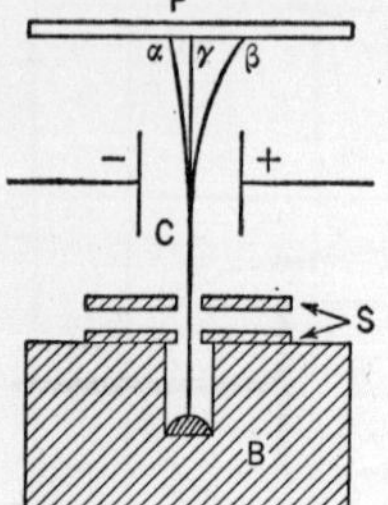

Fig. 7. Identification of Radiations from Radium.

(1) **α rays.** These are slightly deflected from their course towards the negative electrode. They consist of doubly charged helium ions He^{++}, moving with a velocity of about 10,000 miles per second.

(2) **β rays.** These are strongly deflected towards the positive electrode and are electrons moving with velocities ranging from 50,000 to 180,000 miles per second.

(3) **γ rays.** These are not deflected by the field and consist of electromagnetic waves moving with the velocity of light. They are similar to X rays, but their wave lengths are generally shorter, 0.01 to 1 Å, and hence they are more penetrating.

Brilliant investigations by Rutherford, Soddy, Mme. Curie, and others soon disclosed the nature of radioactive change. Soddy advanced the *theory of radioactive disintegration,* now completely accepted. It was proved that radium emits α rays, producing a gas, *radon,* which in turn emits α rays and produces a solid element, *radium A,* which also is radioactive. Ramsay determined the atomic weight of radium as 226, and that of radon as 222; the difference is 4, corresponding to the mass of the helium atom or of the α particle. This indicated a definite transmutation of radium into radon and helium, thus:

$$\text{Ra} \longrightarrow \text{Rn} + \text{He}^{++} + 2\,\epsilon$$

The three radioactive series, called the *uranium series,* the *actinium series,* and the *thorium series,* respectively, are given in Figure 8. The **half life,** shown in this chart, *is the time in which the radioactivity of the given element diminishes to half its initial value.*

Isotopes. During an investigation which led to the discovery of *ionium,* the parent element of radium, Boltwood found that if the ionium became mixed with thorium he could not separate them. It was found, also, that thorium and radiothorium likewise were inseparable, as were radium and mesothorium I. In 1913, Soddy

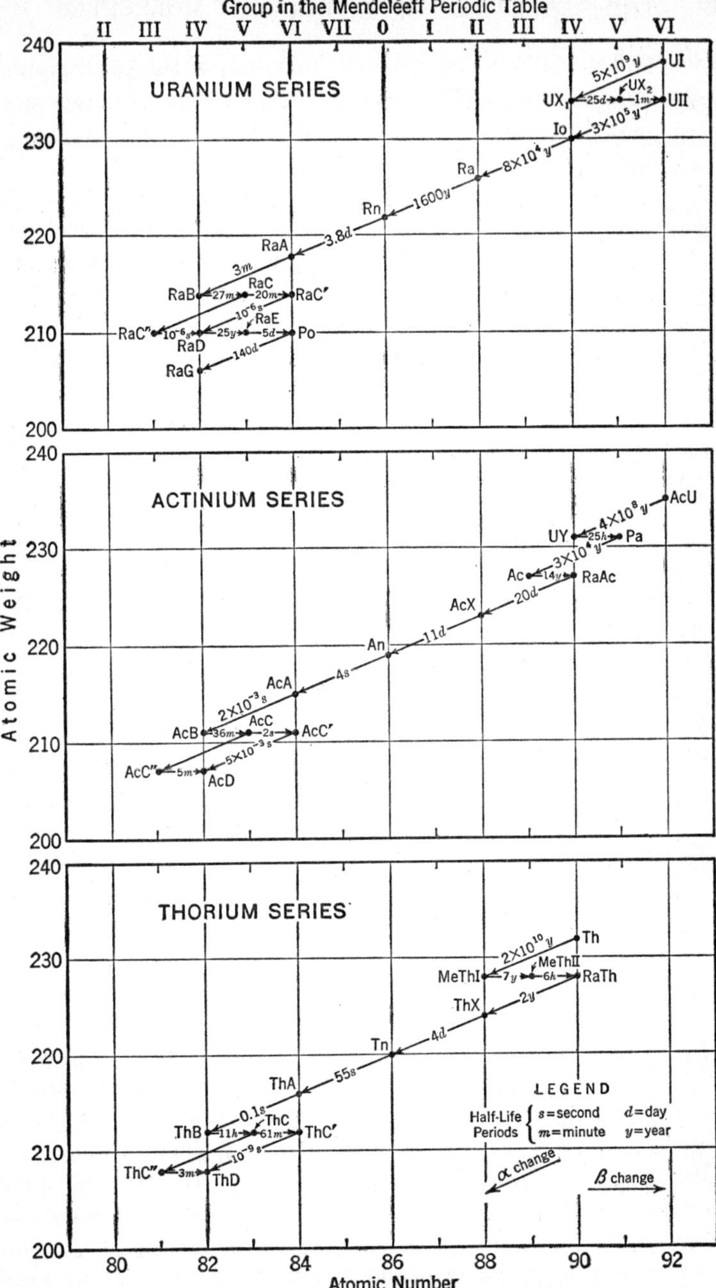

Fig. 8. The Three Radioactive Disintegration Series.

proposed for such inseparable elements the name **isotopes**,[1] because, having the same chemical properties, "they occupy the same place in the periodic table."

By this time the three radioactive disintegration series had been worked out. The end product of each of the series was *lead*, but the atomic weights deduced for the end products were 206, 207, and 208, respectively, and not the known atomic weight of lead, 207.21. Soddy suggested that the atomic weight of lead found in radioactive minerals, and hence of radioactive origin, might be different depending upon whether its parent element was *uranium*, *actinium*, or *thorium*. T. W. Richards, O. Hönigschmid, and others sought to test this idea and obtained convincing results, as shown in Table 7. They found atomic weights of lead ranging from 206.05 to 207.77, thus establishing not only the existence of *isotopes* of lead but also the validity of the radioactive disintegration series.

TABLE 7

ATOMIC WEIGHTS OF LEAD FROM VARIOUS SOURCES

SOURCE OF LEAD	AT. WT.	EXPERIMENTERS
Thorium Minerals:		
Thorite, Norway	207.9	Hönigschmid
Thorite, Ceylon	207.77	Hönigschmid
Thorianite, Ceylon	206.82	Richards and Lembert
Thorianite, Ceylon	206.84	Hönigschmid
"Ordinary lead"	**207.21**	(Accepted value, Intern. Com. on At. Wts., 1941)
Uranium Minerals:		
Pitchblende, Joachimstahl	206.57	Richards and Lembert
Pitchblende, Joachimstahl	206.61	Fajans
Uraninite, South Dakota	206.06	Richards
Cleveite, Norway	206.08	Richards and Wadsworth
Pitchblende, Katanga	206.05	Baxter and Bliss

The existence of isotopes of other elements was established and the isotopic weights were determined by means of **positive-ray analysis** with the **mass spectrograph.** Positive rays are formed in a discharge tube, and pass through a perforated cathode into a space where they are deflected by suitable electric and magnetic fields. Other things being equal the deflection will be proportional to the charge on the ion and inversely proportional to its mass. Thus, if the apparatus is standardized with oxygen and then used under the same conditions with other gases, the isotopic weights of the other gases are determined relative to that of the most

[1] From ἴσος, equal + τόπος, place.

abundant isotope of oxygen taken as 16.00000. Based upon the earlier method of Sir J. J. Thomson, the mass spectrograph was developed by Aston and greatly improved by Hahn, Dempster, Mattauch, and Bainbridge and Jordan, and has become an instrument of high precision.[1]

Truly remarkable results have been obtained which we can only summarize here:

(1) Nearly all the elements as they occur in nature are mixtures of isotopes. Of the common elements only F, Na, Al, Mn, Co, I, Au, and Bi seem to be exceptions. Oxygen itself, the *standard element* for atomic weights, consists of three isotopes with relative masses 16, 17, and 18, of which the isotope of mass 16, O^{16}, greatly predominates. The relative abundances are $O^{16}:O^{17}:O^{18} = 2550 : 1 : 5$, which makes the atomic weight of "ordinary oxygen" 0.027 per cent higher than that of the O^{16} isotope.

(2) The isotopic weights are very nearly whole numbers on the basis of $O^{16} = 16.00000$. For most of them the difference is 0.1 per cent or less, and for all but hydrogen it is less than 0.2 per cent. Thus Prout's hypothesis is substantiated for the isotopes of the various atomic species.

The most convenient method of expressing the divergence of any particular isotopic weight from the whole number rule, is to state the *fractional difference* between the isotopic weight and the nearest whole number. This fractional difference is known as the **packing fraction** of an isotope, and usually is expressed in parts per 10,000. Taking chlorine as an example, the actual algebraic difference between the lighter isotope and the nearest whole number is $34.9804 - 35.0000 = -0.0196$. The fractional difference is $-0.0196 \div 35.0 = -0.00056$; hence the packing fraction is -5.6. In other words, the atomic weight of Cl^{35} is 5.6 parts in 10,000 *less* than the integral value 35.0000.

The determination of the packing fractions of the elements by means of the mass spectrograph has led to the results given in Table 8 and plotted in Figure 9, where packing fractions as ordinates are plotted against mass numbers as abscissas. This figure is substantially the same as that first given by Aston[2] but

[1] For details regarding the mass spectrograph in its various forms see Meldrum and Gucker, *Introduction to Theoretical Chemistry*, pp. 495–516. See also Aston, *Mass Spectra and Isotopes*. Longmans, Green & Co., London, 1933.

[2] Aston, "A New Mass Spectrograph and the Whole Number Rule," *Proc. Roy. Soc.* (Lond.), **A 115**, 487 (1927).

TABLE 8

Packing Fractions of the Known Atoms

Symbol	Mass Number	Packing Fraction	Symbol	Mass Number	Packing Fraction	Symbol	Mass Number	Packing Fraction
n	1	89.5	Co	59	(− 7.0)	Sa		(− 2.4)
H	1	81.3	Ni	58	(− 7.1)	Eu		(− 2.2)
D	2	73.6	Ni	60	− 6.8	Gd	155, 156, 157	− 1.5
He	3	56.7	Cu	63, 65	− 6.9	Tb		(− 1.4)
He	4	9.6	Zn	64	− 6.8	Dy		(− 1.0)
Li	6	28.1	Zn	66	− 7.3	Ho	165	(− 0.8)
Li	7	25.9	Zn	68, 70	− 6.5	Er		(− 0.6)
Be	9	16.7	Ga	69	− 6.5	Tm	169	(− 0.4)
B	10	16.2	Ga	71	− 6.6	Yb		(0.0)
B	11	11.7	Ge		(− 6.7)	Lu		(+ 0.2)
C	12	3.2	As	75	(− 6.9)	Hf		(0.5)
C	13	5.8	Se		(− 7.2)	Ta		(0.8)
N	14	5.4	Br		(− 7.3)	W		(1.0)
N	15	3.3	Kr	78	− 7.0	Re		(1.2)
O	**16**	**0.00**	Kr	82	− 7.5	Os	188	(1.6)
O	17	2.6	Kr	84	− 7.3	Os	190, 192	(2.0)
O	18	2.7	Kr	86	− 7.1	Ir	191, 193	(2.1)
F	19	2.4	Rb		(− 7.2)	Pt	194, 195, 196	2.0
Ne	20	− 0.5	Sr		(− 6.9)	Pt	198	2.2
Ne	21	− 0.1	Y		(− 6.7)	Hg		(2.4)
Ne	22	− 0.6	Zr		(− 6.4)	Tl	203, 205	2.8
Na	23	− 1.6	Cb		(− 6.2)	Pb	204	2.8
Mg	24	− 3.1	Mo	95	− 5.8	Pb	208	2.7
Mg	25	− 2.4	Mo	96	− 5.6	Bi	209	2.6
Mg	26	− 3.9	Mo	97, 98	− 5.7	Po	210	2.8
Al	27	− 3.6	Ru	96, 99	− 5.7	AcC′	211	3.1
Si	28	− 4.6	Rh	103	(− 5.3)	ThC′	212	3.2
Si	29	− 4.7	Pd		− 5.2	RaC′	214	3.5
Si	30	− 5.5	Ag	107, 109	− 4.8	AcA	215	3.7
P	31	− 4.8	Cd		(− 5.0)	ThA	216	3.8
S	32	− 5.5	In		(− 4.9)	RaA	218	4.2
S	34	− 5.8	Zn	116	− 5.0	An	219	4.2
Cl	35	− 5.6	Zn	118	− 5.1	Tn	220	4.2
Cl	37	− 5.8	Zn	119	− 5.2	Rn	222	4.5
A	36	− 5.8	Zn	122, 124	− 4.6	AcX	223	4.6
A	40	− 6.1	Sb		(− 4.7)	ThX	224	4.6
K	39, 40, 41	(− 6.0)	Te		(− 4.4)	Ra	226	4.9
Ca		(− 6.2)	I		(− 4.4)	Ac	227	4.9
Sc	45	(− 6.9)	Xe	129	− 4.2	RaAc	227	4.8
Ti	48	− 7.1	Xe	132	− 4.1	RaTh	228	5.0
Ti	49, 50	− 7.4	Ce	133	(− 4.0)	Io	232	5.3
V	51	(− 7.4)	Ba		(− 3.7)	Th	232	5.5
Cr	52	− 7.9	La	139	− 3.2	Pa	231	5.4
Mn	55	(− 7.3)	Ce		(− 3.5)	UII	234	5.5
Fe	54	− 7.4	Pr	141	(− 3.4)	AcU	235	5.7
Fe	56	− 7.0	Nd	146, 148, 150	− 2.6	UI	238	6.1

Data from the "Annual Isotope Report" by Hahn, Flügge, and Mattauch, *Ber.*, **73A**, 1 (1940). Values in parentheses are uncertain.

includes also the results of later work which he and other workers have carried out. The **mass number** is simply the whole number nearest the isotopic weight. Thus the mass number of the isotope of arsenic with an isotopic weight 74.934 is 75. It is designated as a superscript, As^{75}.

An inspection of the curve in Figure 9 brings out a number of important facts. The packing fractions of all of the atoms except He^4, C^{12}, and O^{16} lie along a smooth curve which is nearly hyperbolic. Falling steeply from its maximum value of 81.3 for H^1 and crossing the zero axis at O^{16}, this curve passes through a flat minimum value of about -10 near Cr^{52} and then increases almost linearly. It recrosses the zero axis at a mass number of about 175 and thence continues upward toward the higher mass number elements. The curve is very useful, because its regularity allows

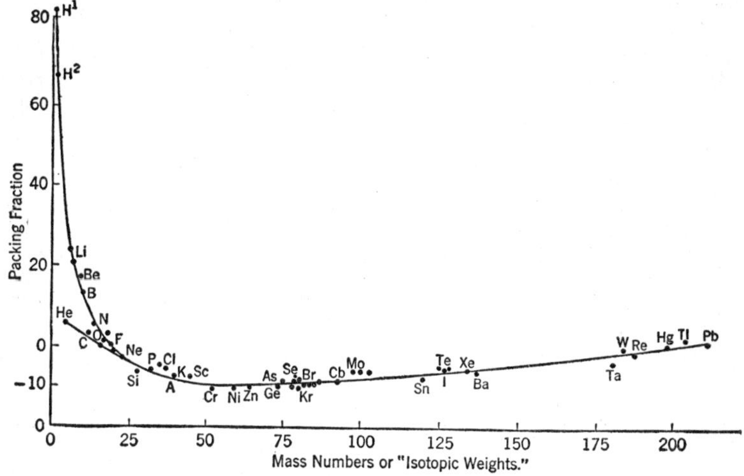

Fig. 9. Curve of Packing Fractions.

us to find, by graphical interpolation, the approximate packing fraction of an element which has not yet been studied in the mass spectrograph. It is also of great theoretical significance in connection with the stability of different atomic nuclei. The relation between packing fraction and the stability of atomic nuclei is well brought out by the fact that the light elements of odd atomic number, which lie along the left branch of the curve, are the elements which are disintegrated most easily by bombardment with α particles or protons. They are much less stable than the elements of even atomic number, which lie along the lower curve. If we extend the curve to the right, in the direction of higher atomic weights, we see that once more the packing fraction is positive; and from this we might expect the nuclei of the heaviest elements to be unstable. This is indeed the case, for it is among these elements that we find radioactivity and spontaneous disintegration. The packing fraction curve then represents the *relative stability* of the elements. The zero line is taken arbitrarily on the basis of the oxygen atom. Elements with a positive packing fraction are less stable than oxygen, while those with a negative packing fraction are more stable. The most stable elements are those with the smallest packing fraction.

(3) The atomic weight of an element is the average of the isotopic weights, obtained by adding the products of the isotopic weights and the fractional abundance of each.

(4) Elements with fractional atomic weights are mixtures of two or more isotopes. For example, chlorine, zinc, cadmium, and tin are mixtures of two, five, eight, and ten isotopes, respectively.

(5) In 1932 H. C. Urey of Columbia University proved the existence of two isotopes of hydrogen, of which the lighter, sometimes called *protium*, H, has the isotopic weight *1*, and the heavier, *deuterium*, D, has the isotopic weight *2*. In ordinary hydrogen the ratio of the two isotopes is about H : D = 6400 : 1 (page 37). Water made from deuterium is called *heavy water*, or *deuterium oxide;* it has a molecular weight of 20, instead of 18 as for ordinary water. A comparison of the properties of ordinary water and heavy water is given in Table 9.

TABLE 9

COMPARISON OF THE PROPERTIES OF ORDINARY AND HEAVY WATER

PROPERTY	H_2O	D_2O
Melting point	0.00° C.	3.82° C.
Boiling point	100.00° C.	101.42° C.
Relative density at 25° C. . . .	1.0000	1.1076
Temperature of maximum density .	4.0° C.	11.6° C.
Surface tension	72.75 dynes/cm.	67.8 dynes/cm.
Heat of fusion	1436 cal./mole	1510 cal./mole
Heat of vaporization	10,484 cal./mole	10,743 cal./mole
Dielectric constant at 25° C. . . .	78.54	78.25
Refractive index (D line of Na, 20° C.)	1.33300	1.32828
Equivalent conductance at 18° C. .	(H_3O^+) 315.2 mhos (K^+) 64.2 mhos	(D_3O^+) 213.7 mhos (K^+) 54.5 mhos
Solubility of NaCl at 25° C. . . .	6.145 *m*	5.653 *m*

A comparison of some of the properties of H and D is shown in Table 10.

TABLE 10

COMPARISON OF THE PROPERTIES OF THE HYDROGEN ISOTOPES

PROPERTY	H_2	D_2
Boiling point	20.38° A.	23.50° A.
Triple point.	13.92° A.	18.58° A.
Heat of fusion	28 cal./mole	47 cal./mole
Heat of vaporization at triple point . . .	217.7 cal./mole	303.1 cal./mole

(6) The physical and chemical properties of isotopes of elements other than hydrogen are virtually identical. The same is true of the properties of their compounds.

(7) Isotopes of certain elements, particularly radioactive isotopes, are useful as *tracers* in following various physical and chemical processes and physiological changes.

A list of isotopes is given in Table 11 on page 54.

The Use of Isotopes as Tracers. Few developments in recent years give greater promise of fruitful application to research than the discovery that isotopes can be used as *tracers*, or *indicators*, to follow the course of reactions. This type of investigation already has led to important results in several widely different fields. In the field of physiology and biochemistry results are particularly significant.

The applicability of isotopes as tracers depends mainly upon two factors: First, isotopic tracers have chemical properties which are virtually identical with those of the ordinary element; and, second, they exhibit differences in certain physical properties, such as density and radioactivity, which make possible their identification and quantitative measurement. Different isotopes of an element enter into the same chemical reactions, forming the same types of compounds, which react in just the same way and with the same vigor. Hydrogen differs in this respect from other elements; although deuterium, D or H^2, behaves like protium, H^1, and forms precisely the same types of compounds, its compounds may show differences in reactivity.

Isotopic tracers may be placed in three classes: (1) Those with atomic mass measurably different from that of the most abundant isotope; (2) naturally radioactive isotopes; (3) artificially radioactive isotopes.

Of the first group *deuterium* and *heavy nitrogen* N^{15} have found the most important application. Deuterium, as the element or in heavy water, may be introduced into inorganic compounds by interaction of heavy water with anhydrides, and into organic compounds by *exchange reactions* with heavy water or by hydrogenation of unsaturated substances. To analyze for it in organic compounds, the substance is burned, the water formed in the combustion collected, and the deuterium content calculated from the density of the water (see page 52). Heavy nitrogen is usually determined from the relative intensities of the lines obtained with the mass spectrograph.

TABLE 11

ISOTOPES OF THE ELEMENTS

(Isotopes of more than 90 per cent abundance are shown in **boldface**; those of less than 1 per cent abundance are shown in *italics*.)

AT. NO.	SYMBOL	ISOTOPES
1	H	**1**, 2
2	He	*3*, **4**
3	Li	6, **7**
4	Be	**9**
5	B	10, 11
6	C	**12**, 13
7	N	**14**, *15*
8	O	**16**, *17*, *18*
9	F	**19**
10	Ne	**20**, *21*, 22
11	Na	**23**
12	Mg	24, 25, 26
13	Al	**27**
14	Si	**28**, 29, 30
15	P	**31**
16	S	**32**, *33*, 34, *36*
17	Cl	35, 37
18	A	*36*, *38*, **40**
19	K	**39**, *40*, 41
20	Ca	**40**, *42*, *43*, 44, *46*, *48*
21	Sc	**45**
22	Ti	46, 47, 48, 49, 50
23	V	**51**
24	Cr	50, 52, 53, 54
25	Mn	**55**
26	Fe	54, **56**, 57, *58*
27	Co	**59**
28	Ni	58, 60, *61*, 62, *64*
29	Cu	63, 65
30	Zn	64, 66, 67, 68, *70*
31	Ga	69, 71
32	Ge	70, 72, 73, 74, 76
33	As	**75**
34	Se	*74*, 76, 77, 78, 80, 82
35	Br	79, 81
36	Kr	*78*, 80, 82, 83, 84, 86
37	Rb	85, 87
38	Sr	*84*, 86, 87, 88
39	Y	**89**
40	Zr	90, 91, 92, 94, 96
41	Cb	**93**
42	Mo	92, 94, 95, 96, 97, 98, 100
43	—	—
44	Ru	96, *98*, 99, 100, 101, 102, 104
45	Rh	**103**
46	Pd	*102*, 104, 105, 106, 108, 110
47	Ag	107, 109
48	Cd	106, 108, 110, 111, 112, 113, 114, 116
49	In	113, **115**
50	Sn	112, 114, 115, 116, 117, 118, 119, 120, 122, 124
51	Sb	121, 123
52	Te	122, 123, 124, 125, 126, 128, 130
53	I	**127**
54	Xe	*124*, *126*, 128, 129, 130, 131, 132, 134, 136
55	Cs	**133**
56	Ba	*130*, *132*, 134, 135, 136, 137, 138
57	La	**139**
58	Ce	*136*, *138*, 140, 142
59	Pr	**141**
60	Nd	142, 143, 144, 145, 146, 148, 150
61	—	—
62	Sm	144, 147, 148, 149, 150, 152, 154
63	Eu	151, 153
64	Gd	*152*, 154, 155, 156, 157, 158, 160
65	Tb	**159**
66	Dy	*158*, 160, 161, 162, 163, 164
67	Ho	**165**
68	Er	*162*, 164, 166, 167, 168, 170
69	Tm	**169**
70	Yb	*168*, 170, 171, 172, 173, 174, 176
71	Lu	**175**, 176
72	Hf	*174*, 176, 177, 178, 179, 180
73	Ta	**181**
74	W	*180*, 182, 183, 184, 186
75	Re	185, 187
76	Os	*184*, 186, 187, 188, 189, 190, 192
77	Ir	191, 193
78	Pt	*192*, 194, 195, 196, 198
79	Au	**197**
80	Hg	*196*, 198, 199, 200, 201, 202, 204
81	Tl	203, 205
82	Pb	204, 206, 207, 208
83	Bi	**209**

(The isotopes of the radioactive elements, 84–92, are shown in Figure 8, page 47.)

From O. Hahn, S. Flügge, and J. Mattauch, *Ber.*, **73A**, 1 (1940).

The second group of isotopic tracers includes only the radioactive isotopes of certain of the heavy metals, such as ThC, which is isotopic with Bi, and RaB, which is isotopic with Pb.[1]

The tracers of the third group have almost completely supplanted those of both the others. The discovery of *artificial radioactivity* has, in fact, greatly extended the application of tracers. In 1934, Curie and Joliot[2] showed that after aluminum was bombarded with alpha particles from polonium it continued to emit *positrons*, positively charged particles of the same mass as the electron. Boron and magnesium were found to behave in the same way. Other elements likewise were rendered radioactive by bombardment with alpha particles and with other projectiles, such as protons, deuterons, and neutrons, accelerated in an electric field. According to Livingood and Seaborg,[3] 330 artificially radioactive isotopes had been produced up to the end of 1939. Radioactive isotopes of all the elements up to and including No. 85, the unknown member of the halogen group, have been produced. To illustrate the formation of an artificially radioactive isotope and its subsequent disintegration, we may consider the case of radioactive nitrogen. The bombardment of boron with alpha particles brings about the change:

$$_{5}B^{10} + {}_{2}He^{4} \longrightarrow {}^{*}_{7}N^{13} + {}_{0}n^{1}$$

The asterisk (*) indicates that the nitrogen isotope of atomic number 7 and atomic mass 13 is radioactive, and the symbol $_{0}n^{1}$ represents the neutron. The subsequent disintegration of the radioactive nitrogen may be represented thus:

$${}^{*}_{7}N^{13} \longrightarrow {}_{6}C^{13} + e^{+}$$

The symbol e^{+} represents the positron. The formation and subsequent disintegration of radioactive phosphorus may be represented thus:

$$_{13}Al^{27} + {}_{2}He^{4} \longrightarrow {}^{*}_{15}P^{30} + {}_{0}n^{1}$$

and

$${}^{*}_{15}P^{30} \longrightarrow {}_{14}Si^{30} + e^{+}$$

Artificially radioactive isotopes have been applied as tracers in various types of investigation, but "the applications [of isotopes as tracers] to chemistry that have been made so far are just the

[1] Some of the applications of the naturally radioactive isotopes as tracers are discussed by Paneth, *Radio-Elements as Indicators*. McGraw-Hill Book Co., New York, 1928.

[2] *Nature*, **133**, 201 (1934).

[3] *Rev. of Modern Physics*, **12**, 30 (1940).

beginning of what is certain to become a very large and fruitful field of research."[1] To indicate the importance of this new research tool we may mention the following applications: (1) To measure the rate of self-diffusion in solid metals, *e.g.*, gold in gold or copper in copper. Using radiogold, McKey has shown that the rate of diffusion of gold is 9.7×10^{-6} mm. per min. (2) To examine precipitation phenomena and to determine solubility of highly insoluble substances. For example, Ferla has studied the completeness of the precipitation of ammonium phosphomolybdate with the aid of radiophosphorus. (3) To study *exchange reactions* such as the following, involving radiobromine:

$$HBr^* + Br \longrightarrow HBr + Br^*$$

It is not certain to what extent the reactivity in such cases is influenced by the emitted radiations; the latter may activate the reactants. (4) To study the phenomena of adsorption and coprecipitation in analytical chemistry. (5) To study the mechanism of reactions, especially in those cases in which kinetic studies alone have failed to reveal the manner in which a reaction actually proceeds. (6) To study biochemical and physiological changes.

Application of Isotopes in Physiology. The application of isotopes as tracers in physiological studies has been particularly significant and gives promise of clarifying this extremely difficult field. The intermediate steps in physiological processes often are uncertain and difficult to study directly. However, if the compound under investigation can be labeled with an easily detectable element, direct evidence of its fate during various changes may be obtained. Isotopic indicators do not affect the chemical properties of the compound and are detectable in small quantities and in high dilution. Heavy nitrogen, N^{15}, has been found useful as a labeling atom, and various artificially radioactive isotopes, such as those of carbon, phosphorus, sulfur, and chlorine, even more so. In carrying out such an investigation the tracer atoms may be introduced into a substance during its synthesis, and the course of the reaction is followed by means of these tagged, or labeled, atoms. A factor limiting the use of artificially radioactive isotopes is their half-life period; this must not be so short that enough decay takes place during the experiment to spoil the sensitiveness of detection. The recently discovered radiohydrogen, H^3, is likely to be much used in this field of investigation.

[1] G. T. Seaborg, *Chemical Review*, **27**, 200 (1940).

Heavy nitrogen, N^{15}, which is present in atmospheric nitrogen to the extent of 0.386 per cent, is present in the same proportion in the nitrogen of the amino acids obtained by hydrolysis of proteins. Schoenheimer and Rittenberg [1] at Columbia University have synthesized alanine and other amino acids from ammonia rich in N^{15} and have used them to determine the fate of ingested amino acids in the animal body. The ammonia rich in N^{15} was prepared by the method developed by Urey. Concentrated ammonium sulfate solution was allowed to flow down a fractionating column into a solution of sodium hydroxide. The ammonia set free ascended the column, under reduced pressure. An exchange reaction took place, the heavy nitrogen N^{15} passing from the ammonium ion into the ammonia molecule. By repeated contact of the ammonia with the ammonium sulfate solution the concentration of the N^{15} in the former increased to over 2 per cent. The amino acids were prepared from this enriched ammonia by the usual methods. The distribution of the nitrogen of a given amino acid throughout the animal body was determined, in the case of rats, by dissecting out the various organs and tissues, liberating the nitrogen as ammonia, oxidizing the latter to nitrogen by means of hypobromite, and analyzing the nitrogen by means of the mass spectrograph. Thus the per cent of the heavy isotope N^{15} concentrated in a given physiological compound, organ, or tissue, was found. Only 0.5 ml. of the gas was required for the analysis. In some experiments both N^{15} and H^2 were concentrated in the same amino acid. These experiments furnished information as to the course which a given amino acid takes in the animal body and the extent to which it is utilized for the formation of various significant physiological compounds, such as *creatinine*.

When an artificially radioactive isotope is used, it is incorporated, usually by synthetic methods, in the compound of which the effect is to be studied. It is usually present only in a very small proportion, the normal analog acting as a *carrier*. The compound is then fed to the animal used in the studies and, when sufficient time has elapsed, the animal is killed and the various organs and tissues dissected out and examined for the radioactive isotope. Since the radioactive and the normal isotopes have identical chemical properties, they will distribute themselves in the same ratio in all parts of the body to which the normal element has gone.

[1] *J. Biol. Chem.*, **127**, 285, 291, 301, 319 (1939).

The presence of the radioactive isotope is detected, and may be quantitatively estimated, by ashing the sample and testing the ash for radioactivity by any of the well-known methods, such as the electroscope or the Geiger counter.

The electroscope consists of a thin gold or aluminum leaf fastened to the top of a vertical metal support. When this system receives an electrical charge, the leaf is repelled from the support, but gradually collapses as the charge leaks off through the air, which is made conducting by the radioactive rays. The intensity of the radioactivity is measured by the rate of collapse of the leaf. The Geiger counter consists of a metal cylinder filled with a suitable gas, and containing an axial wire charged to a potential of several hundred volts. When a radioactive ray passes through this cylinder, it forms a large number of gaseous ions, causing a surge of current which is amplified enough to operate a mechanical counter or flash a light.

Radioactive tracers have been used also in studies of plant metabolism. After growing the plant in soil or solution containing radioactive elements, such as radiophosphorus and radionitrogen, the fate of a given constituent of the soil or solution may be determined by measuring the radioactivity of the various parts of the plant. This may be done by ashing the leaf, stem, or root, as the case may be, and examining the ash for radioactivity, or by testing the various parts of the living plant directly by means of a Geiger counter.

Atomic Numbers. We have seen that X rays are emitted when cathode rays impinge upon solid matter. In a modern X-ray tube, shown in Figure 10, the cathode is a flat spiral tungsten filament *F*, which emits electrons when it is heated by the battery *B*. The electrons are focused by means of the cylinder *C* surrounding the filament and connected to it, and are accelerated toward the anode *A* by about 40,000 volts. The anode is made of a high-melting metal like tungsten or molybdenum, often cooled by water circulating within it. The greater the energy of the cathode rays, the shorter the X rays emitted.

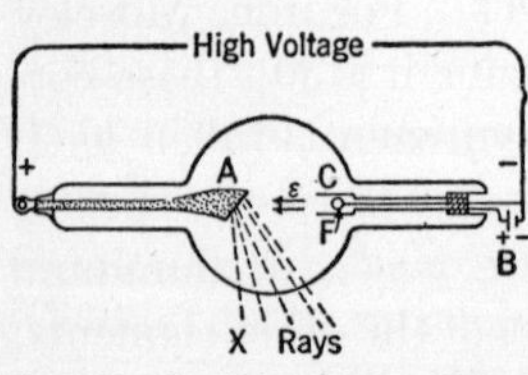

Fig. 10. Coolidge X-Ray Tube.

As early as 1908 Barkla observed that the X rays from a tube consist of a background of *continuous* radiation upon which are superimposed certain radiations of greater intensity, the frequency of which depend upon the material of the anticathode. In 1913 Moseley [1] undertook the systematic examination of these *characteristic* X rays, using various metals as anticathode. A narrow beam of X rays was allowed to fall on a crystal of potassium ferrocyanide which acted as an atomic *diffraction grating* and dispersed the radiations according to their wave lengths (see page 173). The results were recorded on a photographic plate as *line spectra*, and the wave length λ of each line was calculated. Moseley found that the X-ray spectra obtained in this way were very simple, consisting of several pairs of lines. He studied the K series, in which the $K\alpha$ line was more intense than the $K\beta$ line. The lines showed a regular shift towards shorter wave length with increasing atomic weights of the elements used. Moseley deduced the simple relationship:

$$\sqrt{\nu} = A(Z - 1)$$

where ν is the *frequency* (*i.e.*, the reciprocal of the wave length) of the $K\alpha$ line of the X-ray spectrum, A is a constant, and Z, the **atomic number** of the element, is its ordinal number when all the elements are arranged in the order in which they occur in the periodic table. This relationship is shown graphically in Figure 11. For iron, Moseley found that Z is 26; for copper Z is 29; for zinc it is 30; these correspond to their ordinal numbers when hydrogen is taken as 1, helium as 2, and so on. In all, Moseley studied the X-ray spectra of thirty-eight elements. Taking the *atomic number* of aluminum as 13, he was able to fix the atomic numbers of the other elements. The number of missing elements between hydrogen and uranium could then be predicted with certainty.

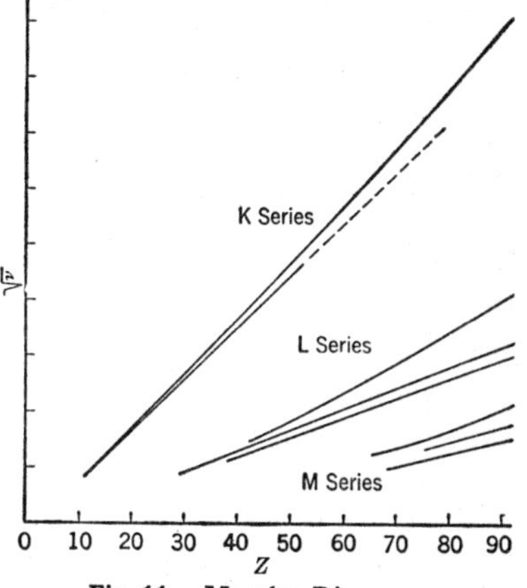

Fig. 11. Moseley Diagram.

Rutherford's previous studies of the scattering of α particles by thin sheets of metal had indicated that each atomic nucleus carried

[1] *Phil. Mag.*, (6) **26**, 1024 (1913); (6) **27**, 703 (1914). Moseley's work was done at Manchester. He was killed at Gallipoli in 1915 during the first world war.

a positive charge equal to about half the atomic weight of the element. Barkla's studies of X-ray scattering had shown that the number of electrons in each atom was also equal to about half its atomic weight. Moseley's work indicated that the integral change from one atom to the next was due to an increase in the nuclear positive charge, and also in the number of external electrons, and that each was equal numerically to the *atomic number* of the element. In 1920 this was confirmed by Chadwick, working in Rutherford's laboratory at Cambridge.[1] His accurate measurement of the scattering of α particles by various metals showed close agreement between the calculated charge on the nucleus and the atomic number found by Moseley. For example, he found 29.3 for copper, 46.3 for silver, and 77.4 for platinum; these correspond to the atomic numbers of 29, 47, and 78, respectively. This led to the extremely important conclusion: *The* ***atomic number*** *of an element is the number of excess positive charges on the nucleus of its atom.* It is regarded as the most fundamental characteristic of an element.

Structure of the Atom. We may now review briefly the part which these discoveries have played in establishing the picture of the structure of the atom that we hold today.

In 1896 Sir J. J. Thomson, the famous Cambridge physicist, proved that the *electron*, the unit of negative electricity, identical with the cathode ray and with the β particle of radioactive discharge, is a constituent of all matter. The mass of this particle has been found to be $\frac{1.008}{1845}$, or 0.000546 on the atomic weight scale. In 1904 Thomson suggested that an atom consists of electrons distributed throughout a diffuse sphere of positive electricity, the charge of which was sufficient to balance the negative charges of the electrons and so to yield a neutral atom.

From his study of the scattering of α particles by gold and other metals, Rutherford showed that this could not be the correct picture of an atom. He proved that the atom has a core, or *nucleus*, which is very small compared to the atom as a whole and which carries a positive charge. He calculated that the number of positive charges on the nucleus was about one half the atomic weight of the element. Consequent upon these discoveries, Rutherford in 1911 put forward his *nuclear theory* of atomic struc-

[1] *Phil. Mag.*, (6) **40,** 734 (1920).

ture. He assumed that the atom consists of a small positively charged nucleus surrounded by negatively charged electrons, which compose the bulk of the atom. The number of electrons corresponds to the number of positive charges on the nucleus; this was verified by the work of Moseley and of Chadwick already cited.

In 1916 G. N. Lewis of the University of California and W. Kossel in Germany, and in 1917 Irving Langmuir of the General Electric Company, reasoning in part from the known properties of the elements as portrayed by the periodic system, advanced definite ideas concerning the distribution of the planetary electrons. They postulated that *the planetary electrons are arranged in successive shells around the nucleus and that the inert gases, representing unusually stable arrangements of electrons, mark the completion of successive shells.* The atoms of elements following a zero group element in any period add successive electrons until, by completion of another shell, the next higher zero group element is reached.

The modern idea is that the *outermost* shell of an atom of the zero group always contains *eight* electrons, except that of helium, which has *two.* The *octet* and the *pair* of electrons in a shell represent stable configurations. The chemical interactions of the elements are ascribed to the tendency of their atoms to exchange or to share electrons in order to acquire electron configurations of maximum stability, *i.e.*, usually an octet, in their outermost shells. Thus, the chemical properties of an element apparently are determined by the number and arrangement of its electrons in the outer shells of its atoms, particularly of those in the outermost shell, the *valence electrons.*

The **nucleus** of the atom is assumed to be made up of *protons* and *neutrons.* The **proton,** represented by the symbol p, is merely the hydrogen atom stripped of its lone electron; its mass is 1.00758 on the *physical* atomic weight scale. The corresponding particle from deuterium is called the **deuteron,** which is represented by d. The **neutron** n is an electrically neutral particle probably composed of 1 proton and 1 electron. Its mass, 1.00895, is nearly the same as that of the proton, and its size also must be comparable if it is a constituent of the minute atomic nuclei. The isotopic weight is very nearly equal to the sum of the weights of the protons and neutrons in the nucleus, while the atomic number of any element equals the number of protons or of planetary electrons.

Little is known regarding the way these particles are arranged in the nucleus. According to prevalent views the α particle is composed of 2 neutrons and 2 protons. Since the α particle is ejected in many radioactive disintegrations, it probably is combined as a structural unit in the nucleus of the atom. The most abundant isotopes of the four elements that make up 90 per cent of the earth's crust, O^{16}, Mg^{24}, Si^{28}, and Fe^{56}, have isotopic weights that are multiples of the atomic weight of helium. In general, elements with even atomic numbers are much more abundant than those with odd atomic numbers, indicating the greater stability of the former.

The atom models described by Lewis, Langmuir, and Kossel represented the atom as a *static* system. Since this model would not explain such atomic phenomena as the emission of light in characteristic line spectra, Niels Bohr in 1913, reasoning from relationships in spectra, built up a *dynamic* atom. He postulated that the electrons revolve in circles around the nucleus, obeying the ordinary laws of mechanics. An electron in any particular orbit is attracted towards the nucleus because of the opposite charges on the two particles; but this attractive force is just balanced by the centrifugal force tending to spin the electron away from the atom. Bohr postulated further that only certain orbits are possible for the electrons in an atom and that an electron revolving in one of these orbits radiates no energy. He designated each orbit by a *quantum number*, indicating the *size* of the orbit. When an electron passes from one orbit to another it liberates or absorbs an amount of energy equal to the difference in energy in the two orbits.

Although Bohr's theory of atomic structure explains the spectrum of hydrogen and of ionized helium, it is not adequate for more complicated atoms. Sommerfeld introduced the idea of elliptical as well as circular orbits for many of the stationary states of the atom. The slight differences in energy explained the existence of groups of spectral lines of slightly different frequencies. Sommerfeld introduced a second quantum number describing the *shape* of the orbit, which might be more or less elliptical.

In order to explain the splitting of spectral lines into a number of components in a strong electrical field (the *Stark effect*) or magnetic field (the *Zeeman effect*), a third quantum number was introduced to describe the *plane of the orbit in space*, with reference to the direction of the applied field. Finally in 1925 Ullenbeck and Goudsmit introduced a fourth quantum number to explain the fine structure of the spectral lines. This corresponds to the *spin of the electron* around its own axis, which may be either in the same direction as the rotation of the electron around the nucleus, or in the opposite direction.

The four quantum numbers required to describe an electron, therefore, correspond to (1) its *size*, (2) its *shape*, (3) its *orientation in space* with reference to an applied field, and (4) the *electronic spin*.

The distribution of electrons in an atom is governed by an important rule known as **Pauli's exclusion principle,** which states that *no two electrons in an atom can have the same four quantum numbers*. Orbits of the same size, shape, and orientation can be occupied at most by pairs of electrons of opposite spin.

More recently Schroedinger has shown that all the results of the *quantum mechanics* of the atom can be derived from a differential equation analogous to that which describes the propagation of a wave. This has led to the development of *wave mechanics*. The solutions of the equation for any particular atomic system represent a system of standing waves which correspond approximately to the electron orbits of the older theory. These solutions give the electron distribution in space, or the *probability* of finding an electron at a given point in space. The probability is greatest in the positions of the orbits of the Bohr theory, but has definite values at other points, so that, in this picture, the clear-cut orbits become hazy and less definite.

The main interest to the chemist of the theory of atomic structure lies in its use in representing the structure of molecules and in explaining the differences in the chemical nature of compounds. The distribution of the planetary electrons in the atoms of all the elements is given in Table 12.

The Structure of Molecules

The study of the structure of molecules has been centered mainly upon the number and nature of the *valence bonds* of the constituent atoms. Much light has been thrown on this subject by the application of the concepts of atomic structure. It is assumed that the chemical properties of the elements are determined by the number of *valence electrons* in the atom, *i.e.*, by the number of electrons

TABLE 12

THE DISTRIBUTION OF ELECTRONS IN THE ATOMS OF THE ELEMENTS

SHELL (X-RAY NOTATION) →		K	L		M			N				O
PRINCIPAL QUANTUM NUMBER (SHELL) n =		1	2		3			4				5
ELECTRON SUBSHELL →		1s	2s	2p	3s	3p	3d	4s	4p	4d	4f	5s
ELEMENT	AT. NO.											
H	1	1										
He	2	2										
Li	3	2	1									
Be	4	2	2									
B	5	2	2	1								
C	6	2	2	2								
N	7	2	2	3								
O	8	2	2	4								
F	9	2	2	5								
Ne	10	2	2	6								
Na	11	2	2	6	1							
Mg	12	2	2	6	2							
Al	13	2	2	6	2	1						
Si	14	2	2	6	2	2						
P	15	2	2	6	2	3						
S	16	2	2	6	2	4						
Cl	17	2	2	6	2	5						
A	18	2	2	6	2	6						
K	19	2	2	6	2	6		1				
Ca	20	2	2	6	2	6		2				
Sc	21	2	2	6	2	6	1	2				
Ti	22	2	2	6	2	6	2	2				
V	23	2	2	6	2	6	3	2				
Cr	24	2	2	6	2	6	5	1				
Mn	25	2	2	6	2	6	5	2				
Fe	26	2	2	6	2	6	6	2				
Co	27	2	2	6	2	6	7	2				
Ni	28	2	2	6	2	6	8	2				
Cu	29	2	2	6	2	6	10	1				
Zn	30	2	2	6	2	6	10	2				
Ga	31	2	2	6	2	6	10	2	1			
Ge	32	2	2	6	2	6	10	2	2			
As	33	2	2	6	2	6	10	2	3			
Se	34	2	2	6	2	6	10	2	4			
Br	35	2	2	6	2	6	10	2	5			
Kr	36	2	2	6	2	6	10	2	6			
Rb	37	2	2	6	2	6	10	2	6			1
Sr	38	2	2	6	2	6	10	2	6			2
Y	39	2	2	6	2	6	10	2	6	1		2
Zr	40	2	2	6	2	6	10	2	6	2		2
Cb	41	2	2	6	2	6	10	2	6	4		1
Mo	42	2	2	6	2	6	10	2	6	5		1
—	43	2	2	6	2	6	10	2	6	6		1 (?)
Ru	44	2	2	6	2	6	10	2	6	7		1
Rh	45	2	2	6	2	6	10	2	6	8		1
Pd	46	2	2	6	2	6	10	2	6	10		

TABLE 12 (*Continued*)

THE DISTRIBUTION OF ELECTRONS IN THE ATOMS OF THE ELEMENTS

Shell (X-ray Notation) →		*K–M*	*N*				*O*			*P*			*Q*
Principal Quantum Number (Shell) n =			4				5			6			7
Electron Subshell →			4*s*	4*p*	4*d*	4*f*	5*s*	5*p*	5*d*	6*s*	6*p*	6*d*	7*s*
Element	At. No.												
Ag	47	Data for shells *K*, *L*, and *M* are the same as shown for Pd on the preceding page.	2	6	10		1						
Cd	48		2	6	10		2						
In	49		2	6	10		2	1					
Sn	50		2	6	10		2	2					
Sb	51		2	6	10		2	3					
Te	52		2	6	10		2	4					
I	53		2	6	10		2	5					
Xe	54		2	6	10		2	6					
Cs	55		2	6	10		2	6		1			
Ba	56		2	6	10		2	6		2			
La	57		2	6	10		2	6	1	2			
Ce	58		2	6	10	1	2	6	1	2			
Pr	59		2	6	10	2	2	6	1	2	(?)		
Nd	60		2	6	10	3	2	6	1	2	(?)		
—	61		2	6	10	4	2	6	1	2	(?)		
Sm	62		2	6	10	5	2	6	1	2	(?)		
Eu	63		2	6	10	7	2	6		2			
Gd	64		2	6	10	7	2	6	1	2	(?)		
Tb	65		2	6	10	8	2	6	1	2	(?)		
Dy	66		2	6	10	9	2	6	1	2	(?)		
Ho	67		2	6	10	10	2	6	1	2	(?)		
Er	68		2	6	10	11	2	6	1	2	(?)		
Tm	69		2	6	10	12	2	6	1	2	(?)		
Yb	70		2	6	10	13	2	6	1	2	(?)		
Lu	71		2	6	10	14	2	6	1	2			
Hf	72		2	6	10	14	2	6	2	2			
Ta	73		2	6	10	14	2	6	3	2	(?)		
W	74		2	6	10	14	2	6	4	2			
Re	75		2	6	10	14	2	6	5	2	(?)		
Os	76		2	6	10	14	2	6	6	2			
Ir	77		2	6	10	14	2	6	7	2	(?)		
Pt	78		2	6	10	14	2	6	8	2			
Au	79		2	6	10	14	2	6	10	1			
Hg	80		2	6	10	14	2	6	10	2			
Tl	81		2	6	10	14	2	6	10	2	1		
Pb	82		2	6	10	14	2	6	10	2	2		
Bi	83		2	6	10	14	2	6	10	2	3		
Po	84		2	6	10	14	2	6	10	2	4		
—	85		2	6	10	14	2	6	10	2	5	(?)	
Rn	86		2	6	10	14	2	6	10	2	6		
—	87		2	6	10	14	2	6	10	2	6		1 (?)
Ra	88		2	6	10	14	2	6	10	2	6		2
Ac	89		2	6	10	14	2	6	10	2	6	1	2 (?)
Th	90		2	6	10	14	2	6	10	2	6	2	2 (?)
Pa	91		2	6	10	14	2	6	10	2	6	3	2 (?)
U	92		2	6	10	14	2	6	10	2	6	4	2 (?)

in the outermost shell of the planetary system. *The reaction of one element with another is due to a tendency of the reacting atoms to rearrange their valence electrons so as to form systems of greater stability.*

As we have seen, the *pair* and the *octet* are considered the most stable electron configurations. A *pair* forms the outermost shell of the helium atom; an *octet* forms the outermost shell of the atoms of each of the other zero group gases. The atoms of other elements, in their reactions with one another, tend to achieve these stable configurations by losing or gaining electrons in their valence shells. Obviously, only the elements of lowest atomic number, H, Li, and Be, can acquire the stable configuration of the pair; all the others tend to acquire the octet configuration.

The tendency of atoms to form more stable configurations can be satisfied (1) by *transferring* valence electrons from one atom to the other and (2) by *sharing* electrons between the atoms. The *sharing* of electrons may be effected either (*a*) by the contribution of one electron by each atom, or (*b*) by the contribution of both electrons by one atom. The nature of the resulting compound definitely depends upon which of these three processes is involved. We shall consider each type of reaction a little more fully.

Electrovalence. *The* ***electrovalent bond*** *is the type of valence bond which holds atoms together when one or more electrons have been transferred from one of the atoms to the other.* The loss of electrons by one atom leaves it positively charged; the gain of electrons by the other atom renders it negatively charged. The former has become a positive ion, a *cation;* the latter has become a negative ion, an *anion.* The bond holding the two atoms together is merely the electrostatic attraction between the two oppositely charged particles. A compound made up in this way is known as an **electrovalent compound.** As an example we may take the formation of sodium chloride, simplifying the case by using the chlorine atom instead of the chlorine molecule and using the atomic models of Kossel. The structures of the two atoms and of the resulting compound are shown in Figure 12. As the diagram represents, the single valence electron of the sodium atom has gone to the chlorine atom, which initially had seven valence electrons. By this process both atoms acquire an octet of electrons in their outermost shells, and sodium and chloride ions are formed. In such compounds there is usually no stable *molecule.* In the solid state the ions form a crystal by taking up alternate positions in a space lattice; in the liquid state or in solution the ions are no longer bound to one another but are free to move. Although we still represent such substances by empirical formulas, like NaCl, and we still express their weights in *moles*, this is purely conventional. Actually,

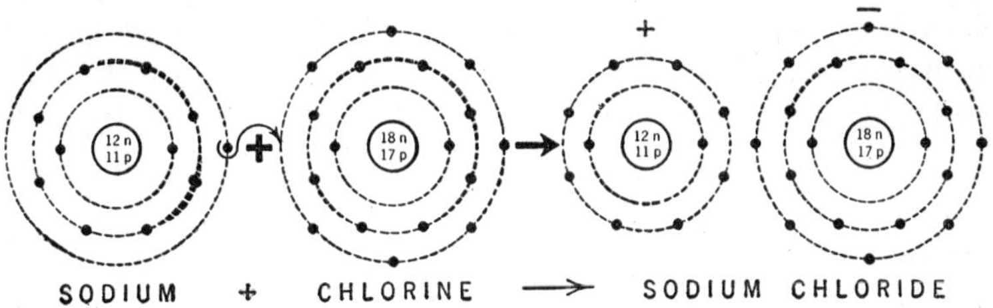

Fig. 12. Formation of an Electrovalent Compound.

the formulas are only the simplest representations of the composition of the compounds, and the "molecular weights" merely the weights on the atomic weight scale corresponding to these formulas.

The formation of electrovalent compounds, *i.e.*, the formation of ions, is not possible for all elements. Electrovalence is limited, practically, to those atoms which can form ions by losing 1, 2, or 3 electrons or by gaining 1 or 2. The elements which lose electrons most easily are the active metals: the alkali metals, each of which has but one valence electron and forms univalent ions, and the alkaline earth metals, each of which has two valence electrons and forms bivalent ions. The alkaline earth metals are less active than the alkali metals, because the work of removing the second electron is much greater than that of removing the first. The work of removing three electrons is so much greater that this is about the limit of ionization of atoms in forming chemical compounds. The total ionizing potentials for the removal of 1, 2, and 3 electrons, respectively, forming Na^+, Mg^{++}, and Al^{+++} are 5.12 volts, 22.58 volts, and 53.0 volts, while the formation of Sn^{++++} from Sn would require 101.9 volts, or the expenditure of 2,300,000 calories per mole. In any particular group of the periodic table the ionizing potential decreases, and hence the metallic properties become stronger, as we go from lighter to heavier elements. This is because the valence electrons of the higher elements are in orbits further removed from the nucleus and so are less strongly held than those of the lighter elements.

The acquisition of electrons to form negative ions is less easily correlated with other atomic properties, but it is limited to those elements, such as Cl and S, one or two lower in atomic number than the rare gases.

Covalence. *The **covalent bond** is formed by a **sharing** of electrons between the atoms.* The formation of *covalent compounds* involves no transfer of electrons from one atom to the other and hence no formation of *ions* as in electrovalent compounds. Usually the sharing involves two electrons per valence bond. The two

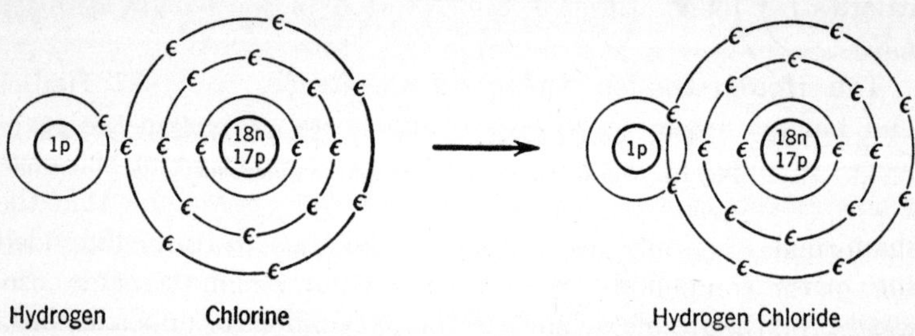

Fig. 13. Formation of a Covalent Compound.

electrons shared form part of the outermost shell of each atom, as will be seen from an examination of the covalent structure of hydrogen chloride shown in Figure 13, where the union of a hydrogen atom with a chlorine atom is represented.

The following are examples of compounds which involve only covalent valence bonds. In each case the atom is represented by the symbol together with the valence electrons as dots.

$$\begin{array}{c}\mathrm{H}\\ :\underset{\cdot\cdot}{\ddot{\mathrm{O}}}:\mathrm{H}\end{array} \qquad \begin{array}{c}\mathrm{H}\\ \mathrm{H}:\underset{\cdot\cdot}{\ddot{\mathrm{N}}}:\mathrm{H}\end{array} \qquad \begin{array}{c}\mathrm{H}\\ \mathrm{H}:\underset{\cdot\cdot}{\ddot{\mathrm{C}}}:\mathrm{H}\\ \mathrm{H}\end{array}$$

Water — Ammonia — Methane

$$:\ddot{\mathrm{N}}:\underset{\cdot\cdot}{\ddot{\mathrm{O}}}:\ddot{\mathrm{N}}: \qquad :\ddot{\mathrm{N}}:\underset{\cdot\cdot}{\ddot{\mathrm{O}}}: \qquad \begin{array}{c}:\ddot{\mathrm{Cl}}:\\ :\underset{\cdot\cdot}{\ddot{\mathrm{Cl}}}:\underset{\cdot\cdot}{\ddot{\mathrm{C}}}:\underset{\cdot\cdot}{\ddot{\mathrm{Cl}}}:\\ :\underset{\cdot\cdot}{\mathrm{Cl}}:\end{array}$$

Nitrous Oxide — Nitric Oxide — Carbon Tetrachloride

The atoms in the diatomic molecules of elementary gases are held together by strong covalent forces, which must be overcome before such gases will enter into reactions with other elements. This accounts for the relative stability of nitrogen, chlorine, and hydrogen at ordinary temperatures. The structures of these molecules may be represented thus:

H:H	$\begin{matrix}\cdot\cdot\ \cdot\cdot\\ :\text{Cl}:\text{Cl}:\\ \cdot\cdot\ \cdot\cdot\end{matrix}$	$\begin{matrix}\cdot\cdot\ \cdot\cdot\\ :\text{N}:\text{N}:\end{matrix}$
Hydrogen	Chlorine	Nitrogen

The separation of the hydrogen molecule into its two atoms has been effected, but in the atomic form the element is highly reactive. The recombination of hydrogen atoms to form hydrogen molecules is attended by the evolution of intense heat, 103,800 calories per mole; this has been utilized in the *atomic hydrogen torch.*[1]

The Heitler-London Theory of Covalence. In 1927 Heitler and London advanced an interesting theory to explain the covalences of different elements. A detailed tabulation of the electronic arrangements of the various elements would show that the main shells are divided into subshells and these in turn subdivided into pairs of levels which correspond to orbits of the same size, shape, and position but in which the electrons have opposite spins. Two electrons in one of these levels are said to be *paired,* that is, their spins are in opposite directions so that they neutralize each other. If there is only one electron in any such level, it is said to be *unpaired.* Heitler and London assumed that covalent bonds are pairs of electrons of opposite spins shared between atoms. The maximum covalence due to shared electrons is equal to the number of unpaired electron spins in the atom. This can be determined for the normal state of the atom from a study of its spectrum. The atom in different states may have different numbers of paired electrons, but these numbers must differ by even numbers. This explains the fact that covalences usually differ by two. The theory amplifies that discussed in the foregoing pages by showing the significance of the electron-pair bond in terms of wave mechanics and in many cases it yields useful results. Its application is beyond the scope of this book.

Co-ordinate Valence. *Valence bonding of this kind is a special type of covalence in which both electrons of the pair are contributed by one atom.* It is a type of valence bonding found in the *ammonium* ion, in *nitrate, sulfate,* and other similar anions, and in complex ions. As an example we may consider the formation of the ammonium ion. The older theories of valence could not explain why the

[1] G. Bartlett, *J. Chem. Ed.*, **4,** 38 (1927).

nitrogen in ammonia, with its valences already satisfied, should take on something in addition. We may represent the addition of the proton, H^+, thus:

$$\begin{array}{c}\mathrm{H}\\ \cdot\cdot\\ \mathrm{H:N:H}\\ \cdot\cdot\end{array} + \mathrm{H^+} \longrightarrow \left[\begin{array}{c}\mathrm{H}\\ \cdot\cdot\\ \mathrm{H:N:H}\\ \cdot\cdot\\ \mathrm{H}\end{array}\right]^+$$

The fourth hydrogen is attached by a co-ordinate bond for which both electrons are furnished by the nitrogen. Once the ion is formed, however, the hydrogen atoms are indistinguishable. The positive charge on the ammonium ion is *on the ion as a whole;* its position cannot be allocated definitely. The use of deuterium atoms has proved that the hydrogen taken on by the ammonia is not always the one which comes out as water when the ammonium ion is treated with a base,[1] thus:

$$NH_4^+ + OH^- \longrightarrow NH_3 + H_2O$$

We may illustrate the formation of co-ordinate bonds by the following examples:

(1) The reaction of auric chloride with chloride ion to give chloraurate ion:

$$\begin{array}{c}\quad\ \ \cdot\cdot\\ \quad\ \ \mathrm{:Cl:}\\ \cdot\cdot\quad\cdot\cdot\\ \mathrm{:Cl:Au}\\ \cdot\cdot\quad\cdot\cdot\\ \quad\ \ \mathrm{:Cl:}\\ \quad\ \ \cdot\cdot\end{array} + \left[\mathrm{:\overset{\cdot\cdot}{\underset{\cdot\cdot}{Cl}}:}\right]^- \longrightarrow \left[\begin{array}{c}\cdot\cdot\\ \mathrm{:Cl:}\\ \cdot\cdot\quad\cdot\cdot\quad\cdot\cdot\\ \mathrm{:Cl:Au:Cl:}\\ \cdot\cdot\quad\cdot\cdot\quad\cdot\cdot\\ \mathrm{:Cl:}\\ \cdot\cdot\end{array}\right]^-$$

(2) The formation of cupric ammonia ion from ammonia and cupric ion:

$$4\begin{array}{c}\mathrm{H}\\ \cdot\cdot\\ \mathrm{H:N:}\\ \cdot\cdot\\ \mathrm{H}\end{array} + \mathrm{Cu^{++}} \longrightarrow \left[\begin{array}{ccccc} & & \mathrm{H} & & \\ & & \cdot\cdot & & \\ & \mathrm{H} & \mathrm{H:N:H} & \mathrm{H} & \\ & \cdot\cdot & \cdot\cdot & \cdot\cdot & \\ \mathrm{H:N} & : & \mathrm{Cu} & : & \mathrm{N:H}\\ & \cdot\cdot & \cdot\cdot & \cdot\cdot & \\ & \mathrm{H} & \mathrm{H:N:H} & \mathrm{H} & \\ & & \cdot\cdot & & \\ & & \mathrm{H} & & \end{array}\right]^{++}$$

(3) The formation of hydrogen ion, H_3O^+, from water and a proton:

$$\begin{array}{c}\mathrm{H}\\ \cdot\cdot\\ \mathrm{:O:H}\\ \cdot\cdot\end{array} + \mathrm{H^+} \longrightarrow \left[\begin{array}{c}\mathrm{H}\\ \cdot\cdot\\ \mathrm{:O:H}\\ \cdot\cdot\\ \mathrm{H}\end{array}\right]^+$$

[1] G. N. Lewis, *J. Am. Chem. Soc.*, **55**, 3502 (1933).

The structure of *nitrate, sulfate,* and *phosphate* ions, each of which involves one co-ordinate linkage, may be represented as follows:

$$\left[\begin{array}{c} :\ddot{O}: \\ :\ddot{\underset{..}{O}}:\ddot{N}:\ddot{\underset{..}{O}}: \end{array}\right]^{-} \qquad \left[\begin{array}{c} :\ddot{O}: \\ :\ddot{\underset{..}{O}}:\ddot{\underset{..}{S}}:\ddot{\underset{..}{O}}: \\ :\underset{..}{O}: \end{array}\right]^{--} \qquad \left[\begin{array}{c} :\ddot{O}: \\ :\ddot{\underset{..}{O}}:\ddot{\underset{..}{P}}:\ddot{\underset{..}{O}}: \\ :\underset{..}{O}: \end{array}\right]^{---}$$

Nitrate Sulfate Phosphate

Comparison of Electrovalent and Covalent Compounds. The question naturally arises: How may one predict whether a given compound is electrovalent or covalent in structure? There are certain marked differences in properties which offer an answer to this question.

(1) Ionization in the pure state. Electrovalent compounds consist of ions held together by electrostatic attraction of the positive charges of one kind of ion and the negative charges of the other. They are ionized, then, even in the solid state. When such a substance is heated sufficiently, it melts and the ions are no longer held rigidly in the crystal lattice. They are free to move and conduct the electric current. The fused chlorides of the metals, like NaCl, KCl, and $CaCl_2$, are good conductors in the fused state. Covalent compounds, however, are very poor conductors in the liquid state. There are no ions present in such a liquid and therefore nothing to carry the current. Common examples of covalent compounds are the halides of the nonmetals (such as CCl_4), water, and many organic substances.

(2) Ionization in aqueous solution. Electrovalent compounds, to the limit of their solubility, dissociate into their ions when dissolved in water. Hence, their solutions are good conductors. Covalent compounds that do not react with water give almost completely nonconducting solutions. Certain compounds, such as hydrogen chloride and the other hydrogen halides, $AlCl_3$, $FeCl_3$, and $SnCl_4$, which are nonconducting or at least poor conductors in the fused state, give solutions which rank as good conductors. This is because they react with the water, forming electrovalent compounds which dissociate, thus:

$$HCl + H_2O \longrightarrow H_3O^+ + Cl^-$$
$$FeCl_3 + 6\,H_2O \longrightarrow Fe(H_2O)_6^{+++} + 3\,Cl^-$$

(3) Boiling point. In general, electrovalent compounds have much higher boiling points than the covalent compounds, because the particles in an electrovalent substance are held by electrostatic attraction whereas no such attraction exists among the molecules of a covalent substance. It is easier, then, to separate the molecules of the covalent substance than to separate the ions of the electrovalent substance. In Table 13 are given the boiling points of a number of compounds of each of these two groups.

TABLE 13

COMPARISON OF ELECTROVALENT AND COVALENT COMPOUNDS

Electrovalent Compounds		Covalent Compounds	
Substance	Boiling Point	Substance	Boiling Point
CaO	2850° C.	$FeCl_3$	315° C.
$BaCl_2$	1560	$HgCl_2$	304
$AgCl$	1550	$SbCl_3$	223
KCl	1500	$AlCl_3$	182
$NaCl$	1413	$AsCl_3$	130
SnS	1230	$SnCl_4$	114
$CoCl_2$	1049	H_2O	100
$CdCl_2$	960	CCl_4	77
$ZnCl_2$	732	HCl	− 83

PROBLEMS AND EXERCISES

1. Given that the isotopes of lithium, Li^6 and Li^7, are mixed in the ordinary element in the proportion of 8.3 per cent to 91.7 per cent, calculate the atomic weight of lithium.

***2.** Assuming the abundance ratios of the oxygen isotopes given on page 54, calculate the atomic weight of the O^{16} isotope on the chemical scale.

3. Assuming that the effect of substituting two deuterium atoms for hydrogen atoms is just twice that of substituting one deuterium atom, compute the relative density of DHO at 25° C. (see Table 9, page 52).

4. Devise methods employing radioactive isotopes for showing that:

(*a*) A dynamic equilibrium exists between an insoluble salt and a saturated solution of its ions.

(*b*) A precipitate of barium sulfate adsorbs ferric ions from a solution of ferric nitrate.

(*c*) Phosphate cannot be completely precipitated by the addition of calcium chloride to a solution of a phosphate.

* Here and in succeeding chapters, the more difficult problems are marked with an asterisk.

5. With reference to electrons show:
   (*a*) The formation of rubidium sulfide from the elements.
   (*b*) The formation of sulfuric acid from sulfur trioxide.
   (*c*) The reaction of carbon with sulfur and the action of chlorine with the product.
   (*d*) The formation of the cadmium ammonia complex ion.
   (*e*) The oxidation of cuprous ion to cupric.

READING LIST

Meldrum and Gucker, *Introduction to Theoretical Chemistry.* American Book Company, New York, 1936. Pages 437–598 deal with the subject matter of this chapter in considerable detail.

S. Glasstone, *Textbook of Physical Chemistry.* D. Van Nostrand Company, New York, 1940. Pages 1–172 cover radiations and structure in a very thorough manner.

F. Soddy, *The Interpretation of the Atom.* G. P. Putnam's Sons, New York, 1932. An interesting summary of the properties of the atom and knowledge regarding structure.

A. S. Eve, *Rutherford.* The Macmillan Company, New York, 1939, 451 pp. A fascinating story of the life and work of this great pioneer worker in radioactivity and nuclear structure.

F. W. Aston, *Mass Spectra and Isotopes.* Edward Arnold & Co., London, 1933.

G. T. Seaborg, *Chem. Rev.*, **27,** 199–285 (1940), gives a good summary of the applications of artificially radioactive isotopes as tracers. This review does not include biochemical or physiological applications.

Ridenour and Yost, *Chem. Rev.*, **18,** 457–495 (1936), gives a summary of the methods of producing and detecting artificially radioactive elements.

A. K. Brewer, "Isotopes in the Study of Plant Growth," *J. Chem. Ed.*, **18,** 217 (1941). An interesting study of the absorption of radiosodium and radiophosphorus by the growing plant.

G. Hevesy, "Applications of Radioactive Indicators to Biology," *Ann. Rev. Biochem.* **9,** 641 (1940). This article describes the applications of radioactive indicators in biology and in biochemistry.

CHAPTER 4

THE IDEAL GAS

Boyle's Law and Charles's (Gay-Lussac's) Law. Gases are distinguished from liquids and solids by the fact that their volume changes enormously with changes in temperature and pressure. In 1660 Robert Boyle [1] studied the change in the volume of a gas with pressure, at constant temperature. Within his experimental error of about 0.5 per cent, he found that *the volume occupied by a fixed mass of a gas is inversely proportional to the pressure, if the temperature remains constant.* ***Boyle's law*** may be expressed mathematically by the equations:

$$PV = K \text{ or } P_1V_1 = P_2V_2 \ (T \text{ and } w \text{ constant})$$

where P, V, T, and w designate respectively the pressure, volume, temperature, and weight of the gas. The graph of Boyle's law, using P and V as variables, is a rectangular hyperbola as shown in Figure 14, with a plot of some of Boyle's original data.

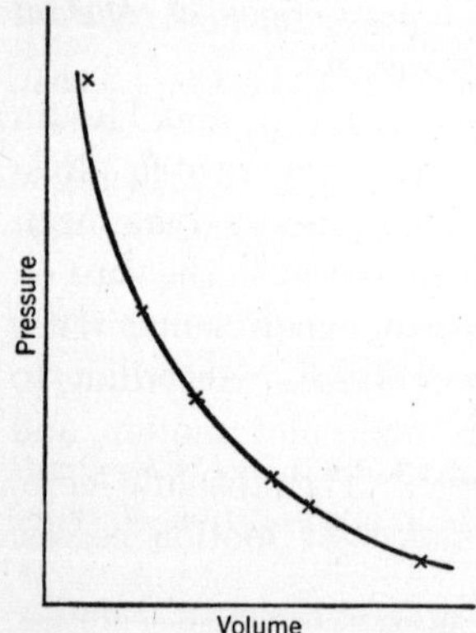

Fig. 14. Boyle's Law Hyperbola.

For different quantities of the same gas, the pressure is proportional to the weight, hence

$$PV = kw \text{ (constant } T \text{ and the same gas)}$$

The effect of temperature upon the volume of a gas was not studied until more than a century after Boyle's work. In 1787 Charles, the French physicist, found that hydrogen, nitrogen, oxygen, air, and carbon dioxide all expanded equally between

[1] Robert Boyle, youngest son of the Earl of Cork, was born in Ireland in 1627. Always financially independent, he devoted his life to science. At 20 he was elected to the Invisible College which in 1663 developed into the Royal Society. In *The Sceptical Chymist* he applied Francis Bacon's inductive method to end the era of alchemy and begin that of scientific chemistry. He introduced the term *analysis* and the modern definition of an element as a *simple substance.* In addition to his study of gases, he showed that the boiling point of a liquid depends upon the pressure, and introduced ice and salt as a freezing mixture. He first used litmus as an indicator, and prepared wood alcohol and acetone. He died in 1691.

0 and 80° C. In 1802 his compatriot Gay-Lussac[1] found that a given mass of any gas expands $\frac{1}{273}$ of its volume at 0° C., for each degree it is heated at constant pressure. The volume V of a gas at any temperature t° C., therefore, is related to the volume V_0 at 0° C. by the equation:

$$V = V_0 + \left(\frac{t}{273}\right)V_0 = V_0\frac{273 + t}{273} \quad (P \text{ and } w \text{ constant})$$

The volumes at any two centigrade temperatures are related by the equation:

$$\frac{V_1}{V_2} = \frac{273 + t_1}{273 + t_2} \quad (P \text{ and } w \text{ constant})$$

Setting $273 + t = T$, Charles's law becomes simply:

$$\frac{V_1}{V_2} = \frac{T_1}{T_2} \quad (P \text{ and } w \text{ constant})$$

T is called the **absolute temperature,** for reasons given below. ***Charles's law*** *states that the volume of a given mass of gas, at constant pressure, varies directly as the absolute temperature.*

Symbols used for the absolute temperature are °A. and °K. (in honor of William Thomson, Lord Kelvin, the great Scotch physicist who showed the importance of this scale in thermodynamics). The term *absolute temperature* was introduced because the zero on this scale, − 273.16° C. according to present experimental data, apparently marks the lowest possible temperature. According to the kinetic-molecular hypothesis, heat is molecular motion and temperature is a measure of its intensity. The absolute zero, 0° A., is the temperature at which all molecular motion ceases.

[1] Joseph Louis Gay-Lussac (1778–1850) received an excellent education in Paris. There he became assistant to Berthollet, who once remarked to him, "Young man, your destiny is to make discoveries." This was indeed the case, for he held professorships of physics and chemistry in Paris and devoted his whole life to brilliant research. From the very beginning he was interested in the behavior of gases and made two daring balloon ascensions in 1804 to test the composition of the air and the magnetic effects at high altitudes. In addition to establishing the law of combining volumes, he also proved that the volume of any gas is proportional to the absolute temperature. He did considerable excellent work in physics, and made important contributions to almost every branch of chemistry. Most of his papers appeared in the *Annales de Chimie et de Physique* which he edited for many years. His classic work on iodine and its compounds and cyanogen and its compounds was most important. In collaboration with Thénard, he reduced potassium to the metallic state with iron, isolated boron from boric acid, studied the properties of chlorine, and carried out some of the earliest fundamental work in organic chemistry.

Although the absolute zero has not been reached in the laboratory, a temperature of 0.0005° A. was attained in the Cryogenic Laboratory of the University of Leyden, Holland, in 1935.

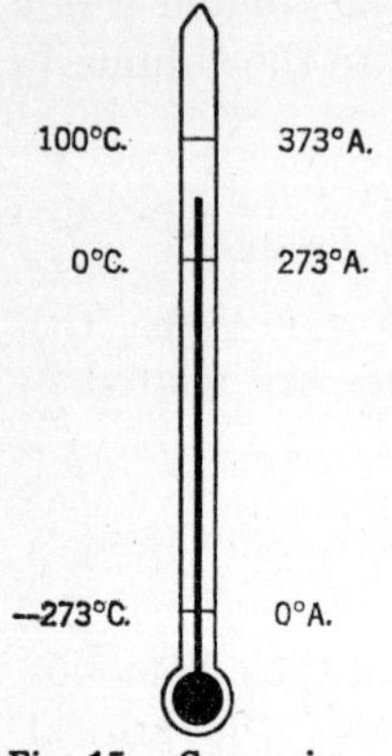

Fig. 15. Comparison of Temperature Scales.

Neither Boyle's law nor Charles's law expresses the behavior of real gases exactly. Both of them, however, are valid within a few tenths of a per cent for any gas at moderate pressures and well above its critical temperature. Thus oxygen, hydrogen, nitrogen, and air obey Boyle's and Charles's laws satisfactorily at room temperature, while carbon dioxide and ammonia, with critical temperatures of 31° C. and 132° C. respectively, show appreciable deviations, the cause of which is discussed on page 102.

The Equation of State of the Ideal Gas. In order to calculate the volume of a gas when pressure and temperature are changed at the same time, it is convenient to combine Boyle's and Charles's laws into a single equation. *Such an expression, relating the volume, pressure, and temperature of a substance, is called an* ***equation of state.***

Starting with a volume V_1 of gas at a pressure P_1 and temperature T_1, and changing the pressure and temperature to P_2 and T_2, the final volume V_2 may be calculated by assuming that the change is made in two steps, according to the following scheme:

$$\boxed{V_1P_1T_1} \xrightarrow[T \text{ constant}]{\text{Change } P_1 \quad (1)} \boxed{V'_1P_2T_1} \xrightarrow[P \text{ constant}]{\text{Change } T \quad (2)} \boxed{V_2P_2T_2}$$

V'_1 is the intermediate volume of the gas at the original temperature T_1, but at the pressure P_2. We can calculate it by means of Boyle's law:

$$P_1V_1 = P_2V'_1$$

The final volume is calculated by means of Charles's law:

$$\frac{V'_1}{T_1} = \frac{V_2}{T_2}$$

Combining these equations so as to eliminate the intermediate volume V'_1 we find:

$$\frac{P_1V_1}{T_1} = \frac{P_2V_2}{T_2} \ (w \text{ constant})$$

This relationship holds for a fixed mass w of gas, whatever the values of P, V, and T, so that we may write:

$$\frac{PV}{T} = \text{a constant}$$

As in the case of Boyle's law, the numerical value of the constant depends upon the weight of gas. If we are dealing with *one mole* of any gas, the constant is designated by R. For n moles, the equation becomes:

$$PV = nRT$$

which is *the equation of state of the ideal gas.* Since neither Boyle's nor Charles's law is exact, the equation of state of the ideal gas holds only approximately for real gases, describing their behavior under moderate pressures and considerably above the critical temperature.

The Gas Constant *R*. This constant is so fundamentally important for the gas laws and occurs in so many relations of physical chemistry that we should understand clearly not only how it may be evaluated but also its physical significance. We could evaluate R by determining the volume of a known weight of gas at any known pressure and temperature, but it is simpler to take the known values at standard conditions. At 273.16° A. and a pressure of 1 atmosphere, one mole of the ideal gas occupies 22.414 liters. Substituting these values in the above equation gives the desired value of R thus:

$$R = \frac{P_0V_0}{T_0} = \frac{1 \times 22.414}{273.16} \text{ l. atm. per deg. per mole}$$
$$= 0.08205 \text{ l.} \times \text{atm.} \times \text{deg.}^{-1} \times \text{mole}^{-1}$$

Evidently its numerical value will depend upon the *units* in which we express P, V, and T. If we express volume in ml., the corresponding value of R is 82.05. Using other units of pressure and volume, we obtain the following values:

$$R = 8.314 \times 10^7 \text{ ergs} \times \text{deg.}^{-1} \times \text{mole}^{-1}$$
$$= 8.314 \text{ joules} \times \text{deg.}^{-1} \times \text{mole}^{-1}$$
$$= 1.987 \text{ cal.} \times \text{deg.}^{-1} \times \text{mole}^{-1}$$

This tabulation emphasizes the fact that the units must be stated clearly in order to give meaning to the gas constant.

The **heat capacity** of a substance is the amount of heat required to raise the temperature 1 degree. The constant R therefore has the dimensions of heat capacity per mole, since it can be expressed in calories per degree per mole. This also can be seen from a consideration of the first equation, term by term:

$$P = \frac{\textit{force}}{\textit{area}} = \frac{\textit{force}}{(\textit{length})^2}$$

$$V = (\textit{length})^3$$

therefore

$$PV = \textit{force} \times \textit{length} = \textit{energy}$$

and

$$\frac{PV}{T} = \frac{\textit{energy}}{\textit{temperature}} = \textit{heat capacity}$$

An imaginary experiment will show the significance of the gas constant. Place a mole of a gas in a cylinder fitted with a frictionless piston, illustrated in Figure 16. Suppose the initial temperature of the system is T, the volume of the gas is V, and the pressure is P inside and outside the cylinder. If we slowly raise the temperature of the gas 1 degree and allow the piston to move so as to keep the pressure inside the cylinder always equal to the external pressure P, we can obtain mechanical work from the gas by means of a suitable mechanism connected to the piston. The work is equal to the product of the force exerted upon the piston, multiplied by the distance through which it moves:

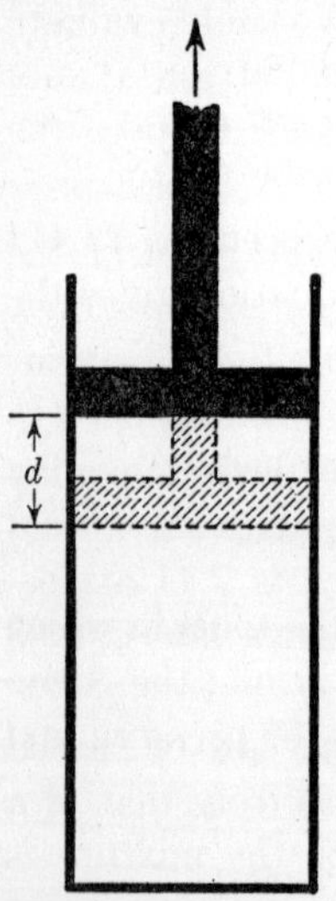

Fig. 16. Work Done by Expanding Gas.

$$w = fd$$

Now the pressure is equal to the force per unit area, or the force is equal to the pressure multiplied by the area of the piston:

$$f = Pa$$

hence

$$w = Pad = P\Delta V$$

where ΔV is the increase in volume, which can be calculated from the gas laws. Initially we have:

$$PV = RT$$

After the temperature has risen 1° C., and the volume has increased to $V + \Delta V$:

$$P(V + \Delta V) = R(T + 1)$$

Subtracting $PV = RT$ from $P(V + \Delta V) = R(T + 1)$, we find:

$$P\Delta V = R \times 1$$

We have just seen that the product of pressure and volume is work, so that *R represents the work done by one mole of a gas expanding against a constant pressure, when the temperature rises 1 degree.*

Dalton's Law of Partial Pressures. In 1801 John Dalton studied the behavior of gases, both pure and mixed, and discovered a generalization known as ***Dalton's law of partial pressures:*** *The total pressure exerted by a mixture of gases is the sum of the partial pressures of the components, each of which equals the pressure which that gas would exert if it were alone in the same volume under the same conditions.* Thus in a mixture of three components, A, B, and C, the total pressure is:

$$P_{\text{total}} = p_{\text{A}} + p_{\text{B}} + p_{\text{C}} \quad (V \text{ and } T \text{ constant})$$

for example if, at a constant temperature, 250 ml. of nitrogen under 720 mm. pressure and 380 ml. of oxygen under 650 mm. pressure were put into a 1-liter flask, the final pressure is found as follows:

$$\begin{array}{lcr} p_{\text{N}_2} \times 1000 = 720 \times 250 & \text{or} & p_{\text{N}_2} = 180 \text{ mm.} \\ p_{\text{O}_2} \times 1000 = 380 \times 650 & \text{or} & p_{\text{O}_2} = 247 \text{ mm.} \\ \hline & & \text{Total } P = 427 \text{ mm.} \end{array}$$

Dalton's law of partial pressures describes *approximately* the behavior of mixtures of permanent gases at moderate pressures. The deviations from this law are comparable with the deviations from Boyle's and Charles's laws. When Dalton's law is applied to mixtures including vapors at higher pressures, the deviations may be large. Thus, at a total pressure of 60 atmospheres the actual partial pressure of ammonia mixed with nitrogen is 7.44 atmospheres, while the pressure calculated from Dalton's law is 9.03 atmospheres, which is 21.4 per cent larger.

One of the most useful applications of Dalton's law of partial pressures is in calculating the volume of a dry gas from that of a gas collected over water. The total pressure of the mixture is equal to the partial pressure of the gas plus the partial pressure of the water vapor. At any particular temperature, the pressure of the water vapor in equilibrium with liquid water is a constant quantity, known as the **aqueous vapor pressure.** The vapor pressure of water has been determined up to the *critical temperature,*

374° C., above which water cannot exist as a liquid. Consequently, if we know the temperature, we can read the aqueous vapor pressure from a table and calculate the volume of the dry gas, thus:

$$P_{\text{gas}} = P_{\text{total}} - P_{H_2O}$$

The values of the vapor pressure of water, from temperatures below the freezing point (supercooled liquid) up to the critical temperature, are shown in Table 14. Notice that the vapor pressure increases more and more rapidly as the temperature rises. At 100° C. it reaches 760 mm., but continues to increase, logarithmically, until it reaches 217.72 atmospheres at the critical temperature, 374° C.

TABLE 14

THE VAPOR PRESSURE OF WATER AT DIFFERENT TEMPERATURES

TEMP. ° C.	V.P. MM. MERC.	TEMP. ° C.	V.P. MM. MERC.	TEMP. ° C.	V.P. MM. MERC.
− 15	1.4	22	19.8	92	567.0
− 10	2.1	23	21.1	94	610.9
− 5	3.2	24	22.4	96	657.6
0	4.6	25	23.8	98	707.3
5	6.5	30	31.8	100	760.0
10	9.2	35	42.2		
15	12.8	40	55.3		(ATM.)
16	13.6	45	71.9	100	1.000
17	14.5	50	92.5	110	1.414
18	15.5	60	149.4	120	1.959
19	16.5	70	223.7	200	15.34
20	17.5	80	355.1	300	84.78
21	18.7	90	525.8	374	217.72

Condensed from *International Critical Tables*, III, 211–212.

When a gas is collected over water and the level of the water inside and outside the container is equalized, the total pressure of the gases inside must equal the barometric pressure B. If the vapor pressure of water is a, and P_1 is the pressure of the gas, then by Dalton's law:

$$B = P_1 + a \qquad \text{or} \qquad P_1 = B - a$$

Knowing the volume V_1 of the gas collected over water at the temperature T_1 and partial pressure P_1, we can calculate V_2, that of the dry gas at the pressure P_2 and temperature T_2, by the following modification of the ideal gas law equation:

$$\frac{(B - a)V_1}{T_1} = \frac{P_2V_2}{T_2}$$

Graham's Law of Diffusion. ***Diffusion*** *is the process by which a substance expands because of the motion of its particles, tending to fill all the available volume.* It is the process by which gases mix with one another, liquids mix, or dissolved substances spread throughout a solution. Diffusion in gases is rapid compared to the process in solution. If two cylinders containing different gases are placed mouth to mouth, they will soon contain a homogeneous mixture of the two. Diffusion takes place even when the heavier constituent originally is placed below the lighter. Thus if a bulb of bromine is broken at the bottom of a tall vessel containing air, the dark red bromine vapor will rapidly diffuse until it is distributed uniformly, despite the fact that the density of the bromine vapor is over five times that of the air. This is true except in an *extremely high* column or for the very large particles of a suspension. Under these conditions the gravitational field causes a concentration of the heavier particles in the lower part of the vessel, but this effect is not observable for molecular mixtures under ordinary laboratory conditions.

In 1829 Thomas Graham discovered that *the rates at which different gases diffuse under identical conditions are inversely proportional to the square roots of their densities.* **Graham's law of gaseous diffusion** may be expressed by the mathematical equation:

$$\frac{r_1}{r_2} = \frac{\sqrt{d_2}}{\sqrt{d_1}}$$

where r_1 and r_2 are the rates of diffusion of the gases whose densities are d_1 and d_2 respectively. The process may be studied most conveniently by measuring the rates at which different gases diffuse through a porous plug or through a small hole in a metal plate, under the same average pressure. This relationship may be used to determine gas densities, if one standard density is known. For instance, if we know that the density of oxygen is 1.43 g./l. under standard conditions, and we find that the rate of diffusion of hydrogen is 4 times as great as that of oxygen under the same conditions, we can write:

$$\frac{1}{4} = \frac{\sqrt{d_2}}{\sqrt{1.43}} \qquad \text{whence} \qquad d_2 = \frac{1.43}{16} = 0.0894 \text{ g./l.}$$

The molecular weights of two gases are proportional to their densities, thus:

$$\frac{M_1}{M_2} = \frac{22.4 \times d_1}{22.4 \times d_2}$$

Hence measurements of rates of diffusion allow us to determine molecular weights. The molecular weights may be related to the rates of diffusion by an equation exactly like the preceding one, or they may be related to the *time* required for a definite volume of gas to diffuse, under the same conditions. The *times* of diffusion are inversely proportional to the rates, so that the equation is:

$$\frac{t_1}{t_2} = \frac{\sqrt{M_1}}{\sqrt{M_2}}$$

where t_1 and t_2 represent the times required for the diffusion of equal quantities of two gases of molecular weights M_1 and M_2. Thus for oxygen and ethylene:

$$\frac{t_1}{t_2} = \sqrt{\tfrac{32}{28}} = \sqrt{1.14} = 1.07$$

Graham's law of diffusion, like the other gas laws, is only an approximate relationship, but often it is useful for a rapid approximate determination of the molecular weight of an unknown gas.

The Kinetic Theory of Ideal Gases

So far we have taken up the laws which describe in general the behavior of all gases. All of these laws are generalizations based upon experiment, and completely independent of any theory of the *nature* of a gas. We shall now show how they can be derived mathematically from the simple idea that a gas consists of a very large number of molecules in rapid motion. This is the *kinetic theory* of gases, one of the most complete and interesting theories ever developed, which involved the united efforts of many men in the last two centuries.

Daniel Bernouilli, the Swiss mathematical physicist, developed a kinetic theory of gases as early as 1738. Unfortunately, he was unable to put his theory to the rigorous test of experiment, and his work had little influence upon his contemporaries. Dalton's success in explaining chemical facts by means of the atomic theory revived the attempt to treat the behavior of gases from the molecular point of view. Clausius and Krönig independently published papers in 1857 in which they developed the kinetic theory equation and derived from it the simple gas laws. The theory was further developed and extended by Maxwell, Kelvin, and Boltzmann, and its successful applications furnished a logical argument for the reality of molecular motion. It remained for Jean Perrin, the brilliant French physical chemist, to furnish a virtual *proof* of molecular motion by his quantitative study of the Brownian movement of colloidal particles suspended in a liquid or gas. He showed that the motion of the colloidal particles was due to ceaseless molecular bombardment and that such a system furnished a large-scale model of molecular motion.

The Postulates of the Kinetic Theory of Gases. The following statements embody all the assumptions necessary for the derivation of the kinetic theory equation:

(1) *A gas consists of an enormous number of very small particles (molecules) moving rapidly in straight lines, and frequently colliding with each other and with the walls of the container.* The pressure exerted upon the walls is the result of molecular bombardment.

(2) *The molecules are perfectly elastic, so that they lose no energy during collisions.* A tennis ball, dropped from a height upon a hard floor, bounces up and down for some time. However, since it is not perfectly elastic, it gradually comes to rest. So also the pressure of a gas composed of molecules which were not perfectly elastic would diminish slowly with time. Finally the molecules would collect into droplets of liquid. Actually, we know that gaseous pressure remains constant indefinitely as long as the temperature and mass of gas remain the same.

(3) *The molecules do not appreciably attract each other or the walls of the container.* The only force which they exert is a repulsion when they collide.

(4) *The volume occupied by the molecules is not appreciable compared to the total volume of the gas.* This is corroborated by the fact that when a gas under atmospheric pressure is liquefied it shrinks to only about 0.1 per cent of its former volume. When steam is formed from water at 100° C., it occupies a volume 1700 times as great as the liquid; hence we can conclude that the free space between the molecules is at least 99.94 per cent of the total volume occupied by the gas, while only 0.06 per cent is occupied by the molecules.

(5) *The mean kinetic energy of the molecules is proportional to the absolute temperature.* Whatever the substance, the proportionality factor is a constant, so that the mean kinetic energy of the molecules of different gases is the same at any given temperature.

The Derivation of the Kinetic Equation.[1] Consider a cube (Figure 17), d cm. on a side, which contains n gaseous molecules, each of mass m. Even 1 cc. of gas contains so many billions of molecules that their *average* velocity u is constant at any temperature, although the actual velocity of individual molecules varies over a wide range. Similarly, the individual molecules strike all the different faces of the cube in a random fashion, but the *average* behavior of all the molecules is the same as that of a gas in which one third of the molecules move back and forth perpendicular to each of the three pairs of faces of the cube.

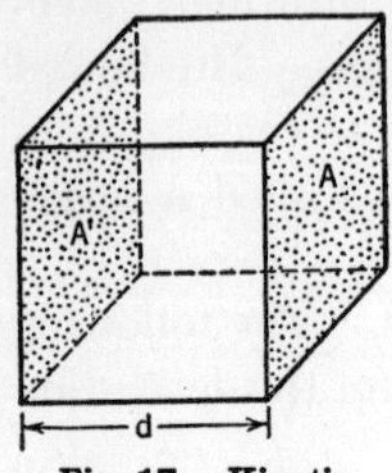

Fig. 17. Kinetic Theory of Gases.

Considering the molecules which move perpendicularly between the faces A and A', we shall calculate the force upon one of these faces, and then the pressure, which is exactly the same as that exerted upon any part of the surface of the container. Any molecule, moving back and forth between parallel faces, travels a distance $2\,d$ cm. between collisions with the face A. Since the molecule is moving with a velocity of u cm./sec., it will strike the face $u/2\,d$ times each second. At each collision with the face, the velocity of the molecule changes by an amount $2\,u$ cm./sec. If the molecule stopped at the face, its velocity would change by an amount u, but when it rebounds with the same speed in the opposite direction, the change is twice as great.

Since the acceleration a of a particle is the rate of change of its velocity, or the change in velocity per second, it will be equal to the number of collisions per second multiplied by the change in velocity at each collision:

$$a = \frac{u}{2\,d} \times 2\,u = \frac{u^2}{d} \text{ cm.} \times \text{sec.}^{-2}$$

According to the fundamental law of physics, the *force* exerted upon the face A by each molecule will be the product of the mass times the acceleration:

$$f = ma = \frac{mu^2}{d} \text{ dyne (for 1 molecule)}$$

[1] A more rigorous derivation of the kinetic equation may be found in Hugh S. Taylor's *Treatise on Physical Chemistry*, 2d ed. D. Van Nostrand Company, Inc., New York, 1931. Chapter III, "The Kinetic Theory of Gases and Liquids." See also Loeb, *The Kinetic Theory of Gases*. McGraw-Hill Book Company, Inc., New York, 1927. Chapter II, "The Mechanical Picture of a Perfect Gas."

Since $\frac{1}{3}$ of all the molecules strike this face, the total force which all of them will exert upon it will be $n/3$ times that which one molecule exerts, or:

$$F = \frac{mnu^2}{3\,d} \text{ dyne (for all molecules)}$$

The *pressure* is the force per unit area:

$$P = \frac{F}{d^2} = \frac{mnu^2}{3\,d^3} \text{ dyne} \times \text{cm.}^{-2}$$

Since d^3 is simply the volume of the cube, V, we find:

$$P = \frac{mnu^2}{3\,V} \quad \text{or} \quad PV = \tfrac{1}{3}\,mnu^2 \text{ erg}$$

This is the fundamental equation of the kinetic theory of gases, which we will designate as **the kinetic theory equation.** From it we shall proceed to derive nine important equations describing the behavior of the ideal gas.

Derivation of the Laws of the Ideal Gas from the Kinetic Theory Equation. (1) Boyle's law. For any particular gas, the average mass of the molecules will be constant. For a fixed weight of the gas, the number of molecules also will be constant. Since the kinetic theory also assumes that the average velocity of the molecules is constant at any fixed temperature, the product mnu^2 will be a constant for a constant quantity of gas at a constant temperature. Substituting this result into the kinetic equation we find:

$$PV = K \quad (w \text{ and } T \text{ constant})$$

This is the familiar expression for Boyle's law, which therefore follows as a consequence of the postulates of the kinetic theory of gases.

(2) The laws of Gay-Lussac and Charles. In deriving Boyle's law from the kinetic equation, we have made no assumption about the velocity of the molecules, except that its average value was constant at any fixed temperature. In order to derive Charles's law, we must use the fifth postulate of the kinetic theory, taking into account the change of molecular velocity with temperature. The kinetic energy of any moving particle is defined as half the product of its mass times its velocity. For an individual molecule:

$$k.\,e. = \tfrac{1}{2}\,mu^2$$

Substituting this expression into the kinetic equation we find:

$$PV = \tfrac{2}{3}\, n(\tfrac{1}{2}\, mu^2) = \tfrac{2}{3}\, n(k.\ e.)$$

According to the fifth postulate of the kinetic theory, the kinetic energy is proportional to the absolute temperature, or:

$$k.\ e. = k'T$$

Substituting this value into the previous equation gives:

$$PV = \tfrac{2}{3}\, k'nT = nkT$$

The constant k is known as **Boltzmann's constant.** Solving this equation for V we find:

$$V = \frac{nk}{P}\, T$$

For a fixed quantity of gas at constant pressure, both n and P are constant, and for the volumes at two different temperatures we find:

$$V_1 = \frac{nk}{P}\, T_1 \qquad \text{and} \qquad V_2 = \frac{nk}{P}\, T_2$$

Dividing the first equation by the second gives:

$$\frac{V_1}{V_2} = \frac{T_1}{T_2}$$

which is Charles's law. This experimental generalization is therefore also a consequence of the kinetic theory of gases.

(3) The equation of state of the ideal gas. Returning to the equation $PV = nkT$, if we are dealing with one mole of gas, $n = N$ (Avogadro's number) and we have:

$$PV = NkT$$

This equation is exactly the same as the equation of state of the ideal gas, if we set $Nk = R$. Boltzmann's constant then is seen to be the gas constant for one molecule, instead of for one mole of gas. The kinetic theory therefore enables us to derive the equation of state of the ideal gas, although it does not fix the numerical value of the gas constant R. R is an experimental and not a theoretical constant, the evaluation of which depends upon an experimental study of gases in the laboratory.

(4) Avogadro's law. For any two gases the following relationship holds according to the kinetic theory equation:

$$P_1V_1 = \tfrac{1}{3}\, n_1m_1u_1^2 \qquad \text{and} \qquad P_2V_2 = \tfrac{1}{3}\, n_2m_2u_2^2$$

If the volumes and pressures are the same, $P_1V_1 = P_2V_2$, hence

$$n_1m_1u_1^2 = n_2m_2u_2^2$$

If the temperatures are equal, then according to the kinetic theory the *kinetic energies* of the molecules are equal:

$$\tfrac{1}{2}\,m_1u_1^2 = \tfrac{1}{2}\,m_2u_2^2 \qquad \text{or} \qquad m_1u_1^2 = m_2u_2^2$$

Dividing this equation into the preceding one gives:

$$n_1 = n_2 \quad (P,\ V, \text{ and } T \text{ equal})$$

This means that Avogadro's law describes the behavior of ideal gases. Real gases show the same deviations that they show in the case of the other ideal gas laws.

(5) Dalton's law of partial pressures. In a vessel containing a mixture of ideal gaseous molecules of different masses, the pressure upon the walls will be the sum of the pressures exerted by each of these different gases, *i.e.:*

$$P = p_{\rm A} + p_{\rm B} + p_{\rm C} + \cdots$$

Since we have assumed that the molecules of ideal gases exert no influence upon each other except when they collide, we can derive equations for the behavior of each gas, independent of the others which may be present in the vessel. These equations would be:

$$p_{\rm A}V = \tfrac{1}{3}\,n_{\rm A}m_{\rm A}u_{\rm A}^2 \qquad p_{\rm B}V = \tfrac{1}{3}\,n_{\rm B}m_{\rm B}u_{\rm B}^2 \qquad p_{\rm C}V = \tfrac{1}{3}\,n_{\rm C}m_{\rm C}u_{\rm C}^2 \cdots$$

Each of these partial pressures is the same as the pressure of the same gas alone, in the same volume and at the same temperature. Thus Dalton's law of partial pressures follows as a corollary of the kinetic theory of gases.

(6) Graham's law of gaseous diffusion. In deriving the kinetic theory equation, we assumed that, at any particular temperature, the gaseous molecules of the same mass moved with the same average velocity u. Rearranging the kinetic theory equation $PV = \frac{1}{3}\,mnu^2$, we can solve for the velocity and find:

$$u = \sqrt{\frac{3\,PV}{mn}}$$

Since mn is the mass of the gas in the volume V, mn/V is the density d at the particular pressure P. Gas densities usually are given at a pressure of 1 atmosphere, which we will designate by $\boldsymbol{d}$. For an ideal gas, the density is proportional to the pressure, so that:

$$\frac{\boldsymbol{d}}{1} = \frac{d}{P} \qquad \text{or} \qquad \boldsymbol{d} = \frac{mn}{PV}$$

Comparing two gases at the same temperature we find that:

$$\frac{u_1}{u_2} = \sqrt{\frac{d_2}{d_1}}$$

If we make the reasonable assumption that the rate at which a gas diffuses is proportional to the rate at which the molecules move, then we would write:

$$\frac{r_1}{r_2} = \sqrt{\frac{d_2}{d_1}}$$

This is simply **Graham's law of diffusion,** which is another experimentally established law which can be derived from the kinetic theory equation.

(7) **Molecular velocities.** The actual molecular velocities also can be calculated from the kinetic theory equation. To simplify numerical calculations, we shall take one mole of gas, for which the equation of state is $PV = RT$. Solving the kinetic theory equation as before for u gives:

$$u = \sqrt{\frac{3\,PV}{mn}} = \sqrt{\frac{3\,RT}{M}}$$

where M is the molecular weight, equal to mn. Notice that the velocity is inversely proportional to the *square root* of the molecular weight and to the *square root* of the absolute temperature. The latter relationship comes from the fact that it is the kinetic energy, involving u^2, which is assumed to be proportional to T. In order to evaluate u for any gas at 0° C., we only need to substitute the known values for R (from page 77), T, and M, thus:

$$R = 8.314 \times 10^7 \text{ ergs} \times \text{deg.}^{-1} \times \text{mole}^{-1}$$

and

$$T = 273.16^\circ \text{ A.}$$

whence

$$u = \sqrt{\frac{3 \times 8.314 \times 10^7 \times 273.2}{M}} \text{ cm.} \times \text{sec.}^{-1}$$

$$= \frac{261{,}000}{\sqrt{M}} \text{ cm.} \times \text{sec.}^{-1}$$

The fastest-moving gas molecules are those of the lightest gas, hydrogen, with a molecular weight of 2.016, the square root of which is 1.420. Their velocity at 0° therefore would be:

$$u = 183{,}900 \text{ cm./sec.} = 1.839 \text{ km./sec.} = 68.6 \text{ miles/min.}$$

A hydrogen molecule, moving with this velocity for six hours, travels a distance equal to the circumference of the earth at the equator. A comparison of this velocity with some other high velocities is made in Table 15. It is perhaps surprising to find that, although the hydrogen molecule moves much faster than the fastest airplane or rifle bullet, it moves slowly in comparison to the earth in its motion around the sun.

TABLE 15

A Comparison of Some High Velocities

	Km. per Sec.	Miles per Min.
Airplane speed record (1939)	0.210	7.8
Velocity of sound in dry air at 0°	0.331	12
Muzzle velocity of rifle bullet	0.823	31
German 75-mile shell (1917)	1.7	63
Hydrogen molecule at 0°	1.8	68
Earth's orbital velocity	29.8	1100

The enormous velocities which we have calculated above are required by the kinetic theory, in order to account for gas pressure by the bombardment of molecules. It might seem a very difficult task to measure such velocities directly, yet the velocity of light, which is much greater still, has been measured very accurately. Actually, the most successful methods of measuring molecular velocities are based upon Fizeau's method for measuring that of light. In 1927 two independent applications of this principle were made by Costa, Smyth, and K. T. Compton and, with greater precision, by Eldridge of the University of Iowa. Figure 18, adapted from Compton's article, illustrates the experimental arrangements. The central axle *A* carries two thin circular metal disks, D_1, D_2, around the periphery of which are cut a series of rectangular slots, a few of which appear in the drawing. The axle and disks form a rotor which is mounted inside a closely fitting jacket *J*. The space between is evacuated as completely as possible by means of suitable pumps, so as to prevent collisions of the

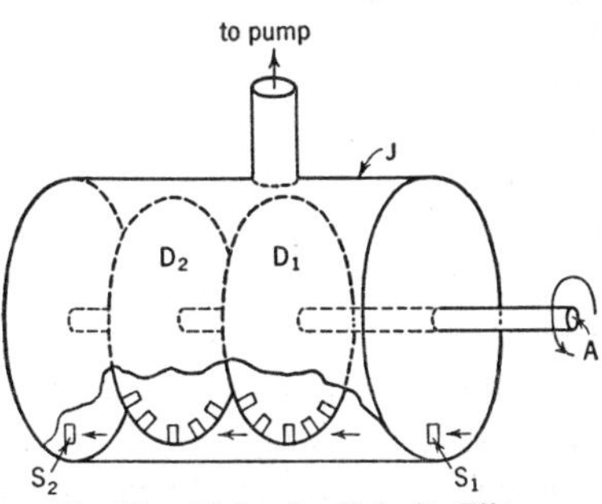

Fig. 18. Molecular Velocity Filter.

gas under investigation with any other molecules. The gas is admitted to the apparatus through the slit S_1 and passes in a straight stream toward the outlet slit S_2. As the rotor whirls around, the disk D_1 chops the gas stream into puffs which move toward the disk D_2 with their initial velocity. If the rotor is moving at exactly the right speed, a slot on the disk D_2 comes in line just in time to allow each puff of gas to pass through it. If the rotor is turning too fast or too slow, the disk D_2 will cut off the gas stream, and keep it from reaching the second slit S_2. The speed of the rotor is varied up to 6000 revolutions per minute, until the maximum number of molecules passes through the apparatus and reaches the detecting device beyond S_2. Then, the molecular velocities corresponding to the known temperature of the entering gas can be calculated from the speed of the rotor, the distance between the disks, and their diameters. These velocities agree within experimental error with those predicted by the kinetic theory.

(8) The heat capacity of gases. Another important extension of the kinetic theory equation enables us to calculate the heat capacity of gases and provides a physical criterion of the number of atoms in the molecule of a gas. According to the postulates of the kinetic theory, heat is a form of molecular motion. In the ideal gas, the only motion is the translational motion of the molecules. If the volume of the ideal gas is held constant, all the heat which it absorbs appears as kinetic energy — in other words, as an increase in the average velocity of the molecules. The increase in the kinetic energy, per degree, therefore is the *heat capacity of the gas at constant volume.* The kinetic energy of one mole of a perfect gas can be calculated immediately from the equations we have already derived. For n molecules, we have found that $PV = \frac{2}{3}n(k.e.)$, where $k.e.$ is the kinetic energy per molecule. For a mole of gas, $n = N$ (Avogadro's number) and we may write:

$$PV = \tfrac{2}{3}N(k.e.) = \tfrac{2}{3}(K.E.)$$

where $K.E.$ is the kinetic energy per mole. We need only divide this equation by the equation $PV = RT$ and rearrange terms to find:

$$(K.E.)_T = \tfrac{3}{2}RT$$

This is the kinetic energy at a temperature T. Similar calculations will show that at a temperature 1 degree higher it will be:

$$(K.E.)_{T+1} = \tfrac{3}{2}R(T + 1)$$

Subtracting the first of these equations from the second gives the change in kinetic energy per degree, which is the same as the heat capacity at constant volume, C_V:

$$C_V = (K.E.)_{T+1} - (K.E.)_T = \tfrac{3}{2}R$$

Naumann, in 1867, made this interesting derivation from the kinetic theory equation.

When we heat a gas at constant pressure, more energy will be required to raise its temperature, because it will expand continually against the pressure of the atmosphere. If we heat a gas 1 degree at constant volume, the pressure will increase. If we reduce the pressure to its original value, the gas will cool unless heat is added. This additional heat is exactly equal to the work which the gas has to do against the constant atmospheric pressure, when it is heated one degree. This, as we have shown on page 78, is equal to R. *The molal heat capacity of a perfect gas at constant pressure, C_P, therefore, is greater by R than the molal heat capacity at constant volume, C_V:*

$$C_P = C_V + R = \tfrac{3}{2}R + R = \tfrac{5}{2}R = 4.95 \text{ cal. per deg. per mole}$$

This reasoning may be extended to diatomic molecules, where, in addition to the kinetic energy of translation we have to consider, at ordinary temperature, the kinetic energy of rotation of the molecules around their common center of gravity. In the derivation of the kinetic equation, the factor 3 enters because the molecules are equally likely to be moving along any one of the three perpendicular axes in space. A molecule of the ideal gas has *3 degrees of freedom* of motion, and three co-ordinates are required to define its position. In the case of a diatomic molecule, two additional degrees of freedom are introduced, as shown in Figure 19. The molecule can rotate, and this rotation can be resolved into motion around the two axes at right angles to the line joining the centers of the atoms. Rotation around the line of centers involves no more energy than the rotation of the perfect gas molecule, which is neglected in the kinetic theory. The diatomic gas molecule therefore has in all *5 degrees of freedom.*

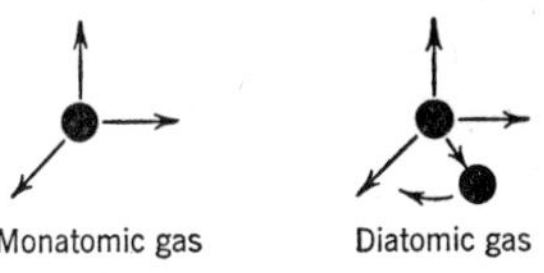

Fig. 19. Degrees of Freedom.

Another way of defining the number of degrees of freedom of a molecule is the number of independent variables required to define its position completely. For a monatomic gas, this is the three dimensions of space. For two *independent* monatomic particles, three co-ordinates would be required for each, or six for the pair. However, if the pair are joined to form a molecule, they remain a fixed distance apart. Three co-ordinates are required to locate the first atom, but the second then must lie on the surface of a sphere, the radius of which is the distance separating the atoms. We need only specify two more co-ordinates — the latitude and longitude — in order to fix the position of the second atom. Thus the diatomic molecule has only 5 degrees of freedom instead of 6.

From the equation $C_V = \frac{3}{2} R$ for a monatomic gas, we see that the gas has a heat capacity of $\frac{1}{2} R$ for each of its three degrees of freedom. Similarly, a diatomic gas would have a heat capacity of $\frac{1}{2} R$ for each of 5 degrees of freedom, or a total of $\frac{5}{2} R$ for the value of C_V. A determination of the heat capacities of monatomic and diatomic gases could be used to check these conclusions, but another method of comparison is simpler. This involves the use of the Kundt dust tube apparatus to determine the velocity of sound in the gas. From this quantity a simple calculation gives the ratio between the molar heat capacity at constant pressure, C_P, and that at constant volume, C_V. The molar heat capacity ratio, designated by the Greek letter gamma is defined as:

$$\gamma = \frac{C_P}{C_V}$$

Since the molar heat capacities will be different for monatomic and diatomic gases, so also will be their ratios. The predictions of the kinetic theory are summarized in Table 19.

TABLE 16

THEORETICAL MOLAR HEAT CAPACITIES AND HEAT CAPACITY RATIOS FOR GASES

TYPE OF GAS	C_V	C_P	$\gamma = \frac{C_P}{C_V}$
Monatomic	$\frac{3}{2} R$	$\frac{5}{2} R$	1.67
Diatomic	$\frac{5}{2} R$	$\frac{7}{2} R$	1.40

Chemical evidence had indicated that mercury vapor was monatomic. In 1876 Kundt and Warburg found that the heat capacity ratio for this substance was exactly that indicated by the theory for a monatomic gas. A few years later the theory was applied to gases about which chemical methods could tell nothing. When Ramsay discovered and studied the rare gases of the atmosphere, he found no elements with which they would combine. However, he determined the heat capacity ratio for each of these gases, found that it was 1.67, and hence concluded that their molecules were monatomic. On this assumption he determined their atomic weights from gas densities and found that, in order to include them in the periodic table, he had to add a new column, Group 0, which Mendeléeff had not suspected. The ratios of the molar heat capacities of a number of monatomic and diatomic gases are given in Table 17. The ratios agree perfectly with the results of chemical investigation, and furnish a valuable independent method of determining the complexity of a molecule. The simple kinetic theory yields results which are remarkably satisfactory when dealing with gases near room temperature.

TABLE 17

THE HEAT CAPACITY RATIO (γ) FOR VARIOUS GASES

Gas	$\gamma = \frac{C_P}{C_V}$	Gas	$\gamma = \frac{C_P}{C_V}$
Hg	1.67	H_2	1.410
A	1.668	O_2	1.401
Ne	1.64	N_2	1.404
Kr	1.68	Cl_2	1.355
Xe	1.66	NO	1.400
Na	1.68	CO	1.404
K	1.69	HCl	1.41

(9) The law of atmospheres. Another consequence of the kinetic theory of gases is ***the law of atmospheres,*** *which states that the pressure of a gas (or its density or concentration) decreases exponentially with the height of the column, provided the temperature is constant.* The mathematical formulation of this law, which will be derived on page 635, is:

$$\log \frac{P_1}{P_2} = \log \frac{d_1}{d_2} = \log \frac{C_1}{C_2} = 0.4343 \frac{Mg}{RT} (h_2 - h_1)$$

Here the values of pressure P, density d, and concentration C, correspond to those of the height h. M is the molecular weight of the gas, T the absolute temperature, g the acceleration of gravity (the normal value of which is 980.665 cm. $\times$ sec.$^{-2}$ or 980.665

dynes × g.$^{-1}$) and R the gas constant, which must be expressed in ergs × deg.$^{-1}$ × mole^{-1}.

For any particular gas at a definite temperature, the term $0.4343 \frac{Mg}{RT}$ will have a constant value which we may call K. If h_1 is taken as the datum line from which all of our measurements are made, we can set $(h_2 - h_1) = h$, let P_0 equal the pressure at the datum line and P the pressure at the height h, and the equation of the law of atmospheres then becomes:

$$\log \frac{P_0}{P} = Kh$$

If at any given height h the pressure has fallen to some fraction, *e.g.*, $\frac{1}{2}$, of its value at the surface, this equation shows that at a height $2h$ it will be $\frac{1}{4}$ of the value at the surface, and so on. In other words, as the height increases in *arithmetical* progression (h, $2h$, $3h$, etc.) the pressure decreases in a *geometrical* progression ($\frac{1}{2}$, $\frac{1}{4}$, $\frac{1}{8}$, etc.). Of course, there is nothing unique about the factor $\frac{1}{2}$. If we had picked the height at which the pressure had fallen to $\frac{1}{3}$ of the value at the surface, then the pressure at twice this height would be $\frac{1}{9}$ of that at the surface.

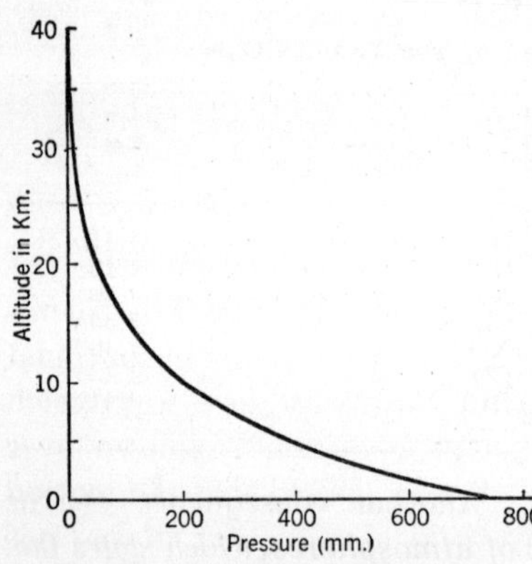

Fig. 20. The Earth's Atmosphere.

The equation of the law of atmospheres, derived from the kinetic theory, can be tested by measurements of the atmospheric pressure at different altitudes above the surface of the earth. Figure 20 shows a graph for the pressure as a function of the altitude, based upon the flights of 321 sounding balloons made in the summer months.[1] These results show the simple relationship between pressure and altitude, which we have deduced for an atmosphere of uniform temperature, free from convection currents. Near the surface of the earth, the atmosphere is turbulent, with marked dif-

[1] The data for this figure and the accompanying table were taken from *Physics of the Air*, 2d ed. by W. J. Humphreys. McGraw-Hill Book Co., New York, 1920, p. 74.

ferences in temperature and frequent wind storms. This region would not be expected to behave like an *ideal* atmosphere. At about 11 km. above the surface of the earth, however, the stratosphere begins — a vast region of constant temperature, to which the laws of the ideal atmosphere are found to apply. Above 11 km. the pressure is halved for every increase in altitude of 4.5 km. The agreement between experiment and theory, shown in Table 18, affords further verification of the kinetic theory.

TABLE 18

THE DECREASE IN ATMOSPHERIC PRESSURE WITH ALTITUDE

Altitude (Km.)	Difference in Altitude (Km.)	Observed Pressure	
		Atmospheres	Mm. Mercury
0	0	1	762.6
5.6	5.6	$\frac{1}{2}$	381.3
10.5	4.9	$\frac{1}{4}$	190.7
15.0	4.5	$\frac{1}{8}$	95.3
19.6	4.6	$\frac{1}{16}$	47.7
24.1	4.5	$\frac{1}{32}$	23.8
28.6	4.5	$\frac{1}{64}$	11.9
33.1	4.5	$\frac{1}{128}$	6.0

The Brownian Movement. In 1827 the Scotch botanist Robert Brown (1773–1858) examined suspensions of pollen under the microscope and found that the small particles of pollen were in continual motion — darting back and forth, up and down, in a way which suggested perpetual motion. This phenomenon is known ever since as the **Brownian movement.** Brown proved that the motion was not due to animalcules, and others showed that it was not caused by thermal eddy currents, like the visible motion of dust particles in a beam of sunlight. It was a property of the solution itself, and it was indeed perpetual motion, since colloidal quartz particles, enclosed in the rocks since past geologic ages, were found to move with equal vigor.

Fifty years after the discovery of the Brownian movement, the Belgian, Carbonelle, offered the first satisfactory explanation of its cause. He suggested that the colloidal particles were bombarded incessantly by the molecules of the liquid about them. The molecules are invisible, but the colloidal particles, millions of times as large, are supposed to obey the same laws of motion as gaseous molecules, and hence serve as a large-scale model of the motion of individual molecules. Carbonelle's ideas were not tested experimentally until many years later. In 1908 Jean Perrin, professor of physical chemistry at the University of Paris, took up this difficult experimental problem. The first difficulty was the preparation of suspensions with particles of uniform size, so that each "molecule" would behave exactly like its neighbors. He was able to prepare uniform suspensions of gamboge and of mastic, with which he could make quantitative measurements. He could not measure *directly* the mean velocity of a single colloidal particle, because it was continually jostled by the molecules of the liquid, unlike a gaseous molecule which moves many times its own diameter between collisions. In his own words, "the entanglements of the trajectory are so numerous and so rapid that it is impossible to follow them, and the trajectory seen is always infinitely shorter and more simple than the real trajectory." In order to avoid this difficulty, Perrin carried out ingenious studies of the distribution of the colloidal particles in the gravitational field, which established just as conclusively the analogy with gases and the predictions of the kinetic theory.

Perrin's Study of the Colloidal Atmosphere. Perrin immediately saw that if the Brownian movement were really due to molecular bombardment the distribution of the colloidal particles should obey the same law of atmospheres deduced for ideal gases. In his own words: [1]

Let us suppose that it is possible to obtain an emulsion [2] with the granules all identical, an emulsion which I shall call, for shortness, *uniform.* It appeared to me at first intuitively that the granules of such an emulsion should distribute themselves as a function of the height in the same manner as the molecules of a gas under the influence of gravity. Just as the air is more dense at sea level than on a mountaintop, so the granules of an emulsion, whatever may be their initial distribution, will attain a permanent state where the concentration will go on diminishing as a function of the height from the lower layers, and the law of rarefaction will be the same as for the air.

A closer examination confirms this conception and gives the law of rarefaction by precise reasoning, very similar to that which enabled Laplace to correlate the altitude and the barometric pressure. . . . It

[1] *Brownian Movement and Molecular Reality* by Jean Perrin, translated by F. Soddy. Taylor, and Francis, London, 1910, p. 23.

[2] Actually Perrin used *sols,* since gamboge and mastic are *solids.* For the distinction between these terms see page 532.

shows clearly that the *concentration of the granules of a uniform emulsion decreases in an exponential manner as a function of the height,* in the same way as the barometric pressure does as a function of the altitude.

The only difference between gas molecules and colloidal particles is that the former move *in vacuo,* while the latter are buoyed up by the liquid surrounding them. If m is the mass of one colloidal particle, the molecular weight $M = mN$. Since the *effective* mass of the colloidal particle is decreased by the liquid it displaces, we may write $m = V(D - d)$, where V is the volume of the colloidal particle, D its density, and d the density of the liquid. We then find for the colloidal atmosphere:

$$\log \frac{C_0}{C} = \frac{NV(D - d)g(h_2 - h_1)}{RT}$$

The only difference between the earth's atmosphere and the colloidal atmosphere is an enormous difference in scale. Instead of requiring sounding balloons sent to great heights, Perrin carried out his studies of suspensions in a small glass cell, only 0.1 mm. (100 μ) high. Such a cell was made by boring a shallow hole in a microscope slide. After the drop of suspension was placed in the cell, a cover glass was sealed over the top to prevent evaporation. The cell was placed on the stage of a powerful microscope, and carefully leveled. In a room at constant temperature the suspension reached a steady state in about three hours, and maintained this distribution indefinitely.

By using a high-powered objective lens, Perrin could focus sharply on a layer of the emulsion about 1 μ thick, and count the number of particles in this layer. Of course, the particles kept moving in and out of the layer, but the average of many individual counts was a constant quantity. Perrin then raised or lowered the objective by a definite small distance, and repeated the counting at other levels. The change in concentration with changing level was very large within the cell. A schematic diagram of the colloidal atmosphere, and the appearance of individual layers, is shown in Figure 21. A series of photographs showing various stages in the settling of colloidal protein particles under the influence of a centrifugal field, is shown on Plate XIV, facing page 548.

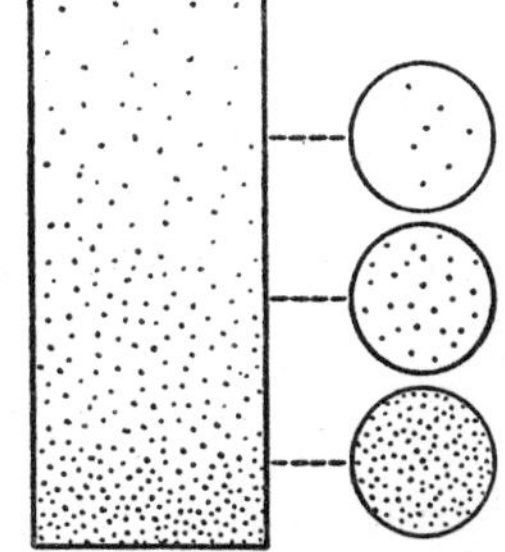

Fig. 21. The Colloidal Atmosphere.

Perrin studied a large number of different suspensions, and made thousands of individual counts in order to verify the law of the colloidal atmosphere. His conclusions are best summarized in his own words.

> My most careful series has been done with granules of gamboge having a radius of 0.212 μ. The readings have been made in a cell having a height of 100 μ in four equidistant horizontal planes cutting the vessel at the levels:
>
> $$5\ \mu,\ 35\ \mu,\ 65\ \mu,\ 95\ \mu$$
>
> These readings . . . relate to 13,000 granules and give, respectively for these levels, concentrations proportional to the numbers:
>
> $$100,\ 47,\ 22.6,\ 12$$
>
> which are practically equal to the numbers:
>
> $$100,\ 48,\ 23,\ 11.1$$
>
> which are exactly in a geometrical progression. Thus the exponential distribution cannot be doubted, each elevation of 30 μ here decreasing the concentration to about half its value.

A corresponding decrease in the concentration of the earth's atmosphere requires a distance 150 million times as great! From a study of a large number of different suspensions, in which he varied the size and density of the particles as much as possible, Perrin concluded that, within the limits of his experimental error, particles in Brownian movement in a suspension behaved exactly according to the laws of the kinetic theory.

> It may be interesting to observe that the largest of the granules for which I have found the laws of perfect gases followed are already visible in sunlight under a strong lens. They behave as the molecules of a perfect gas, of which the gram molecule weighed 200,000 tons.

The student grounded in the kinetic and atomic theories may not realize that at the turn of the century a group of able scientists, vigorously headed by Wilhelm Ostwald, attacked the atomic theory as a dogma, like the old phlogiston theory, which did more harm than good. It was Perrin's work which silenced this criticism and brought the atomic theory into universal favor. As Ostwald said, "The agreements of the Brownian movement with the requirements of the kinetic hypothesis . . . justify the most cautious scientist in now speaking of the experimental proof of the atomic theory of matter."

PROBLEMS AND EXERCISES

1. If a sample of 175 ml. of oxygen, collected over water at 30° C. when the barometric pressure is 745 mm. of mercury, is dried and reduced to standard conditions, what volume will it occupy?

2. If 250 ml. of nitrogen at 730 mm. pressure is mixed with 400 ml. of oxygen at 700 mm. pressure, all at a constant temperature of 20° C., calculate the final pressure of the mixture, (*a*) in a total volume of 300 ml., dry, (*b*) in a total volume of 350 ml. over water.

3. A sample of nitrogen collected over water at 35° occupies a volume of 200 ml. when the barometer reads 760 mm. What volume will it occupy if it is measured over water at 20° at a barometric pressure of 735 mm.?

4. Under standard conditions, oxygen diffuses through a capillary at the rate of 15.7 ml. per minute, while an unknown gas diffuses at the rate of 10.6 ml. per minute. If the density of oxygen is 1.429 g. per l., what is the density of the unknown gas?

5. (*a*) If one liter of hydrogen passes through the capillary of a diffusion apparatus in 1 min., 35 sec., how long will the same volume of methane take to pass through the same capillary? (*b*) What is the molecular weight of an unknown gas, one liter of which passes through the same capillary in 5 min., 55 sec.?

6. Calculate the average velocity of the molecules of oxygen gas (*a*) at 0° C., (*b*) at 100° C.

7. The average velocity of the molecules of a certain gas at 0° C. is 299 m./sec. Calculate the molecular weight of the gas.

8. (*a*) To what temperature would hydrogen gas have to be cooled in order to reduce the mean speed of its molecules to that of the molecules of oxygen at 20° C.? (*b*) To what temperature would xenon have to be heated in order to increase the average speed of its molecules to that of the molecules of helium at − 50° C.?

9. What would be the molecular weight of a gas the molecules of which move with the speed of sound in air at 0° C.?

10. Show that, for an ideal gas, the equation, PV/wT = a constant, expresses the relation between pressure, volume, temperature, and mass.

11. Show from the kinetic theory that the equation, $PV = nRT$, holds for an ideal gas or gas mixture.

* **12.** (*a*) Taking the density of mercury at 0° C. as 13.60 g./cc. and the normal acceleration of gravity as 980.7 cm./sec.^{2}, show that the normal atmosphere is 1.013×10^6 dynes per square cm. (*b*) Calculate R in dyne cm. per deg. per mole and check the value on page 77. (*c*) Calculate the value of R in cal. per deg. per mole and check the value on the same page. One calorie is 4.183 joules.

* **13.** If the volume of a gas is a function of P and T, the total derivative of V may be expressed by the fundamental equation of partial differentiation as: $dV = (\partial V/\partial P)_T\, dP + (\partial V/\partial T)_P\, dT$. Evaluate $(\partial V/\partial P)_T$ and $(\partial V/\partial T)_P$ from the equations for Boyle's and Charles's laws respectively, substitute in the equation above, rearrange, and integrate to prove PV/T = constant.

* **14.** (*a*) Calculate the constant k in the equation, $\log C_0/C = kMh$, for air, the "molecular weight" of which is 29.0, from the fact that the pressure is halved for an increase in altitude of 4.5 km., and the assumption that the pressure is proportional to the concentration. (*b*) Using the value of k from (*a*) and assuming that each gas individually obeys the atmospheric formula, calculate the partial pressures of N_2 and O_2 at a height of 40 km. in an *ideal* isothermal atmosphere, if their partial pressures at the ground are 0.780 and 0.220 atm. respectively. How much does the composition of the atmosphere change with height, according to this calculation?

* **15.** Using the same constant determined in problem 14, calculate the partial pressure of bromine vapor at a height of 1 km. in an ideal isothermal atmosphere, if it is in contact with liquid bromine at 0° C. at the bottom. The vapor pressure of bromine at this temperature is 65.9 mm. of mercury.

READING LIST

A. Findlay, *The Spirit of Chemistry*. Longmans, Green & Co., New York, 1930. An excellent general discussion of "The Three States of Matter" is given in Chapters VII and VIII, pages 96–130.

Sir William Bragg, *Concerning the Nature of Things*. Harper & Brothers, New York, 1925. Covers gases, liquids, and solids in an elementary way.

J. B. Perrin, *Brownian Movement and Molecular Reality*. Trans. by F. Soddy. Taylor and Francis, London, 1910.

Otto Maass, "The Gaseous State of Aggregation," Chapter III in *A Treatise on Physical Chemistry*, 2d ed. edited by Hugh S. Taylor. D. Van Nostrand Company, New York, 1931.

S. Glasstone, *Textbook of Physical Chemistry*. D. Van Nostrand Co., New York, 1940. This book is a detailed treatise, comprising 1289 pages. See especially pages 184–188 and 238–277.

Leonard B. Loeb, *Kinetic Theory of Gases*. McGraw-Hill Book Company, New York, 1927. Chapter II, "The Mechanical Picture of a Perfect Gas," Chapter VIII, "The Reality of Molecular Motions, Brownian Movements," and Chapter IX, "Specific Heats and the Kinetic Theory."

CHAPTER 5

THE BEHAVIOR OF REAL GASES

Deviations from the Ideal Gas Laws. We have seen that the ideal gas laws hold approximately for gases at and above room temperature, and at pressures no greater than a few atmospheres. Even under these conditions, real gases show appreciable deviations from the ideal gas laws, and these become much larger at high pressures and at temperatures near the critical temperature. Since the ideal gas laws all can be deduced from the kinetic theory, a closer inspection of the postulates of this theory will give a clue to the deviations shown by real gases.

TABLE 19

Change of *PV* with Pressure for Real Gases

P (Atm.)	*PV*		
	O_2 (0°)	CO_2 (40°)	H_2 (0°)
1	1.0000		1.0000
50	0.9568	0.8500	1.0330
100	0.9265	0.3090	1.0639
200	0.9140	0.4675	1.1336
300	0.9625	0.6485	1.2045
400	1.0515	0.8230	1.2775
600	1.2690	1.1570	1.4226
800	1.5030	1.4790	1.5665
1000	1.7355	1.7800	1.7107

Boyle's law states that, at constant temperature, $PV = K$. We have already seen that a plot of P against V gives a rectangular hyperbola, but another plot is more useful in showing the *deviations* from this law. If we plot PV against P, the result, for any gas obeying Boyle's law, is a straight line, parallel to the axis of P. In Table 19 we have set down experimental values of the product PV for three common gases at pressures up to 1000 atmospheres In each case the value of PV at 0° and 1 atmosphere is taken as unity. These data are plotted in Figure 22 to show how they deviate from Boyle's law. The curve for oxygen is typical of most gases at room temperature. The product PV first *decreases* with increasing pressure, then passes through a minimum value and finally *increases* nearly linearly when the pressure becomes very high. Carbon dioxide at 40° C., a temperature only slightly above the critical point (31.1°), shows a much larger initial decrease than oxygen. At moderate pressures, the value of PV is only *one third* as large as at one atmosphere. At high pressures its behavior is much more nearly like that of both other gases. Hydrogen shows a different type of curve, with a continual increase in PV all the way. The same is true of helium and neon but this type of curve is exceptional near room temperature.

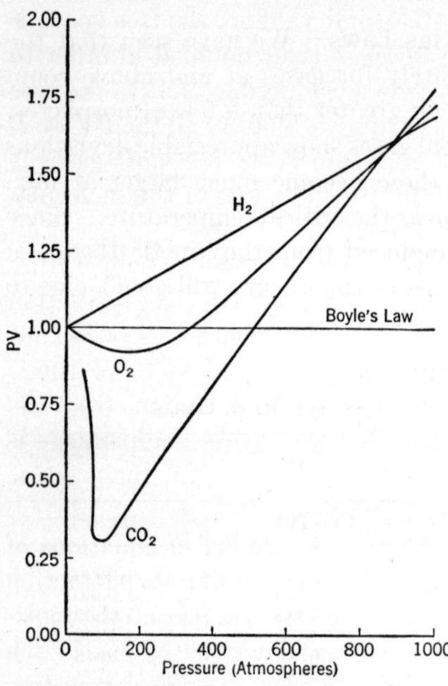

Fig. 22. Boyle's Law and Real Gases at High Pressure.

In deriving the kinetic equation for the ideal gas, we made two assumptions which are not justified when we are dealing with real gases. First, we assumed that *the molecules exerted no attraction upon one another*. If this were true at all temperatures, the gas could not liquefy, since it is the cohesive forces between the molecules of a liquid which keep it in that state even when it fills only part of the volume of a container. The ideal gas would not liquefy but would remain a gas until it shrinks to a point at the absolute zero. All real gases, however, have been liquefied; and even when the liquid is vaporized, the residual attraction between the molecules may show itself in deviations from the ideal gas law. When such a gas is compressed, the external pressure is augmented by the cohesive force between the molecules. *Less* than twice the pressure is required to halve the volume, so that the product PV decreases with increasing pressure. This accounts for the decreasing part of the PV curve, and for the unusual decrease in the case of gases like CO_2, which are near their critical temperature where the cohesive forces are unusually large.

A second simplifying assumption was that *the molecules occupied no appreciable volume,* so that practically the whole volume of the container represented the "free space" in which they could move. This assumption is justified for a gas at low pressure, but it becomes less applicable when the pressure is increased. If the molecules take up an appreciable part of the total volume, the free space is reduced and the pressure must be *more* than doubled in order to halve the volume. This effect causes the product PV to *increase* with pressure, and accounts for the upward slope of all the PV *vs.* P curves at high pressures. The complete curve for most gases is affected by both the attraction and the finite size of the molecules and so takes the form shown in Figure 22.

In the case of hydrogen, helium, and neon at room temperature the PV curves increase steadily, indicating that the attraction between the molecules is negligible. This conclusion is borne out by the fact that these gases liquefy only at very low temperatures. It is the volume of the molecules which causes deviations from the ideal gas law at ordinary temperatures, but, as the temperature is lowered, the attraction becomes appreciable even in these gases, and the PV curve is of the usual type.

Equations of State for Real Gases. A number of equations of state have been suggested, which take into account the attraction between the molecules of real gases, and the volume of the molecules. One of the best-known of these was derived by the Dutch physicist van der Waals in 1873. He considered that the attraction between the molecules will not affect the average velocity of those in the body of the gas, which are attracted equally from all sides. However, the molecules approaching the walls of the container will be slowed down because of the uncompensated attraction of the molecules in the body of the gas. The result is what may be called an **internal pressure** acting upon the gas. Assuming that the force of attraction is proportional to the concentration, the result of *doubling* the concentration is to double (1) the number of retarded molecules near the wall and (2) the force of attraction upon each of these molecules, since it now is attracted by twice as many molecules in the body of the gas. Doubling the concentration therefore will quadruple the internal pressure. In general, the internal pressure will be proportional to the *square* of the concentration or to the square of the reciprocal of the volume. It may be represented by a term a/V^2, where the proportionality factor a is a measure of the force of attraction. Since the internal pressure augments the pressure P applied to the gas, the *effective* pressure will be $(P + a/V^2)$.

In calculating the effect of the volume of the molecules, van der Waals pictured them as hard spheres which restrict the "free space," reducing it from V to $(V - b)$, where b represents four times the actual volume of the molecules of a mole of gas. The complete van der Waals equation of state for one mole of gas therefore is:

$$\left(P + \frac{a}{V^2}\right)(V - b) = RT$$

This equation may be rearranged into the form:

$$PV = RT - \frac{a}{V} + \frac{ab}{V^2} + bP$$

At low pressure, P is small and V is large; hence the last three terms become small in comparison with RT and the equation reduces to that of the ideal gas. At higher pressures the equation of van der Waals describes the behavior of real gases much more satisfactorily than do the simple gas laws.

The van der Waals equation is notably superior to the ideal gas law equation in the neighborhood of the critical temperature, where it gives the general characteristics of the P–V curves. The constants a and b which, unlike R, are characteristic of the particular gas, may be evaluated from experimental values of the volume occupied by one mole of gas under several known conditions of temperature and pressure. They can then be used, with considerable success, to calculate the critical temperature, pressure, and volume of the gas. Usually, however, the process is reversed and the constants are determined from the critical data (page 124).

In general, the value of the attraction constant a determined from experimental P–V–T curves decreases at higher temperatures and cannot be regarded as truly constant. Since the time of van der Waals, many equations of state for real gases have been suggested to reproduce experimental data more accurately, although none of them has a sound theoretical basis. In 1917, F. G. Keyes, at the Massachusetts Institute of Technology, who has carried out many studies of P–V–T relationships among gases, proposed the equation:

$$\left(P + \frac{a}{(V - l)}\right)(V - \delta) = RT$$

Here a and l are constants characteristic of the gas, while δ is an exponential function of the volume of the gas. Although calculations using this equation are difficult, it will reproduce the behavior of real gases considerably more accurately than the van der Waals equation. Table 20 gives a comparison of the observed pressures required to give certain observed volumes for 1 mole of carbon dioxide at 48° C., and the pressures calculated from the ideal gas law, the van der Waals equation, and the Keyes equation, respectively.

TABLE 20

A COMPARISON OF THREE EQUATIONS OF STATE FOR ONE MOLE OF CO_2 AT 48° C.

V IN ML.	P IN ATMOSPHERES AND DEVIATIONS, ΔP, IN PER CENT						
	Measured P	Ideal Gas P	ΔP	van der Waals P	ΔP	Keyes P	ΔP
1320	18.40	19.9	+ 8	18.5	+ 1	18.40	0.0
1100	21.75	24.0	+ 10	21.9	+ 1	21.72	− .1
880	26.41	30.0	+ 14	26.8	+ 2	26.52	+ .5
660	33.92	40.0	+ 18	34.4	+ 1	33.97	+ .2

Keyes and Kenney, *Am. Soc. Refrigerating Eng.*, Dec. 4, 1916.

The Measurement of Gas Density. *The* ***density*** *of a gas is the weight of 1 liter under known conditions of temperature and pressure. The* ***standard density*** *is measured in grams per liter, at 0° C. and a pressure of one atmosphere.* There are two general methods of measuring gas densities — (1) the *Regnault density bulb* and (2) the *density balance.*

(1) The Regnault density bulb was introduced by that well-known French physical chemist of the last century. As illustrated in Figure 23, it consists of a glass or fused silica bulb with a side-arm containing a stopcock S. It is cleaned, evacuated, and weighed. Then it is connected, by means of the ground joint J, to a supply of the purified gas, immersed in a thermostat, and filled with the gas at a known temperature and a pressure read from a barometer connected directly to the gas system. When the bulb has been weighed filled with gas, the weight of the gas is determined by subtracting that of the evacuated bulb. The volume of the bulb, found from the weight of water which it will hold, is usually between 500 ml. and 2 liters, depending upon the accuracy desired.

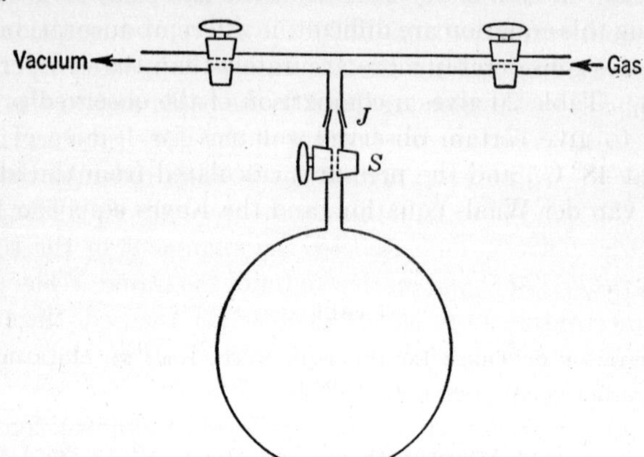

Fig. 23. Regnault Gas Density Bulb.

(2) The density balance. This method involves the accurate measurement of the *pressures* at which the densities of two gases become equal. One form of the apparatus is shown in Figure 24. It is made entirely of fused quartz. The buoyancy bulb *E*, of

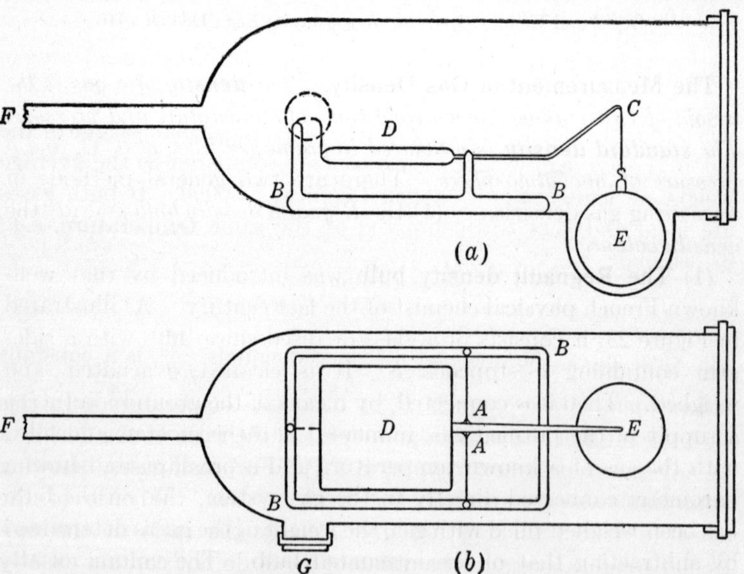

Fig. 24. The Torsion Gas-Density Balance. (*a*) Elevation. (*b*) Plan.

about 2 ml. capacity, is suspended by a fine fiber from the end C of a light rod. It is counterbalanced by a flat plate D of approximately equal surface, to minimize the effect of adsorption of the gas. The moving system in this case is supported by the fine torsion fibers A–A, which are fused to the beam and to the heavier frame B, which rests on the bottom of the glass tube serving as a jacket for the balance. Purified gas is admitted into the jacket through the tube F until it buoys up the bulb E. The balance point of the beam is indicated by the alignment of the reference fibers on the end of D and on the center of the frame. The position is read accurately through a microscope focused through the window G. The balancing pressure is read on an elaborate mercury barometer connected to the tube F.

When the balancing pressure of the gas of unknown density has been read, that of the standard gas is determined. The densities of the two gases must be equal at balance, and a knowledge of the density of the standard gas at once gives that of the other.

The Molecular Weights of Ideal Gases. For 1 mole of an ideal gas the equation of state is:

$$PV = RT$$

and the molecular weight M is given by the equation:

$$M = dV = \frac{d}{P} RT$$

where d is the density in g. per liter. The molecular weight of the gas is the average weight of a molecule, compared to the average weight of a molecule of oxygen taken as 32.0000. If both gases are ideal and they are compared at the same temperature, *e.g.*, 0°, we find:

$$\frac{M}{M_{O_2}} = \left(\frac{d}{P}\right) \div \left(\frac{d}{P}\right)_{O_2}$$

For ideal gases, the quotient $\frac{d}{P}$, since it equals $\frac{M}{RT}$, is a constant independent of the pressure P, at constant temperature. In this case the ratio of the molecular weights is the ratio of the densities at any given pressure, *e.g.*, at S.T.P. For real gases, showing appreciable deviations from the ideal gas law, the ratio of the densities at S.T.P. does not give exactly the ratio of the molecular weights, because the different gases do not contain exactly the same number of molecules at a pressure of 1 atmosphere.

There are two general methods of correcting for deviations from the ideal gas law and determining exact molecular weights. Both of these are based upon the experimental fact that, at pressures up to about 1 atmosphere, the deviation of any gas from the ideal gas law may be represented by the equation:

$$PV = P_0V_0(1 - AP)$$

where A is known as the **compressibility coefficient** of the gas. As the pressure is reduced to zero, AP becomes zero, and the gas behaves ideally, so that $P_0V_0 = RT$. As before, we can substitute for the molecular weight $M = dV$, and thus obtain an equation for the molecular weight of a real gas:

$$M = \frac{d}{P}(1 - AP)RT$$

If the compressibility coefficient A of the gas is known, the determination of its density d at any convenient pressure P, *e.g.*, 1 atmosphere, will suffice to calculate its molecular weight. Two slightly different methods of obtaining the same result are the *method of limiting density* and the *method of limiting pressure.*

(1) **The method of limiting density.** As the pressure is reduced to zero, the quotient d/P approaches a limiting value which we may call $(d/P)_0$ and which is known as *the* ***limiting density*** *of the gas.* The preceding equation shows that the molecular weight of the gas is given by the simple equation:

$$M = \left(\frac{d}{P}\right)_0 RT$$

The limiting density of a gas can be determined by plotting the values of d/P against the pressure P, and extrapolating to the axis of ordinates, where $P = 0$. If we solve the equation before the preceding one for d/P, we find:

$$\frac{d}{P} = \frac{M}{RT(1 - AP)}$$

Since A is much smaller than unity for the common gases, the right-hand term of this equation may be divided out to obtain:

$$\frac{d}{P} = \frac{M}{RT}(1 + AP)$$

This shows that the quotient d/P is a linear function of P, which is verified by direct measurement of the densities of gases at pressures below 1 atmosphere. The extrapolation of d/P to obtain the limiting density therefore consists in drawing a straight line through the values of d/P, and extending it to its intersection with the axis of ordinates, where $P = 0$.

As an example of the determination of the limiting density of a gas, we may take the study of the density of oxygen, carried out by Baxter and Starkweather.[1] Using Regnault gas density bulbs, they found the following values at 0° C.:

Pressure (atm.)	**1**	$\frac{3}{4}$	$\frac{1}{2}$	$\frac{1}{4}$
Density (g./l.)	1.42897	1.07149	0.71415	0.35699
$\frac{d}{P}$	1.42897	1.42865	1.42830	1.42796

As shown in Figure 25, a graphical extrapolation of these data gives the value of 1.42767 for the *limiting density* of oxygen at 0° C.

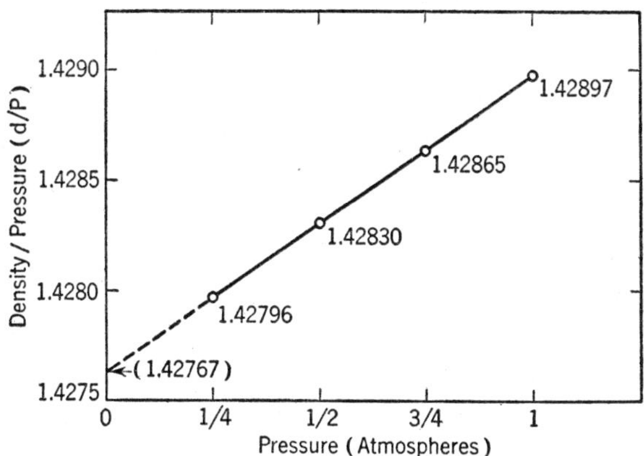

Fig. 25. The Limiting Density of Oxygen.

An important application of the method of limiting densities is the determination of the atomic weights of rare gases of the zero group, which form no compounds and hence cannot be studied by the usual chemical methods. The method of limiting densities has been applied with equal success to other elementary gases and to gaseous compounds in which the atomic weight of one of the

[1] Baxter and Starkweather, *Proc. Nat. Acad. Sci.*, **10**, 479 (1924), **14**, 57 (1928). Gregory Paul Baxter, professor of chemistry at Harvard University and Chairman of the International Committee on Atomic Weights, is famous for his systematic studies of the atomic weights of the elements and for his work on the densities of gases and other physico-chemical and analytical problems.

constituent elements is to be determined. In any case, the ratio of the limiting densities is the ratio of the exact molecular weights:

$$\frac{\text{Molecular weight of gas}}{32.0000} = \frac{\text{Limiting density of gas}}{\text{Limiting density of oxygen}}$$

Rearranging this equation, we may write for the molecular weight of the gas:

$$M = \text{Limiting density of gas} \times \frac{32.0000}{\text{Limiting density of oxygen}}$$

$$M = \text{Limiting density of gas} \times \text{Molar volume}$$

The molecular weight of oxygen divided by its limiting density gives the true molar volume — the volume which one mole of an ideal gas would occupy under standard conditions. The value is:

$$\text{Molar volume} = \frac{32.0000 \text{ g.}}{1.42767 \text{ g./l.}} = 22.4146 \text{ liters}$$

The molecular weight of any gas now may be determined by multiplying its limiting density by this limiting value of the molar volume. As an example of the accurate determination of molecular and atomic weights by the method of limiting density, we may take the study of propylene, C_3H_6, by Batuecas.[1] He obtained the following results at 0° C.:

Pressure (atm.)	**1**	$\frac{2}{3}$	$\frac{1}{2}$
Density (g./l.)	1.9148	1.2681	0.9478
$\left(\frac{d}{P}\right)$	1.9148	1.9021	1.8956

The limiting density of propylene calculated from these data is 1.8766 g./l. The molecular weight therefore is:

$$1.8766 \text{ g./l.} \times 22.4146 \text{ l.} = 42.062 \text{ g.}$$

Taking the atomic weight of hydrogen as 1.0080, and subtracting from the molecular weight the weight of 6 gram atoms of hydrogen gives 36.014 g. as the weight of 3 gram atoms of carbon, and 12.005 as the atomic weight of carbon. This is only 0.04 per cent lower than the present accepted value of this atomic weight, namely, 12.010.

(2) The method of limiting pressure. This method of determining molecular weights accurately from gas densities is particularly

[1] Batuecas, *J. Chim. Phys.*, **31**, 165 (1934).

applicable to measurements with the density balance. We have seen that the molecular weight of a real gas is given by the equation:

$$M = \frac{d}{P}(1 - AP)RT$$

If the density balance has been used at the temperature T to determine the pressures at which two gases have the same density d, the ratio of the two molecular weights would be given by the equation:

$$\frac{M_1}{M_2} = \frac{RT\frac{d}{P_1}(1 - A_1P_1)}{RT\frac{d}{P_2}(1 - A_2P_2)} = \frac{P_2(1 - A_1P_1)}{P_1(1 - A_2P_2)}$$

From this equation, the ratio r of the two *pressures* will be:

$$r = \frac{P_1}{P_2} = \frac{M_2(1 - A_1P_1)}{M_1(1 - A_2P_2)}$$

As the pressure approaches zero, the value of r approaches the ratio of the molecular weights, $\frac{M_2}{M_1}$. If r is determined at several pressures below 1 atmosphere, plotted against P_1, and extrapolated to $P_1 = 0$, this limiting value of r is the ratio of the molecular weights. If one of the molecular weights is known, the other may be found.

This method has been used successfully by Cawood and Patterson,[1] who determined the molecular weights of a number of gases by comparison with oxygen. Some of the values which they obtained were: CO_2, 44.0101; C_2H_4, 28.0556; CF_4, 87.989; CH_3F, 34.0318.

Molecular Weights from Vapor Densities. When we are dealing with liquids and solids which vaporize without decomposition at temperatures that are not too high, we may determine their vapor densities. The density of the vaporized substance at a measured temperature and pressure is multiplied by the gram molecular volume under the same conditions to give the molecular weight of the substance. The *Dumas method* and the *Victor Meyer method* are the best known applications of this procedure.

[1] Cawood and Patterson, *Trans. Roy. Soc.* (Lond.), **A 236,** 77 (1937).

The **Dumas method,** originated by J. B. Dumas in 1827, utilizes a glass bulb of about 200 ml. capacity, with a side tube which may be sealed off. The bulb is dried and weighed full of air. Into it is introduced a quantity of the substance, usually a liquid, in considerable excess of the amount necessary to fill the bulb when vaporized. The bulb is then heated in a constant temperature bath at a temperature above the boiling point of the substance. A bath of boiling water is satisfactory if the substance boils below 100° C.; for higher-boiling substances an oil bath may be used. As the substance boils, the air is driven out so that when vaporization is complete the bulb contains only the vapor of the substance at the temperature of the bath and at barometric pressure. The side tube of the bulb is now sealed off; it is then cooled, dried, and weighed, together with any glass removed in the sealing. This gives the weight of the bulb plus the vapor.

The side tube is next scratched with a file and carefully opened under water, which fills the bulb. After its outer surface has been dried, the bulb plus the water is weighed. From the weight of water the volume of the bulb is computed, which is also the volume of the vapor and of the air originally present.

The weight of the air subtracted from that of the bulb plus air gives the weight of the empty bulb. This weight, subtracted from that of the bulb plus the vapor, gives the weight of the vaporized substance occupying the bulb at the measured temperature and pressure. Dividing the weight by the volume gives the density of the vapor under these conditions. Multiplying this density by the theoretical gram molecular volume calculated for the same conditions gives the molecular weight of the substance. Thus if 0.820 g. of a substance fills a 200-ml. bulb at 73° C. and 750 mm., the density under the given conditions will be $\frac{0.820}{0.200}$ or 4.10 g. per l. The gram molecular volume under the same conditions is $22.4 \times \frac{346}{273} \times \frac{750}{760}$, or 29.5 l. The molecular weight of the substance then is 4.10×29.5 or 120.9 g.

The **Victor Meyer method** employs the apparatus developed in 1878 by Victor Meyer, then professor of chemistry at Zurich. It consists of a glass tube about 40 cm. long and 1 cm. in diameter, terminating at the lower end in a cylindrical bulb about 10 cm. long and 3 cm. in diameter. Near the top of the tube is a side tube, which is attached by rubber tubing to a eudiometer. The Victor Meyer tube is thermostated by circulating vapor or liquid at a suitable temperature through a jacket which surrounds the whole tube except the very top. When the apparatus is thus heated, the enclosed air is at the temperature of the jacket and at atmospheric pressure. The eudiometer is filled with water and connected with a suitable leveling tube or bulb. A suitable quantity of the substance, sealed off and weighed in a small glass bulb, is dropped into the Victor Meyer tube, which is then stoppered. When the small bulb breaks, the substance vaporizes and expels an equal volume of air into the eudiometer, where it is collected over water and measured, together with the room temperature and the barometric pressure. *The volume of air measured in the eudiometer is the same as that which the substance would occupy at room temperature and under barometric pressure, if it were gaseous under those conditions.* This volume, corrected to the dry basis at S.T.P., corresponds to the weight of the substance taken. The corresponding weight of the vapor is calculated for 22.4 liters, giving the molecular weight of the substance.

The Victor Meyer method has been used with electrically heated iridium apparatus for the determination of the molecular weights of substances up to 2000° C.

The Liquefaction of Gases. Most liquids at room temperature can be converted into gases by heating or by reducing the pressure. Similarly, most solids at room temperature can be liquefied and finally vaporized. On the other hand, gases at room temperature cannot always be converted into the liquid or solid state. In the eighteenth century Lavoisier suggested that, if the surface of the earth were to fall to the temperature of interstellar space, the gases of the atmosphere might condense to liquids. Before the end of that century, sulfur dioxide and ammonia had been liquefied by cooling, and in 1823 Michael Faraday at the Royal Institution in London obtained liquid chlorine. His apparatus is

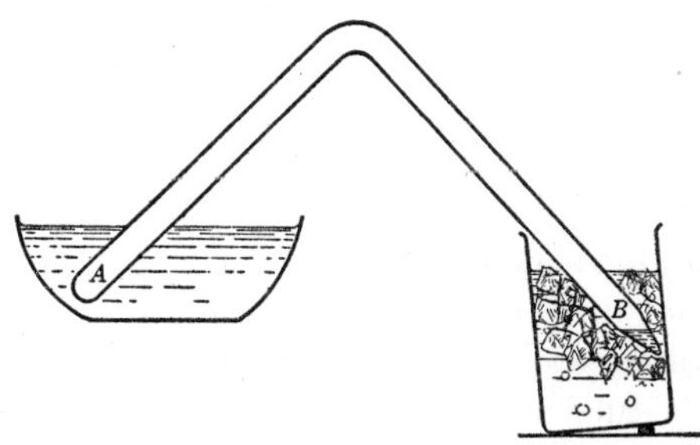

Fig. 26. Faraday's Method of Liquefying Chlorine.

shown in Figure 26. If crystals of chlorine octahydrate at *A* are heated to 30° by means of a water bath while the other end of the tube is cooled with a freezing mixture of ice and salt, liquid chlorine collects in the cold end of the tube at *B*. Somewhat later, Faraday continued these experiments and succeeded in liquefying hydrogen sulfide, hydrogen chloride, and a number of other gases by the same method. He was unable, however, to liquefy oxygen, nitrogen, and hydrogen, which were therefore called **permanent gases.**

In the early attempts to liquefy gases, it was assumed that the application of sufficient pressure would change any gas into a liquid. However, in 1869 Thomas Andrews, professor of chemistry in Belfast, Ireland, studied carbon dioxide, and showed that, while it could be liquefied easily at temperatures up to 31.1° C., above this *critical* temperature no amount of pressure would change the gas into a liquid. *The* ***critical temperature*** *of a substance is the highest temperature at which it can exist as a liquid. The* ***critical pressure*** *and* ***critical density*** *are the vapor pressure and density at the critical temperature.* As we shall see in discussing liquids (page 129), at the critical temperature the density of a liquid becomes equal to that of the vapor in contact with it. Also, the surface tension of a liquid in contact with its vapor decreases to zero at the critical temperature so that there is no *interface* and the meniscus which separates the two phases disappears. This can be demonstrated in the case of liquids like ether, which do not have too high a critical temperature and pressure, using a tube like that shown in Figure 27. The liquid is put into the heavy glass tube and boiled to drive out all the air, after which the top of the tube is sealed. If the tube then is heated slowly, the liquid-vapor meniscus flattens out and becomes indistinct, finally disappearing at the critical temperature. As the vapor cools again to this temperature, striations first appear in the tube and then the meniscus reappears, reforming the liquid surface. This experiment is quite spectacular, but the tube must be protected adequately by means of shatterproof glass to prevent possible injury in case of breakage.

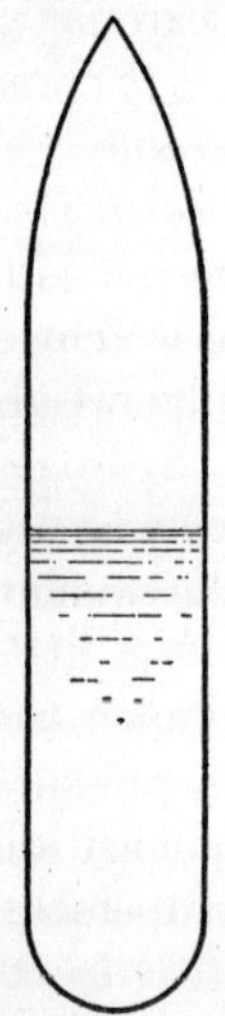

Fig. 27. Tube to Show Critical Phenomena.

In Table 21 we have collected the critical constants and boiling

TABLE 21

CRITICAL CONSTANTS AND BOILING POINTS OF SOME COMMON SUBSTANCES

SUBSTANCE	D_c IN G./ML.	P_c IN ATM.	T_c IN °A.	T_b IN °A.	$\frac{T_b}{T_c}$
Helium	0.0693	2.26	5.3	4.3	0.81
Hydrogen	.0310	12.8	33.3	20.5	.62
Nitrogen	.3110	33.5	126.1	77.4	.61
Carbon monoxide	.311	35	134	81.2	.61
Oxygen	.430	49.7	154.4	90.2	.58
Carbon dioxide	.460	73.0	304.3	—— *	——
Hydrogen chloride	.42	81.6	324.6	188.2	.58
Hydrogen sulfide	——	88.9	373.6	213.7	.57
Ammonia	.235	111.5	406.1	239.8	.59
Chlorine	.573	76.1	417.2	238.6	.58
Sulfur dioxide	.52	77.7	430.4	263.2	.59
Diethyl ether	.263	35.5	467.0	307.8	.66
Benzene	.304	47.7	561.7	353.4	.63
Water	.4	217.7	647.2	373.0	.58
Mercury	4–5	> 200	> 1823	630.1	.35

Data from *I. C. T.*, **I**, 102 and **III**, 248 and sections preceding.

* Carbon dioxide does not exist as a liquid under a pressure of one atmosphere.

points of a number of common substances. As this table shows, the critical pressure usually increases with the critical temperature, although the critical pressures of hydrogen chloride, hydrogen sulfide, ammonia, and water are larger than would be expected on this basis, and those of ether and benzene are much smaller. The boiling point at a pressure of one atmosphere, T_b, is a little less than $\frac{2}{3}$ of the absolute critical temperature, T_c — giving the average 0.60 for the values tabulated here.

All of the gases liquefied before the time of Andrews had critical temperatures at or near room temperature, as Table 21 shows. The discovery that a gas must be cooled below its critical temperature before it can be liquefied suggested that the early workers had tried to liquefy the "permanent" gases at temperatures above their critical values. Immediately experiments were carried out at lower temperatures, and in 1877 Pictet and Cailletet, working independently, succeeded in liquefying oxygen in small quantities by allowing it to expand suddenly from a high pressure. In 1891 the British chemist Sir James Dewar, head of the Royal Institution, made large quantities of liquid air and developed his ingenious vacuum-jacketed flask for its storage.

Such a **Dewar flask,** or **thermos bottle,** shown in Figure 28, consists of a double-walled vessel made of glass. The space between the flasks is evacuated as completely as possible to reduce the loss of heat, which would be rapid through a gas at ordinary pressure.

The inner walls usually are silvered in order to cut down the radiation of heat. Liquid air may be kept in such a flask with the loss by evaporation of only a few per cent of its volume per day.

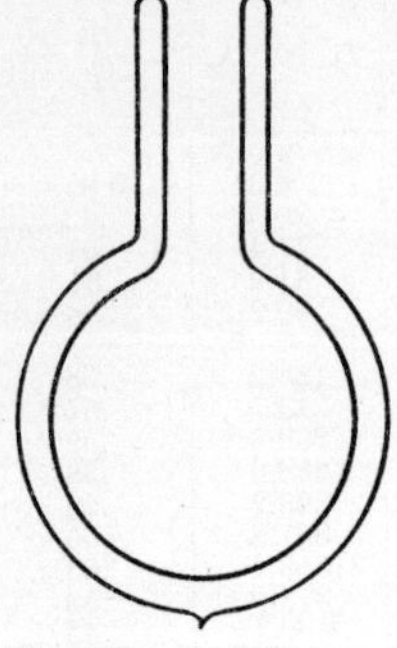

Fig. 28. One Type of Dewar Flask.

The Joule-Thomson Effect. The commercial methods of producing liquid air all are based, to a greater or less extent, upon a principle discovered and studied by James Joule, working with William Thomson, later Lord Kelvin, professor of natural philosophy at Glasgow. They found that, when a gas under high pressure is allowed to expand freely to a lower pressure, the temperature of the gas almost always changes during the process. In order accurately to measure the change in temperature, they used an apparatus fitted with a porous plug, shown diagrammatically in Figure 29. The plug consisted of a packing of cotton or silk, held in place by two perforated disks of metal. The gas under pressure P_1 diffused through the plug and emerged at the lower pressure P_2. The temperature of the gas before and after expansion was determined by means of sensitive thermometers, not shown in the diagram. The observed change in temperature, due to this free expansion, was corrected for the small loss of heat from the apparatus. *The change in temperature, per unit change in pressure, when a gas expands freely (without doing work) is called the* ***Joule-Thomson coefficient***, μ. It may be defined by the equation:

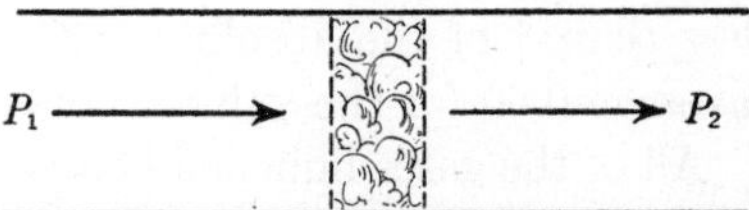

Fig. 29. Joule-Thomson Porous Plug Experiment (Schematic).

$$\mu = \frac{dT}{dP}$$

If the temperature is given in centigrade degrees and the pressure in atmospheres, the Joule-Thomson coefficient represents the *decrease* in temperature for a *decrease* in pressure of one atmosphere. Joule and Thomson found that the coefficient was positive for practically all gases — *i.e.*, the gas cools on free expansion. The only exception which they found was hydrogen, which *warms* on free expansion at room temperature. Further study has shown

facing page 116 *Press Association*

Plate II. GILBERT NEWTON LEWIS

(*For biographical note see page 334.*)

that the Joule-Thomson coefficient decreases in absolute magnitude with increasing temperature, and also with increasing pressure, as shown for air by the data collected in Table 22.

TABLE 22

JOULE-THOMSON COEFFICIENTS, IN DEGREES PER ATMOSPHERE, FOR AIR AT DIFFERENT TEMPERATURES AND PRESSURES

P IN ATM.	0	25	50	100	150	200
90° A.	2.045	− 0.005	− 0.014	− 0.026	− 0.035	− 0.041
120	1.265	.059	.013	− .010	− .026	− .036
150	0.833	.847	.641	.130	.025	− .017
180	.602	.619	.555	.299	.135	.029
210	.459	.458	.420	.295	.182	.080
240	.361	.345	.315	.247	.175	.101
270	.285	.266	.244	.196	.148	.099
300	.227	.212	.195	.159	.124	.089

Data from *I. C. T.*, V, 144. The values in the second column are obtained by extrapolation to zero pressure.

At any definite pressure, the temperature at which the Joule-Thomson coefficient of a gas is zero, is called the **inversion temperature** *of that gas.* From Table 22 we see that the inversion temperature for air at 200 atmospheres pressure is about 160° A., while the value at atmospheric pressure would be considerably above room temperature. The inversion temperature of hydrogen, however, is far below room temperature. At − 80.5° C., there is no change in temperature when hydrogen expands from 113 atmospheres pressure to one atmosphere. At lower temperatures, the Joule-Thomson coefficient for hydrogen is positive, *i.e.*, it cools on expansion. The inversion temperature of helium is − 173° C., even lower than that of hydrogen. This accounts for the great difficulty in liquefying helium.

All liquids absorb heat when they evaporate. The Joule-Thomson effect may be considered as a residue of the heat of vaporization. The temperature of a gas falls as it passes through the porous plug, because the attraction between the molecules retards the speed of those which are escaping, diminishing their kinetic energy, and thus lowering their temperature. This is the same influence which causes a decrease in the product *PV* for most real gases, as explained on page 102. The Joule-Thomson coefficient of a perfect gas always would be zero. For hydrogen and helium at room temperature, the attraction between the molecules is negligible in comparison with the molecular size, which acts like a repulsion and yields a negative Joule-Thomson effect. The same is true of other gases at high pressures, where the deviations of PV are also positive.

The Liquefaction of Air. The practical application of the Joule-Thomson effect to the liquefaction of air on a commercial scale was made in 1895 by Karl Linde, professor of thermodynamics in the Technical Institute in Munich. In the following year Hampson, in England, developed a somewhat simpler liquefier which is used especially in small installations. Both are based on the same general principles, the Joule-Thomson effect and regenerative cooling of the incoming air. First the air is dried and purified to prevent the stoppage of the valves with ice or solid carbon dioxide. Then it is compressed to about 200 atmospheres pressure and circulated through coils of tubing in which the heat of compression is removed by cooling water or refrigerating brine. Finally it passes to the liquefier, a simplified drawing of which is shown in Figure 30. The compressed air passes through the *inner* copper tube T_1 of a heat interchanger and escapes through the valve V, where it expands to atmospheric pressure.

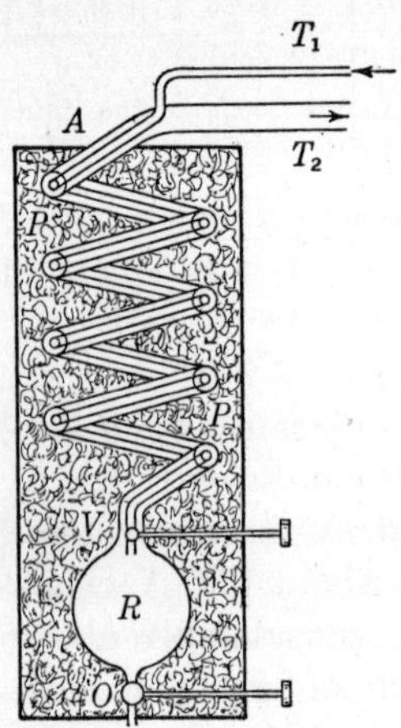

Fig. 30. Schematic Diagram of Linde's Air Liquefier.

The valve takes the place of the porous plug in the experiment described above, and the expanding air is cooled by the Joule-Thomson effect. The exhaust air, on its way back to the compressor, passes up the *outer* tube T_2 of the heat interchanger, in this way cooling the incoming gas to a still lower temperature before it reaches the valve V. This process is known as **regenerative cooling.** Since the Joule-Thomson coefficient increases as the temperature is lowered, the temperature of the escaping gas soon sinks below the boiling point of liquid air, and drops of the liquid accumulate in the receiver R, whence they are drawn off through the outlet valve O. The double tube T actually is wound in the form of a very long spiral, and forms such an effective regenerative cooler that practically all of the cold gained from the expansion is put back into the incoming gas, and the low-pressure gas returns to the compressor at room temperature. An idealized representation of the process of regenerative cooling is shown in Figure 31.

A more efficient system, which would extract heat even from a perfect gas, puts the compressed gas through an engine where it does mechanical work as it expands and loses an equal quantity of heat. George Claude, the French chemist, overcame the mechanical difficulties and developed a practical machine for liquefying air, in which 95 per cent of the heat is extracted as mechanical work and only 5 per cent by the Joule-Thomson effect.

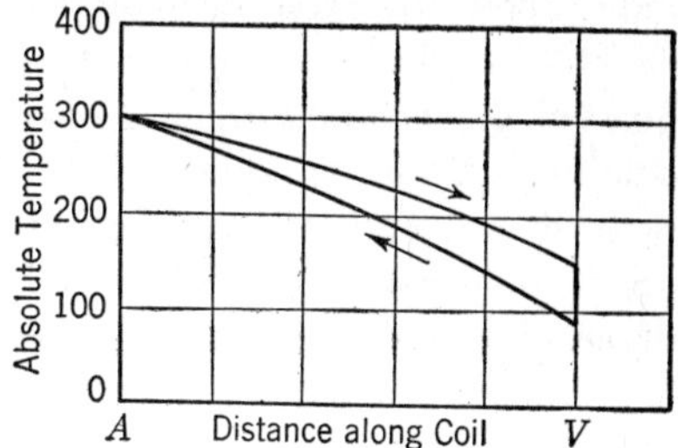

Fig. 31. Regenerative Cooling in the Liquefaction of Air.

The Liquefaction of Hydrogen and Helium. This is more difficult than the liquefaction of air, because these gases must be cooled to such a low temperature before heat can be extracted by free expansion. Dewar, at the Royal Institution, first liquefied hydrogen in 1898 by cooling the gas to − 205° C. and allowing it to escape through a valve from a pressure of 180 atmospheres. An apparatus for preparing liquid hydrogen in the same way, precooling the gas with liquid air, was worked out by Travers at about the same time. This is the basis of all subsequent apparatus. Liquid hydrogen in turn was used by Kammerlingh Onnes to cool helium gas to 15° A., after which it was liquefied by expansion. This work was carried out in the Cryogenic Laboratory of the University of Leiden, Holland, in 1907.

Although the uses of liquid hydrogen and helium are limited to experimental work at low temperatures, liquid air has industrial applications. If it is allowed to evaporate, the nitrogen (b.p. − 196° C.) evaporates first and leaves nearly pure oxygen (b.p. − 183° C.). By circulating the liquid air through a fractionating column, the two gases can be separated more economically, and this is done in the process of liquefying the air. The liquefied gases usually are allowed to evaporate and are stored in strong steel cylinders. In 1926, 81,000,000 cubic feet of oxygen were prepared in this way in Europe. Most of this was used in oxyacetylene welding and in the cutting of steel with the oxygen torch. Liquid oxygen is used in explosives. If a cylinder of charcoal is impregnated with liquid oxygen, it may be detonated by a cap and provides a powerful explosive, comparable to dynamite. This oxygen-charcoal explosive has been used to some extent in mining and quarrying. Liquid oxygen is also used in airplanes flying at great heights. A flask of liquid oxygen is lighter than a tank of the compressed gas, and its evaporation can be controlled to deliver as much as necessary. Compressed oxygen is used in some chemical processes and also in the treatment of certain diseases like pneumonia where the patient cannot obtain from the air enough oxygen to prevent cyanosis.

The rare gases of the atmosphere, once chemical curiosities, are now important by-products of the manufacture of liquid air, from which they are separated by fractionation. The most abundant of these gases, argon, is used in large quantities to fill electric light bulbs. It is inert and does not react chemically with the tungsten filament; also its presence slows down the rate of evaporation of the filament and thus retards the blackening of the lamp. Neon is separated from argon by a fractionation process developed by Claude. A Claude plant which produces 50 cubic meters of oxygen per hour will also furnish 100 liters of neon per day. The gas finds wide commercial use in neon lamps, since it glows with a brilliant orange-red color when a high-tension electric current is sent through it. The neon lamp is much more efficient than an incandescent-filament lamp, and finds use in airplane beacons because its light will penetrate mist and fog.

The chief commercial source of helium is the fractionation of natural gas from certain districts in Texas. The low-boiling helium is separated from the less volatile hydrocarbons and nitrogen. In 1928 the production was 6,000,000 cubic feet. Helium is used as a lifting gas in dirigibles, since it is 90 per cent as efficient as hydrogen and is not inflammable. It also has important applications in preventing "caisson disease," or "bends," in caisson workers and divers. A mixture of this gas and oxygen is used instead of air for these workers under high pressure. Helium is much less soluble in the blood than is nitrogen, and is eliminated more quickly when the pressure is released, with less danger of forming minute bubbles in the capillary blood vessels, which cause the painful and dangerous cramps in those who come out too quickly from a space in which the air is under pressure.

The Isothermals of a Gas and Liquid. In his study of gases under pressure, Andrews sealed up a sample in a small tube over mercury and determined its volume at different temperatures and pressures. He plotted his results as isothermal curves, or isotherms. *A curve representing the change in the volume of a system*

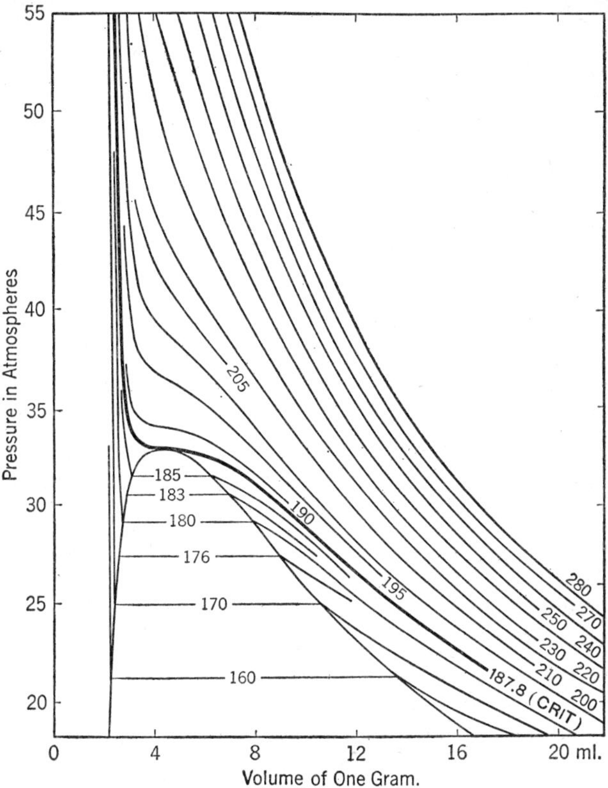

Fig. 32. Isotherms of Isopentane.

with changing pressure, at any constant temperature, is called the ***isothermal or isotherm*** *of the system at that temperature.* Amagat and others improved upon Andrews' methods. Some of Amagat's results for isopentane, $(CH_3)_2CHC_2H_5$, are shown in Figure 32. The isotherm of a perfect gas is a rectangular hyperbola, as we saw on page 74. However, the isotherms of real gases deviate from this curve, because of departures from Boyle's law; but permanent gases show no appreciable deviations over the range of this diagram. Even isopentane at 280° C. shows a normal gaseous isotherm, but as the temperature is reduced the isotherm shows a decided irregularity which becomes a point of inflection, with a horizontal tangent, at the critical temperature, 187.8° C. Below this point, the isotherm is divided into two curves by a horizontal straight section. The right-hand curve corresponds to the isotherm of the gas, the horizontal portion to that of the gas and liquid in contact, and the left-hand steep curve to that of the liquid. Thus if we start with 1 gram of the gas at 160° C., its volume at a pressure of about 19 atmospheres is represented by the right-hand end of the bottom curve. As the volume is decreased, the pressure gradually increases along that curve, until, at about 21 atmospheres the gas starts to liquefy. Under these conditions the pressure applied to the system just equals the vapor pressure of the liquid at that temperature, and the volume can be decreased, without increasing the pressure, until all the gas is liquefied. Then the pressure rises rapidly with decreasing volume, for the compressibility of the liquid is much less than that of the gas. At successively higher temperatures, the horizontal portions of the isotherms become shorter, because the densities of the gas and liquid are closer together and more of the material is in the gaseous state. At the critical temperature the horizontal line has shrunk to a point.

Andrews stressed the *continuity* between the liquid and gaseous phases, which his experiments demonstrated. At the critical point, all differences between the gas and the liquid disappear, and the two are identical. Above this temperature the gas alone exists, while below this temperature either gas or liquid may exist, depending upon the pressure. If we pass from a gas to a liquid, or *vice versa*, below the critical temperature, there will be a discontinuous change, but if we make the change through the critical region, there is no such discontinuity. Thus we could change gaseous carbon dioxide to the liquid form without any discontinuity in its properties by first heating it to the critical temperature, then increasing the pressure until it exceeded the critical pressure, and finally allowing the substance to cool down to the original temperature. This illustrates the continuity of the liquid and gaseous phases, which Andrews concluded were not different in kind but "only distant stages of a long series of continuous physical changes."

Van der Waals' Equation and the Critical Temperature. In deriving his equation for the behavior of real gases, van der Waals also stressed the continuity of the liquid and gaseous states. He showed that the constants a and b in his equation could be used to calculate the critical constants of a gas, or could be deduced from them if they were known.

If we take the van der Waals' equation,

$$\left(P + \frac{a}{V^2}\right)(V - b) = RT$$

multiply it out and arrange in powers of V, we have:

$$V^3 - \left(b + \frac{RT}{P}\right)V^2 + \left(\frac{a}{P}\right)V - \frac{ab}{P} = 0$$

Such a third-degree equation in V will have three roots, one of which will be a real number and all of which may be real numbers. That means that if we set the pressure and temperature at any values we choose, the equation can be solved for V, and there will be either one or three values of V which will satisfy the equation. If we put into the equation different values of T and plot the values of P and V for any fixed values of the constants a and b, we obtain a series of curves like those in Figure 32. At high temperatures, there is only one real value of V for a given value of P, while at low temperatures there are three such values, which lie closer together as the temperature increases. The whole series of curves is strikingly like those which Andrews had found experimentally, except that S-shaped portions take the place of his horizontal lines. From this comparison, we see that the three roots of the equation coincide, giving three identical values for V, at the critical temperature. The corresponding value for the volume must be the critical volume,

$$V = V_c \qquad \text{or} \qquad V - V_c = 0$$

Since any algebraic equation is equal to the products of the equations defining the roots, this equation must be:

$$(V - V_c)^3 = 0 \quad \text{or} \quad V^3 - 3\,V_cV^2 + 3\,V_c^2V - V_c^3 = 0$$

Since the coefficients of this equation must be exactly the same as those of the equation above, arranged in decreasing powers of V, provided we insert the values of the critical pressure and temperature, we find on equating coefficients:

$$3\,V_c = b + \frac{RT_c}{P_c},\quad 3\,V_c^2 = \frac{a}{P_c},\quad \text{and}\quad V_c^3 = \frac{ab}{P_c}$$

Solving for the critical constants in terms of the constants of the equation of state, gives the values:

$$V_c = 3\,b,\quad T_c = \frac{8\,a}{27\,Rb},\quad \text{and}\quad P_c = \frac{a}{27\,b^2}$$

Solving instead for the constants of the equation of state, we find:

$$a = 3\,P_cV_c^2,\quad b = \frac{V_c}{3},\quad \text{and}\quad R = \frac{8\,P_cV_c}{3\,T_c}$$

In testing his equation, van der Waals calculated values of a and b for carbon dioxide from values of the volume of the gas at different pressures and, solving for the critical temperature, found 305.5° A. or 32.3° C., which is in good agreement with the observed value of 31.1°. However, tests with other gases generally did not give nearly such satisfactory agreement, which shows that the van der Waals' equation is not quantitatively applicable to most real gases.

PROBLEMS AND EXERCISES

1. Baxter and Starkweather found the following values for the densities of nitrogen at 0°: 1.25036 g./l. at 1 atm., 0.83348 g./l. at $\frac{2}{3}$ atm., and 0.41667 g./l. at $\frac{1}{3}$ atm. From these data calculate the limiting density of nitrogen and, combining it with the limiting density of oxygen, calculate the molecular weight of nitrogen and its atomic weight. Compare this with the present accepted value of the atomic weight.

2. Baxter and Starkweather found the following values for PV, for argon at 0°: 1.00000 at 1 atm., 1.00030 at $\frac{2}{3}$ atm., and 1.00060 at $\frac{1}{3}$ atm. From these data calculate the value of P_0V_0 and the limiting density of argon, if the observed density at 1 atm. is 1.78364 g./l. From the value of the limiting gram-molecular volume, calculate the atomic weight of argon.

3. Moles and Salazar found that at 0° C. the densities of carbon monoxide were: 1.25000 g./l. at 1 atm. and 0.624875 g./l. at $\frac{1}{2}$ atm. From these data find the limiting density of carbon monoxide and the atomic weight of carbon.

4. Moles and Sancho have found for the density of ammonia at 0° the following values: 0.77143 g./l. at 1 atm. and 0.38281 g./l. at $\frac{1}{2}$ atm. Calculate the limiting density of ammonia and hence its molecular weight, and the atomic weight of nitrogen, if that of hydrogen is 1.0080.

5. From the values of the densities in the preceding problem and those given on page 109 for the corresponding densities for oxygen, calculate the molecular weight of ammonia at 1 atm. and $\frac{1}{2}$ atm. pressure, and compare with the limiting value determined in the preceding problem. How much error is involved in the values calculated from the densities at the higher pressures?

6. In the determination of the molecular weight of ether by the Dumas method, 0.560 g. of ether filled a bulb containing 210 ml. at 70° C. and 770 mm. pressure. Calculate from these data the molecular weight of ether.

7. In the determination of the molecular weight of a substance by the Victor Meyer method, 0. 2312 g. of substance was used, and 34.06 ml. of air was collected in the eudiometer and measured over water at 22° C. and under 758 mm. pressure. Find the molecular weight of the substance.

8. The application of the Victor Meyer method to determine the molecular weight of bromine gave the following results: weight of bromine = 0.1536 g.; 24.26 ml. of air collected over water at 23° C. and 738 mm. Find the molecular weight of bromine.

READING LIST

Sydney Young, *Stoichiometry.* Longmans, Green and Company, 2d ed., London, 1918. Pages 1–53; 173–221.

S. Glasstone, *Textbook of Physical Chemistry.* D. Van Nostrand Company, New York, 1940. See especially pages 277–314.

Alembic Club Reprint, No. 12, "The Liquefaction of Gases." The Alembic Club, Edinburgh, 1912. This contains papers by Faraday from 1823 to 1845.

Leonard B. Loeb, *Kinetic Theory of Gases.* McGraw-Hill Book Company, New York, 1927. Chapter V, "The More Accurate Equation of State, or van der Waals' Equation."

E. F. Burton, H. G. Smith, and J. O. Wilhelm, *Phenomena at the Temperature of Liquid Helium.* Reinhold Publishing Corporation, New York, 1940. Chapters I, "Historical Introduction," II, "The Liquefaction of Gases" (many diagrams), and III, "The Measurement of Temperature."

CHAPTER 6

LIQUIDS

In general, the properties of liquids are intermediate between those of gases and of solids. The molecules of a gas move in a completely random fashion, so far apart that their mutual attraction and their volume ordinarily may be neglected in deriving the kinetic theory equation. At the other extreme, the units in a crystalline solid are held in definite positions in the crystal lattice. The molecules in liquids are practically in contact, as in solids, but they lack the completely ordered arrangement of crystals, and their mutual attraction and their volumes cannot be neglected as in gases. This makes their theoretical treatment more difficult than that of gases or solids. However, considerable progress has been made in recent years. Although much of the quantitative treatment is beyond the scope of this work, some of the concepts will be useful qualitatively in interpreting different properties of liquids.

Density. The density of a liquid can be measured in several ways. (1) The first is based upon the **principle of Archimedes,**[1] which states that *a body immersed in a fluid is buoyed up by a force equal to the weight of the fluid it displaces.* A sinker, which usually consists of a sealed glass tube weighted with lead shot, shown in Figure 33, is weighed in air and then in a liquid of known density. Its volume is calculated from these data. Then it is immersed in the liquid under investigation and weighed again. The difference between the weight in air and the weight in the liquid is the weight of liquid displaced; hence the density of the liquid is calculated easily. For accurate work, the buoyancy of the air must be taken into consideration. The sinker would weigh more *in vacuo* than in air, because it would no longer be buoyed up by the air it displaces. The correction added to the weight in air in order to give that *in vacuo* is the weight of the air displaced by the object, minus that displaced by the weights. The weights usually are made of brass, with a density of 8.4 g./ml.

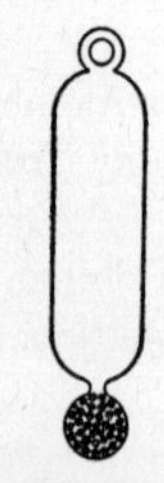

Fig. 33. Density Sinker.

[1] Greek mathematician and physicist of the third century B.C.

(2) Another method of measuring the density of a liquid is by means of the **hydrometer.** A submerged weighted float, with a long graduated stem, is put into the liquid as shown in Figure 34. The denser the liquid, the more the hydrometer will be buoyed up and the higher the stem will project above the surface. The reading of the scale at the surface gives the density directly. Hydrometers are made with different scales for heavy and light liquids. They can be read to about 0.1 per cent.

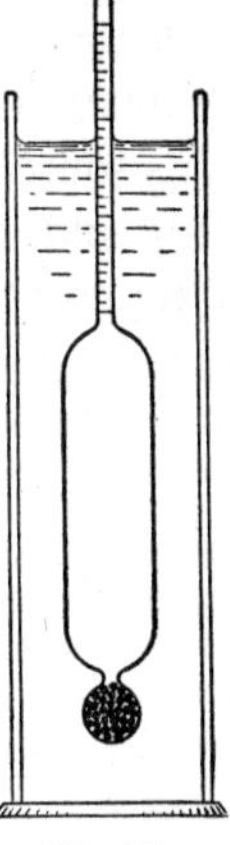

Fig. 34. Hydrometer.

(3) More accurate methods of determining the density of a liquid employ a volumetric flask, illustrated in Figure 35, or a pycnometer, one type of which is shown in Figure 36. In each case the apparatus is cleaned carefully to remove grease and is standardized by weighing it empty and then filled with water at a known temperature. The level of the water in the neck of the flask is adjusted to the mark with a capillary tube, while that in the pycnometer is adjusted by touching a wedge of filter paper to the fine tip and thus drawing the water down to the mark etched on the other arm. The sensitivity of the instrument is determined by the ratio of the diameter of the small tube to the total volume. Thus the water in the neck of a 100-ml. flask cannot be adjusted with as great percentage accuracy as that in the arm of a 10-ml. pycnometer, which probably is only $\frac{1}{100}$ as large in diameter. Such a pycnometer is sensitive to about 0.001 per cent.

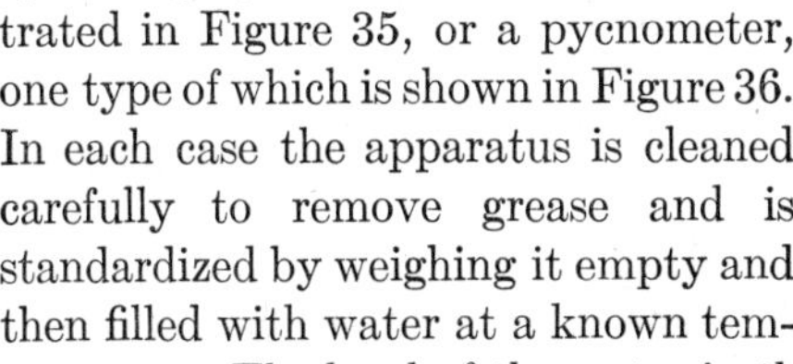

Fig. 35. Volumetric Flask.

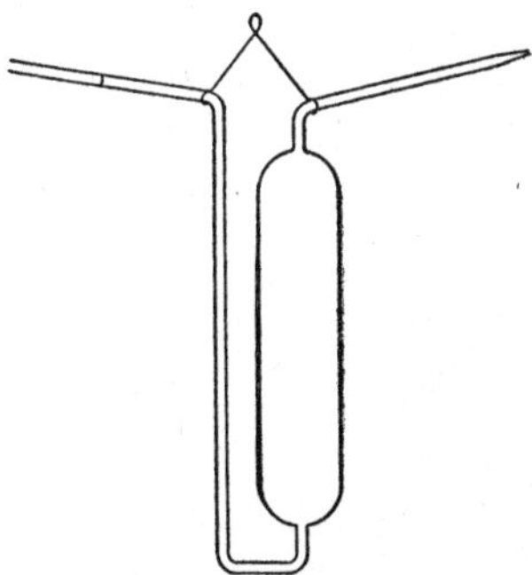

Fig. 36. Pycnometer.

The density of a liquid changes with temperature much more rapidly than that of a solid, as we might expect from the smaller intermolecular forces and from the fact that the molecules usually are more widely spaced. As a result, the coefficient of expansibility will be correspondingly greater, and the temperature must be adjusted more accurately in determining the density of a liquid. In the case of benzene, for example, the coefficient of expansibility is 0.0014 per degree and, in order to measure its density with an accuracy of 0.001 per cent, the temperature must be controlled within $\frac{1}{140}$° C., and a control of ±0.001° C. would be advisable in order to eliminate error from this source. An inspection of Table 23 will show how the densities and specific volumes of water and mercury change with temperature.

TABLE 23

THE DENSITIES AND SPECIFIC VOLUMES OF WATER AND MERCURY AT DIFFERENT TEMPERATURES

Temp. in ° C.	Water		Mercury	
	D in G./Ml.	*V* in Ml./G.	*D* in G./Ml.	*V* in Ml./G.
− 10	0.9979	1.0021	13.620	0.07342
0	.999868	1.000132	13.596	.07355
1	.999927	1.000073		
2	.999968	1.000032		
3	.999992	1.000008		
4	1.000000	1.000000		
5	.999992	1.000008	13.583	.07362
10	.999728	1.000272	13.571	.07369
15	.999127	1.000874	13.559	.07375
16	.998970	1.001031		
17	.998802	1.001199		
18	.998623	1.001379		
19	.998433	1.001569		
20	.998232	1.001771	13.546	.07382
21	.998021	1.001983		
22	.997799	1.002206		
23	.997567	1.002439		
24	.997326	1.002682		
25	.997074	1.002935	13.534	.07389
30	.995676	1.004343	13.522	.07396
35	.994059	1.005976	13.510	.07402
40	.992246	1.007815	13.497	.07409
50	.98807	1.01207	13.473	.07422
60	.98324	1.01705	13.449	.07436
70	.97781	1.02270	13.424	.07449
80	.97183	1.02899	13.400	.07463
90	.96534	1.03590	13.376	.07476
100	.95838	1.04343	13.352	.07490

Data from *I.C.T.*, **III**, 25 and 26 and **II**, 458.

Orthobaric Densities. Ordinarily the densities of gases and liquids are measured at atmospheric pressure. However, in a study of the properties of liquids and their vapors it is interesting to compare what is known as the orthobaric densities of the two. *The **orthobaric density** of a liquid or vapor is its density measured at a pressure equal to that of the vapor in contact with the liquid at the temperature of the experiment.* At any one temperature, the orthobaric densities of the liquid and vapor, therefore, are comparable because they are measured at the same pressure. However, the experimental pressure is not the same at different temperatures, since the vapor pressure of a liquid increases exponentially with increasing temperature.

The orthobaric density of a liquid *decreases* with increasing temperature, while that of the vapor *increases.* If the orthobaric densities of liquid and of vapor are plotted against the temperature, they approach each other more and more rapidly and become equal at the critical temperature. This is shown in Figure 37, which is a plot of the data of Sydney Young for *benzene.* Recent work by Maass has shown that the densities near the critical temperature may not behave quite so simply as these data indicate, but the general shape of the curve is typical of most substances which have been studied.

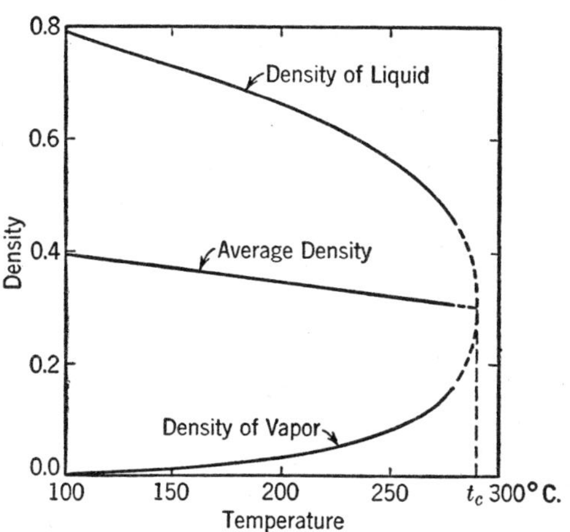

Fig. 37. Orthobaric Densities and Law of Rectilinear Diameter for Benzene.

In 1886 Cailletet and Mathias found that a plot of the average of the orthobaric densities of the liquid and its vapor was very nearly a straight line up to the critical temperature. This is illustrated in Figure 37 for *benzene.* In this case, the average density d_m is given by the equation:

$$d_m = \frac{(D + d)}{2} = 0.4501 - 0.0005248\,t + 0.0000000693\,t^2$$

where D and d are the densities of the liquid and vapor respectively, and t is the centigrade temperature. This equation holds from the melting point of the solid benzene to the critical temperature, so that it expresses the average orthobaric density over the whole range of existence of the liquid. The average density is very nearly a linear function of the temperature, as the very small coefficient of the quadratic term indicates. This generalization of Cailletet and Mathias often is called the **law of the rectilinear diameter.** It holds most exactly for normal liquids, like hydrocarbons and their derivatives. The curvature of the mean density line becomes more pronounced in the case of more polar liquids like ammonia, water, organic alcohols, and other liquids which are considered to be associated.

TABLE 24

THE ORTHOBARIC DENSITIES IN G./ML., OF THREE ORGANIC SUBSTANCES

SUBSTANCE	DIETHYL ETHER		*n*-PENTANE		METHANOL	
TEMP. (° C.)	*D*	*d*	*D*	*d*	*D*	*d*
40	0.6894	0.003731	0.6062	0.0034		
60	.6658	.006771	.5850	.0060		
80	.6402	.01155	.5624	.0101	0.7355	0.001465
100	.6105	.01867	.5377	.0163	.7140	.003984
120	.5764	.02934	.5107	.0250	.6900	.007142
140	.5385	.04488	.4787	.0386	.6640	.01216
160	.4947	.06911	.4394	.0591	.6340	.01994
180	.4268	.1135	.3867	.0935	.5980	.03186
190	.3663	.1620	.3485	.1269	.5770	.04010
193.8	**0.2625**					
197.2			**0.2323**			
200					.5530	.05075
220					.4900	.08635
225					.4675	.1003
230					.4410	.1187
235					.4054	.1438

D and *d* represent the densities of liquid and gas respectively.

This law often is useful in determining the critical density more accurately than it can be measured directly. The critical density is the density of the substance at the critical temperature, which we shall call t_c in centigrade degrees. If the equation for the average density at temperatures below the critical temperature has been determined, substitution of the critical temperature in the equation gives the critical density.

Cohesion, Adhesion, and Surface Tension. *The internal pressure in liquids is due to the force of attraction between the molecules.* This force is termed ***cohesion*** *because it is exerted between like particles.* It is very intense over short distances, but decreases much more rapidly than the force of gravitation as the distance is increased.

The spherical shape of rain drops and the tenacity with which wet pieces of glass, paper, or cloth stick together are all illustrations of the force of cohesion in water. Although a long stream of water will not cling to the end of a rod but will break up into drops, a column of water confined in a tube will show considerable tensile strength. The arrangement for demonstrating this property is shown in Figure 38. A glass tube is bent in the shape shown, cleaned, filled over half full of water, heated to boil out the air, and then sealed. If the tube is tilted so as to fill one arm with water, it may be brought back to the position shown, and the column of water will fill the upright tube. It is held by the adhesion between the water and the glass at the top, and by the cohesion of the water molecules in the column, which act like a liquid rope and support the weight of the column. When it is jarred, the water will break away at some point and the column will fall until the liquid stands at the same height in the two arms. This experiment is possible only with those liquids which wet glass and adhere to it. ***Adhesion*** *is the force between two unlike substances, like water and glass.*

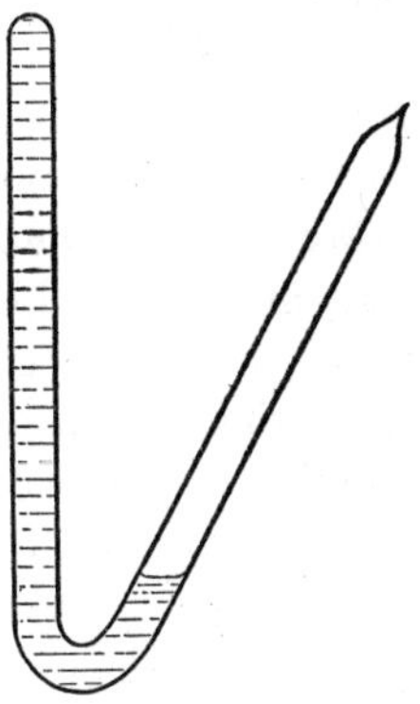

Fig. 38. Demonstrating the Tensile Strength of a Liquid.

Why does a rain drop draw itself into a sphere and mercury form nearly spherical drops when it is placed upon a piece of glass? In each case the liquid assumes the shape with the minimum surface as though it were encased in an invisible elastic bag. *The force which draws the drop together is* ***surface tension,*** which is another manifestation of cohesion between the molecules. In Figure 39, we focus our attention on two different molecules — one in the interior of the liquid and one at the surface. In each case we have drawn a circle representing the effective range of molecular forces. In the center of the solution, the attractive forces of the surrounding molecules are exerted equally from all sides, but at the surface they are all exerted sideways or downward, with no corresponding force attracting the molecule from the space above. As a result, the molecules at the surface are all drawn toward the body of the liquid and this tends to reduce the area of the surface. *If we consider a line 1 cm. long in the surface of the liquid, the force with which the surface on one side of the line pulls the surface on the other side is defined as the* **surface tension.** Usually it is represented by the Greek letter gamma, γ, and is expressed in dynes per centimeter.

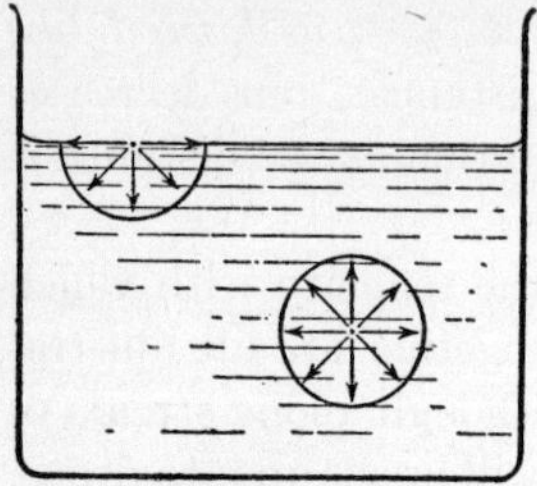

Fig. 39. Molecular Forces in a Liquid.

Methods of Determining Surface Tension. (1) The du Noüy ring method. This method, although not the most accurate, is the most straightforward, and finds frequent application in measuring the surface tension of biological fluids. One form of the apparatus is shown in Figure 40. A ring of platinum wire about 4 cm. in circumference is cleaned with great care and suspended from the arm *A* of the torsion balance. The pointer arm *B* is set at zero, and the adjusting screw *C* is turned until the torsion of the wire raises the arm *A* into a horizontal position, just clearing the support *D*. The knob *E* is now turned to raise the platform until the small amount of liquid in the watch glass touches the wire. The pointer arm *B* then is turned clockwise slowly, so that the torsion of the wire pulls the ring upward. At the same time, the knob *E* is turned to lower the liquid and keep the arm *A* in a horizontal position. The maximum pull on the ring, just before it is torn from the surface, measures the surface tension of the liquid. The torsion corresponding to different readings of the pointer *B* is found by preliminary experiments, in which small weights are hung on the ring.

The downward pull on the ring is practically all due to the surface tension of the *two* surface films, one on the outside and one on the inside of the ring, and we may write:

$$F = 2\,\gamma C \qquad \text{whence} \qquad \gamma = \frac{F}{2\,C}$$

where F is the force in dynes necessary to tear away the ring and C is its circumference in centimeters. The shape of the water sur-

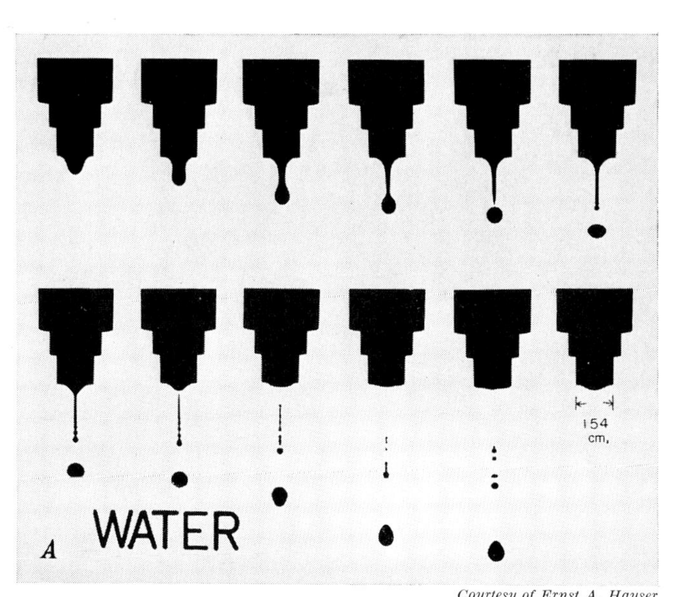

Courtesy of Ernst A. Hauser

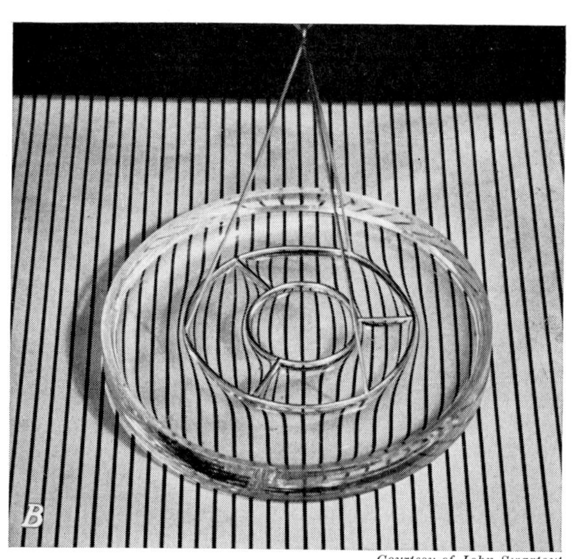

Courtesy of John Swartout

facing page 132

Plate III. (A) SILHOUETTE PHOTOGRAPHS OF DROP FORMATION (B) WATER SURFACE IN CONTACT WITH DU NOÜY RING

face and its pull on the ring are shown in Plate III, facing page 132.

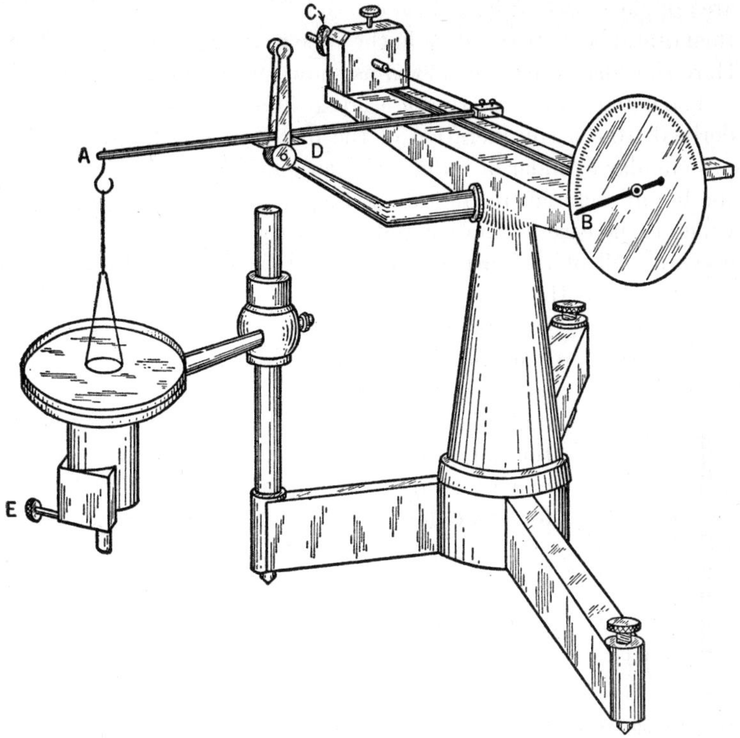

Fig. 40. The du Noüy Ring and Torsion Balance.

(2) The capillary rise method. The action of a sponge or a piece of blotting paper in sucking up a liquid, and the rise of oil in a lamp wick are all due to surface tension. In every case, the liquid wets the solid, that is, the force of adhesion is sufficient to cause it to spread over the surface. If a capillary tube is put into a liquid which wets its surface, the capillary becomes in effect a *tube* of the liquid, and surface tension draws the liquid up into the capillary in order to reduce the total surface of the liquid, as shown in Figure 41 (*a*). If a capillary tube is put into a liquid like mercury which does not

(*a*) Capillary Rise (*b*) Capillary Depression

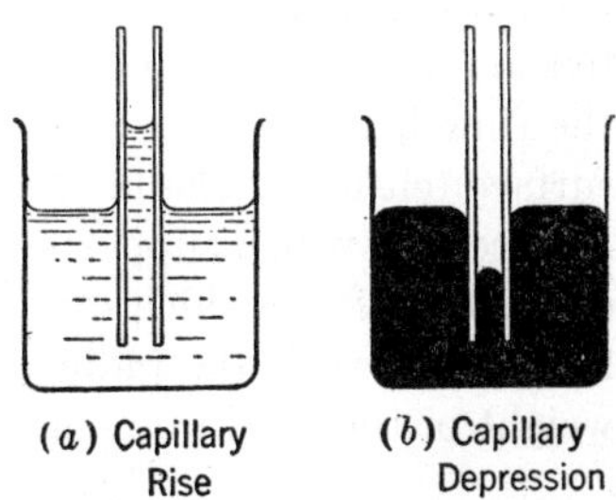

Fig. 41. Capillary Action.

wet the glass, the surface of the mercury will be increased by the area of glass with which it is in contact and the surface tension will then draw the mercury *down* in the tube to reduce the total surface. Here the surface will be curved as shown in Figure 41 (*b*).

The equation for the rise of a liquid in a capillary tube is easily derived from a consideration of the forces involved. If the tube is a circular cylinder of radius r, its circumference will be $2\pi r$. If the liquid meniscus in the tube is tangent to the wall of the tube, which is the case for most liquids against a tube of *clean* glass, the upward pull of the surface tension will be $2\pi r\gamma$. This will pull liquid up into the tube until the weight of the column of liquid just balances the pull. Neglecting the small hemispherical meniscus, the weight in dynes will equal the volume of the cylindrical section, $\pi r^2 h$, multiplied by its density d and by the acceleration of gravity g, which is 980.6 dynes per g. under standard conditions. Equating the two forces we find:

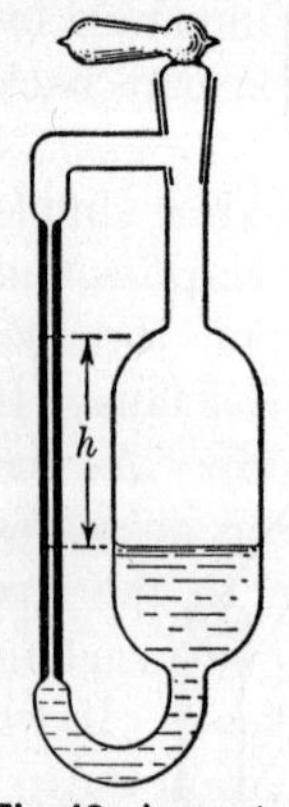

Fig. 42. Apparatus for Measuring Capillary Rise.

$$2\pi r\gamma = \pi r^2 hdg \qquad \text{or} \qquad \gamma = \tfrac{1}{2} rhdg$$

Figure 42 shows an apparatus used by T. W. Richards, and more recently improved by Grinnell Jones, for precise measurements of surface tension by the capillary rise. Since the height of rise h depends upon the radius of the tube, the cylinder in which the bulk of the liquid is contained must be so large that its capillary effect is negligible, or the results must be corrected for the errors introduced.

(3) The drop-weight method. This method is based upon the weight of drops of the liquid falling slowly from the end of a tube which is held in a vertical position. If the drop forms slowly, it reaches a point when it no longer can be supported by the surface tension of the liquid and breaks away. The weight of the drop at the time it breaks away from the tip therefore is a measure of the surface tension of the liquid. If we assume that the length of the surface film which supports the drop is equal to the circumference of the tube from which it falls, the total pull of the surface will be $2\pi r\gamma$, where r is the radius of the tip. Equating this to Wg, the weight of the drop in dynes, and solving for γ gives:

$$\gamma = \frac{mg}{2\pi r}$$

Unfortunately this equation is only an approximation, since the mechanism of drop-formation is more complicated than we have assumed. It has been investigated through silhouettes taken with a high-speed camera. Some of these are shown in Plate III, facing page 132. Six stages in the formation of a drop at the end of a tube are illustrated in Figure 43. The drop grows reversibly through the first three stages represented here, but when it reaches the fourth stage (*d*) it becomes unstable, the neck of the drop quickly pinches off and the drop falls, often accompanied by one or more smaller drops which form as the thin neck snaps back under the action of surface tension.

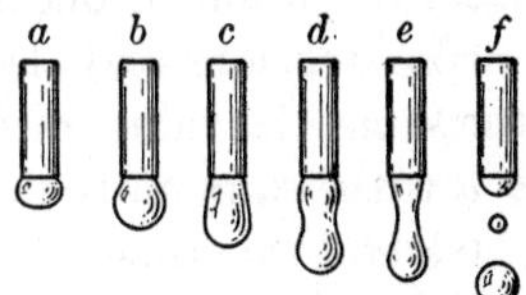

Fig. 43. Stages in the Formation of a Drop.

A number of studies of the deviations from the preceding simple formula have been made, among which the work of Harkins and Brown [1] is outstanding. The deviations depend upon the size of the drop relative to the size of the tube from which it falls. If the drop is *very large,* the simple equation fits exactly. As the size of the drop decreases in proportion to the tip, the calculated surface tension is too small. If we write the equation thus:

$$\gamma = \left(\frac{mg}{r}\right)F$$

the constant F will have the value $\frac{1}{2}\pi = 0.159$ for an infinitely large drop, and the values given in Figure 44 for the corresponding value of $r/V^{\frac{1}{3}}$, where V is the volume of the drop and r as before is the radius of the tube. Since the radius of a spherical drop is $\sqrt[3]{3\,V/4}$, $V^{\frac{1}{3}}$ is proportional to the radius, and $r/V^{\frac{1}{3}}$ is a measure of the ratio of the radius of the tip to that of the drop. If the size of the tip is chosen so that $r/V^{\frac{1}{3}}$ is between 0.76 and 0.94, the

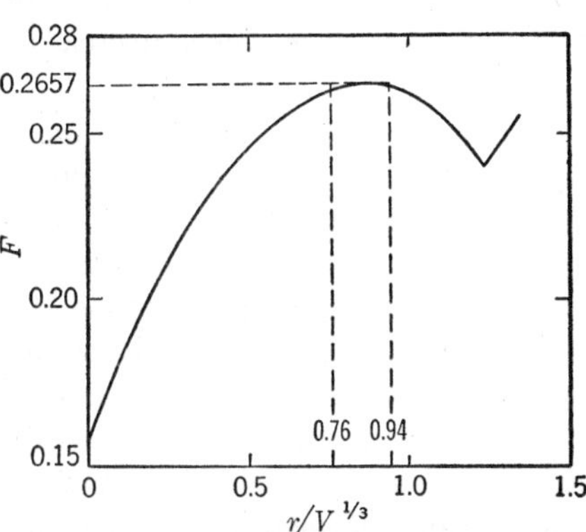

Fig. 44. Drop-Weight Function for Different Ratio of Radius of Tip to Size of Drop.

[1] W. D. Harkins and F. E. Brown, *J. Am. Chem. Soc.*, **41**, 499 (1919).

value of F will be constant within less than 1 per cent of the maximum value of 0.2657, as shown in the figure.

The drop-weight method is most suitable for measuring the surface tension of one liquid relative to that of another. If the surface tensions and also the densities of the two liquids are nearly the same, the values of F will not be very different, and if the ratio γ/d is the same in the two cases, the values of F will be identical.

Careful experiments show that there is a slight difference in the value of the surface tension, depending upon the gas present above the liquid surface. Thus the surface tension of water in contact with air saturated with water vapor is about 0.1 per cent lower than that of water in contact with the water vapor alone. The presence of gases like carbon dioxide or hydrogen sulfide, which are soluble in water, causes a decrease of about 1 per cent in the surface tension, while hydrogen has no appreciable effect. From our picture of molecular forces in a liquid, we would expect that the nature of the gaseous phase might make an appreciable difference in the force exerted upon a molecule in the surface. If the molecules of the gas exert an appreciable attraction upon the molecule of the liquid in the surface, this attraction will decrease the force holding the molecule in the liquid surface, hence decreasing the surface tension.

When two immiscible liquids are in contact, there will be a definite boundary or **interface** separating them. This liquid boundary is maintained by the **interfacial tension** of the liquid-liquid interface, just as the liquid-gas or liquid-vapor interface is maintained by the surface tension. The drop-weight method is a convenient one for measuring interfacial tension. Here the size of the drop will depend upon the *difference in density* of the two liquids as well as the interfacial tension. In the case of a liquid drop falling in air, the density of the latter is small enough in comparison so that we neglected it in our discussion, although it must be considered in exact work. The determination of interfacial tension is important in connection with the theory of colloidal behavior, and interfacial tensions are significant in physiological processes.

The surface tensions of a number of different pure liquids are collected in Table 25. The values for water and for benzene are known most accurately, and these liquids usually are taken as standards in calibrating apparatus used for the determination of the surface tensions of other liquids.

TABLE 25

THE SURFACE TENSION, IN DYNES PER CM., OF DIFFERENT LIQUIDS MEASURED AGAINST AIR AT 20° C.

SUBSTANCE	FORMULA	γ	SUBSTANCE	FORMULA	γ
Water	H_2O	72.75	Methyl acetate	$CH_3 \cdot C_2H_3O_2$	24.6
Glycerol	$CH_2OH \cdot CHOH \cdot CH_2OH$	63	Ethyl acetate	$C_2H_5 \cdot C_2H_3O_2$	23.9
Glycol	$CH_2OH \cdot CH_2OH$	48	*n*-Propanol	C_3H_7OH	23.8
Nitrobenzene	$C_6H_5NO_2$	43.9	Methanol	CH_3OH	22.6
Aniline	$C_6H_5NH_2$	42.9	Ethanol	C_2H_5OH	22.3
Pyridine	C_5H_5N	38	Isopropanol	$(CH_3)_2CHOH$	21.7
Benzene	C_6H_6	28.88	Diethyl ether	$C_2H_5OC_2H_5$	17.0

The influence of structure upon the surface tension is marked, as a glance at the table will show. The surface tensions of all the monohydroxy alcohols in the paraffin series are nearly the same. That of water is unusually large, probably due to association of the molecules through hydrogen bonds. This type of association is cut down in the alcohols because one of the hydrogen groups attached to the oxygen is replaced by a bulkier alkyl group. In ether, both of the hydrogens of water are replaced by alkyl groups, and thus the surface tension is reduced even further. In glycol and glycerine, on the other hand, additional hydroxyl groups are added and the surface tension increases with each additional group, until that of glycerol is not far from that of water.

A comparison of the surface tensions of benzene and pyridine is interesting. The cohesional force is greater in pyridine, due no doubt to the possibility of hydrogen bonds between a hydrogen in one molecule and the nitrogen in another. This nitrogen, like the oxygen in the alcohols, must have some unshared electrons in its valence shell. The higher surface tension of aniline and nitrobenzene may be due to the same type of intermolecular force.

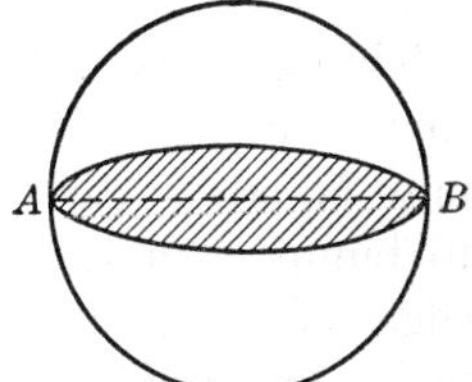

Fig. 45. Pressure in a Bubble.

Pressure in a Drop or Bubble. We have seen that the surface tension of a liquid draws it together so that it becomes approximately spherical in shape. It is a simple matter to calculate the pressure inside such a drop, by considering it as cut into two halves by the diametral plane *AB*, as shown in Figure 45. The force of surface tension which is pulling these two halves together is equal to the product of the circumference of the circle times the surface tension:

$$\text{Force} = 2\pi r\gamma \text{ (in dynes)}$$

The pressure is simply the quotient of the force divided by the area:

$$P = \frac{2\,\pi r\gamma}{\pi r^2} = \frac{2\,\gamma}{r} \text{ (in dynes per square centimeter)}$$

It follows that the pressure in the drop *increases* as the radius of the drop *decreases*.

The situation is exactly similar in the case of a bubble of gas in a liquid. Here also the surface tension of the liquid draws the gas bubble into a nearly spherical shape, and the pressure inside the bubble is given by the same equation which holds for the pressure inside a drop of liquid. In the case of a soap bubble, or any other formed by a thin shell of liquid surrounding a bubble of gas, the pressure is *twice* that inside a bubble completely immersed in a liquid, because the surface film has two sides, and is so thin that the radii of the two are practically the same.

The effects of surface tension on bubbles are often important. When a gas is introduced into a liquid through a tube immersed under the surface, the gas bubbles out irregularly, and the liquid usually is drawn up into the tube after each bubble is ejected. As the pressure of the gas is built up, the liquid is forced down the tube and the bubble of gas grows at the end of the tube. With increasing size of the bubble, the exterior pressure due to surface tension decreases and the bubble grows more rapidly until it breaks away. The gas pressure now is much *less* than that due to the surface tension on the small bubble remaining, which is sucked back into the tube, starting the whole process over again. A determination of the maximum pressure in the growth of the bubble is one method of measuring surface tension.

The bumping of boiling liquids also is dependent upon the pressure required to start the growth of a very small bubble. Very pure liquids in carefully cleaned apparatus are particularly likely to bump. Air dissolved in the liquid, pieces of dirt, or rough edges of small scratches on the beaker or flask, act as nuclei on which the bubbles can start and thus reduce bumping. If none of these inequalities are present, the only nuclei for bubbles are the spaces between the molecules of the liquid in its normal state. If our equation is valid under these circumstances, it shows that the pressure is enormous in a bubble of molecular dimensions. At the normal boiling point the vapor pressure of the liquid is one atmosphere, which is not enough to form such a small bubble. The liquid therefore **superheats** — *i.e.*, its temperature rises above the normal boiling point before bubbles start to form. Once a bubble starts and grows beyond the molecular dimensions, it expands with almost explosive violence, the nearby molecules of liquid evaporate into it, and bumping results. The tendency to bump may be overcome by putting into the liquid some inert, porous substance, such as a bit of unglazed porcelain. The air in the small pores furnishes nuclei for the formation of bubbles in the liquid. The same result is attained by the boiling-tubes invented by the Russian chemist Markownikoff, one of which is shown in Figure 46. It is made by drawing out a piece of glass tubing into a thin capillary which is sealed near the end to form a small air pocket. This touches the bottom of the flask, and the bubbles come off smoothly from the open end of the tube.

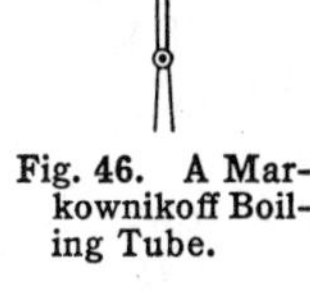

Fig. 46. A Markownikoff Boiling Tube.

Surface Tension and Temperature. As the temperature rises, the surface tension of a liquid decreases to zero at the critical temperature. Hence, when a liquid is heated gradually up to the critical temperature, the meniscus separating the liquid and vapor gradually flattens out, until it becomes horizontal and finally disappears at the critical temperature. Various equations have been suggested to express the change of surface tension with temperature, the first of which was advanced by Roland von Eötvös (*pronounced* ût'vûsh), professor of physics in the University of Budapest, in 1886. He found that the product of the surface tension multiplied by the $\frac{2}{3}$ power of the molecular volume was a linear function of the temperature. Setting the molecular volume equal to M/D, where M is the molecular weight and D is the density of the liquid, the Eötvös equation may be written:

$$\gamma\left(\frac{M}{D}\right)^{\frac{2}{3}} = a - kT$$

Since the surface tension vanishes at the critical temperature T_c and the density does not, the equation also may be written in the form:

$$\gamma\left(\frac{M}{D}\right)^{\frac{2}{3}} = k(T_c - T)$$

In 1893 Ramsay and Shields studied the surface tensions of many liquids over a wide range of temperature, and showed that the equation of Eötvös did not hold within the limits of their experimental accuracy. They changed it to:

$$\gamma\left(\frac{M}{D}\right)^{\frac{2}{3}} = k(T_c - \delta - T)$$

In the Ramsay-Shields equation the value of δ, an empirical constant, usually is 6°. This equation is quite satisfactory over a wide range of temperature, but is not valid near the critical temperature, since it predicts that the surface tension vanishes 6° below the critical temperature.

The symbol k used for the constant of these three different empirical equations must not be confused with the Boltzmann constant k, introduced on page 86.

Ramsay and Shields found that the value of the constant k in their equation was about 2.12 for many substances. They assumed that substances showing an abnormally *low* value of this constant were associated into complex molecules, like $(H_2O)_2$, $(H_2O)_3$, or higher polymers, so that their true molecular weights in the liquid state were greater than a single formula weight. For example, in the case of water they found that the constant was 1.04. If we call M the formula weight and M' the *true* molecular weight in solution, we have the two equations:

$$\gamma\left(\frac{M'}{D}\right)^{\frac{2}{3}} = 2.12(T_c - \delta - T) \quad \text{and} \quad \gamma\left(\frac{M}{D}\right)^{\frac{2}{3}} = 1.04(T_c - \delta - T)$$

Dividing the first equation by the second, we find:

$$\left(\frac{M'}{M}\right)^{\frac{2}{3}} = \frac{2.12}{1.04} \quad \text{or} \quad \frac{M'}{M} = \left(\frac{2.12}{1.04}\right)^{\frac{3}{2}}$$

The ratio M'/M is called the *degree of association,* which may be designated by x. In this case $x = 2.9$, indicating that liquid water is chiefly $(H_2O)_3$.

More recent studies indicate that the value of k varies widely for different substances. In organic compounds it is determined chiefly by the size of the molecule. It lies between 2.0 and 2.5 for most substances containing less than twelve carbon atoms in the molecule, but it is much higher for heavier molecules. Thus it is 2.90 for benzophenone and 5.95 for tristearin. On the basis of the reasoning of Ramsay and Shields, the degree of association in these two substances would be 0.63 and 0.21 respectively; in other words these molecules would have to be *dissociated* in the liquid state. The chemical nature of these substances argues against any such behavior. These and other facts led Sugden to conclude that the value of the Ramsay-Shields constant cannot be considered a quantitative measure of association in the liquid state. For substances of low molecular weight, a value of the constant which is less than 2 indicates abnormality, but this now is considered to be due to general intermolecular forces throughout the liquid rather than the formation of individual polymeric molecules.

A more successful modification of the Eötvös equation has been made by Katayama of the Tohuku Imperial University in Japan. In 1916 he showed that the *difference in orthobaric density* between the liquid and the vapor should be substituted for the density of the liquid in the equation of Eötvös. His equation therefore is:

$$\gamma\left(\frac{M}{D - d}\right)^{\frac{2}{3}} = k(T_c - T)$$

The equation of Katayama holds accurately up to the critical temperature and gives the value zero for the surface tension at this temperature.

In 1924 Sugden showed that the surface tension of a given liquid could be expressed as a function of temperature alone by means of an equation of the form:

$$\gamma = \gamma_0\left(1 - \frac{T}{T_c}\right)^{\frac{6}{5}}$$

where γ_0 is a constant and T/T_c is the *reduced temperature.* The Sugden equation holds well for normal liquids over the whole range of temperature, as shown in Figure 47, where it is tested by plotting $\gamma^{\frac{5}{6}}$ against the temperature. The result is a straight line for normal liquids, but a line with appreciable curvature for the two associated liquids, acetic acid and methanol. These are plotted to the same scale, but with axes offset to avoid confusion with the other lines.

In 1923 Macleod found a simple equation connecting the surface tension of a liquid under its own vapor pressure, with the difference in density of the liquid and the vapor. The equation of Macleod is:

$$\gamma = C(D - d)^4$$

where the constant C is characteristic of the particular liquid.

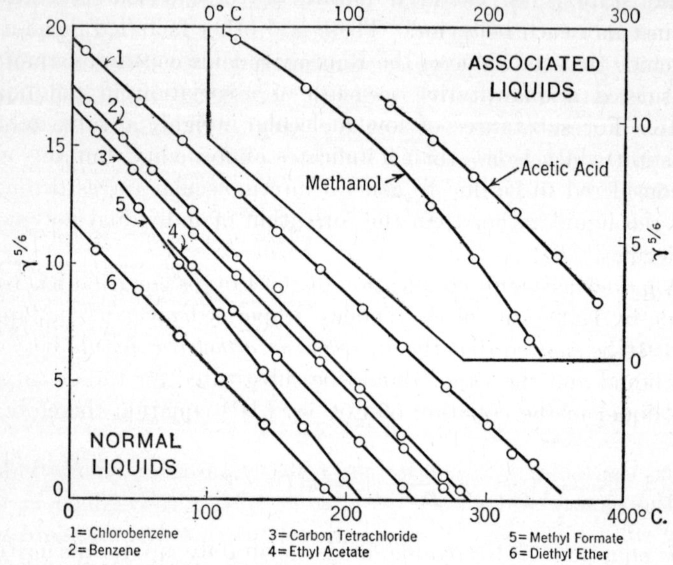

Fig. 47. Test of the Sugden Equation for Surface Tension.

Molecular Volumes and the Parachor. A study of the molecular volumes of compounds in the liquid state has brought out some interesting relationships. In 1855 Hermann Kopp, professor of chemistry at Heidelberg, set out to measure the molecular volumes of liquids at the normal boiling points, where he thought that they would be comparable. He found that the molecular volumes determined under these conditions were nearly additive and he computed values of the *atomic volumes* in compounds. He found that the atomic volume of an element was nearly the same in different compounds of the same type, but might be decidedly different in different types of compounds. Thus the atomic volume of oxygen was 12.2 ml. in a carbonyl group, =CO, but only 7.8 ml. in a carboxyl group, —COOH. This shows that the atomic volume which he calculated is partly an ***additive property****, depending on the kind of atom involved*, and partly a ***constitutive property****, depending upon the type of combination.*

In 1924 Sugden suggested that the molecular volumes of different substances would be more truly comparable at temperatures where their surface tensions were equal, rather than at their boiling points. This is because the surface tension is related to the cohesive forces in the liquid, comparable to internal pressures of thousands of atmospheres. Although no exact relation between internal pressure and surface tension is known, Sugden thought that the internal pressures would be more nearly equal in different liquids having the same surface tension. By taking the fourth root of the Macleod equation he obtained the relationship:

$$\gamma^{\frac{1}{4}} = C^{\frac{1}{4}} (D - d)$$

By choosing for all the measurements a suitable standard surface tension, γ_1, at a sufficiently low temperature, the value of d_1 will be negligible compared to D_1 and the molecular volume will be:

$$\frac{M}{D_1} = \frac{MC^{\frac{1}{4}}}{\gamma_1^{\frac{1}{4}}}$$

Since the factor $\gamma_1^{\frac{1}{4}}$ is the same in every case, the *relative* values of the molecular volumes of different substances defined in this way will be independent of the value chosen for the standard surface tension. As a matter of convenience, the factor is taken as unity, and *we define the molecular volume at a surface tension of 1 dyne per cm., or* ***parachor***, [*P*], *by means of the equation:*

$$[P] = MC^{\frac{1}{4}}$$

Sugden concludes that the *parachor* is a true molecular volume, since it is about 0.77 the volume of the liquid at the critical temperature, and $[P]^{\frac{2}{3}}$, which has the dimensions of *area,* is proportional to the collision diameters of the simple molecules in the gas phase. The study of a large number of compounds provided data for the calculation of atomic parachors and also the parachors due to various atomic arrangements. The latter are known as **structural parachors.** In Table 26 are collected some of these atomic and structural parachors.

Sugden found that the calculated values of the parachors agreed with the observed values within 1 or 2 per cent. The structural parachors are the same in groupings of the same structure, regardless of the atoms involved. Thus the parachor of the double bond

TABLE 26

SOME ATOMIC AND STRUCTURAL PARACHORS

C = 4.8	S = 48.2	Triple bond = 46.6	3-membered ring = 16.7
H = 17.1	F = 25.7	Double bond = 23.2	4-membered ring = 11.6
N = 12.5	Cl = 54.3		5-membered ring = 8.5
P = 37.7	Br = 68.0	O_2 in esters = 60.0	6-membered ring = 6.1
O = 20.0	I = 91.0		

Sugden, *The Parachor and Valency*, George Routledge & Sons, London (1930), page 38.

is the same in compounds in which the links are C=C, C=O, C=S, C=N, and N=O. As an example of the calculation of the parachor of a compound, let us take benzene, based on the Kekulé structure of alternate single and double bonds in the ring:

$$\begin{aligned} C_6 &= 6 \times 4.8 = 28.8 \\ H_6 &= 6 \times 17.1 = 102.6 \\ \text{3 double bonds} &= 3 \times 23.2 = 69.6 \\ \text{6-membered ring} &= 6.1 \\ [P] \text{ observed} = 206.2 \qquad [P] \text{ calculated} &= 207.1 \end{aligned}$$

The parachor has found important applications in organic chemistry in deciding among several structural formulas suggested to account for various chemical reactions. One example will be given. Acetaldehyde, $CH_3 \cdot CHO$, readily polymerizes to the trimer, $(CH_3 \cdot CHO)_3$. There is a change of the parachor from $(3 \times 121.2) = 363.6$ to 298.7. This indicates that some of the C=O double bonds have been changed to C—O—C single bonds. The decrease of 64.9 corresponds to a loss of three double bonds (69.6) rather than two (46.4) and suggests the cyclic structure I instead of the chain structure II.

```
          O
        /   \
CH3 · CH     HC · CH3
      |       |
      O       O
        \   /
       HC · CH3

          I

[P] (calc.) = 300.1
```

```
        CH2
         |
       HCOH
         |
        CH2
         |
       HCOH
         |
        CH2
         |
        HCO
         II

[P] (calc.) = 317.2
```

The parachor observed for the polymer agrees very closely with that of the cyclic structure and invalidates the other.

Viscosity. *The* ***viscosity*** *of a liquid is a measure of its resistance to flow, which may be called its* ***internal friction.*** Some liquids, like heavy oils or molasses in January, move very sluggishly, while others, like water and ether, flow easily. It is comparatively easy to solder a tank watertight, but much more difficult to make it tight enough to prevent the leakage of gasoline, which has a much lower viscosity.

One of the most accurate methods of measuring viscosity is based upon the rate of flow of the liquid through a capillary tube, under a definite pressure. The French physician and physiologist Jean Louis Marie Poiseuille investigated this subject in connection with his study of the circulation of the blood through the arteries and veins of the body. The absolute unit of viscosity is named in his honor the **poise.** In 1844 Poiseuille found experimentally that the rate of flow of water through a capillary is proportional to the pressure and to the fourth power of the radius of the tube, and inversely proportional to its length. This law holds for *streamline flow.* If the flow becomes *turbulent,* the friction increases and Poiseuille's law no longer is followed.

Poiseuille's equation usually is stated thus:

$$\frac{V}{t} = \frac{\pi r^4 P}{8\,\eta l} \qquad \text{or} \qquad \eta = \frac{\pi r^4 P t}{8\,V l}$$

Here V is the volume of liquid flowing in time t, P is the pressure, r is the radius of the tube, and l its length. The proportionality factor η is known as the **coefficient of viscosity** or simply the **viscosity.** In the C.G.S. system, η has the dimensions of dyne $\times$ sec. $\times$ cm^{-2}, or **poise.**

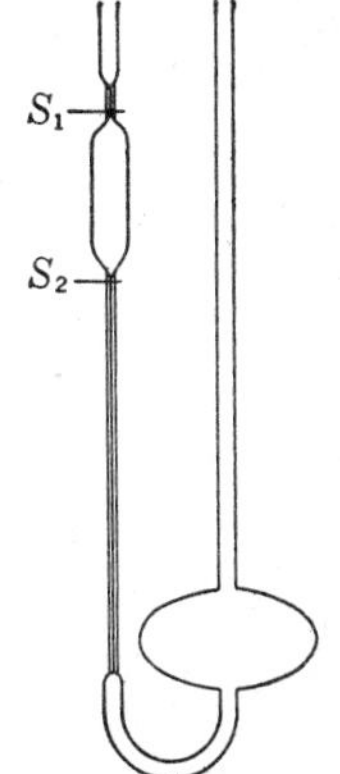

Fig. 48. Washburn's Viscometer.

The Measurement of Viscosity. The measurement of absolute viscosity is difficult, requiring a uniform capillary tube of circular cross section which must be measured with extreme precision, since the fourth power of the radius of the tube enters the equation for the viscosity. The measurement of viscosities relative to a standard liquid, usually water, is a much simpler procedure. An apparatus for measuring relative viscosities was devised by the German physical chemist Wilhelm Ostwald. The modification of his apparatus shown in Figure 48 was developed by Washburn and Williams at the University of Illinois. It is made of fused quartz. The liquid under investigation is measured into the large bulb from a pipet. The apparatus is mounted vertically in a thermostat and suction applied to the left-hand tube to draw the liquid up above the scratch S_1. The liquid is then allowed to flow through the capillary, which in this case is 0.5 mm. in diameter and 195 mm. long, into the large bulb. The interval between the times when the liquid meniscus passes the marks S_1 and S_2 is the time required for the liquid (about 9 ml.) to pass through the capillary. It may be measured by a stop-watch, or more accurately by a chronograph recorder. Grinnell Jones, professor of physical chemistry at Harvard University, has developed an automatic timer, employing a photoelectric cell, which eliminates the personal factor in visual timing and gives an accuracy of 0.01 second. His apparatus gives results accurate to 0.01 per cent.

In any of these modifications of the Ostwald viscometer, the liquid is forced through the capillary by the hydrostatic pressure of the column of liquid itself. Since this is proportional to the density of the liquid, the **relative viscosity** η/η_0 is given by the equation:

$$\frac{\eta}{\eta_0} = \frac{Dt}{D_0 t_0}$$

where D and D_0 are the densities of the liquid under investigation and of water, and t and t_0 are the times required for the two liquids to pass through the capillary.

Another method of measuring viscosity is to determine the rate of fall of a steel ball in a tube containing the liquid. This is much used industrially, *e.g.*, in the determination of the viscosity of lubricating oils.

TABLE 27

THE VISCOSITIES OF SEVERAL LIQUIDS AT DIFFERENT TEMPERATURES
COEFFICIENT OF VISCOSITY η IN MILLIPOISES

TEMP. ° C.	WATER	METHANOL	ETHANOL	ETHER	BENZENE
– 10	26.0			3.23	
0	17.94	8.08	17.9	2.842	9.00
10	13.10	6.90	17.5		7.57
20	10.09	5.93	17.2	2.332	6.47
30	8.00	5.15	16.8	2.128	5.61
40	6.54	4.49	16.5	1.97	4.92
50	5.49	3.95	16.1		4.36
60	4.70	3.49	15.8	1.66	3.89
70	4.07		15.5		3.50

The Change of Viscosity with Temperature and Pressure. The viscosity of a liquid depends upon the *size*, *shape*, and *chemical nature* of the molecules which compose it. In general, in a series of similar compounds the viscosity increases with increasing molecular size. This is illustrated in the case of the paraffin hydrocarbons, which pass from mobile liquids like gasoline to heavy lubricating oils. Here a change in shape is involved as longer chains are formed. Chemical forces between neighboring molecules also influence viscosity. Thus the viscosity of water is nearly twice as great as that of methanol, probably because the strong force of the hydrogen bond tends to keep adjacent molecules in the same relative positions and thus opposes their flow.

The viscosity of a liquid increases when it is subjected to increased pressure, as shown by the work of P. W. Bridgman, professor of physics at Harvard University. It decreases as the temperature is raised, as shown in Table 27. As the pressure is increased, the molecules are crowded more closely and they have less free space left in which they can move. As the temperature is raised, the liquid expands and the available free space is increased. In each case the change of viscosity parallels the free space in which the molecules can pass each other.

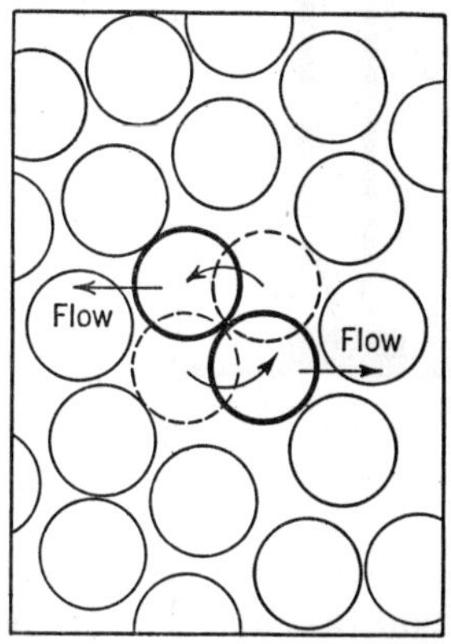

Fig. 49. Molecular Flow in a Liquid.

This point of view has been treated mathematically in the development of an interesting theory of the liquid state by Henry Eyring, professor of physical chemistry at Princeton University. He pictures the process of liquid flow in molecules which can be represented by spheres as follows: On the average, the molecules are arranged in the manner shown in Figure 49. The distribution is somewhat ordered but allows an appreciable free space in which the molecules can move. We may think of two molecules colliding to form a double molecule, which rotates through about 90° to allow the molecules to pass each other. A series of these rotations comprise the viscous flow. The surrounding molecules only need to move slightly from the centers of their free spaces in providing a "hole" large enough to allow a pair of molecules to pass each other.

The Vapor Pressure of Liquids. *The **vapor pressure** of a liquid is the pressure exerted by the vapor in equilibrium with the liquid.* The vapor pressure changes with temperature and with increased total pressure; hence in stating a vapor pressure, the temperature must be specified, and also the pressure, if much above atmospheric.

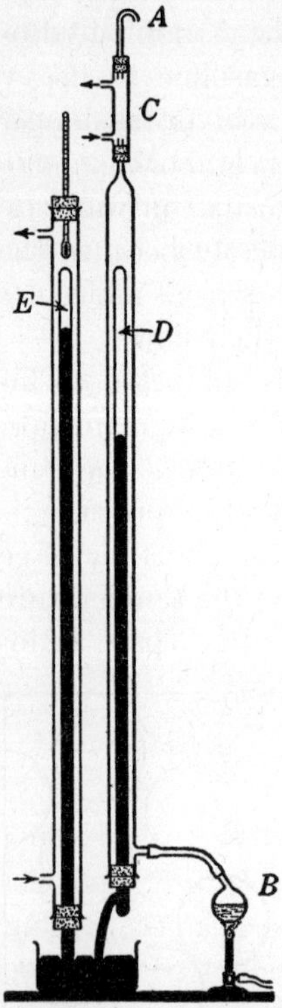

The Measurement of Vapor Pressure. Two general methods may be used to determine the vapor pressure of a substance: (1) The **static method** is illustrated in Figure 50. A sample of the pure material is carefully freed from dissolved gases and introduced into a barometric tube *D* at a definite temperature, which is maintained constant by the vapor from the liquid boiling in the bulb *B*. The heights of the column containing the substance and of the barometer *E* are corrected for temperature. The difference in height is the vapor pressure of the substance at the boiling point of the liquid in *B*. The temperature of the jacket may be lowered by applying suction through the tube *A* and boiling the liquid under reduced pressure. The method may be adapted to high pressures by substituting an air-column manometer for the evacuated barometric column, and applying the same high pressure to it and to the tube containing the liquid under investigation.

Fig. 50. Static Method of Measuring Vapor Pressure.

(2) If the vapor pressure of the substance is small, the **dynamic method** devised by Regnault in 1845 is more accurate. It is based upon the assumption that at low pressure the vapor behaves like a perfect gas and obeys Dalton's law of partial pressures. Under these conditions if a liquid evaporates into an inert gas, its partial pressure at equilibrium will be equal to the vapor pressure, and the ratio of its partial pressure p_1 to the total pressure P will be the same as the ratio of the number of moles of vapor n_1 to the total number of moles of vapor and inert gas $(n_1 + n_2)$:

$$\frac{p_1}{P} = \frac{n_1}{(n_1 + n_2)}$$

In practice, a known amount of the inert gas at a known pressure is passed through the liquid slowly enough to become saturated with the vapor at the temperature of the experiment. The total amount of material evaporating is determined either from the loss of weight of the liquid, or from the gain in weight of a suitable absorbent.

For example, if 24.0 l. of air, measured at 740 mm. pressure and at a temperature of 150° C., is passed over mercury, 0.516 g. will evaporate. These data suffice to determine the vapor pressure of mercury at 150° C. The number of moles of mercury, n_1, is the weight divided by the molecular weight:

$$n_1 = \frac{0.516}{200.6} = 0.00257 \text{ mole}$$

The number of moles of air, regarded simply as a perfect gas, is given by solving the gas law equation $PV = n_2RT$ for n_2:

$$n_2 = \frac{PV}{RT} = \frac{(\frac{740}{760})24.0}{0.0821 \times 423} = 0.672 \text{ mole}$$

The vapor pressure of mercury at that temperature therefore is:

$$\frac{p_1}{740} = \frac{0.00257}{(0.672 + 0.003)} = 0.00382 \quad \text{or} \quad p_1 = 2.82 \text{ mm.}$$

The Change of Vapor Pressure with Temperature. The vapor pressure of a liquid increases with rising temperature, and the increase becomes rapid as the temperature approaches the boiling point. Several typical vapor pressure curves are plotted in Figure 51, all of which show the same general characteristics.

The relationship between vapor pressure p and absolute temperature T, deduced thermodynamically on page 633, and known as the Clausius-Clapeyron equation is:

$$\frac{d \ln p}{dT} = \frac{L_v}{RT^2}$$

Here L_v is the molal heat of vaporization of the liquid at the absolute temperature T, and R is the gas constant. When the heat of vaporization does not change appreciably with temperature, this may be integrated to yield:

$$\log p = A - \frac{0.4343\, L_v}{RT}$$

This is a linear equation if we take log p as ordinate and the reciprocal of the temperature, $1/T$, as abscissa. The *intercept* on the

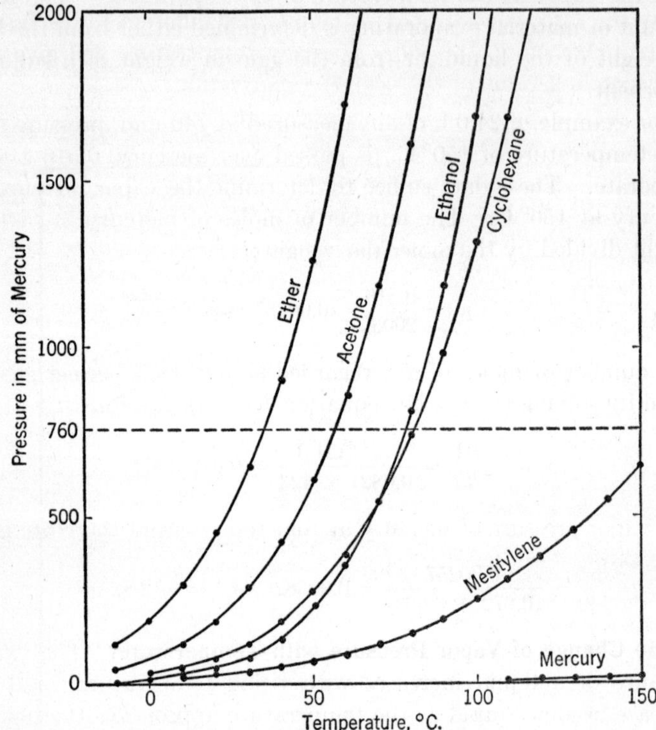

Fig. 51. Some Vapor-Pressure Curves.

ordinate axis is A, and the *slope* $S = -\frac{0.4343\ L_v}{R}$. The heat of vaporization in calories per mole therefore is given by:

$$L_v = -\ 4.469\ S$$

In Figure 52 we have plotted in this way the same data given in the previous figure. The fact that they lie so close to straight lines shows the adequacy of this equation, at least as a good first approximation. If the vapor pressures are known with high precision or if a long range of temperatures is covered, the curvature may become more pronounced, and another term is required for satisfactory agreement. The vapor pressures of many liquids, up to the critical temperature, can be expressed by the equation:

$$\log p = A + \frac{B}{T} + C \log T$$

where the three constants, A, B, and C, are different for each substance. As before, the slope S at any temperature will give the corresponding value of the heat of vaporization.

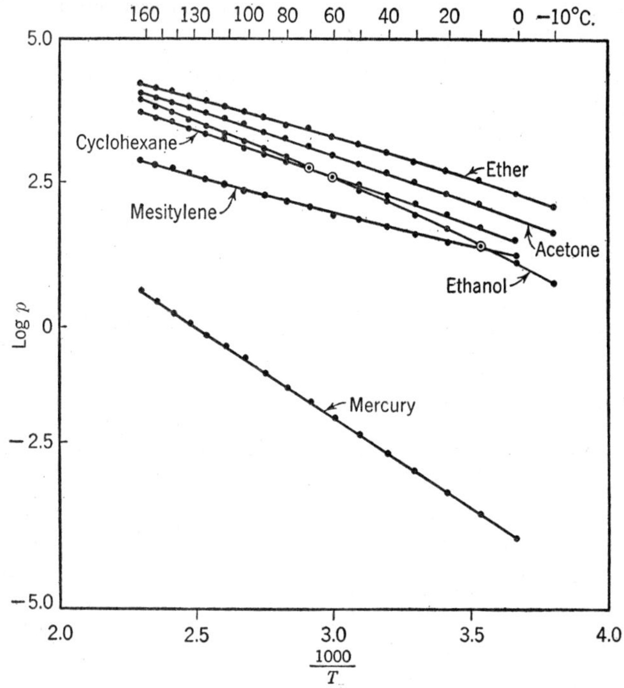

Fig. 52. Some Logarithmic Vapor-Pressure Curves.

The vapor-pressure curve for a liquid extends to the critical temperature, at which its value is the *critical pressure.* Above this temperature the liquid cannot exist. Most liquids can be supercooled below their normal freezing point, if the solid is not present, and the vapor pressure curve of such a supercooled liquid is a continuation of that of the liquid above the freezing point. If a little of the solid is dropped into the supercooled liquid, however, at a constant temperature below the freezing point, the liquid will solidify completely. The vapor pressure of the solid is less than that of the supercooled liquid at the same temperature.

PROBLEMS AND EXERCISES

1. A sinker weighs 11.898 g. *in vacuo* and 6.425 g. in water at 20° C. At this temperature the density of water is 0.9982 g./ml. Calculate the volume of the sinker. If it weighs 7.537 g. in acetone at the same temperature, what is the density of acetone?

2. A sinker which weighs 9.567 g. *in vacuo* is found to weigh 5.031 g. in water at 25° C. and 5.594 g. in benzene at the same temperature. What is the density of benzene?

3. A volumetric flask is standardized by weighing it empty and then filled to the mark with water. It is then filled with methanol and adjusted to the mark at the same temperature. Calculate the density of the methanol from the following data:

Weight of flask *in vacuo*	75.32 g.
Weight of flask + water (20° C.)	322.90 g.
Weight of flask + methanol (20° C.)	272.97 g.

***4.** The same flask standardized in the experiment given above is filled with diethyl ether, thermostated at 0° C. and adjusted to the mark. It is then brought back to room temperature and found to weigh 259.45 g. (*a*) If the *linear* coefficient of expansibility of the Jena glass flask is 5.6×10^{-6} per degree, what is the volume of the flask at 0° C. and the density of ether at this temperature? (*b*) If the cubical coefficient of thermal expansibility of ether averages 0.001535 between 0 and 20° C., calculate the density of ether at 20° C.

5. Using the data of Table 24, page 130, calculate the mean orthobaric densities of diethyl ether and plot these and the densities of liquid and vapor to test the law of the rectilinear diameter.

6. Plot the orthobaric densities of liquid and vapor for methanol and calculate and plot the average densities. Extrapolate this line to the critical temperature, 240.0° C., and thus calculate the critical density of this substance.

7. Describe four methods of determining the density of a liquid. Explain the theory of each and its advantages and disadvantages.

8. Calculate the internal pressure of mercury at 20° C., from the pressure required to compress the vapor, considered a perfect gas, to the volume occupied by the same weight of the liquid.

9. Describe three methods of determining the surface tension of a liquid, explaining the precautions and corrections necessary in each case.

10. A circular du Noüy ring 30.2 mm. in diameter is put in contact with a surface of chloroform at 20° C. A pull of 525 mg. is required to lift the ring from the surface. Calculate the surface tension, assuming the gravitational constant is 980 dynes/g.

11. The minimum pull required to separate a certain du Noüy ring from a benzene surface at 20° C. is found to be 432 mg., while a pull of 413 mg. will separate the same ring from a surface of acetic acid at the same temperature. Taking the value of the surface tension of benzene from Table 25, calculate that of acetic acid.

12. To what height will water rise in a capillary 0.5 mm. in diameter at 20° C.?

13. The capillary of an apparatus for measuring surface tension is tested and found to have a uniform radius of 0.136 mm. Acetone, the density of which is 0.793 g./ml. at 20° C., is found to rise 44.9 mm. in this capillary. If the gravitational acceleration is 980 dynes/g., calculate the surface tension of acetone.

14. In the equation $\gamma = mgF/r$, substitute for the weight m in grams the corresponding value in terms of the volume V of the drop and the density d of the liquid, and solve the equation for V. Show that if γ/d is the same for two liquids falling from the same tip the volumes of the drops also will be the same, and hence the values of F.

15. (*a*) Derive an equation for the relative surface tensions of two different liquids of densities d_1 and d_2, which rise h_1 and h_2 cm. respectively in the same capillary under comparable conditions. (*b*) If water rises 47.5 mm. in a certain capillary at 20°, and ethyl bromide, the density of which is 1.430 g./ml., rises 11.0 mm. under the same conditions, what is its surface tension?

16. Calculate the pressure, in atmospheres, due to surface tension in a drop of aniline 0.001 mm. in diameter at 20° C.

17. Calculate the pressure, in atmospheres, in a bubble of air 0.001 mm. in diameter, immersed in water at a temperature where the surface tension is 50 dynes per cm. To what temperature must the water be heated in order that its vapor pressure may equal the pressure on the bubble, so that the bubble would grow? The data of Table 14 may be plotted to estimate the temperature. What bearing does this calculation have on bumping in boiling water?

18. Compare and explain three different equations relating surface tension with molecular volume and temperature. What conclusions about *association* and *polymerization* in a liquid can be drawn from a study of surface tension at different temperatures?

19. Raise each side of Sugden's surface tension equation to the power $\frac{5}{6}$, and show that if a substance obeys this equation, a plot of $\gamma^{\frac{5}{6}}$ against the centigrade temperature should give a straight line.

20. Sugden found that the difference between the orthobaric density D of a liquid and that of the vapor d was given by the equation:

$$D - d = d_0\left(1 - \frac{T}{T_c}\right)^{\frac{3}{10}}$$

Show that this equation, combined with Katayama's surface tension equation, will yield Sugden's surface tension equation.

21. Derive Macleod's surface tension equation, $\gamma = C(D - d)^4$, from Sugden's density equation, $D - d = d_0(1 - T/T_c)^{\frac{3}{10}}$, and his surface tension equation, $\gamma = \gamma_0(1 - T/T_c)^{\frac{6}{5}}$.

22. Most of the chemical reactions of benzoquinone indicate that it should be represented by formula A, but the peroxide formula B also has been suggested to account for some of its reactions and properties. The value of the parachor of this substance is found to be 236.8. Calculate the parachors corresponding to the two structures and deduce which one probably is correct.

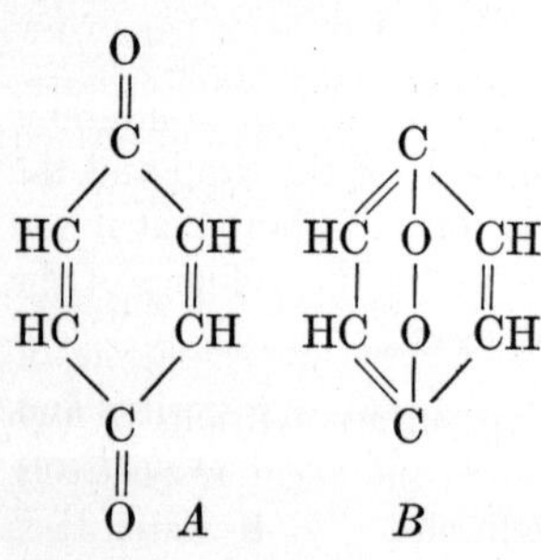

23. A viscometer of the type shown in Figure 48 has a capillary with a uniform diameter of 0.496 mm. and a length of 195 mm. The small bulb delivers 9.04 ml. between the marks S_1 and S_2. It is filled with 65 ml. of liquid, so that the *average* height of the liquid column is equal to 200 mm., which is the vertical distance between the centers of the small bulb and the large reservoir respectively. In this apparatus, the average time required for chloroform, with a density of 1.491 g./ml., to flow out of the bulb is found to be 228.0 sec. Calculate the coefficient of viscosity in poises, assuming the gravitational acceleration is 980 dynes/g.

24. A viscometer is standardized at 20° C., with water, for which the time of flow is found to be 427.5 sec. If mercury flows through this instrument in 48.4 sec., what is its viscosity?

25. If benzene flows through a certain viscometer in 254.7 sec. at 0° C., what will be the time of flow for ether at the same temperature? The densities of the two liquids are 0.9001 and 0.7363 g./ml. respectively.

26. From the general equation for an ideal gas, $PV = nRT$, deduce the equation:

$$\frac{p_1}{P} = \frac{n_1}{(n_1 + n_2)}$$

and explain its use in determining vapor pressures.

READING LIST

Sir William Bragg, *Concerning the Nature of Things.* Harper & Brothers, New York, 1925. Chapter III, "The Nature of Liquids" contains a simple discussion of the properties of liquids and of liquid surfaces, with many excellent illustrations.

Eric K. Rideal, *An Introduction to Surface Chemistry*, 2d ed. The Macmillan Company, New York, 1930.

N. K. Adam, *The Physics and Chemistry of Surfaces.* Oxford University Press, 1930.

P. Lecompte du Noüy, *Surface Equilibria of Biological and Organic Colloids.* Chemical Catalog Company, New York, 1936.

Samuel Sugden, *The Parachor and Valency.* F. S. Crofts & Co., New York, 1930. This book contains a discussion of the liquid state, a description of the theory and practice of the measurement of surface tension, and a discussion of the parachor and its applications to problems of molecular structure and valence.

Emil Hatschek, *The Viscosity of Liquids.* D. Van Nostrand Company, New York, 1928. A complete and well-written presentation of the theory and practice of all methods of measuring viscosity, and an interesting discussion of the viscosity of liquids and their mixtures and of nonelectrolytic and electrolytic solutions.

Joel H. Hildebrand, *Solubility of Non-Electrolytes*, 2d ed. Reinhold Publishing Corporation, New York, 1936. This book deals with general theories of the liquid state and with internal pressure in liquids.

H. E. Edgerton, E. A. Hauser, and W. B. Tucker, "Studies in Drop Formation as Revealed by the High-Speed Motion Camera," *J. Phys. Chem.*, 41, 1017 (1937). This interesting article, from the laboratories of the Massachusetts Institute of Technology, contains many splendid photographs like those reproduced on Plate III, facing page 132.

CHAPTER 7

SOLIDS

The Properties of Solids

Solids may be divided into two classes, *crystalline* and *amorphous.* The former are arranged according to a definite pattern in space, and can be recognized by their crystalline form, while the latter are noncrystalline. Glass is so characteristic an amorphous solid that all such clear substances are often spoken of as *glasses.* Some writers consider that amorphous solids are simply supercooled liquids. In some respects glasses resemble liquids more than crystalline solids. Instead of melting sharply at a definite temperature, they gradually soften. Amorphous solids are plastic under pressure and are distorted permanently, while crystalline solids usually are *elastic.* Instead of slowly yielding and flowing under pressure, they return to their original shape unless they have been strained too far.

All gases and most liquids are ***isotropic,*** *i.e., their properties are the same in all directions.* Most crystalline solids, on the other hand, are ***anisotropic,*** *and show different properties in different directions.* Thus crystalline quartz when heated expands nearly twice as rapidly in directions perpendicular to the crystal axis as it does in directions parallel to this axis. The difference in the optical properties of crystals in different directions accounts for the polarization of light and for the rotation of the plane of polarized light.

The Density of Solids. There are several methods of measuring the density of solids. (1) The most direct is to measure and weigh a piece of the solid of definite dimensions, *e.g.,* a centimeter cube. The density is found by dividing the weight by the volume. This method is applicable only to solids like the metals, which can be machined accurately.

(2) A second method is based upon the principle of Archimedes (page 126). If a sample of a solid is weighed in air and then in water, the difference in weight will equal the weight of the water it displaces. The weight of the sample, divided by the weight of the water displaced, gives its **specific gravity,** that is, the density

of the material relative to that of water at the same temperature. Since the density of water has been determined accurately over a wide temperature range, the density of the solid is found by multiplying its specific gravity by the density of water at that temperature. This method is applicable to most metals or materials which are not affected by immersion in water. It was first used by Archimedes in testing the new crown of Hiero, king of Syracuse, to see if it was pure gold.

(3) A third method, also based upon the principle of Archimedes, may be applied to powdered materials. It makes use of a pycnometer for solids, or specific gravity bottle, shown in Figure 53. This is a small flask, fitted with a ground stopper having a small hole through the center. After the apparatus is cleaned scrupulously inside and out, dried, and weighed, it is filled with water or any nonvolatile liquid of known density, adjusted to a definite temperature in a thermostat, and weighed again. Its volume is determined from the weight and density of the liquid. A weighed sample of the solid is put into the bottle and the rest of the space filled with an inert solvent of known density. The volume once more is adjusted in the thermostat. The final weight determines the volume of the liquid. The volume of the solid is found by difference and its density by dividing its weight by its volume.

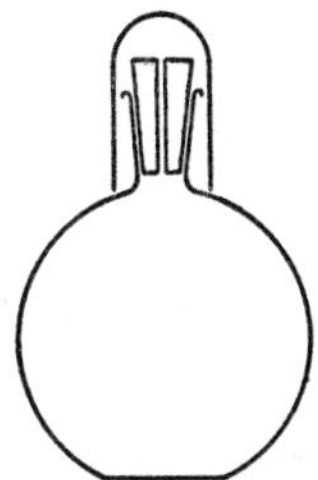

Fig. 53. Specific Gravity Bottle.

(4) The method of floating equilibrium may be applied to very small particles and serves also to determine the homogeneity of the material. The crystals are immersed in a liquid in which they sink, and a heavier liquid is added gradually to form a solution in which they start to rise, and reach **floating equilibrium.** The density of the solid then is equal to that of the solution, which is measured, *e.g.*, in a pycnometer. Air bubbles adhering to the crystals must be removed by applying suction to the system. An advantage of the *flotation method* is that a few small crystals, scrutinized under the microscope and found free of imperfections and entrapped air, suffice for the determination. In determining the density of minerals insoluble in water, various amounts of mercuric iodide may be dissolved in potassium iodide solution. The most concentrated of these solutions has a density of 3.3, which will float most silicates. For substances soluble in water, mixtures

of benzene with ethylene dibromide or methyl iodide will give densities from 0.878 to 2.18 or 2.90, respectively, while the use of methylene iodide would extend the range to 3.325.

The Melting Point. *The **melting point** of a solid is the temperature at which the solid begins to change to liquid, under a pressure of 1 atmosphere.* The melting point of a pure substance is the same as the **freezing point** of the liquid — *the temperature at which both solid and liquid can exist in contact with each other, under a total pressure of 1 atmosphere.* If a piece of ice is put into water above the freezing point, it will melt. If it is put into water supercooled below the freezing point, it will form a nucleus upon which some of the water will freeze. In either case the temperature of the mixture will fall or rise to the freezing point and will remain there indefinitely if the system is insulated from the surroundings.

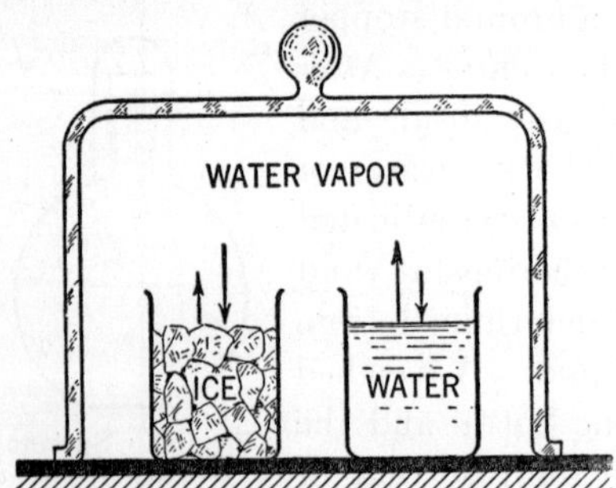

Fig. 54. Water Changing to Ice through the Vapor Phase, Below the Freezing Point.

These facts are explained easily in terms of the vapor pressure. Imagine two beakers, containing respectively ice and water, placed side by side under a bell jar as shown in Figure 54 and kept at a constant temperature. Below the freezing point, the vapor pressure of the supercooled water is greater than that of the ice; hence it will evaporate and condense upon the ice. Only at the freezing point are the vapor pressures of the solid and liquid equal.

The vapor-pressure curve of a solid can be represented over a considerable range of temperature by the equation:

$$\log p = K - 0.4343 \frac{L_s}{RT}$$

where K is a constant, L_s is the latent heat of *sublimation*, and T is the absolute temperature. This is analogous to the equation for the vapor pressure of a liquid, in which the heat of *vaporization* L_v is involved (page 149).

A solid cannot be heated above its melting point, so its vapor-pressure curve must end at this temperature. However, most liquids can be *supercooled*, *i.e.*, cooled below the freezing point, and their vapor-pressure curves continue without a break at this point. Figure 55 shows a plot of the logarithm of the vapor pressure of ice and water against the reciprocal of the absolute temperature. The slope of the curve for ice is steeper than that for the

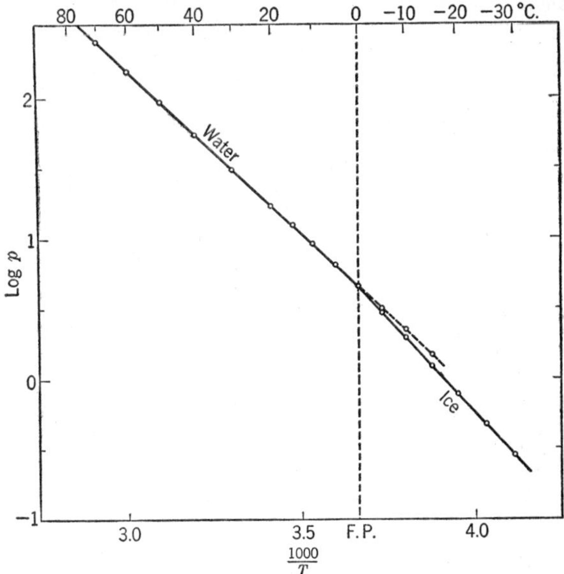

Fig. 55. A Logarithmic Plot of the Vapor Pressure of Water and Ice.

supercooled liquid because the heat of sublimation is greater than the heat of vaporization. This is true for *all* solids and liquids. The two curves intersect at the freezing point.

Hardness. Another important property of solids is their hardness, which can be determined by several methods. (1) The fact that a hard substance will scratch a softer one was used by Mohs in 1820 to define a scale (**Mohs' scale of hardness**) widely used by mineralogists. Ten minerals, with the relative hardness assigned to each, are listed in Table 28. To find the hardness of a substance, we need only find which materials in this list it will scratch and which it will not. The finger nail is slightly above 2 in hardness on the Mohs scale, since it scratches gypsum but not calcite. A penny has a hardness of about 3, a knife blade a little more than 5 and window glass about 5.5. Artificial corundum and silicon carbide are almost as hard as diamond and are widely used as abrasives.

TABLE 28

THE MOHS SCALE OF HARDNESS

1. Talc, $H_2Mg_2(SiO_3)_4$	6. Orthoclase, $KAlSi_3O_8$
2. Gypsum, $CaSO_4 \cdot 2\,H_2O$	7. Quartz, SiO_2
3. Calcite, $CaCO_3$	8. Topaz, $(AlF)_2SiO_4$
4. Fluorite, CaF_2	9. Corundum, Al_2O_3
5. Apatite, $Ca_4(CaF)(PO_4)_3$	10. Diamond, C

(2) Another scale of hardness is that developed by Brinell for testing metals. A spherical ball of hardened steel is forced into the material by means of a press. The weight of the load, in kg., divided by the spherical area of the indentation, in sq. mm., gives the **Brinell number.** The area of the indentation is determined from the depth or the diameter of the hole. Brinell numbers range from 4 for lead and 16 for annealed aluminum to 400 for a hard-worked alloy of platinum with 30 per cent iridium and 470 for certain alloy steels properly heat treated.

The Heat Capacity of Solids. In 1819 P. L. Dulong and A. T. Petit, both at the École Polytechnique in Paris, studied the heat capacities of solid elements and advanced the generalization that *the atomic weight of an element times its specific heat is a constant, about 6.2.* This constant is *the* ***atomic heat capacity*** *of the element and is the quantity of heat required to raise the temperature of 1 gram atom 1° C.* The rule was useful in fixing the atomic weights of a number of the elements.

Dulong and Petit's rule holds for all but a few elements at room temperature. In 1871 Boltzmann explained the rule on the basis of the kinetic theory. He pictured an ideal monatomic solid as a lattice made up of atoms which were held together by powerful crystal forces but which could vibrate slightly about their positions of rest. Rising temperature increased this vibration. As in the case of the ideal gas (page 91), each atom has three degrees of freedom of motion. However, while the energy of the gas molecule is all kinetic, that of the atom in a solid is half kinetic and half potential because of the crystal forces which pull the atom back when it moves. The atom of the solid has, then, *six* instead of *three* degrees of freedom. If the energy is distributed equally among all six, the heat capacity of a perfect monatomic solid at constant volume should be twice that of a perfect gas, or:

$$C_v = 3\,R = 5.96 \text{ cal. per deg. per g. atom}$$

Measurements usually are carried out in calorimeters open to the atmosphere, and consequently they yield the heat capacity at constant pressure C_p, which is larger than C_v because of the work done against the atmospheric pressure as the solid expands.

The difference is much smaller than in the case of gases, amounting to less than 1 calorie unit instead of 1.987 cal. $\times$ deg.$^{-1}$ $\times$ g. atom^{-1}. Moreover, it varies considerably among the elements, depending upon their atomic volumes and coefficients of thermal expansibility and compressibility. In 1907 Gilbert N. Lewis calculated the heat capacity at constant volume for nineteen of the elements. His results are summarized in Table 29. The atomic heat capacity at constant volume averaged 5.9 ($\pm$0.09) except for the four lightest elements, while the deviations from the average value of 6.2 for the atomic heat capacity at constant pressure were twice as great. Lewis concluded: "*Within the limits of experimental error, the atomic heat at constant volume at 20° C. is the same for all the solid elements whose atomic weights are greater than that of potassium.*"

TABLE 29

ATOMIC HEAT CAPACITIES OF SOLID ELEMENTS AT 20° C.

ELEMENT	AT. WT. (1907)	CALORIES PER DEGREE PER GRAM ATOM	
		C_p	C_v
Na	23.0	6.9	6.4
Mg	24.4	6.0	5.8
Al	27.1	5.8	5.6
K	39.1	7.1	6.5
Fe	55.9	6.0	5.9
Ni	58.7	6.1	5.9
Cu	63.6	5.8	5.6
Zn	65.4	6.0	5.7
Pd	107.0	6.1	5.9
Ag	107.9	6.1	5.8
Cd	112.5	6.2	5.9
Sn	119.0	6.4	6.1
Sb	120.0	6.0	5.9
I	127.0	6.9	6.0
Pt	195.0	6.1	5.9
Au	197.0	6.2	5.9
Tl	204.0	6.4	6.1
Pb	207.0	6.3	5.9
Bi	208.0	6.3	6.2
Average		6.2^+	5.9^+
Average deviation		$\pm$ 0.26	$\pm$ 0.15
Average (excluding first four)		6.2	5.9
Average deviation (excluding first four)		$\pm$ 0.18	$\pm$ 0.09

Some of the lighter solid elements show much larger deviations in atomic heat capacity than those given in Table 29. At room temperature the atomic heat capacity of carbon (diamond) is 1.4, of boron 3.3, of silicon 4.7, and of beryllium 3.8. At higher temperatures the heat capacities of these elements approach 6.2. Further study has shown that the heat capacity of all substances decreases greatly at very low temperatures. It is now thought that the heat capacity of crystalline substances actually becomes *zero* at 0° A. The experimental values for the heat capacities of four typical elements are collected in Table 30 and plotted in Figure 56. They all start from near zero at very low temperatures

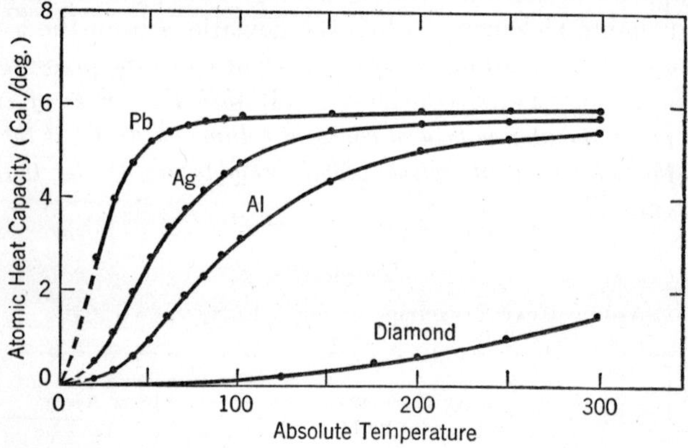

Fig. 56. The Atomic Heat Capacities of Four Elements at Different Temperatures.

and at first increase rapidly. Over the middle part, the curve is nearly linear; then it flattens out at the value of 6.2 (*i.e.*, 3 *R*) predicted by the rule of Dulong and Petit.

The change of heat capacity with temperature was explained by Einstein in 1907 on the basis of the quantum theory. Debye elaborated the theory. He considered that the energy in a crystalline solid consists of vibrations or standing waves of many different frequencies. The limiting (highest) frequency is fixed by the elastic properties of the crystal, which depend upon the masses of the particles and the rigidity with which they are held in the crystal. The heat capacity is governed by the frequency of the vibrations of the crystal and is *low* for crystals having light particles, tightly held, and *high* for those in which the particles are large and loosely held. As the temperature rises, the crystal expands and the crystal forces are decreased; hence the light elements at high temperatures behave like the heavier elements at lower temperatures. Debye introduced the idea of a **characteristic temperature** θ for each element. Dividing the absolute temperature by the characteristic temperature gives the **reduced temperature,** T/θ. According to Debye's ideas, all atomic heat capacity curves for similar elements should be the same function of the reduced temperature, increasing with the *cube* of the reduced temperature near the absolute zero and approaching 3 R at higher temperatures.

TABLE 30

THE ATOMIC HEAT CAPACITY OF FOUR ELEMENTS AT DIFFERENT TEMPERATURES

Temp. ° A.	Diamond (θ = 461)		Aluminum (θ = 96)		Silver (θ = 54)		Lead (θ = 22)	
	C_v	T/θ	C_v	T/θ	C_v	T/θ	C_v	T/θ
20			0.07	0.21	0.41	0.37	2.66	0.91
40			.53	.42	1.91	.74	4.73	1.82
60			1.40	.63	3.30	1.11	5.39	2.73
80			2.25	.83	4.17	1.48	5.64	3.64
90	0.01	0.20	2.67	.94	4.49	1.67	5.70	4.09
100	.06	.22	3.07	1.04	4.73	1.85	5.75	4.55
150	.33	.33	4.36	1.56	5.42	2.78	5.84	6.82
200	.60	.43	5.04	2.08	5.63	3.71	5.87	9.09
250	1.00	.54	5.38	2.61	5.75	4.63	5.90	11.37
300	1.49	.65	5.64	3.13	5.80	5.56	5.95	13.64

Source: Lewis and Gibson, *J. Am. Chem. Soc.*, **39,** 2554 (1917).

In Table 30 we have listed the characteristic temperatures for the four elements, as given by Lewis and Gibson, who define θ as the temperature at which C_v is equal to $\frac{3}{2}$ R. The reduced temperatures corresponding to each value of the atomic heat capacity also are listed in the table. In order to test Debye's predictions, representative values of the heat capacities of all four of these elements are plotted in Figure 57 against the reduced temperature, omitting overlapping points. The heat capacity curves of these four elements, which all crystallize in the cubic system, are the same function of the reduced temperature over the whole experimental range. This verifies Debye's predictions in a remarkable way, and shows a uniformity of behavior which is not suggested by the curves in Figure 56.

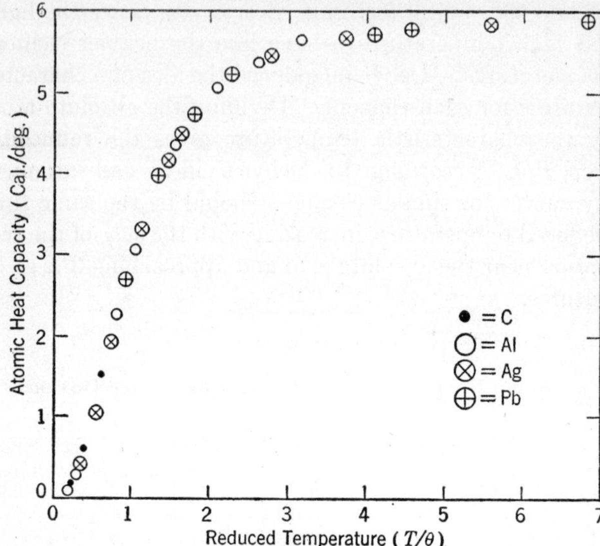

Fig. 57. The Atomic Heat Capacities of Four Elements at Different Reduced Temperatures.

The Properties of Solid Compounds. Certain properties of solid compounds can be calculated from those of the constituent elements. In 1864 Hermann Kopp[1] found that for many solid compounds the ***molecular heat capacity***, *i.e., the quantity of heat required to raise the temperature of 1 mole of the compound 1° C.*, is approximately the sum of the atomic heat capacities of the solid constituents. For liquid or gaseous elements, the heat capacities in solid compounds could be calculated from the molecular heat capacities of their compounds. Thus the molecular heat capacity of silver chloride is 11.7 cal. per deg. per mole. Subtracting 6.2 for the silver gives 5.5 for the chlorine. The difference between calculated and observed molecular heat capacities is about 3 per cent, so that the rule of Kopp, although useful in giving the approximate heat capacity of a solid compound, is by no means exact.

As T. W. Richards pointed out, the decrease in volume during the formation of compounds usually parallels the evolution of heat. Thus, when sodium and potassium react to form a feebly bound

[1] Professor of Chemistry at the University of Heidelberg. This work is described in detail in *Ann. Chem. Pharm. Suppl.*, *3*, **1**, 289 (1864).

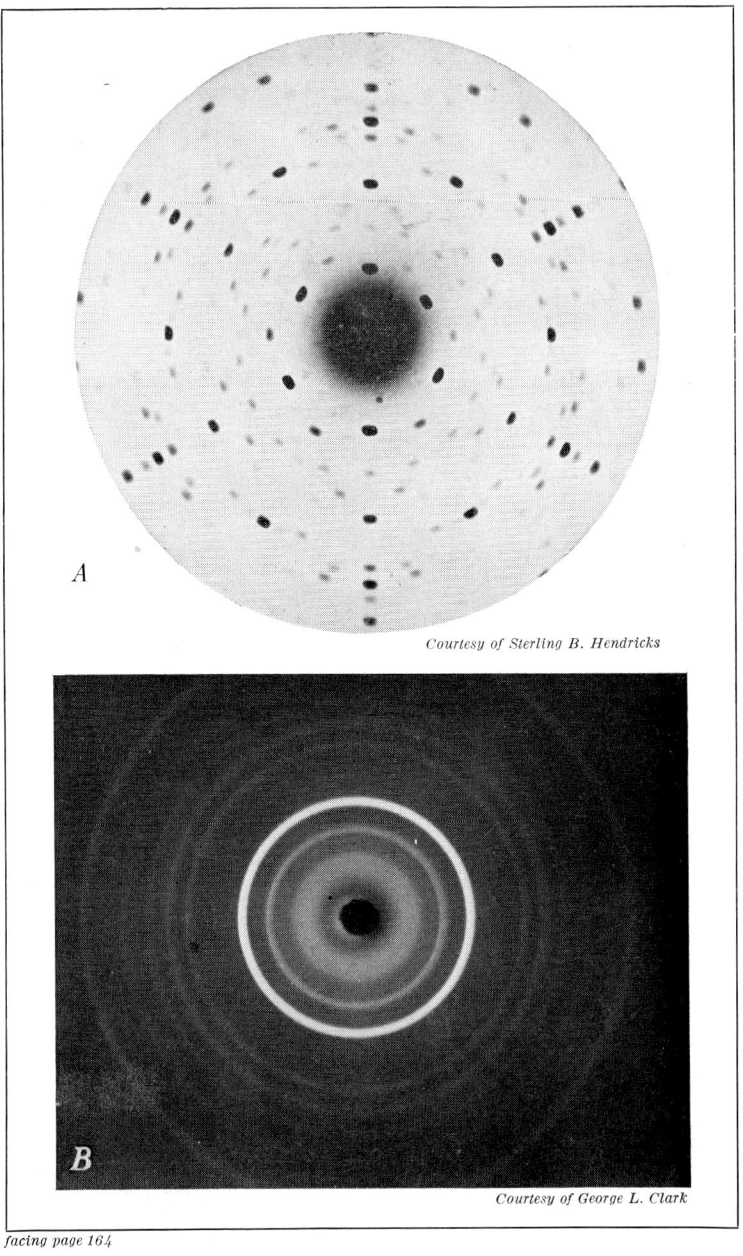

facing page 164

Plate IV. (A) LAUE X-RAY PHOTOGRAPH OF ALUMINA (B) POWDER X-RAY PHOTOGRAPH OF SILICA, SHOWING RINGS OBTAINED WITH FLAT FILM

compound, the decrease in volume is 0.9 ml. per mole and 1 kilocalorie of heat is liberated; when sodium and bromine react to form the tightly bound sodium bromide, the decrease in volume is 15.1 ml. per mole and 86 kilocalories are liberated. The volume change is calculated from the atomic volumes of the constituents and the molecular volume of the compound. As an illustration, we may calculate the change in volume on the formation of one mole of potassium chloride, thus:

Atomic volume of K	45.3 ml.
Atomic volume of Cl (liq.) .	25.1 ml.
Sum	70.4 ml.
Molecular volume of KCl .	37.5 ml.
Contraction in volume . .	32.9 ml.

The close parallel between volume contraction and heat of formation is shown in Figure 58, which gives a comparison of the heats of formation and contractions in volume during the formation of *one gram equivalent* of each of a large number of chlorides.

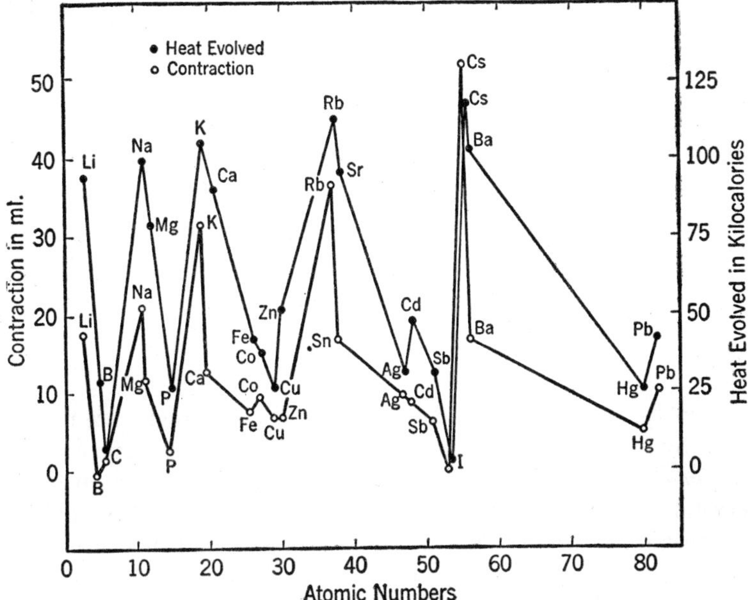

Fig. 58. The Heats and Volume Changes in the Formation of Chlorides. (After T. W. Richards, *J. Frank. Inst.* 198, 6 (1924).)

Crystal Systems and Their Characteristics

Crystal Form. *The most characteristic properties of crystals are the angles between corresponding faces.* The faces of the crystal may not be perfectly developed, but the **interfacial angles** are

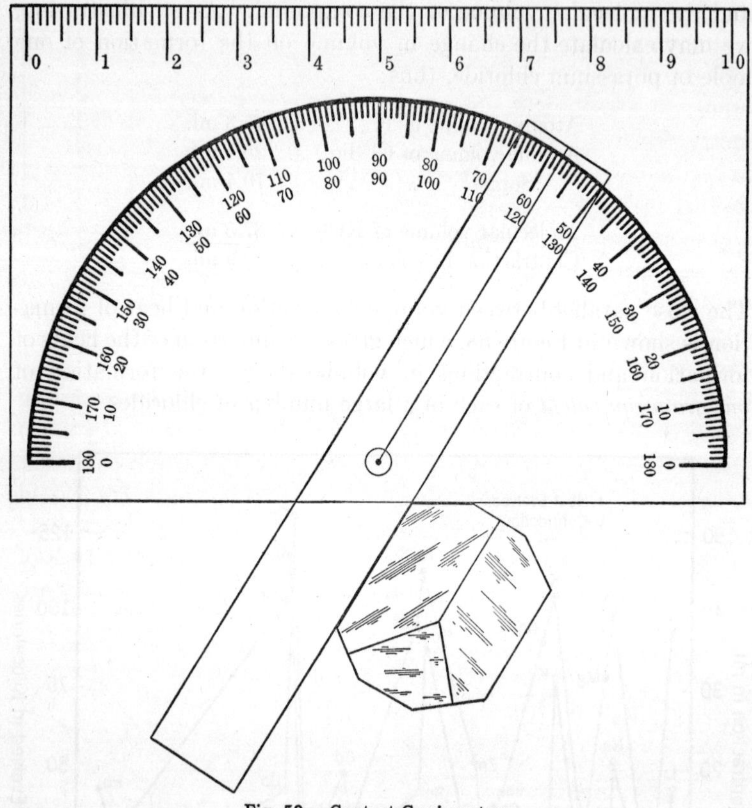

Fig. 59. Contact Goniometer.

always the same for the same substance. These angles are measured by means of an instrument called a *goniometer*. The *contact goniometer*, illustrated in Figure 59, requires a large, perfect crystal. In the *reflecting goniometer*, invented by the English chemist W. H. Wollaston, the crystal is mounted upon a turntable and rotated until a beam of light reflected from one face is seen through a microscope. The crystal then is turned until the beam of light is reflected by the next face, and the angle between the faces is read from a graduated scale. This instrument is more accurate than the contact goniometer and can be used with very small crystals.

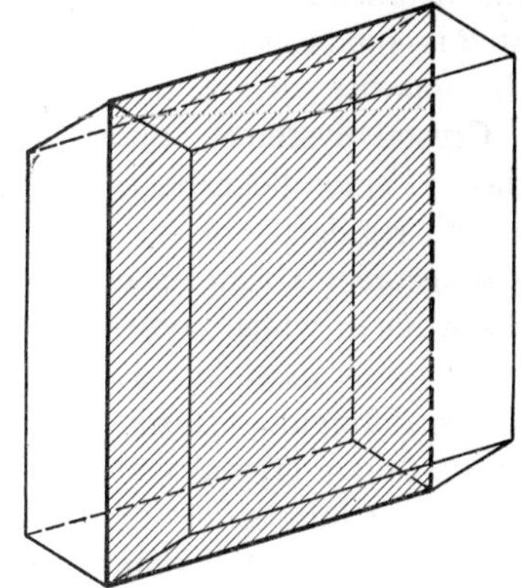

Fig. 60. Plane of Symmetry.

Crystals are classified according to the symmetry which they display. If the crystal can be bisected by a plane into two halves which are mirror images of each other, it possesses a **plane of symmetry,** such as that illustrated in Figure 60. Most crystals have several planes of symmetry. If a crystal can be rotated about a line so that it occupies the same position in space several times during one revolution, it is said to have an **axis of symmetry** in that line. If the crystal occupies the same position twice during the revolution, it is said to possess an axis of **binary** (twofold) **symmetry,** such as the line CC' in Figure 61. Notice that two other binary axes of symmetry would be furnished by the lines AA' and BB' in this figure. Axes of higher symmetry than binary are

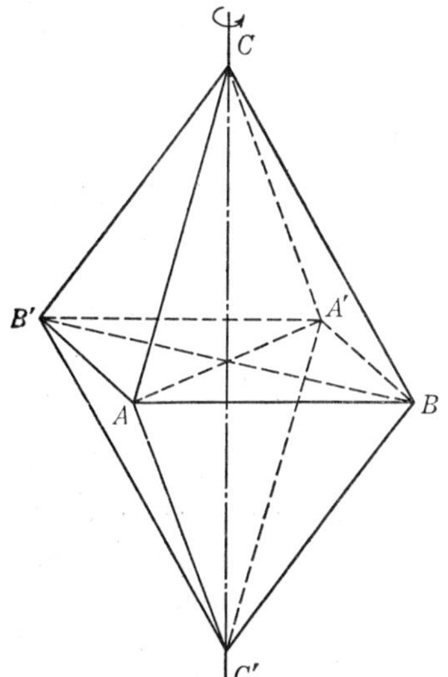

Fig. 61. Axis of Symmetry.

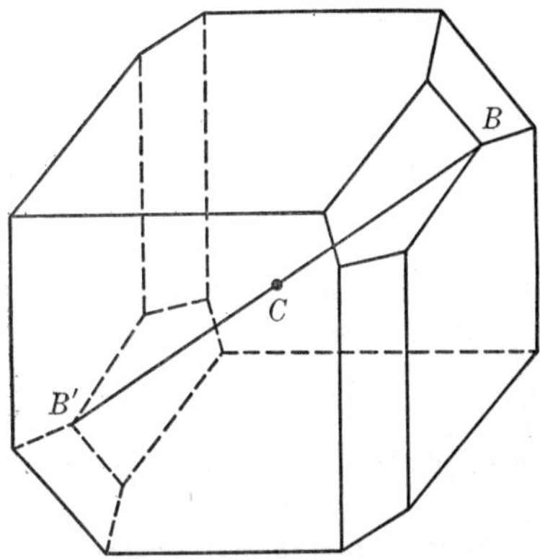

Fig. 62. Center of Symmetry.

trigonal (threefold), *tetragonal* (fourfold), and *hexagonal* (sixfold). A crystal has a **center of symmetry** if any line through this point intersects opposite faces of the crystal in equidistant points. Thus the crystal in Figure 62 possesses the center of symmetry *C* and the distance *BC* along the line intersecting one point on the surface at *B* is equal to the distance *B′C* from the intersection of the line on the opposite surface.

Crystal Systems. Shortly after Dalton enunciated his atomic theory, crystallographers advanced the hypothesis that the observed regularity of crystal form reflected a regularity of atomic arrangement within the crystal. This led to a systematic study of the ways in which points (representing the centers of the atoms) could be arranged in space in recurring patterns. The symmetries of the different patterns in space were then studied and divided into six main **crystal systems,** most of which were subdivided further into a number of different **forms.** Crystals are described with reference to **crystallographic axes,** *which are 3 or 4 straight lines of conveniently chosen length, passing through a common origin and inclined at definite angles.*

Different crystals in the same system may differ in the lengths of the axes, and these can be determined only by careful measurements with a goniometer. The six crystal systems may be described conveniently in terms of their crystallographic axes as follows:

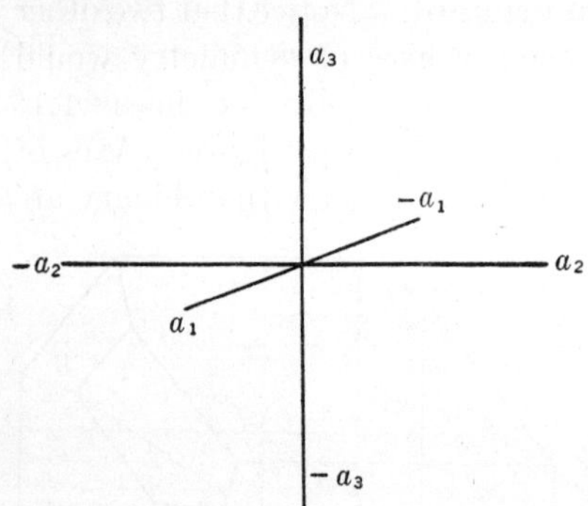

Fig. 63. Isometric (Regular) Axes.

(1) The **isometric, or regular, system** has *three axes of equal length intersecting at right angles.* Among the crystal forms in this system are the *cube,* the *octahedron,* the *dodecahedron,* and the *tetrahedron.* Diamond, gold, silver, copper, platinum, iron, galena (PbS), halite or rock salt (NaCl), cuprite (Cu_2O), garnet, pitchblende (U_3O_8), pyrite (FeS_2), and sphalerite (ZnS) are typical substances crystallizing in this system.

(2) The **tetragonal system** has *three axes at right angles, only two being equal in length* (a_1, a_2 in Figure 64). Among the crystal forms in this system are the *prism,* the *pyramid,* and the *sphenoid* (wedge). Stannite (Cu_2FeSnS_4), rutile (TiO_2), zircon ($ZrSiO_4$),

scheelite ($CaWO_4$), and chalcopyrite ($CuFeS_2$) are minerals crystallizing in the tetragonal system.

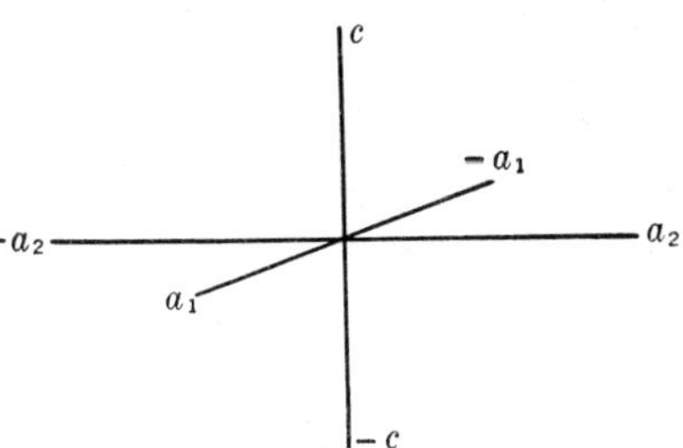

Fig. 64. Tetragonal Axes.

(3) The **hexagonal system** has *four axes, three of equal length in one plane, at angles of 60° and 120° to each other, the fourth (c) intersecting the others at right angles and being either longer or shorter.* Among the forms of this system are the *prism*, the *pyramid*, and the *rhombohedron.* Arsenic, antimony, bismuth, graphite, tellurium, molybdenite (MoS_2), beryl ($Be_3Al_2(SiO_3)_6$), corundum (Al_2O_3), hematite (Fe_2O_3), calcite ($CaCO_3$), cinnabar (HgS), and quartz (SiO_2) crystallize in the hexagonal system.

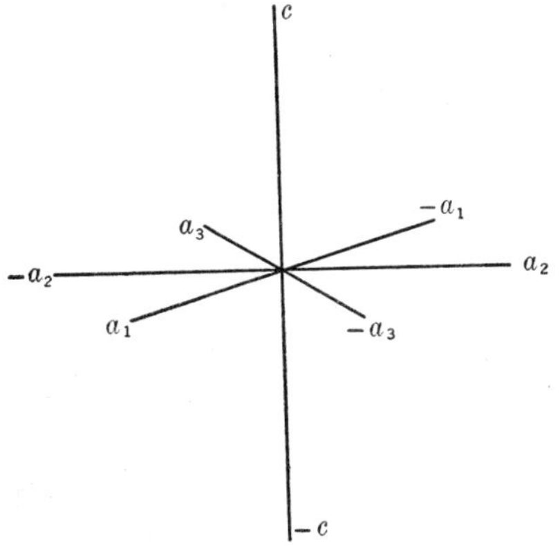

Fig. 65. Hexagonal Axes.

(4) The **orthorhombic system** has *three axes at right angles and unequal in length.* Any axis may be chosen as the vertical (*c*) axis. The *b* axis is longer than the *a* axis. *Prisms* and *pyramids* are common forms of orthorhombic crystals. Sulfur, stibnite (Sb_2S_3), pyrolusite (MnO_2), aragonite ($CaCO_3$), topaz ($(AlF{\cdot}OH)_2SiO_4$), niter (KNO_3), and anhydrite ($CaSO_4$) are minerals crystallizing in the orthorhombic system.

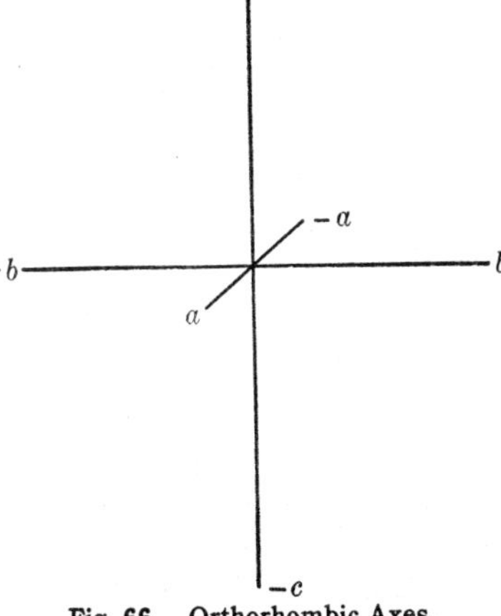

Fig. 66. Orthorhombic Axes.

(5) The **monoclinic system** has *three axes of unequal lengths, two of which (a and c) intersect at an oblique angle, while the third axis b is*

perpendicular to the plane of the other two. Monoclinic materials crystallize in *prisms* and *pyramids.* Monoclinic crystals have only one plane (a–c) of symmetry and one axis (b) of binary symmetry. Familiar minerals which crystallize in the monoclinic system are: cryolite (Na_3AlF_6), orthoclase ($KAlSi_3O_8$), borax ($Na_2B_4O_7 \cdot 10\,H_2O$), and gypsum ($CaSO_4 \cdot 2\,H_2O$).

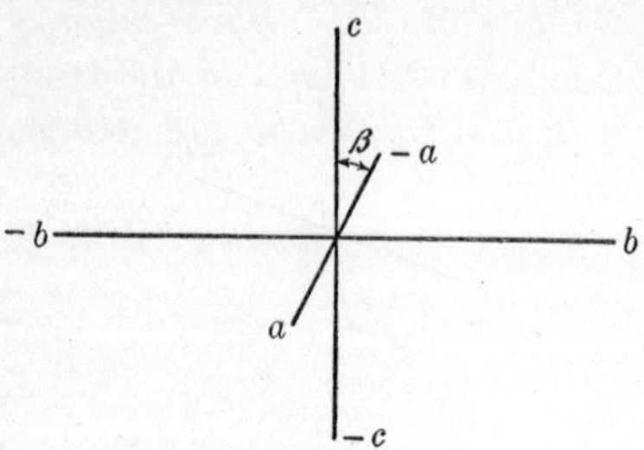

Fig. 67. Monoclinic Axes.

(6) The **triclinic system** has *three axes of unequal length, intersecting at oblique angles. Prisms* and *pyramids* are among the forms found. Triclinic crystals have a center of symmetry, but no plane or axis of symmetry. The few triclinic minerals seldom show well-developed crystals. One of these has the same composition as orthoclase ($KAlSi_3O_8$) with axial lengths and angles which are only slightly different, hence the name *microcline.*

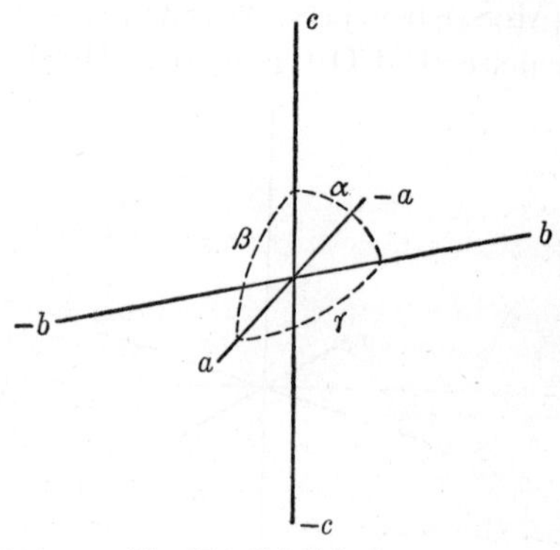

Fig. 68. Triclinic Axes.

Designation of Crystal Faces. Often there are many crystal forms in the same crystal system, and the same substance may crystallize in several different forms. Two important systems of designating the different crystal faces with reference to the crystallographic axes are *the parameters* and *the Miller indices.*

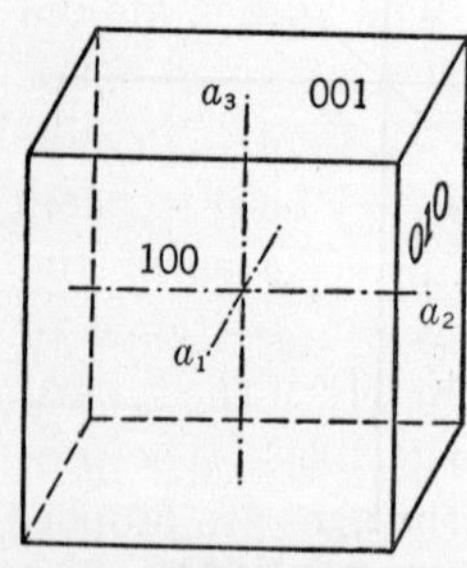

Fig. 69. Miller Indices of Cubic Faces.

(1) ***The parameters*** *of a face are the ratios of its intercepts upon the crystallographic axes, measured in terms of the corresponding unit axial lengths.* In the cube, Figure 69, each face intercepts one of the axes at equal distances from the center and is parallel to the other two, so that the intercepts would be 1, ∞, and ∞. The parameters are

always simple integers or proper fractions and most frequently are 1 or ∞.

(2) ***The Miller indices*** *of a crystal face are the integral ratios of the reciprocals of the parameters.* The Miller indices of the front face of the cube then would be 1, 0, and 0. These are written

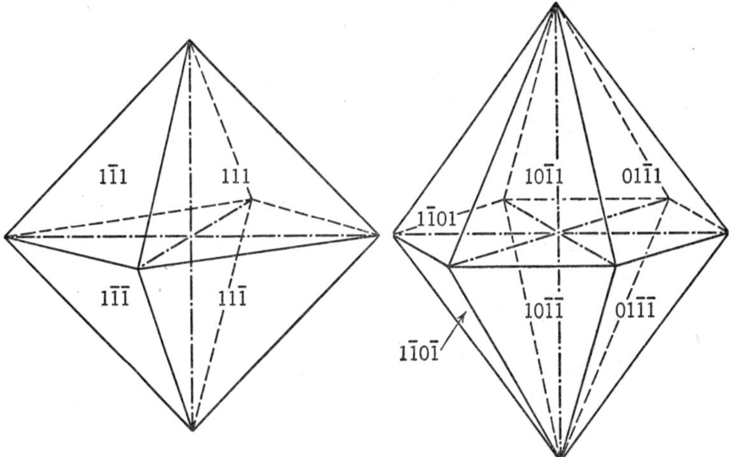

Fig. 70. **Some Miller Indices of Isometric Octahedron.**

Fig. 71. **Some Miller Indices of Hexagonal Pyramid.**

together as 100 (read *one, zero, zero*). The numbers always refer to the axes numbered a_1, a_2, and a_3 respectively in the isometric system and to other axes in alphabetical order in the other systems. The negative sign on top of a number indicates that the face cuts the negative end of the corresponding axis. The Miller indices of some of the faces of representative crystal forms are given in the figures and should be self-explanatory. Figure 72 shows a crystal typical of orthorhombic sulfur. Two pyramids, set base to base, are capped by two obtuser pyramids. The projections of the central pyramidal faces cut the axes at distances proportional to the axial lengths a, b, and c; therefore the parameters of the typical face are 1, 1, 1, and the Miller indices are written 111. The projections of the terminal pyramidal faces upon the axes are proportional to 1 a, 1 b, and $\frac{1}{2}$ c: hence the Miller indices are 221. The indices of several of the faces are given on the figure. A simple relationship always exists between the Miller indices of different faces of a crystal, and this is known as the **law of rational indices.**

The crystallographer's choice of axes and planes in describing crystals on the basis of space groups of points is arbitrary, and his only criterion is to make the indices of the principal planes as simple as possible. The actual determination of the arrangements

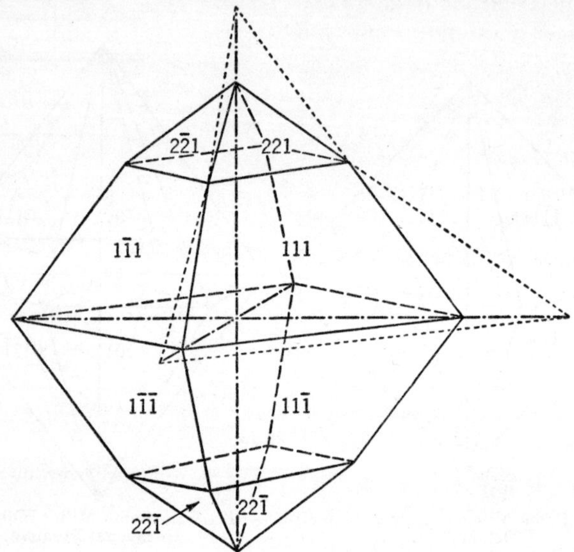

Fig. 72. Some Miller Indices of Orthorhombic Sulfur Crystal.

of atoms in the structural units depends upon X-ray methods which we shall now consider. In nearly every case, these studies have corroborated the earlier choice of axes and planes based on crystallographic data.

X-Ray Patterns and Crystal Structure

There are four principle methods of employing X rays in the study of crystal structure — Laue patterns, the X-ray spectrometer, the rotating crystal method, and the powder method. We will consider them in this order.

Laue Patterns. In 1912 M. von Laue in Munich suggested that if crystals were built up of regular arrangements of atoms in space they should diffract X rays like three-dimensional gratings. Friedrich and Knipping tested this suggestion by means of the arrangement shown in Figure 73. A fine beam of X rays is selected with the aid of two pinholes in the lead sheets *S*. This beam passes through the crystal C, where it is diffracted. The resulting pattern of spots is recorded upon the photographic plate P. If the beam of X rays passes along a crystallographic axis of the crystal, the pattern will show the symmetry around that axis. In general such a photograph will indicate the symmetry of the crystal and the way in which it is orientated, even if the external faces of the crystal are imperfect. Figure 74 illustrates the diffraction pattern of potassium chloride when the beam of X rays passes through it along one of the axes. A more complicated pattern is shown on Plate IV, facing page 164. The method may be used to analyze simple crystals; it has also been extended to complex structures, but the details are more complicated than in the case of other methods.

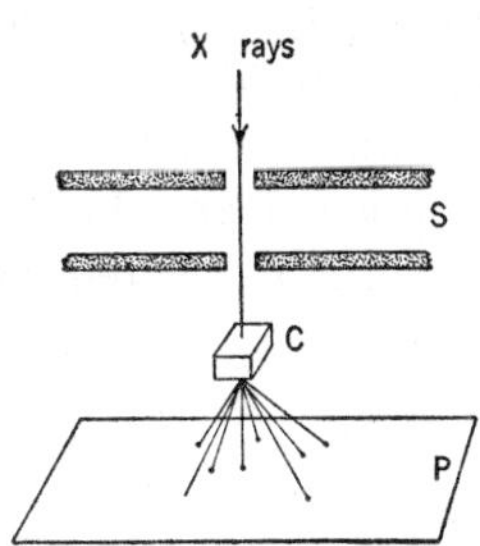

Fig. 73. Laue Diffraction Method.

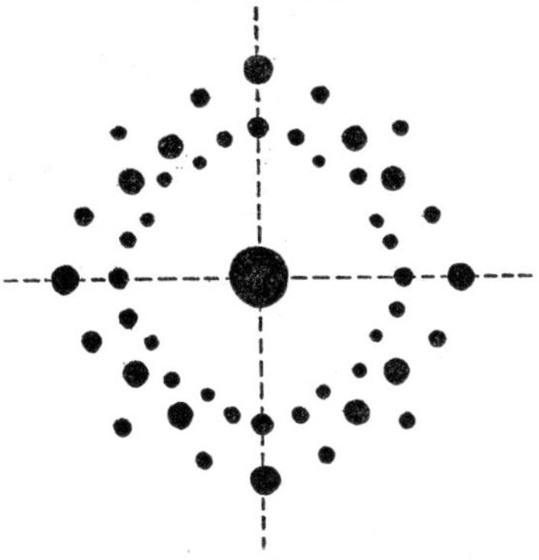

Fig. 74. Laue Pattern for KCl.

The X-ray Spectrometer. The *X-ray spectrometer* was developed by Sir W. H. Bragg, Director of the Royal Institution of Great Britain, and his son W. L. Bragg, now Director of the Cavendish Laboratory in Cambridge. Their apparatus, which is somewhat like an optical spectrometer, is illustrated in Figure 75. X rays generated in the tube T at the left are collimated by the lead slits S_1 and fall upon the crystal C, from the face of which they are "reflected" through the second slit system S_2 and pass into the ionization chamber I, which measures their intensity.

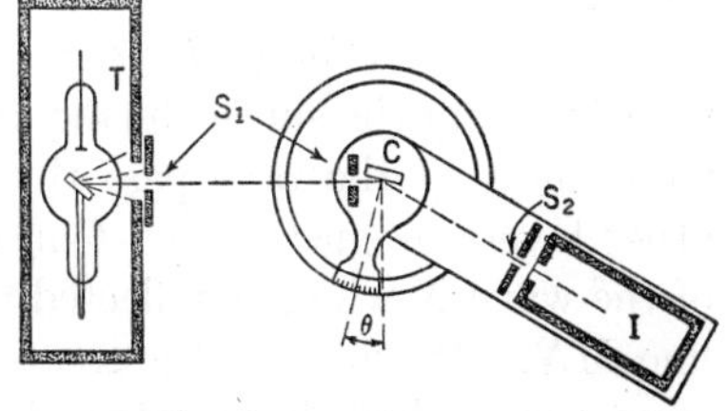

Fig. 75. Bragg X-Ray Spectrometer.

The "reflection" of X rays is not like that of light from a polished surface. Visible light is reflected almost entirely from the surface, and does not penetrate more than a few atomic layers into the interior of the material. X rays, on the other hand, are much more penetrating, as shown by their formation of Laue spots after they pass through a whole crystal. Most of the "reflection" occurs inside the crystal, from the planes of atoms contained in a thickness sometimes as great as a millimeter. This type of reflection is not greatly influenced by the surface of the crystal, but we speak of it "as reflection from the crystal face."

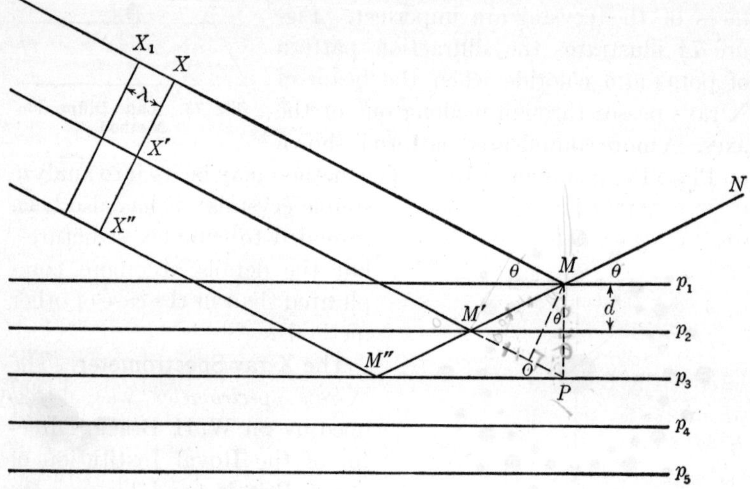

Fig. 76. X-Ray Reflection from a Crystal.

The mechanism of the reflection of X rays may be visualized by reference to Figure 76. Suppose a bundle of X rays falls obliquely upon the face of a crystal, represented by the outer plane of atoms p_1. *If the* ***incident rays*** *make an angle θ with the surface, the* ***reflected rays*** *are those which leave the crystal at the same angle with the opposite direction on the surface.* Part of the incident rays are reflected from the surface plane of atoms, p_1, in the direction MN, while most of the rays pass through and are reflected from the other layers in succession. Consider a part of the straight front of the wave X which is reflected from the plane p_2 along the same line MN. It will travel a greater distance than that part of the same wave which is reflected along MN from the surface plane. According to the well-known laws of the interaction of light waves, these will reinforce each other only if the second is one or more whole wave lengths behind the first. If this condition is not fulfilled, the waves will interfere and destroy each other. These two cases are illustrated in Figure 77. In the first case the peaks of the waves coincide and they reinforce each other; in the second case they are a half wave length apart and neutralize each other.

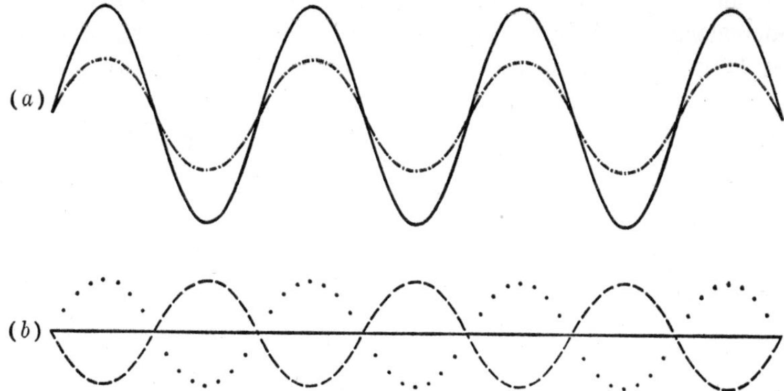

Fig. 77. Two Waves (*a*) Reinforce and (*b*) Destroy Each Other. (Original Waves Dotted and Dashed; Final Wave Full Line.)

The difference in path of the two portions of the wave is calculated easily by means of a simple geometrical construction. From M drop the line MP perpendicular to the face p_1, and extend $X'M'$ to meet p_3 in P. The triangle MPM' is isosceles because of the equality of the angles of reflection and of the distances between atomic planes. The distance $M'M$ is equal to $M'P$. Drop the perpendicular MO to $X'P$ from M. The angle OMP is equal to θ, hence $OP = MP \sin \theta$. Now $MP = 2\,d$, where d is the distance between the successive atomic planes, and OP is the difference in path of the two parts of the wave. If they are to reinforce each other, this difference must be some multiple of the wave length of the X rays, which we shall call λ. The desired relation therefore is:

$$n\lambda = 2\,d \sin \theta$$

where n is 1, 2, 3, or any integer. This is the fundamental equation of the X-ray spectrometer. For X rays of a definite wave length, a series of angles, θ_1, θ_2, etc., will give reflections corresponding to values of $n = 1$, 2, etc. These are often called the **first order spectrum,** the **second order spectrum,** etc. If the distance d between atomic planes in the crystal is known, the X-ray spectrometer can be used to determine the wave length λ of X rays. If X rays of a known wave length are used, the distance between atomic planes can be determined, and from these distances in different directions can be found the arrangement of the atoms in space.

In carrying out an experiment, the crystal is mounted in position on the table, which is set in a series of positions corresponding to increasing values of θ. The ionization chamber is set at an angle of $2\,\theta$ in each case to receive the reflected beam of X rays. The

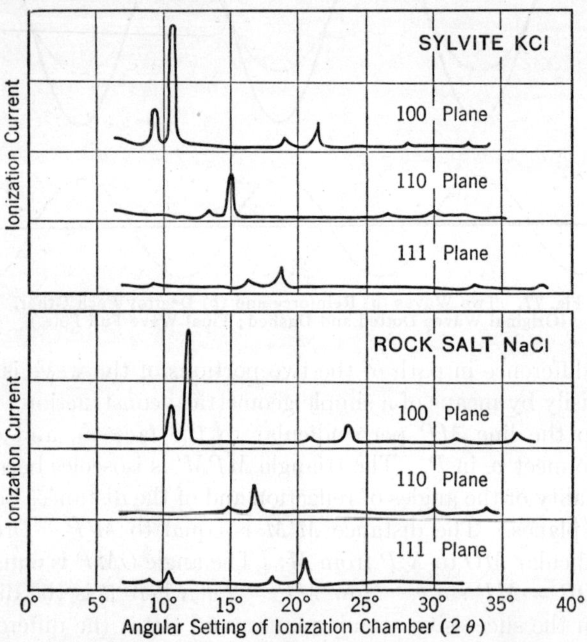

Fig. 78. Typical X-Ray Spectra. (After Bragg and Bragg, ***X Rays and Crystal Structure***, **p. 86.**)

intensity of this beam is measured directly by the current flowing through the ionization chamber. The plot of current against angle takes the form illustrated in Figure 78, showing a series of peaks. In this case the incident beam of X rays came from a palladium target, which gives two strong lines (the K_α and K_β); hence the double series of peaks on the graph. After a graph has been obtained for one reflecting plane, the crystal is turned so as to reflect from the other principal faces. Since the crystals here tested were isometric, crystallizing in cubic form, three planes were investigated — the 100, 110, and 111 planes.

Space Lattices. Consider first the case of potassium chloride. The settings of the ionization chamber corresponding to the larger of the two peaks (the K_α line) reflected from the 100 plane, divided by two, give the angle of reflection, θ. The peaks occur at values of θ of 5° 23′, 10° 49′, and 16° 20′. Since

$$\sin 5° 23' : \sin 10° 49' : \sin 16° 20' = 0.0938 : 0.1877 : 0.2812 = 1 : 2 : 3,$$

these peaks represent reflections of the first, second, and third orders from the 100 face of sylvite.

Comparing the three faces, we find that the first order reflections occur at 5° 23′, 7° 37′, and 9° 23′ respectively for the 100, 110, and 111 faces. Rearranging the fundamental equation of the X-ray spectrometer, we find that:

$$\frac{1}{d} = \frac{2 \sin \theta}{n\lambda}$$

If X rays of constant wave length are employed for a series of reflections of the same order, the ratio of the distances between reflecting atomic planes will be given by:

$$\frac{1}{d_1} : \frac{1}{d_2} : \frac{1}{d_3} = \sin \theta_1 : \sin \theta_2 : \sin \theta_3$$

In the case of the sylvite planes this gives:

$$\begin{aligned} \frac{1}{d_{100}} : \frac{1}{d_{110}} : \frac{1}{d_{111}} &= \sin 5° 23' : \sin 7° 37' : \sin 9° 23' \\ &= 0.0938 : 0.1325 : 0.1630 \\ &= 1 : 1.413 : 1.738 \\ &= 1 : \sqrt{2} : \sqrt{3} \text{ (within experimental error)} \end{aligned}$$

A comparison with Figure 79 shows that these are exactly the relationships in a simple cubic lattice. If the difference between successive 100 planes is taken as 1, that between successive 110 planes is half the diagonal across one face of the unit cube, or $\sqrt{\frac{1}{2}}$. Since DEO and DOF are similar triangles, and DE is $\sqrt{\frac{3}{2}}$:

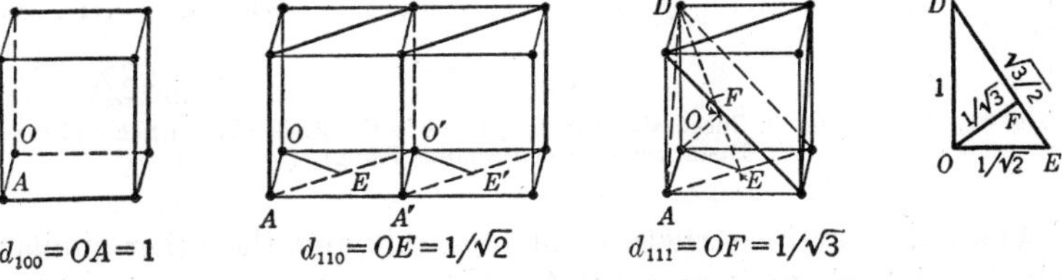

Fig. 79. Relationship between Planes in a Simple Cubic Lattice.

$$\frac{OF}{DO} = \frac{OE}{DE} \quad \text{or} \quad \frac{OF}{1} = \frac{\sqrt{\frac{1}{2}}}{\sqrt{\frac{3}{2}}}, \text{ hence } \frac{OF}{1} = \frac{1}{\sqrt{3}}$$

The relationship between the interplanar distances in a simple cubic lattice therefore is:

$$\frac{1}{d_{100}} : \frac{1}{d_{110}} : \frac{1}{d_{111}} = 1 : \sqrt{2} : \sqrt{3}$$

The experimental results for sylvite show that the K^+ and Cl^- are indistinguishable in the lattice. However, a study of the rock salt spectrum shows that it consists of alternate Na^+ and Cl^- arranged as shown in Figure 80, and hence this must be the structure of sylvite. It also is the structure of most of the alkali halides and many of the oxides, sulfides, selenides, and tellurides of the divalent metals. In this structure, which is often called the **rock salt lattice,** the 100 and 110 planes contain both kinds of atoms, while the 111 planes are made up alternately of atoms of only one kind. This causes the appearance of the extra peaks in the 111 spectrum of rock salt (near 10°). The ionic arrangement, as well as the corresponding spacings, is illustrated in Figure 81, a type of diagram often used in connection with crystal structure.

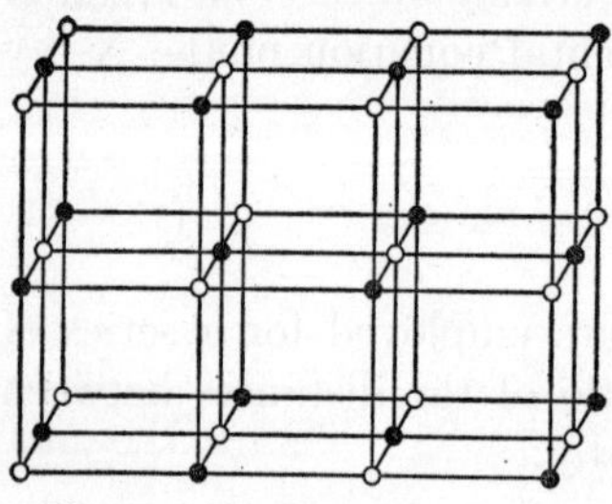

Fig. 80. The Rock Salt (NaCl) Structure.

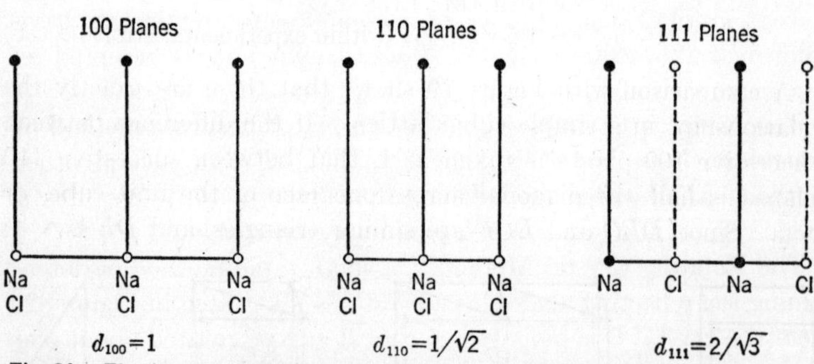

Fig. 81. The Atoms in Successive Crystal Planes in the Rock Salt Lattice and the Distances between Similar Planes.

Once the crystal structures of rock salt and the other similar alkali halides have been worked out, it is easy to determine Avogadro's number from a knowledge of the actual interionic distances and the densities of the salts. Referring to Figure 80, we see that the unit of the sodium chloride crystal is a cube containing four sodium atoms and four chlorine atoms on alternate corners. The points represent merely the *centers* of the atoms; only one eighth of each atom falls within the unit cube, while the rest is contained in the seven other cubes which adjoin each corner. Each unit cube therefore contains $\frac{4}{8}$ or $\frac{1}{2}$ an atom of sodium and the same amount of chlorine. The volume of the unit cube is simply $(d_{100})^3$. One molecular weight of sodium chloride will contain N atoms of *each* element, in the atomic volume V, which is equal to the molecular weight divided by the density, hence:

$$2\,N(d_{100})^3 = V \qquad \text{or} \qquad N = \frac{V}{2(d_{100})^3}$$

The wave lengths of some of the characteristic X rays have been determined by means of fine ruled gratings, and these X rays have been used to find the spacing in the salt crystals. Thus in the unit cube of potassium chloride at 18° C., $d_{100} = 3.14541 \times 10^{-8}$ cm. The density of the solid at the same temperature was found to be 1.98930 g. $\times$ cm^{-3}. Since the molecular weight is 74.553 g. $\times$ mole^{-1}, the corresponding value of Avogadro's number is:

$$N = \frac{74.553}{2 \times 1.98930 \times (3.14541 \times 10^{-8})^3} = 6.0215 \times 10^{23}$$

Recent studies[1] of a number of different salts and metals have confirmed the value of 6.023×10^{23}, which now is accepted as Avogadro's number.

The X-ray spectrometer provides the most accurate method of crystal analysis, but it is more complicated than several other methods which often are adequate. Furthermore, it requires a single crystal of a size which is not always available.

The Rotating Crystal Method. A more rapid method of determining the reflecting angles for a crystal is illustrated in Figure 82. Here the crystal C is mounted so that it can be rotated about one of its axes. As in the case of the X-ray spectrometer, reflections will occur at certain angles, and these will register upon the photographic film F which is bent in the form of an arc of a circle about C

[1] Miller and DuMond, *Phys. Rev.*, **57**, 198 (1940), give a résumé of this work.

as center. The positions of the lines on the film indicate *twice* the angles of reflection from the crystal, and the blackening of the film is a measure of their intensity. This method requires very long exposures but much fewer individual measurements than the readings of the ionization chamber in the X-ray spectrometer.

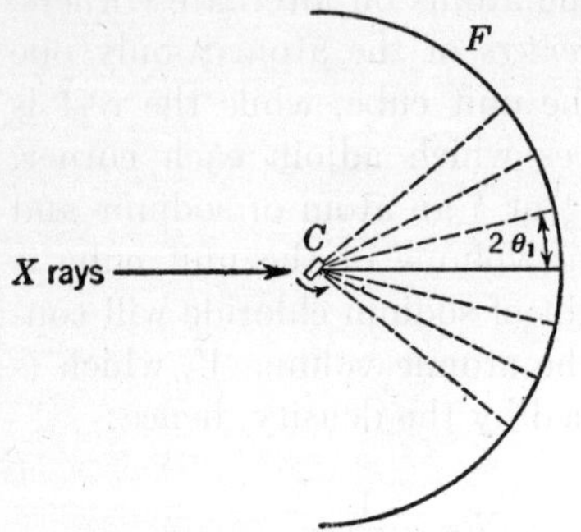

Fig. 82. Rotating Crystal Method of Crystal Analysis.

The Powder Method. In 1916 Debye and Scherrer, at the Technische Hochschule in Zurich, devised a method of analyzing the structure of crystalline powders, which was developed independently by A. W. Hull, of the General Electric Company in this country in 1917. A beam of monochromatic X rays falls upon the crystalline powder P (Figure 83). The powder contains so many different small crystals arranged at random, that it presents all possible orientations of the crystal faces to the beam of X rays. Those faces which lie at exactly the correct angle to the beam of X rays will reflect it at an angle θ given by the usual relationship:

$$\sin\theta = \frac{\lambda}{2\,d}$$

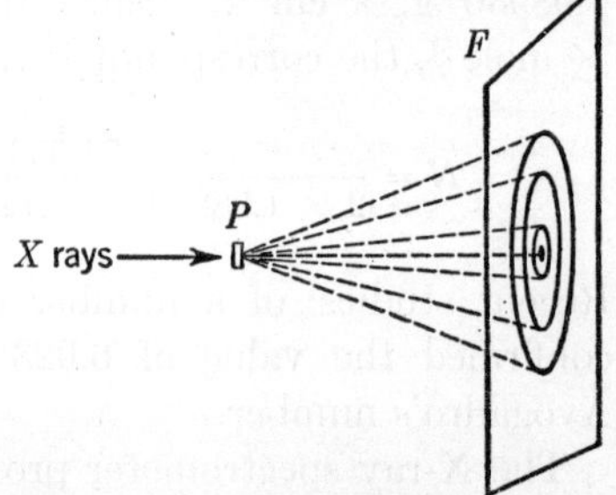

Fig. 83. Diffraction Cones from Crystalline Powders.

Those rays which are reflected at the same angle to the incident beam will fall upon a *cone* having this beam as axis. Rays reflected at a greater angle will fall along a broader cone. The reflected beams are recorded upon a photographic film F, which may be flat, as in Figure 83. This arrangement gives the type of photograph illustrated by Plate IV, facing page 164. Where additional lines, corresponding to the higher order reflections, are desired, the film is bent in the form of a nearly complete circle around P as center (Figure 84 *a*). After an exposure of adequate duration, the film is developed and, when spread out flat, has the appearance of Figure 84 *b* and Plate V, facing page 180. Although

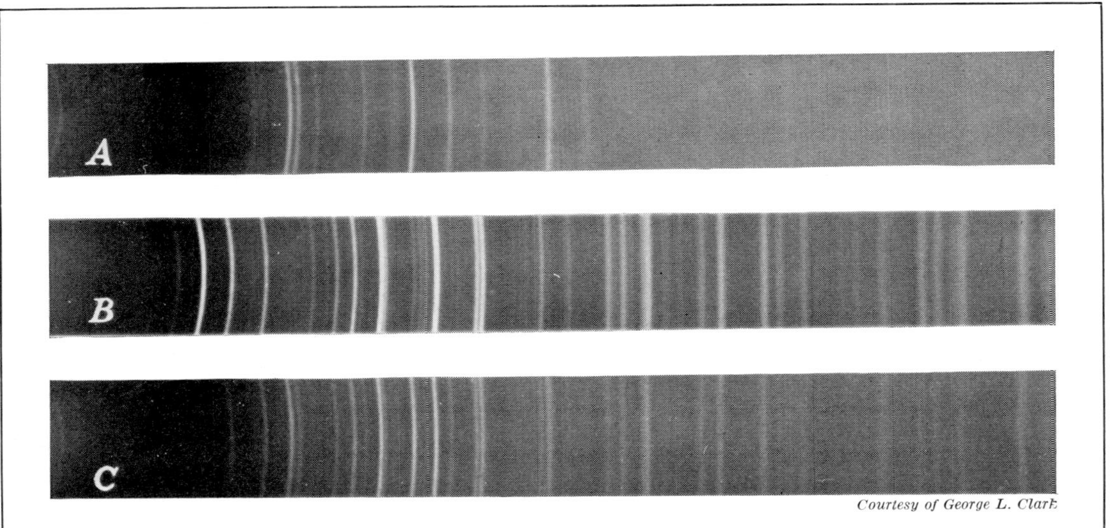

Courtesy of George L. Clark

facing page 180

Plate V. POWDER X–RAY PHOTOGRAPHS WITH CIRCULAR FILM

(A) PbI_2 (B) PbO (C) PbI_2 and PbO in equal amounts.

the method is not applicable to very complicated structures, it is particularly useful in comparing similar crystalline compounds and determining the *relative spacing* with great accuracy.

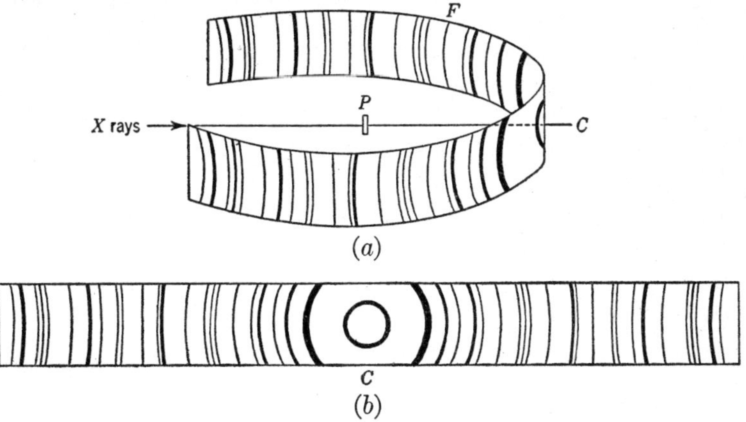

Fig. 84. Film Showing Powder Pattern for NaCl.

Crystal Structure of Some Common Substances. The unit cells of some of the relatively simple crystal lattices in which all of the elements and most simple chemical compounds are found to arrange themselves are given in Figures 85–95.

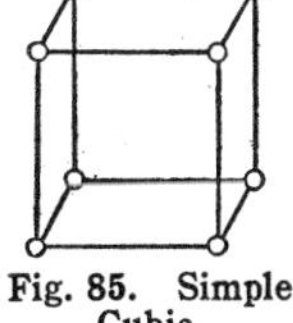

Fig. 85. Simple Cubic.

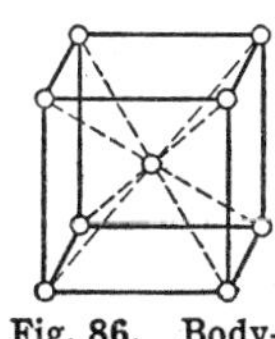

Fig. 86. Body-Centered Cubic.

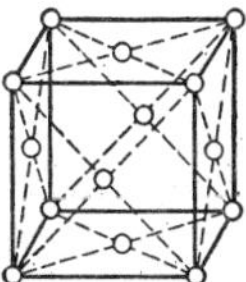

Fig. 87. Face-Centered Cubic.

The **simple cubic, body-centered cubic,** and **face-centered cubic** lattices are three of the simplest possible arrangements.

The **cesium chloride type** of lattice is a body-centered cubic, in which the eight atoms of one kind are arranged at the corners of the cube and the atoms of the other kind are in the center. Each kind of atom by itself forms a simple cubic lattice. The unit cube contains eight atoms of one kind, and only one of the other kind. This is not in conflict with the chemical formula for the compound, since the central atom belongs wholly to the cube, while only $\frac{1}{8}$ of each of the 8 corner atoms lies within the unit cube. The number of

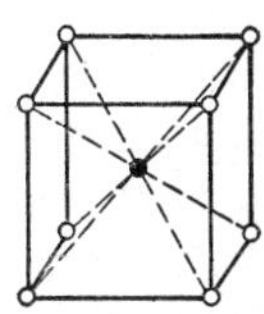

Fig. 88. CsCl Type.

atomic centers in the unit cell has nothing to do with the number of atoms of each element in the molecular formula, but the number of *whole atoms* of each within the boundary of the cell always is proportional to the number in the molecular formula.

The **cuprite (Cu_2O) lattice** consists of a body-centered cubic arrangement of the oxygen atoms, with the copper atoms at the alternate points of the diagonals, half-way between the center and the corners. The copper atoms therefore form a face-centered cubic lattice, in which each atom is equidistant from two oxygen atoms. If the adjacent copper and oxygen atoms are joined, they are found to make up *two* interpenetrating lattices which are independent of each other and not connected in any way. The heavy dashed lines in the figure connect the adjacent atoms in the unit cell, and an extension of the figure will show that this lattice is continued in the adjacent cells, while the four other oxygen atoms in the unit cell form part of the other lattice.

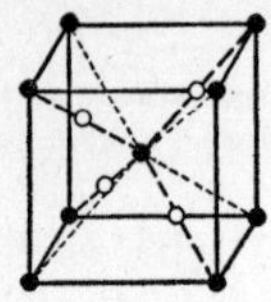

Fig. 89. Cuprite (Cu_2O) Type.

The **blende (ZnS) type** of crystal, one of the first to be analyzed by the Braggs, consists of two identical interpenetrating face-centered cubic lattices, in which each atom is equidistant from four of the other kind. The diamond is built along exactly the same pattern, except that a carbon atom is found at each point in the lattice.

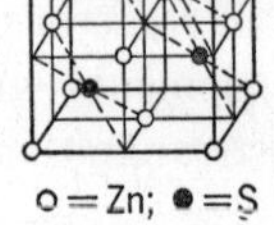

Fig. 90. Blende (ZnS) Type.

In the **fluor (CaF_2) lattice,** the calcium atoms form a face-centered cubic structure, while the fluorine atoms, at the centers of each of the eight small cubes, make up a simple cubic lattice. Each calcium atom is at the center of *eight* neighboring equidistant fluorine atoms, while each fluorine atom is surrounded by *four* equidistant calcium atoms. This is an extension of the zinc sulfide lattice to take in two fluorine atoms instead of one sulfur.

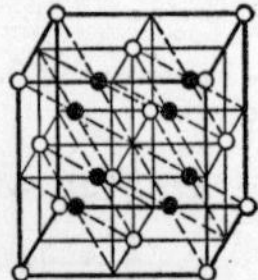

Fig. 91. Fluor (CaF_2) Type.

The **rutile (TiO_2) type** of lattice is tetragonal. The eight titanium atoms lie at the corners of a rectangular prism, while a ninth lies in the center of the prism, surrounded by six oxygen atoms approximately at the corners of

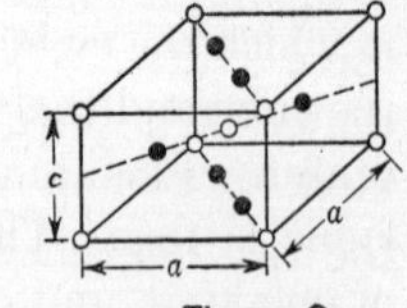

Fig. 92. Rutile (TiO_2) Type.

a regular octahedron. A continuation of the structure would show that this is true of *every* titanium atom. Every oxygen atom is surrounded by three titanium atoms, lying approximately at the corners of equilateral triangles. In the case of rutile itself, the height c is 2.95 Å., while the a axes are each 4.58 Å. Other distances are characteristic of other substances crystallizing in the same system.

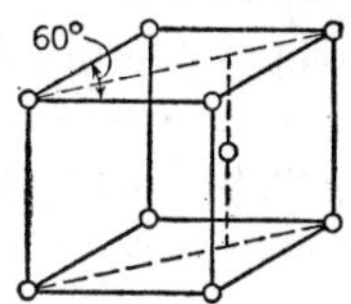

Fig. 93. Hexagonal Close-Packed.

In the **hexagonal close-packed lattice,** eight of the atoms are arranged at the corners of a rhombic prism, the sides of which make angles of 60 and 120° with each other. The ninth atom is halfway between the rhombic planes, on a perpendicular to the bisector of the 60° angles, erected one third of the distance from one edge of the prism, as shown. This lattice represents the closest way in which spheres can be packed, and is the form in which many metals crystallize.

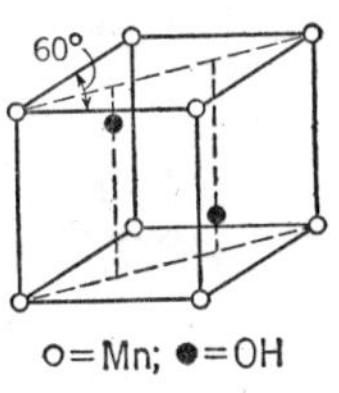

Fig. 94. Mn $(OH)_2$ Type.

The **manganous hydroxide structure** is a hexagonal arrangement in which the two hydroxyl groups are arranged as shown within the rhombic prism. The hydroxyl group is very little larger than the oxygen. The position of hydrogen cannot be determined since it is too light an element and has too few electrons to affect X rays.

The **zincite structure** is a more complicated hexagonal arrangement. The zinc atoms alone approximate a hexagonal close-packed lattice, while the oxygen atoms form a similar lattice which interpenetrates the first. The rhombic planes are alternately zinc and oxygen atoms, and one additional atom of each is arranged on a central axis, perpendicular to these planes. Each atom lies nearly at the center of a tetrahedron of atoms of the other kind. The four neighboring atoms surrounding the two interior atoms in the unit cell are connected to them by dotted lines, to indicate this tetrahedral arrangement.

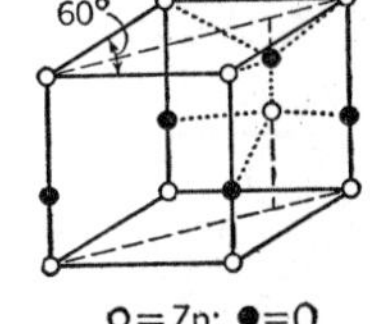

Fig. 95. Zincite (ZnO) Type.

Crystal Forms and Crystal Forces. Crystals may be classified according to the type of unit of which they are composed, and the way these units are held together. The following are the types:

(1) **Atomic lattices.** The unit of such a structure is the atom, and the bonds which hold it together are covalent. Relatively few atomic lattices are known. The best example is the diamond, which crystallizes in a lattice of the blende type, in which each atom is surrounded by four others lying at the corners of a regular tetrahedron. This relationship is more clearly evident if we turn the crystal over on to its 111 plane and draw not the cubic lattice lines, but the lines connecting the neighboring atoms, as in Figure 96 (*a*). These lines evidently correspond with the directions of the

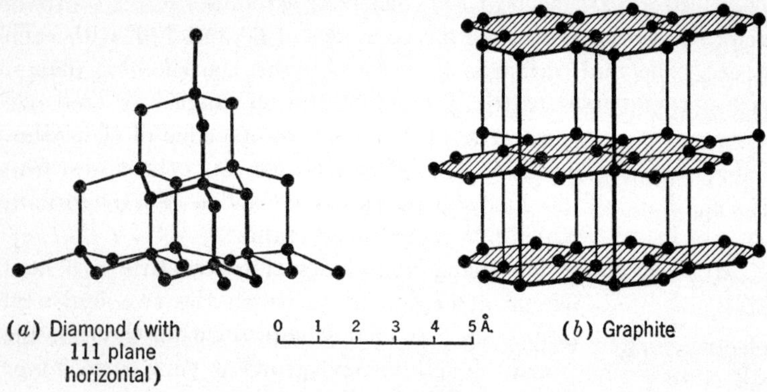

Fig. 96. Comparison of the Structures of Diamond and Graphite.

valence bonds in space. The bonds are covalent as in the case of typical organic compounds. The X-ray patterns from diamond show unusual regularity in the atomic arrangement throughout the whole crystal. The strength of the covalent bonds and the closeness of the atoms, 1.54 Å., account for the great hardness of the diamond and for its very high melting point. The same type of structure is found also in the related elements silicon, germanium, and gray tin, and probably in silicon carbide.

(2) **Molecular lattices** are those in which the forces holding together the atoms in the molecule are much stronger than those holding the molecules together in the lattice. The halogens, each of which has seven electrons to the atom in the valence shell, share electrons to complete their octets, and form stable double molecules which exist in the crystal. Elements of the sixth group in the periodic table, with six valence electrons, form chains in which each atom is linked to two of its neighbors by covalent bonds. In sulfur the arrangement is:

$$\cdot\ddot{\underset{\cdot\cdot}{S}}:\ddot{\underset{\cdot\cdot}{S}}:\ddot{\underset{\cdot\cdot}{S}}:\ddot{\underset{\cdot\cdot}{S}}:\ddot{\underset{\cdot\cdot}{S}}\cdot$$

Closed units, S_8, formed by the union of the atoms at the ends of the chain, are found in rhombic sulfur. In other cases chains or sheets of atoms may be formed, and these are bound less firmly into **chain** or **layer lattices.** Graphite is one of the most interesting of these, because of the difference in its properties from those of diamond. The structure of graphite is very similar to that of diamond, as Figure 96 (*b*) shows. The atoms in the horizontal sheets appear to be coplanar, each surrounded by three neighbors at a distance of 1.42 Å. This is less than the spacing in diamond, but the planes themselves are separated by 3.40 Å., over twice the atomic distance in diamond. The very easy cleavage of graphite is parallel to these planes. Graphite is unusual in having a combination of the atomic lattice and the molecular layer lattice.

(3) **Ionic lattices.** According to our ideas of valence, electrovalent compounds are formed by the transfer of an electron from the metallic to the nonmetallic atom and therefore should form *ionic lattices*. The properties of these lattices bear out this supposition, although X-ray data do not allow us to distinguish with certainty between ions and atoms in crystals. Salts conduct the electric current when fused, yield conducting solutions when dissolved in water, and give other indications of being made up of ions. The form in which these salts crystallize depends upon the charges of the ions and their relative sizes. A comparison of the distances between the centers of the ions in a series of salts of the same type shows that we may consider each ion as a sphere of approximately constant radius. If the radius of any one ion is known, all the others can be calculated. Wasastjerna has calculated a number of ionic radii from a study of molecular refraction, and his results have been corroborated independently. Taking his value of 1.33 Å. for the fluoride ion and 1.32 Å. for the oxide, the radii of a number of the other ions have been calculated. Representative values are collected in Table 31.

(4) **In semi-ionic lattices** the bonds are intermediate between the pure electrovalent and covalent types. Such a bond arises if the pair of electrons is not shared uniformly between the atoms but on the average spends more time near one atom than the other. The pure electrostatic bond changes to this intermediate type if the cation is *small*, with a high ionizing potential, while the anion is *large*, with a low electron affinity. The small anions F^- and O^{--}, with high electron affinity, usually enter into ionic lattices, as do

TABLE 31

Some Ionic Radii in Salts

(In angströms)

6	7	0	1	2	3	4
		He	Li 0.78	Be 0.34		
O 1.32	F 1.33	Ne	Na 0.98	Mg 0.78	Al 0.57	Si 0.39
S 1.74	Cl 1.81	A	K 1.33	Ca 1.06	Sc 0.83	Ti 0.64
Se 1.91	Br 1.95	Kr	Rb 1.49	Sr 1.27	Y 1.06	Zr 0.87
Te 2.11	I 2.20	X	Cs 1.65	Ba 1.43	La 1.22	Ce 1.02

From *Atomic Structure of Minerals*, by W. L. Bragg, Cornell University Press, Ithaca, N. Y., 1937.

the alkali and alkaline earth metals. Larger anions, such as I^-, S^{--}, and Se^{--}, and metals of the transition groups, like Zn and Cd, which form small, high-valent ions, tend to form semi-ionic lattices, in which the atoms are usually closer together than in the truly ionic, and the bonds tend to be directional in character. In the metallic elements of the B subgroups in the periodic table, there is a marked tendency for a tetrahedral arrangement of the valence bonds in crystals. This appears in the blende type of crystal, which is semi-ionic and typical of this type of compound.

(5) The metallic lattice, like the ionic, consists of ions, but these are all positive. The negative particles are valence electrons, which are not held rigidly in place, but are more or less free to move in the lattice, thus carrying the electric current much more easily than the electrons in nonmetals. The true metals crystallize in very simple lattices. Only among the metalloids do more complicated structures appear, in which the bonding, like that in a semi-ionic lattice, is intermediate between the metallic and the atomic or molecular.

The alkali metals all crystallize in the body-centered cubic structure. If we consider the atoms as spheres, this represents a rather loose type of packing, since each sphere touches only eight of its neighbors, leaving large spaces between, as shown in Figure 97. Few other metals crystallize in this arrangement. More are found in the denser face-centered cubic or hexagonal close-packed lattices, in which each sphere touches 12 of its neighbors. The spheres are arranged at the corners of equilateral triangles in the diagonal 111 planes of the face-centered cubic structure, and in the 0001 planes of the hexagonal close-packed. The only difference is that the arrangement is repeated in every *third* layer of the cubic structure and in *alternate* layers of the hexagonal, as shown in Figures 98 and 99.

Fig. 97. Body-centered Cubic Packing of Equal Spheres.

Isomorphism. *Two substances are said to be* ***isomorphous*** *when they are of the same crystal form.* Isomorphous substances usually will form mixed crystals — homogeneous crystalline solids containing the constituents in variable proportions. If the solubilities of the two substances are quite different, mixed crystals may not be formed, but the more soluble substance will deposit from a supersaturated solution upon a crystal of the other substance, and thus will overgrow it. In 1819 Mitscherlich studied

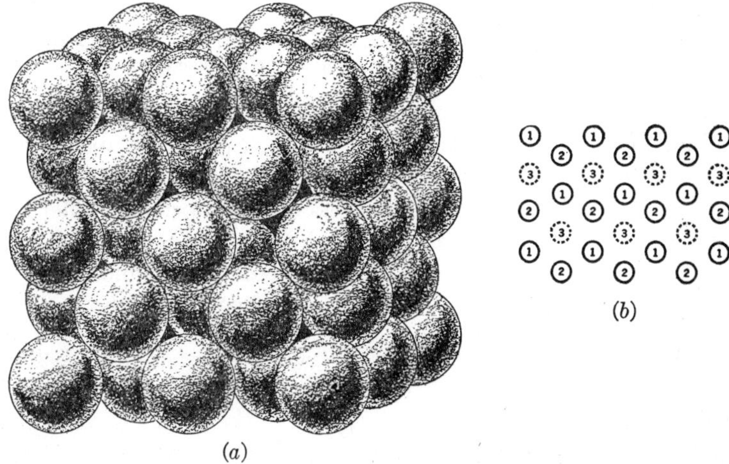

Fig. 98. (*a*) Face-centered Cubic Packing of Equal Spheres. (*b*) The Pattern of Atomic Centers in Successive Layers Parallel to the 111 Plane.

the isomorphism of a number of salts and concluded that isomorphous substances were built on the same molecular pattern — *e.g.*, K_2SO_4 and K_2SeO_4, or Na_3PO_4 and Na_3AsO_4. The atomic weights of a number of elements were deduced from their equivalent weights and a comparison of their compounds with isomorphous compounds of known composition.

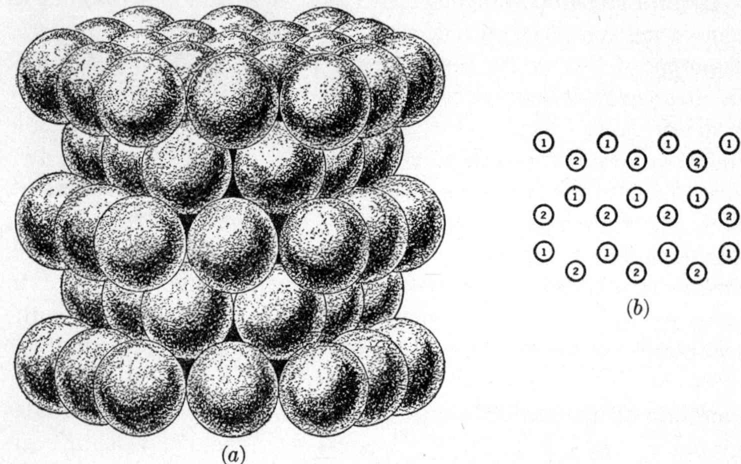

Fig. 99. **(*a*) Hexagonal Close-Packing of Equal Spheres. (*b*) The Pattern of Atomic Centers in Alternate Layers Perpendicular to Hexagonal Axis.**

Chemical similarity is not, however, a necessary or sufficient explanation of isomorphism. Some salts, *e.g.*, NaCl and KCl, although they both form cubic crystals, do not deposit together as mixed crystals. Moreover, many isomorphous substances differ in chemical composition — *e.g.*, NaF and MgO, $CaCl_2$ and K_2S, or $NaNO_3$ and $CaCO_3$. In 1919 Langmuir used the electronic theory of valence to show that the electronic arrangements in the *ions* of the two pairs of salts are identical:

$$\underset{2,8}{Na^+}\underset{2,8}{F^-} \quad \text{and} \quad \underset{2,8}{Mg^{++}}\underset{2,8}{O^{--}}$$

$$\underset{2,8,8}{Cl^-}\ \underset{2,8,8}{Ca^{++}}\ \underset{2,8,8}{Cl^-} \quad \text{and} \quad \underset{2,8,8}{K^+}\ \underset{2,8,8}{S^{--}}\ \underset{2,8,8}{K^+}$$

X-ray studies of crystal structure have shown that substances will be isomorphous (1) *if their formulas are of the same type*, (2) *if the units of structure are within 10 or 15 per cent of the same size, and* (3) *if they are held together by the same type of valence bond.* The difference in valence does not affect the crystal arrangement. As we might expect, careful measurements of crystal angles and arrangement show slight differences between two isomorphous substances and in the series of mixed crystals which they form. These, however, are too small to disturb the general crystalline arrangement.

Polymorphism. Many elements and compounds are found in more than one crystalline form. *Such substances are said to be* ***dimorphous*** *if they exist in two forms and* ***polymorphous*** *if they exist in several modifications.* Carbon existing as diamond and graphite is dimorphous. So is sulfur, which occurs in nature in a rhombic form and also can be obtained in monoclinic crystals. These two crystalline forms change into each other reversibly at a temperature of 95.6° C. Above this temperature the monoclinic form is stable, and below it the rhombic. Two such crystalline forms which change into each other *reversibly* are said to be **enantiotropic.** In the case of carbon no such reversibility can be realized in the laboratory. Diamond has been changed into graphite, but the opposite change has not been achieved. Carbon, therefore, is considered **monotropic,** with only one stable modification — graphite. Among common dimorphous minerals, calcium carbonate usually crystallizes in the hexagonal system as *calcite,* with a density of 2.71, but also is found in the rhombic form of *aragonite,* with a density of 2.92. Aragonite may be transformed into calcite at temperatures above 400° C. Calcite is the stable modification at ordinary temperatures and pressures.

Some Applications of X-ray Analysis. X-ray analysis has been applied to many problems, as diverse as the arrangement of metallic ions in alloys and that of the constituent atoms in organic molecules. The analysis of organic crystals is much more difficult than that of minerals because the light carbon, oxygen, and nitrogen atoms do not diffract X rays nearly so much as do the heavier metals, while the hydrogen atom does not affect the passage of X rays at all. Nevertheless, it has been possible to determine the positions of the atoms of carbon, nitrogen, and oxygen and to infer that of hydrogen in many of these organic compounds.

A study of paraffins and other *aliphatic* molecules shows that they are built upon the diamond pattern — that is, the carbon atoms in the chain are joined in a tetrahedral arrangement, as shown in Figure 100. The successive atoms are 1.54 Å. apart, and if the valence bonds make the tetrahedral angle of 109° 28′, alternate atoms should be 2.52 Å. apart in straight lines. This is verified by the observed separation of 2.54 Å. between these atoms. The distances between doubly bonded carbon atoms (1.34 Å.) and between triply bonded carbon atoms (1.20 Å.) are appreciably less than that between singly bonded ones.

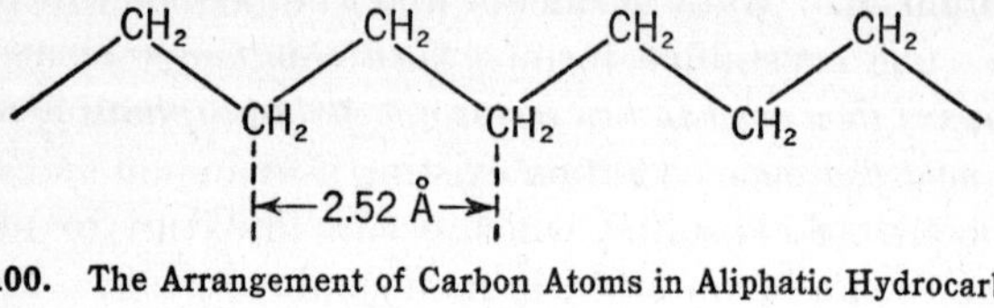

CH_2 CH_2 CH_2 CH_2

CH_2 CH_2 CH_2

←2.52 Å→

Fig. 100. The Arrangement of Carbon Atoms in Aliphatic Hydrocarbons.

Benzene, naphthalene, and other *aromatic* compounds, on the other hand, are built upon the plan of graphite, in flat six-membered rings with neighboring atoms 1.39 Å. apart. The results of these studies therefore corroborate the structures deduced from the reactions of organic compounds. The observed distances in graphite and in the aromatic compounds indicate that these bonds are intermediate between double and single bonds — in fact, that the actual structure resonates between the two forms. In benzoquinone, two carbon-carbon distances of 1.50 and 1.32 Å. respectively, are found. These correspond to the C—C and C═C distances, respectively, and bear out the structural formula usually assigned to this compound, *viz.:*

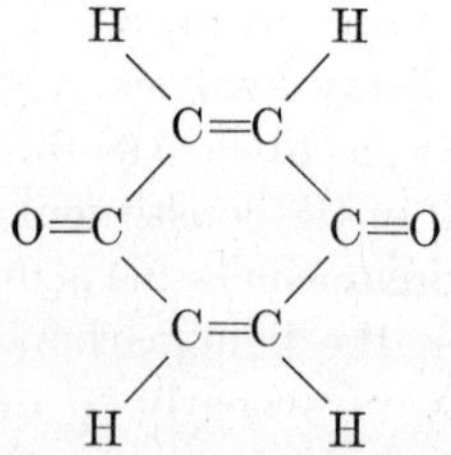

```
      H       H
       \     /
        C═C
       /     \
  O═C         C═O
       \     /
        C═C
       /     \
      H       H
```

In organic crystals, the units are the molecules, within which the distances are those indicated above. The forces acting between the molecules are very much less than between atoms or ions, and the distances are correspondingly greater. The distance between adjacent carbon atoms in different molecules varies between 3.6 and 3.9 Å., which is very little more than the 3.40 Å. separating the layers in graphite.

X-ray studies have helped greatly to explain the structure of fibers, which are so important in the vegetable and animal kingdoms. Cellulose (which forms a large part of wood and plant structure in general), silk, and wool are natural fibers. All fibers are made up of threadlike units, visible under the microscope and arranged more or less parallel to each other. This suggests that the structural units are long *chains*, which may be considered giant molecules. The chemical disintegration of these fibers usually yields simpler molecules, which may have been combined in the fibers by an anhydride structure.

X-ray investigation has shown that fibers give a type of diffraction pattern like that of crystals rotated around an axis, so that the crystal planes perpendicular to the axis of rotation are arranged at all angles, while those parallel to the axis are unchanged. In the fiber the axis is lengthwise and the sharpness of the diffraction pattern is an indication of the alignment of the small crystallite units. *X-ray studies then indicate that the fundamental units in fibers are long chain molecules with definite crystalline structure, arranged more or less exactly parallel to each other.*

Silk and wool are protein fibers, which can be hydrolized to yield a mixture of α-amino acids, the general formula of which is:

$$\begin{array}{c} \mathrm{H} \\ | \\ \mathrm{H_2N—C—COOH} \\ | \\ \mathrm{R} \end{array}$$

where R stands for any univalent organic radical. At the beginning of this century, Emil Fischer showed that these amino acids can combine to form long chains by the elimination of water between carboxyl and amino groups on adjacent molecules, thus:

$$\mathrm{H_2N—\underset{\displaystyle R}{\overset{\displaystyle H}{C}}—CO\boxed{OH + H}NH—\underset{\displaystyle R'}{\overset{\displaystyle H}{C}}—COOH} \longrightarrow$$

$$\mathrm{H_2N—\underset{\displaystyle R}{\overset{\displaystyle H}{C}}—CO—NH—\underset{\displaystyle R'}{\overset{\displaystyle H}{C}}—COOH}$$

The group —CO—NH— is called the **peptide linkage** and is considered characteristic of all proteins. If the protein chain is formed with the usual tetrahedral angle between the adjacent C—C bonds and also between C—N bonds, and if the bonds are

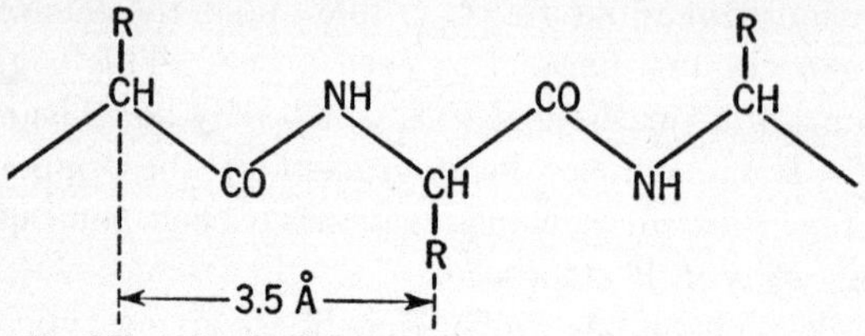

Fig. 101. The Probable Constitution of a Protein Chain.

1.54 Å. and 1.37 Å. long respectively, the side chains (*R* groups) in a protein chain should project from alternate sides at a distance of 3.5 Å., as shown in Figure 101. Silk is made up of the protein *fibroin*, which apparently consists chiefly of alternate residues of the two simplest amino acids, glycine and alanine, the formulas for which are respectively:

$$H_2N\text{—}\overset{\displaystyle H}{\underset{\displaystyle H}{C}}\text{—}COOH \qquad \text{and} \qquad H_2N\text{—}\overset{\displaystyle CH_3}{\underset{\displaystyle H}{C}}\text{—}COOH$$

X-ray studies show that these are joined as shown in Figure 102 into long chains in which the —NH— groups are separated by distances of 3.5 Å., while the chain repeats itself at intervals of 7.0 Å.

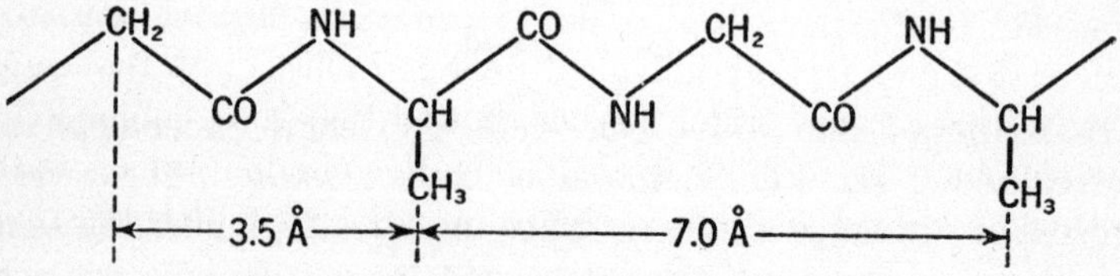

Fig. 102. The Probable Constitution of Fibroin.

In wool, the amino acids entering into the chains are more complex than in silk, with longer side-chains. The structure is repeated at distances of 5.1 Å. along the wool fiber axis, which indicates that the chain in unstretched wool is *folded* as shown in Figure 103. The crystalline substance in unstretched wool is known as *α-keratin*. When the fiber is stretched, this is changed into *β-keratin*, in which the pattern repeats itself every 7.0 Å. along the fiber axis, as in fibroin. However, the distance between groups which occupy identical positions in the α-keratin structure becomes 10.2 Å. in the β-keratin structure. This is illustrated for the two

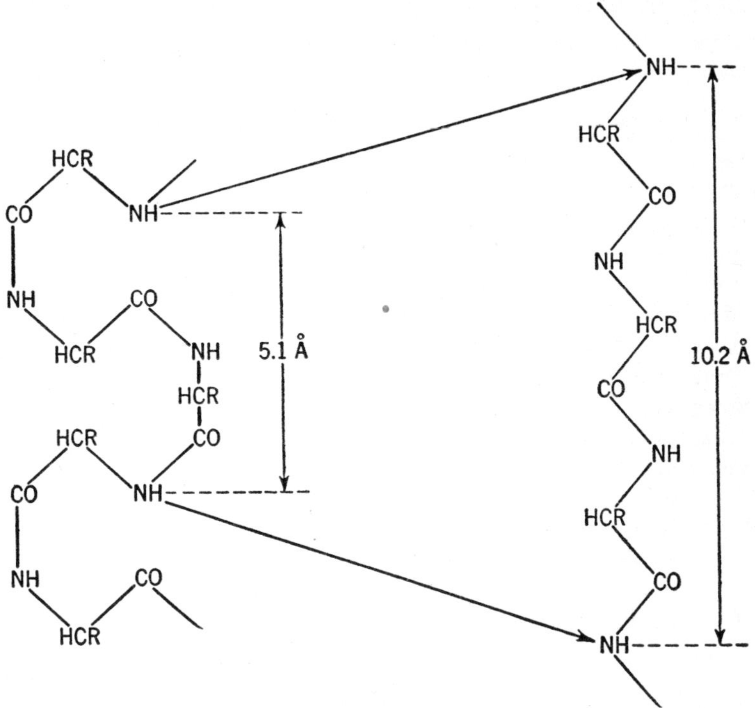

Fig. 103. The Probable Relation between Unstretched and Stretched Molecular Chains in Wool.

NH groups in Figure 103. This doubling in length under a pull can be realized if the wool is immersed in hot water. The reverse process of shrinkage also takes place most readily under the same conditions — a fact readily appreciated by anyone who has ever tried to don a pair of woolen socks which had been washed in hot water.

PROBLEMS AND EXERCISES

1. Outline three methods of determining the density of a solid, explaining the theory of each and its advantages and disadvantages.

2. A rectangular piece of brass 155 mm. long, 13 mm. wide, and 5.7 mm. high is found to weigh 96.5 g. What is the density of the brass?

3. A sample of aluminum weighs 42.35 g. in air and 26.75 g. in water at 20° C. Calculate its density.

***4.** Assuming that King Hiero's crown contained only gold and silver and weighed 5.89 per cent less in water at 20° C. than in air, what per cent of silver did it contain? The specific gravity of gold is 19.3 and that of silver is 10.6. Assume that the density of each metal is the same in the alloy as in the pure element.

***5.** A piece of beeswax weighs 10.47 g. in air. When tied to a lead sinker weighing 4.35 g. and submerged under water, the system weighs 3.61 g. If the density of lead is 11.35 g./ml., what is the density of beeswax?

6. A certain density bottle weighs 17.520 g. empty and 37.882 g. filled with water at 25° C. When 9.947 g. of glycolamide, $CH_2OH \cdot CONH_2$, are put into this bottle, 9.009 g. of *n*-heptane are required to fill it. If the density of water is 0.9971 g./ml. and that of *n*-heptane is 0.6794 g./ml. at 25° C., calculate the density of glycolamide at the same temperature.

7. A sample of Pyrex glass weighed 49.229 g. in air and 27.234 g. in water at 25° C. Calculate its density.

8. In determining the density of urea at 25° C., the following data were obtained:

Weight of density bottle filled with *n*-heptane .	31.3940 g.
Weight of empty bottle	17.5194 g.
Weight of bottle + urea + *n*-heptane . . .	32.8057 g.
Weight of bottle + urea	20.4090 g.

If the density of *n*-heptane at 25° C. is 0.6794 g./ml., calculate that of urea.

9. Discuss the atomic heat capacities of solid elements and compounds, including the law of Dulong and Petit, the law of Kopp, and the change of heat capacity with temperature.

10. State the first and second laws of crystallography and explain the characteristics of the main crystal classes.

11. Draw an octahedron (Figure 70) and a hexagonal pyramid (Figure 71). Letter all the corners. Indicate clearly all axes of symmetry, stating the multiplicity of each. Indicate also all planes of symmetry. Do either of these forms have a center of symmetry?

12. Make a diagram consisting of a square array of at least 10 rows of 10 dots, each representing the centers of atoms in a two-dimensional crystal. Draw lines through these to make: (1) a square with sides parallel to the rows; a series of rhombs with vertical and horizontal axes in the ratio (2) 1 : 2, (3) 1 : 3, (4) 2 : 3, (5) 3 : 4. Taking the spacing of the dots in the rows as the unit axes, calculate the Miller indices of each figure, and show that the **law of rational indices** in a two-dimensional crystal follows from the assumption that *only those lines are found in which the atoms are relatively close together.*

13. Name and explain four methods of X-ray analysis.

14. Derive the fundamental equation of the reflection of X rays by atomic planes in crystals.

15. List the different types of crystal lattices, classified according to the units in the lattice and the types of bond which hold them together.

16. Show that the number of atomic centers of each type of atom in the unit cells of blende, rutile, cuprite, fluor, and zincite is consistent with the chemical formula of each of these substances.

17. Determine the number of units co-ordinated around an ion or atom of each kind, in each of the space lattices shown in Figures 85–95. Compare the co-ordination in lattices which are: atomic, ionic, and metallic respectively.

18. Discuss the use of X-ray analysis in the study of fibers.

READING LIST

J. R. Partington, *A Text-Book of Inorganic Chemistry*, 3d ed. The Macmillan Co., New York, 1930. The treatment of crystallography is fairly detailed, and many illustrations of crystalline form, isomorphism, and polymorphism are discussed under the chemistry of the different elements.

T. W. Richards, "Compressibility, Internal Pressure, and Change of Atomic Volume," *J. Franklin Institute*, **198**, 1 (1924).

William E. Ford, *Dana's Manual of Mineralogy.* John Wiley & Sons, New York, 1929. This well-known handbook contains a copiously illustrated discussion of crystallographic terms and crystal systems. Most of the book is devoted to a description of particular minerals.

Sir William Bragg, *Concerning the Nature of Things.* Harper & Brothers, New York, 1925. The last half of this book contains an excellent elementary presentation of the nature of crystals.

Sir W. H. Bragg and W. L. Bragg, *X Rays and Crystal Structure*, 4th ed. Harcourt, Brace & Company, New York, 1924. This classic volume contains a clear and interesting introduction to the methods of X-ray analysis, with some of the results of these studies.

W. L. Bragg, *Atomic Structure of Minerals.* Cornell Univ. Press, Ithaca, N. Y., 1937. A clear and interesting treatment of this field.

R. W. G. Wyckoff, *The Structure of Crystals*, 2d ed. Chemical Catalog Company, New York, 1931. Supplementary volume, 1934. A detailed treatment of the whole subject by one of the foremost American authorities.

C. W. Stillwell, *Crystal Chemistry.* McGraw-Hill Book Company, New York, 1938. This book is a very interesting treatment of the results obtained from crystal analysis. The laws governing the formation of crystals of different types are discussed on the basis of the modern theories of Pauling and others. Chapter XII, "Natural Fibers," and Chapter XIII, "Synthetic Fibers," devote 70 pages to an interesting discussion of these topics.

CHAPTER 8

THERMOCHEMISTRY

Thermochemistry *may be defined as the study of thermal changes caused by chemical reactions and physical processes.* Chemical and physical changes almost always are accompanied by the liberation or absorption of heat. If heat is evolved, the reaction is **exothermic**; if heat is absorbed, it is **endothermic.** The combustion of coal in a fire and the mixing of concentrated sulfuric acid and water are familiar examples of *exothermic* processes, while the chilling effect of the evaporation of moisture from the skin and the freezing action of a mixture of ice and salt illustrate *endothermic* processes. In many other cases, the effects are less obvious. For example, the solution of sugar in water or the precipitation of silver chloride causes much smaller thermal effects, but these, like the larger ones, can be measured in a suitable **calorimeter,** as any apparatus for measuring heat changes is called.

The thermal changes which occur during chemical or physical processes are just as characteristic as the changes in chemical or physical properties. They are closely related to the *driving force* of the reaction. By means of the principle of Le Chatelier, a knowledge of the heat of a reaction allows us to predict the direction and extent to which the equilibrium will shift if the temperature changes.

Thermal Units and Heat Capacity. Heat is a form of energy; hence the unit of heat in the c.g.s. system is the **erg** (= 1 dyne × cm.) or the **joule** (= 10^7 ergs). The joule is equal to 1 volt × 1 coulomb. These quantities, as sanctioned by international agreement, are defined on page 370. Different amounts of energy are required to warm equal weights of different substances through the same temperature interval. *The amount of energy required to raise the temperature of a substance 1° C. is called the* ***heat capacity*** *of the substance.* Heat capacities of liquids may be measured by means of a calorimeter shown schematically in Figure 104. This consists of a Dewar flask D from which the leakage of heat is very small, fitted with a tight cover C to prevent evaporation. An insulated electrical heating coil H supplies electrical energy to the liquid under investigation, which nearly fills the calorimeter and is mixed uniformly by the propeller-stirrer S. The temperature is read on a sensitive thermometer T or determined by means of an electrical resistance thermometer or a thermel (multiple thermocouple). A measured quantity of electrical energy is supplied to the material, and the rise of temperature is read on the thermometer. After suitable corrections for the heat of stirring and the gain or loss of heat to the room, the heat capacity of the whole system is simply the total energy supplied, divided by the total change in temperature. Subtracting the heat capacity of the calorimeter, which is determined separately, gives the heat capacity of the material under investigation. From this we can determine the heat capacity per gram, *i.e.*, the **specific heat capacity** which is a characteristic property of the substance.

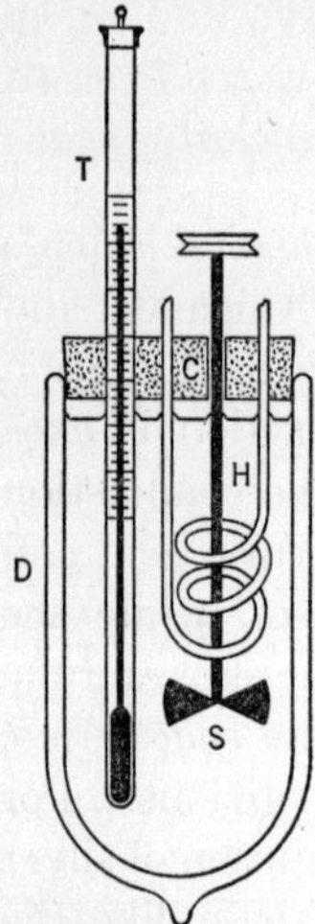

Fig. 104. A Simple Calorimeter.

Water is taken as a standard substance in calorimetry. A careful study of its thermal properties has been completed recently by Osborne, Stimson, and Ginnings [1] at the National Bureau of Standards in Washington. Their results, plotted on a large scale in Figure 105, show that the specific heat capacity changes with temperature — decreasing slightly to a minimum at about 35° and then increasing to 100°. The calorie usually is considered as the amount of energy required to raise the temperature of 1 gram of water 1 degree centigrade. Following the procedure of Bichowsky and Rossini [2] we shall take as the unit of heat the ***calorie**, defined as 4.1833 joules.* This corresponds to the heat required to raise the temperature of 1 gram of water from 15° to 16°, or from 59° to 60°, but it depends only upon the electrical units and not upon a study of the heat

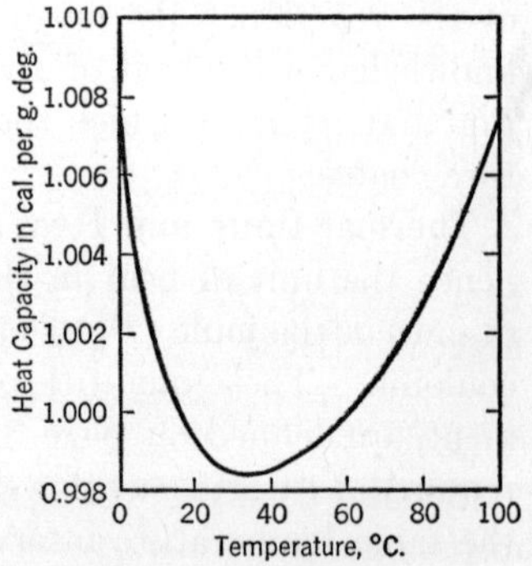

Fig. 105. The Specific Heat Capacity of Water.

[1] Osborne, Stimson, and Ginnings, *Bur. Standards J. Research*, **23,** 197 (1939).
[2] Bichowsky and Rossini, *The Thermochemistry of the Chemical Substances.*

capacity of water. Table 32 gives the heat capacity of water, in joules and defined calories, taken from Osborne, Stimson, and Ginnings. The value of the 15°-calorie, 20°-calorie, and mean calorie ($\frac{1}{100}$ of the energy required to raise 1 g. of water from 0° to 100°) can be read from this table. *The* ***kilogram calorie*** *(**kcal.**)*

TABLE 32

THE SPECIFIC HEAT CAPACITY OF WATER AT DIFFERENT TEMPERATURES

TEMP. °C.	HEAT CAPACITY/G.		TEMP. °C.	HEAT CAPACITY/G.	
	J./Deg.	Cal./Deg.		J./Deg.	Cal./Deg.
0	4.2169	1.0080	40	4.1769	.9987
5	4.2014	1.0043	50	4.1790	.9992
10	4.1914	1.0019	60	4.1827	1.0000
15	4.1850	1.0004	70	4.1879	1.0013
20	4.1811	.9995	80	4.1947	1.0029
25	4.1788	.9989	90	4.2034	1.0050
30	4.1777	.9987	100	4.2143	1.0076
35	4.1774	.9986	Mean	4.1883	1.0014

or ***large calorie*** *is 1000 times as large as the calorie, or the amount of heat required to raise 1 kg. of water 1° C.* The specific heat capacities of some representative substances are given in Table 33.

TABLE 33

THE SPECIFIC HEAT CAPACITIES, IN CALORIES PER GRAM, OF SOME REPRESENTATIVE SUBSTANCES (AT 25° C. UNLESS OTHERWISE NOTED)

Substance		Substance	
Aluminum	0.2116	Potassium chloride, KCl	0.164
Copper	.0921	Ethanol, C_2H_5OH	.581
Iron	.1075	Benzene, C_6H_6	.411
Mercury (liquid)	.03325	Carbon tetrachloride, CCl_4	.200
Ice (− 10° C.), H_2O	.478	Diethyl ether, $(C_2H_5)_2O$	.539
Aragonite, $CaCO_3$	.196	*n*-Hexane, C_6H_{14}	.527

Source of table: *I.C.T.* V, pp. 92 *et seq.*

Physical Changes: Latent Heats. When ice is heated at 0°, it melts, but the temperature does not rise until all the ice has changed to water. The heat, which was absorbed in melting the ice, disappears without causing a rise of temperature; hence it was called *latent* (hidden) *heat* by Joseph Black, the Scotch chemist who discovered this phenomenon in 1760. An identical amount of heat is liberated when the same quantity of water freezes. It is known as the *latent heat of fusion.* Similarly, when water is vaporized, it absorbs a large quantity of heat — *latent heat of evaporation* — which reappears when the water vapor condenses. The evaporation of perspiration from the skin enables the body to maintain a uniform temperature even in the hottest summer weather. On a larger scale, the evaporation of water from the ocean makes the seashore cooler in summer.

Latent heats are involved in all changes of state, and in most changes from one crystalline form of a solid to another. Thus when the familiar tetragonal white modification of tin changes to the cubic gray form, stable below 18° C., 0.6 kcal. of heat per mole is liberated. This represents the *latent heat of transition* from white to gray tin.

The heat of vaporization per gram l_v and per mole L_v for a number of elements and compounds, as well as the boiling points on the absolute scale, are given in Table 34. Trouton, in 1884, showed that *the molar heats of vaporization are proportional to the absolute boiling points.* This is ***Trouton's rule,*** which may be expressed thus:

$$L_v = KT_b = 21\ T_b$$

Trouton's rule is a useful approximation, which holds qualitatively over a wide range of temperature, although the "constant"

TABLE 34

HEATS OF VAPORIZATION AND TROUTON'S RATIO

SUBSTANCE	T_b ° A.	l_v CAL./G.	L_v CAL./MOLE	$K = \frac{L_v}{T_b}$
Helium	3	5.5	22	7.3
Oxygen (O_2)	90.2	50.9	1,629	18.1
Ammonia	240	327	5,560	23.2
Methanol	337.9	263.1	8,165	24.2
Ethanol	351.7	200.8	9,250	26.3
Benzene	353.4	94.3	7,362	20.8
Water	373	564.5	10,571	28.3
Acetic acid	391.5	96.8	5,810	14.8
Aniline	456	104	9,678	21.2
Naphthalene	491	75.5	9,670	19.7
Phosphorus (P_4)	560	130	16,100	28.8
Mercury	630.1	70.8	14,200	22.5

The data in this table are taken from Bichowsky and Rossini, *The Thermochemistry of the Chemical Substances*, supplemented by *I.C.T.* and Fiock, Ginnings, and Holton, *B. of Standards J. Research*, **6,** 881 (1931) for methanol and ethanol.

(Trouton's ratio) shows a systematic increase with temperature. The constants also are abnormally high for many liquids like water and ammonia, which are known to be *polar*. This is because more energy is required to separate polar molecules from the surface of the liquid, to which they are held by forces of cohesion.

Table 35 gives the latent heats of fusion of a number of representative substances, together with their melting points on the absolute scale T_m. The heats of fusion per gram l_f vary widely and without regularity. The heats of fusion per mole L_f, on the other hand, show a general increase with the absolute melting point. The molar heat of fusion of most elements is about 2.2 times the absolute melting point:

$$L_f = 2.2\ T_m$$

This relationship, analogous to Trouton's rule for heats of vaporization, is confined to elements and does not hold for most compounds, as the table shows.

TABLE 35

HEATS OF FUSION OF VARIOUS SUBSTANCES

SUBSTANCE	T_m ° A.	l_f CAL./G.	L_f CAL./MOLE	$\frac{L_f}{T_m}$
Oxygen (O_2)	54.5	3.30	106	1.9
Argon	84	6.64	265	3.2
Acetone	178	23.4	1360	7.6
Ammonia	195	83.5	1420	7.3
Mercury	233	2.74	550	2.4
Carbon tetrachloride	249	4.35	670	2.7
Water	273	79.76	1437	5.3
Benzene	278.6	30.3	2367	8.5
Phosphorus (yellow)	317	5.00	155	0.5
Aluminum	932	85	2300	2.5
Copper	1356	50	3200	2.4
Nickel	1725	73	4300	2.5

These data are taken from Bichowsky and Rossini, *The Thermochemistry of the Chemical Substances*, supplemented by *I.C.T.*

Heat Content: ΔH. Since 1437 cal. is absorbed in melting one mole of ice, the water at 0° C. must contain 1437 cal. $\times$ mole^{-1} more heat than the ice at the same temperature. There is no direct method of measuring the total heat content of a system, but we can determine the *change in heat content* during the process, by measuring, in a calorimeter, the heat liberated or absorbed *at constant pressure*. In the case cited above, if we call the molal heat content of the ice H_i and that of the water H_w, then the change in heat content during the melting of ice, ΔH, will be:

$$\Delta H = H_w - H_i = L_f$$

In general, for any physical or chemical process, we can define the ***change in heat content*, ΔH,** *as the heat content of the products of the process, H'', minus the heat content of the factors, H':*

$$\Delta H = H'' - H'$$

Thus in every case ΔH is the heat *absorbed* during the process. If the process is reversed, the *sign* of ΔH is changed; hence we must always specify exactly the process under consideration. For instance, if we were considering the freezing of one mole of water, which could be represented by the equation:

$$H_2O\ (l) \longrightarrow H_2O\ (s)$$

the change in heat content would be

$$\Delta H \longrightarrow H_i - H_w = - L_F$$

The same considerations apply to chemical reactions, and the information contained in the two preceding equations is usually condensed into a single thermochemical equation, which expresses the chemical reaction, or physical change, and also the change in heat content ΔH which accompanies it. Thus we may write:

$$H_2O\ (l) \longrightarrow H_2O\ (s) \ - \ 1437 \text{ kcal. } (\Delta H_{273})$$

The value of ΔH corresponds to the change in heat content for the reaction *as it is written; i.e.*, for the change of *1 mole of water into ice.* The absolute temperature at which the process occurs is indicated in the subscript to the ΔH, unless it is stated explicitly elsewhere. This temperature must be stated since ΔH changes with temperature, as we shall see on page 215.

Isothermal Heat Changes. *A latent heat change is defined as the heat liberated or absorbed when a change in physical state occurs at constant temperature.* The same restriction of constant temperature must be placed upon all other thermochemical processes, if the results are to have definite significance. *Processes which take place at a constant temperature are called* ***isothermal processes****, and the corresponding heat changes are* ***isothermal heat changes.*** Heats of solution and dilution and of all chemical reactions are recorded as isothermal heat changes.

If the process is endothermic, the isothermal heat change is measured easily. The reaction is carried out in a calorimeter which is suitably protected from thermal leakage, and the temperature is kept constant by adding a measured quantity of heat, usually by means of an electrical resistance coil. The increase in the heat content of the system during this isothermal process is exactly equal to the quantity of heat which is added to keep the temperature constant.

If the process is exothermic, the heat of the reaction can be measured by balancing it with a process which *absorbs* a known quantity of heat. For instance, the evaporation of a known weight of a volatile substance like ether, from a bulb immersed in the calorimeter, could be used to keep the temperature of the system constant. It would then be a measure of the decrease in heat content of the system. Another method has been used more extensively. First, we measure exactly the rise of temperature, ΔT, when the reaction takes place in a calorimeter in which all thermal leakage is prevented. *Such a process, carried out without gain or loss of heat, is an* **adiabatic process.** If the process cannot be made completely adiabatic, the heat exchange can be measured and a correction applied for it. The system is then cooled to the original temperature, and the rise of temperature, ΔT, which accompanied the reaction, is exactly duplicated by means of measured electrical heating. This quantity of heat is exactly equal to that which would have to be *extracted* from the system at its final temperature, in order to restore it to its original condition. It therefore corresponds to the isothermal heat of the reaction at the *initial temperature.*

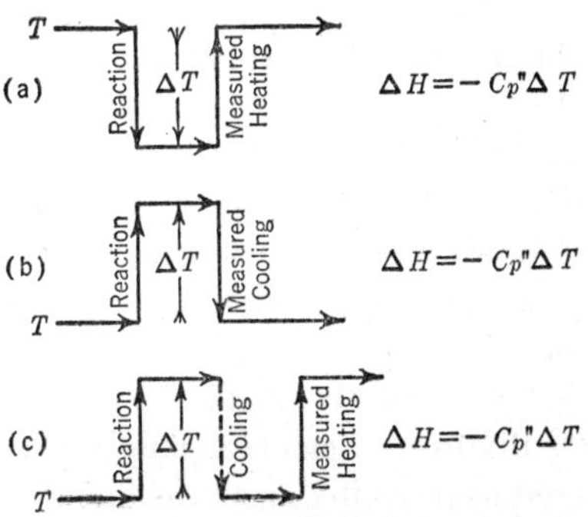

Figure 106 illustrates the different processes. In (*a*) we have an *endothermic* process occurring adiabatically, followed by an adiabatic heating to the same initial temperature. This is equivalent to the case in which heat is added electrically to balance the fall of temperature caused by the reaction. In (*b*) we have an *exothermic* process balanced by the *absorption* of heat. In (*c*) we have the process equivalent to (*b*), in which we measure the electrical energy required to bring about the same rise in temperature caused by the reaction.

(a) $\Delta H = -C_p''\Delta T$

(b) $\Delta H = -C_p''\Delta T$

(c) $\Delta H = -C_p''\Delta T$

Fig. 106. Measuring Isothermal Heats of Reaction.

In (*a*) and (*c*), we could calculate the *decrease* in heat content (heat liberated) in the isothermal process at the *initial* temperature, by multiplying the change in temperature, ΔT, by the heat capacity at constant pressure, C_p'' of the *products* of the reaction (plus that of the calorimeter).

$$-\Delta H = C_p''\Delta T$$

Similarly, if the heat capacity of the *factors*, C_p', had been used, the resulting decrease in heat content would refer to the isothermal process at the *final* temperature. This fact was first distinguished clearly by T. W. Richards,[1] in 1903.

Heats of Solution and Dilution. Intermediate between the physical processes (fusion, evaporation, and other changes of state) and chemical reactions are the processes of solution and dilution. In the mixing of two ideal gases, or of two similar liquids which form an *ideal* solution, there should be no change in total heat content. This condition is nearly fulfilled in the mixing of many pairs of organic liquids. Similarly, if a solid dissolves in a liquid to form an ideal solution, the change in heat content should correspond to the latent heat of fusion of the solid. This relationship holds for naphthalene or diphenyl dissolved in benzene, and for other organic substances.

In the case of solutions in water and other polar liquids, there may be large changes in heat content, particularly when the solutes are electrolytes. Here the behavior of an ideal solution is complicated by electrical effects, as well as more or less definite chemical reactions between solvent and solute.

When we dissolve a salt in water, there may be either an increase or a decrease in heat content. Often the sign of ΔH is different for the solution of anhydrous and hydrated forms of the same substance. This is illustrated by the case of calcium chloride. When "anhydrous" calcium chloride (the *calcined* material frequently used as a drying agent) is dissolved in water to form a dilute solution, the change is *exothermic* and the temperature rises. If the experiment is repeated with the same amount of the salt in the form of the hexahydrate, $CaCl_2 \cdot 6\,H_2O$, the change is *endothermic*. Thus the heat content decreases when the anhydrous salt is dissolved, and increases when the hydrated salt is employed. A similar relationship holds for many salts which can form crystalline

[1] T. W. Richards, *J. Am. Chem. Soc.*, **25**, 209 (1903).

hydrates. However, many anhydrous salts, such as ammonium nitrate, dissolve in water with a marked absorption of heat. These usually are salts which form no crystalline hydrates. *Fully hydrated salts and those which do not form crystalline hydrates usually dissolve with the absorption of heat, while anhydrous salts which can form crystalline hydrates dissolve with the liberation of heat.*

In general, *the* **heat of solution** *of a substance is the heat absorbed when one mole of the substance is dissolved in an infinitely large quantity of the solvent* — *i.e.*, a quantity of solvent so large that further dilution causes no measurable thermal effect.

The dilution of a solution from one concentration to another also involves thermal changes which are described by thermochemical equations. The concentrations of the initial and final solutions usually are represented by the relative numbers of moles of solute and solvent, and the thermal term is the change in heat content, ΔH, or the heat *absorbed* in the process. Thus we may write:

$$CaCl_2 \cdot 50\ H_2O + 350\ H_2O \longrightarrow CaCl_2 \cdot 400\ H_2O + 0.325 \text{ kcal.}$$

This means that a solution containing 1 mole of calcium chloride and 50 moles of water (about 1.1 *m*) is diluted with 350 moles of water to form a solution containing 1 mole of calcium chloride in 400 moles of water (about 0.14 *m*). The corresponding change in heat content is 0.325 kcal. — *i.e.*, 0.325 kcal. is absorbed in the process of dilution. The expressions $CaCl_2 \cdot 50\ H_2O$ and $CaCl_2 \cdot 400\ H_2O$ do not represent chemical compounds, but simply the mole ratio of salt to water in the solution.

The symbols (s) for *solid*, (l) for *liquid*, and (g) for *gas* frequently are used in these equations to designate the exact state of a substance. Thus $CaCl_2 \cdot 6\ H_2O$ (s) represents 1 mole of the crystalline hexahydrate of calcium chloride, and not a solution. The symbol aq (an abbreviation for *aqua*) is used to denote an infinitely large quantity of water — *i.e.*, such a large amount that further addition of water causes no measurable thermal change. If a solution of calcium chloride is infinitely dilute, we would write $CaCl_2 \cdot aq$.

A calorimeter for measuring heats of dilution, developed by T. W. Richards and his associates,[1] is shown in Figure 107. The calorimeter C_1 is a platinum vessel, supported on thin wedges of cork within the "submarine" jacket B, from which it is insulated by

[1] Richards and Rowe, *J. Am. Chem. Soc.*, **42,** 1621 (1920); **43,** 770 (1921); **44,** 704 (1922); Richards and Gucker, *ibid.*, **51,** 712 (1929).

means of a 2.5-cm. air space. A lid, fitted to the submarine jacket with a gasket, is supplied with tubes through which the necessary connections are made between the calorimeter and the outside. The submarine assembly is immersed in a well-stirred water-bath A, fitted with a tight wooden cover J and thermally insulated from the room by a heavy layer of felt F. The difference in temperature between the calorimeter and the bath is measured by means of the 6-junction thermel[1] D, D and kept within $\pm$ .003° during an experiment, by heating the bath when necessary, with the coils of bare resistance wire I, I, or cooling it by means of a stream of cold water not shown in the diagram. This suffices to make the process adiabatic.

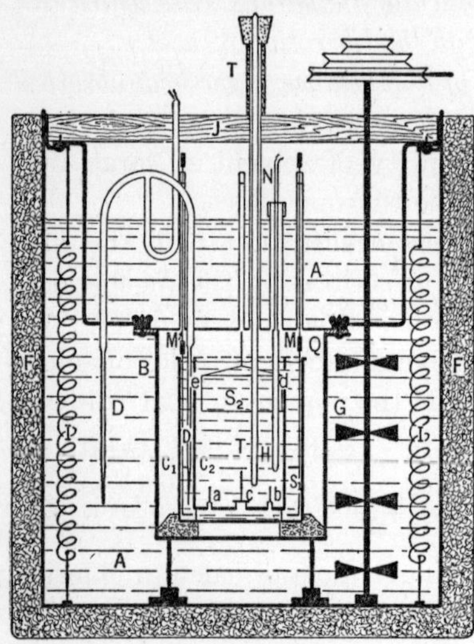

Fig. 107. A Calorimeter for Measuring Heats of Dilution.

The solution is contained in an inner platinum can C_2, while an equal volume of water fills the annular space between C_2 and C_1. The liquids are stirred by the two-stage reciprocating stirrers S_1 and S_2, moving in opposite directions. The calorimeter is heated to the desired temperature by means of the insulated resistor H. The temperature is measured to $\pm$ 0.0001° by means of the platinum resistance thermometer T. When the plugs a, b, c, d, and e are pulled out, the stirrers mix the liquids efficiently, and the change in temperature ΔT is measured with an accuracy of about $\pm$ 0.0002°. Knowing the heat capacity of the solution and that of the calorimeter, the change in heat content is calculated. The results given in the last part of Table 36 were obtained with this apparatus.

Heats of Reaction. *The **heat of reaction** is the heat absorbed in the reaction of the number of moles of material represented in the chemical equation.* In order to distinguish among the many dif-

[1] A "thermel" consists of a thermoelectric couple, made by joining dissimilar metallic wires, or of two or more such couples connected in series.

ferent chemical reactions, it is customary to speak of the **heat of neutralization, heat of combustion, heat of formation,** etc., referring to the heat absorbed in these particular reactions.

Heats of neutralization and of other reactions between solutions, are measured conveniently in a calorimeter such as that described for heats of dilution.

TABLE 36

SOME HEATS OF SOLUTION AND OF DILUTION (18° C.)

Reaction	
$CaCl_2 + 400\ H_2O \longrightarrow CaCl_2 \cdot 400\ H_2O$	− 18.09 kcal.
$CaCl_2 \cdot 2\ H_2O + 398\ H_2O \longrightarrow CaCl_2 \cdot 400\ H_2O$	− 12.03 kcal.
$CaCl_2 \cdot 4\ H_2O + 396\ H_2O \longrightarrow CaCl_2 \cdot 400\ H_2O$	− 1.97 kcal.
$CaCl_2 \cdot 6\ H_2O + 394\ H_2O \longrightarrow CaCl_2 \cdot 400\ H_2O$	+ 4.54 kcal.
$CaCl_2 \cdot 400\ H_2O + aq \longrightarrow CaCl_2 \cdot aq$	− 0.43 kcal.
$NaOH \cdot 25\ H_2O + 25\ H_2O \longrightarrow NaOH \cdot 50\ H_2O$	+ 0.123 kcal.
$NaOH \cdot 50\ H_2O + aq \longrightarrow NaOH \cdot aq$	+ 0.086 kcal.
$H \cdot C_2H_3O_2 \cdot 25\ H_2O + aq \longrightarrow H \cdot C_2H_3O_2 \cdot aq$	− 0.154 kcal.
$NaC_2H_3O_2 \cdot 25\ H_2O + aq \longrightarrow NaC_2H_3O_2 \cdot aq$	− 0.314 kcal.

Heats of combustion are measured in the calorimetric bomb developed by Berthelot, one of the outstanding French chemists of the late nineteenth century. A recent modification of this apparatus, used by R. S. Jessup at the National Bureau of Standards for measuring the heat of combustion of diamond and graphite, is shown in Figures 108 and 109. The combustible material is weighed into the shallow platinum crucible A, supported on an insulating ring of beryllium oxide B. This is suspended from the lid of a heavy bomb of about 400 ml. capacity, made of "illium," a corrosion-resisting nickel-chromium alloy. After the lid is screwed down upon a gold gasket G, oxygen is admitted through the valve V in the lid, to a pressure of about 30 atmospheres. The bomb is then put into a calorimeter C containing a known weight of water, surrounded by a jacket J immersed in a carefully controlled thermostat. Thus the heat leakage during an experiment can be estimated accurately and a correction applied. A coil of fine iron fuse wire F suspended above the crucible is connected by the wire L_1 to the bomb, and by the wire L_2 to a terminal W, carried out through an insulating bushing in the lid of the bomb. These terminals can be connected to an external battery, which supplies a current sufficient to melt the fine iron fuse wire and thus ignite the substance. The rise in temperature due to the combustion is measured by means of a platinum resistance thermometer T sensitive to 0.0001° C., and the change of heat content is determined

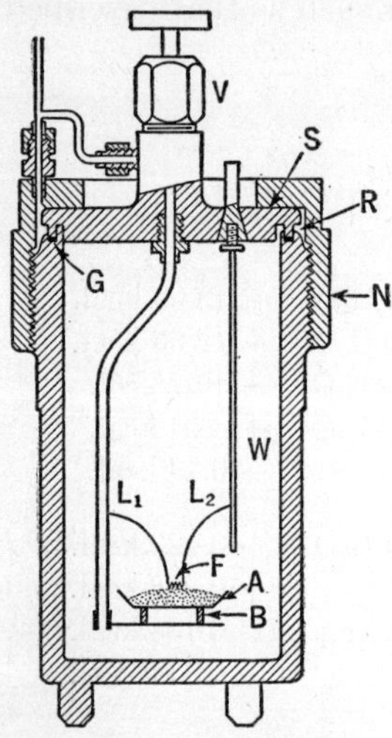

Fig. 108. A Combustion Bomb.

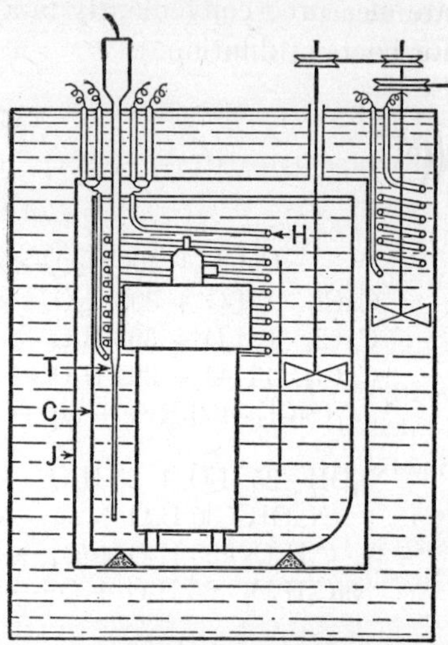

Fig. 109. A Combustion Calorimeter.

from a knowledge of the heat capacity of the system, or a measurement of the electrical energy required to duplicate the rise in temperature. A small correction for the heat evolved in fusing the iron wire is determined experimentally and applied to the observed results.

Since the reaction in the bomb is carried out at *constant volume*, the thermal effect corresponds to the change in what is called the *energy content* of the system. This change, symbolized by ΔE, is not exactly the same as the change in heat content ΔH. The small difference can easily be calculated, as explained on page 621, and thus we can find the value of ΔH.

The heats of combustion of some organic compounds are given in Table 37. The products of combustion are gaseous carbon dioxide, *liquid* water, gaseous nitrogen, and gaseous sulfur dioxide.

Thermochemical Equations. A chemical equation expresses the nature of a chemical reaction and the amount of material changed. Since a definite change in heat content accompanies each chemical reaction, this additional information is conveniently added to the

TABLE 37

HEATS OF COMBUSTION OF CERTAIN ORGANIC COMPOUNDS AT 18° C.

Substance	$-\Delta H$ (*Kcal. per Mole*)
Methane, CH_4 (g)	212.95
Acetylene, C_2H_2 (g)	311.1
Ethylene, C_2H_4 (g)	336.6
Ethane, C_2H_6 (g)	373.05
Methanol, CH_3OH (l)	173.74
Ethanol, C_2H_5OH (l)	326.87
Glycerol, $C_3H_5(OH)_3$ (l)	397.0
Diethyl ether, $(C_2H_5)_2O$ (l)	651.7
Acetic acid, CH_3COOH (l)	208.3
Ethyl acetate, $C_2H_5 \cdot C_2H_3O_2$ (l)	538.5
Glyceryl tributyrate, $C_3H_5(C_4H_7O_2)_3$ (l)	1941.1
d-Glucose, $C_6H_{12}O_6$ (s)	673.0
l-Fructose, $C_6H_{12}O_6$ (s)	675.6
Sucrose, $C_{12}H_{22}O_{11}$ (s)	1349.6
Lactose, $C_{12}H_{22}O_{11}$ (s)	1350.8
Starch $(C_6H_{10}O_5)_x$ (s)	675.8 x
Glycogen $(C_6H_{10}O_5)_y$ (s)	614.1 y
Urea, $(NH_2)_2CO$ (s)	151.6
Glycine, $CH_2(NH_2)COOH$ (s)	233.4
dl-Alanine, $CH_3CH(NH_2)COOH$ (s)	387.5
dl-Valine, $(CH_3)_2CH \cdot CH(NH_2)COOH$ (s)	700.8
Leucine, $(CH_3)_2CH \cdot CH_2CH(NH_2)COOH$ (s)	855.6
Glutamic acid, $C_5H_9NO_4$ (s)	542.4
Cystine, $(SCH_2CH(NH_2)COOH)_2$ (s)	993.9

equation. *A **thermochemical equation** expresses the chemical reaction and also the change in heat content ΔH which accompanies it.* Thermochemical equations obey all the laws of ordinary linear algebraic equations in one or more unknown quantities. Thus we may write:

$$C\ (s) + O_2\ (g) \longrightarrow CO_2\ (g) - 94.45\ \text{kcal.}$$

This equation states that, when 1 mole of carbon unites with 1 mole of oxygen to form 1 mole of carbon dioxide, there is a decrease in heat content of 94.45 kcal. In other words, this reaction *evolves* 94.45 kcal. of heat. We can see at once that the *sign* of the change of heat content will be changed if we write the reaction for the *decomposition* of carbon dioxide into its elements, for the products of this reaction have a greater heat content than the factor.

$$CO_2\ (g) \longrightarrow C\ (s) + O_2\ (g) + 94.45\ \text{kcal.}$$

If two moles each of carbon, oxygen, and carbon dioxide were involved, the change in heat content would be doubled.

$$2\,C\,(s) + 2\,O_2\,(g) \longrightarrow 2\,CO_2\,(g) - 188.90 \text{ kcal.}$$

Often, a reaction can be carried out in several steps. Thus carbon can be burned in a small amount of oxygen to form carbon monoxide, which in turn can be burned to carbon dioxide. The thermochemical equations are:

$$C\,(s) + \tfrac{1}{2}\,O_2\,(g) \longrightarrow CO\,(g) - 26.84 \text{ kcal.}$$
$$CO\,(g) + \tfrac{1}{2}\,O_2\,(g) \longrightarrow CO_2\,(g) - 67.61 \text{ kcal.}$$

Like algebraic equations, these thermochemical equations can be added to eliminate the term CO (g) which occurs on both sides. The other terms are collected as usual, giving the equation:

$$C\,(s) + O_2\,(g) \longrightarrow CO_2\,(g) - 94.45 \text{ kcal.}$$

This is one illustration of a general principle known as the ***law of Hess***, *which states that, in any series of chemical or physical changes the total heat effect is independent of the path by which the system goes from its initial to its final state.* Hess reached this conclusion from an experimental study in 1840, but it is now recognized as a corollary of the law of the conservation of energy.

As a further illustration of the use of thermochemical equations, the heat of formation of calcium chloride hexahydrate, from anhydrous calcium chloride and water, can be calculated from the data of Table 36 as follows:

$$\begin{array}{rll}
CaCl_2 + 400\,H_2O \longrightarrow & CaCl_2 \cdot 400\,H_2O & -\ 18.09 \text{ kcal.} \\
CaCl_2 \cdot 400\,H_2O \longrightarrow & CaCl_2 \cdot 6\,H_2O + 394\,H_2O & -\ \ 4.54 \text{ kcal.} \\
\hline
CaCl_2 + 6\,H_2O \longrightarrow & CaCl_2 \cdot 6\,H_2O & -\ 22.63 \text{ kcal.}
\end{array}$$

The algebraic treatment of thermochemical equations is particularly useful in finding the heat changes in reactions which cannot be measured directly. The most important application is in the heats of organic reactions. Many of these proceed too slowly to be measured directly, or are disturbed by side reactions. In general, it is comparatively easy to measure the heats of combustion of organic substances, and these data, with the heats of combustion of the products, suffice to calculate the heats of formation. For example, the heat of formation of acetylene would be difficult to determine directly, but can be calculated from the heat of combustion of acetylene and of the carbon and hydrogen. The necessary equations, arranged so that they can be added directly, with cancellation of the undesired terms, are:

$$
\begin{array}{rcll}
2\,C\,(s) + 2\,O_2 & \longrightarrow & 2\,CO_2 & -\ 188.90\ \text{kcal.} \\
H_2 + \tfrac{1}{2}\,O_2 & \longrightarrow & H_2O\,(l) & -\ \ 68.37\ \text{kcal.} \\
2\,CO_2 + H_2O\,(l) & \longrightarrow & C_2H_2 + \tfrac{5}{2}\,O_2 & +\ 311.17\ \text{kcal.} \\
\hline
2\,C\,(s) + H_2 & \longrightarrow & C_2H_2 & +\ \ 53.90\ \text{kcal.}
\end{array}
$$

In combining equations which involve water, the term H_2O (l) cannot, of course, be canceled against the term H_2O (g), since they differ by the latent heat of vaporization of water.

The only practical disadvantage in this type of calculation is that the final result is the difference of two or more large numbers, so that its *per cent* of uncertainty is larger than that of any of the heats of combustion. When heats of reaction can be measured *directly*, the results usually can be obtained with greater accuracy. Recently Kistiakowsky and his coworkers at Harvard University have measured directly the heats of hydrogenation and of halogenation of many unsaturated organic compounds. The gaseous mixtures are passed through a catalyst chamber contained in an adiabatic calorimeter. When the rate of heating has become uniform, it is measured accurately for a definite time, during which the quantity of gas flowing through the calorimeter also is measured. A subsequent determination of the rate of heating with a known elec-

TABLE 38

Heats of Certain Organic Addition Reactions in the Gaseous Phase at 355° A.

Reaction			ΔH
$H_2C{=}CH_2 + H_2$	$\longrightarrow$	C_2H_6	− 32.82 kcal.
$H_2C{=}CH{-}CH_3 + H_2$	$\longrightarrow$	C_3H_8	− 30.12 kcal.
$H_2C{=}CH{-}C_2H_5 + H_2$	$\longrightarrow$	C_4H_{10}	− 30.34 kcal.
$H_2C{=}CH{-}C_3H_7 + H_2$	$\longrightarrow$	C_5H_{12}	− 30.14 kcal.
$H_2C{=}CH{-}CH{=}CH_2 + 2\,H_2$	$\longrightarrow$	C_4H_{10}	− 57.07 kcal.
$C_6H_6 + 3\,H_2$	$\longrightarrow$	C_6H_{12}	− 49.80 kcal.
$HC{\equiv}CH + 2\,H_2$	$\longrightarrow$	C_2H_6	− 75.06 kcal.
$HC{\equiv}C{-}CH_3 + 2\,H_2$	$\longrightarrow$	C_3H_8	− 69.70 kcal.
$H_3C{-}C{\equiv}C{-}CH_3 + 2\,H_2$	$\longrightarrow$	C_4H_{10}	− 65.58 kcal.
$H_2C{=}CH_2 + Br_2$	$\longrightarrow$	$C_2H_4Br_2$	− 29.06 kcal.
$H_2C{=}CH{-}CH_3 + Br_2$	$\longrightarrow$	$C_3H_6Br_2$	− 29.41 kcal.
$H_2C{=}CH{-}C_2H_5 + Br_2$	$\longrightarrow$	$C_4H_8Br_2$	− 29.59 kcal.

Kistiakowsky *et al.*, *J. Am. Chem. Soc.*, **57,** 65, 876 (1935); **58,** 137, 146 (1936) **59,** 831 (1937); **60,** 440, 2764 (1938); **61,** 1868 (1939).

trical input allows the calculation of the heat liberated during the catalytic reaction, with an accuracy of about 0.1 per cent. The calorimeter could be used at temperatures up to 150° C., but most experiments were carried out at 80–90°. The results were corrected to a standard temperature of 82° C., by means of the Person-Kirchhoff equation, given on page 216. Some of Kistiakowsky's results are given in Table 38. The final article in the series listed at the foot of the table gives a résumé of the work and discusses the structural factors which influence these heats of reaction.

Heats of Formation. As a basis for thermochemical calculations, the most convenient data are the heats of formation of different substances. *The* ***heat of formation*** *is the heat absorbed when one mole of a substance is formed from its constituents in their standard states. The* ***standard state*** *of each element is taken as the form in which it exists under atmospheric pressure at a standard temperature* (usually 18° or 25° C.). When several modifications of the element are stable at room temperature, one of these is chosen arbitrarily as the standard state. Thus in the case of carbon the modification known as β-graphite has been taken as the standard state by many investigators. However, Bichowsky and Rossini, in their recent authoritative book, *The Thermochemistry of the Chemical Substances*, state: "We have selected diamond as the standard state for carbon because, with respect to heat content, it is the only truly reproducible form of solid carbon." The heat of formation of β-graphite therefore is − 0.22 kcal., corresponding to the equation:

$$\text{C (diamond)} \longrightarrow \text{C } (\beta\text{-graphite}) - 0.22 \text{ kcal.}$$

Similarly, the heat of formation of carbon dioxide corresponds to the reaction:

$$\text{C (diamond)} + O_2 \text{ (g)} \longrightarrow CO_2 \text{ (g)} - 94.45 \text{ kcal.}$$

The heats of formation of a number of substances are listed in Table 39. The symbol $\Delta H°$ is used because the elements and compounds are in their standard states. In *any* reaction, the ***standard change in heat content***, $\Delta H°$, *is the heat absorbed when the reactants and products all are in their standard states.*

The Law of Maximum Work (Heat). A study of Table 39 will show that the exothermic compounds are stable, while the endothermic compounds are unstable. In general, the greater the amount of heat liberated in its formation, the more stable the com-

TABLE 39

HEATS OF FORMATION OF CERTAIN SUBSTANCES FROM THE ELEMENTS AT 18° C.

SUBSTANCE	$\Delta H°$ (KCAL.)	SUBSTANCE	$\Delta H°$ (KCAL.)
Al_2O_3	− 380.0	NH_3 (g)	− 11.00
Fe_2O_3	− 198.5	H_2S	− 5.3
CO_2 (from diamond)	− 94.45	HI	5.91
SO_2 (g)	− 70.92	NO	21.6
H_2O (l)	− 68.37	AsH_3	43.6
H_2O (g)	− 57.80	H (from H_2)	51.90
CuO	− 38.5	C_2H_2	53.9
FeS_2	− 35.5	$Hg(CNO)_2$	64.1
CuS	− 11.6		

Bichowsky and Rossini, *Thermochemistry of the Chemical Substances.*

pound; and the greater the amount of heat absorbed, the more unstable the compound. Thus alumina is so stable that it is hard to decompose into its elements, while copper oxide is considerably less stable. Nitric oxide is not stable at room temperature, although it does not decompose into its elements at a measurable rate, but mercuric fulminate, $Hg(CNO)_2$, explodes violently when it is struck and hence is used in percussion caps.

Such considerations led Berthelot to conclude that the change in heat content during a reaction is a quantitative measure of the intensity of the reaction. He called this principle the *law of maximum work*, although it would be described more accurately as the *law of maximum heat.* Berthelot's "law" is not valid in every case, but it is a useful principle by which to predict the direction in which a reaction will tend to go. Suppose, for example, we wished to predict, from the data of Table 39, whether hydrogen sulfide could be burned to water and sulfur, or water and sulfur would react to liberate oxygen. The equation is:

$$H_2S\ (g) + \tfrac{1}{2}\,O_2 \rightleftharpoons H_2O\ (l) + S\ (s)$$

According to Berthelot's law the reaction will go in the direction in which there is a decrease in heat content. The equations for the heats of formation may be subtracted to give the desired result.

$$\begin{array}{ll} H_2 + \tfrac{1}{2}\,O_2 \longrightarrow H_2O\ (l) & -\ 68.37\text{ kcal.} \\ H_2 + S\ (s) \longrightarrow H_2S\ (g) & -\ 5.3\text{ kcal.} \\ \hline H_2S\ (g) + \tfrac{1}{2}\,O_2 \longrightarrow H_2O\ (l) + S\ (s) & -\ 63.1\text{ kcal.} \end{array}$$

The oxidation of H_2S therefore involves a large decrease in heat content, and this is the direction in which the reaction should go. This is borne out by experience.

Berthelot's law of maximum work (heat) holds in all cases when the change in heat content is large. When the change in heat content is small, however, other factors may cause the reaction to proceed in the direction in which there is an increase in heat content. Equilibrium reactions, which do not go to completion, include many exceptions to Berthelot's law. For example, the esterification of ethyl alcohol and acetic acid:

$$C_2H_5OH + H \cdot C_2H_3O_2 \rightleftharpoons C_2H_5 \cdot C_2H_3O_2 + H_2O$$

comes to an equilibrium when it is two thirds complete, although the heat content of the system increases in the process.

Berthelot himself recognized that all changes of state are exceptions to his rule, since the melting of ice occurs naturally above 0°, although the heat content increases on melting.

Heats of Formation in Homologous Series. A study of the heats of formation of the members of a homologous series of organic compounds shows interesting regularities. Table 40 gives some recent values which Rossini and his collaborators at the Bureau of Standards have obtained for heats of formation of normal paraffin hydrocarbons, C_nH_{2n+2}, normal olefin hydrocarbons, C_nH_{2n}, and normal primary aliphatic alcohols, $C_nH_{2n+1}OH$. These values are plotted in Figure 110. In each series the heat of formation increases with increasing number of carbon atoms. In the first few members of each series the increment for each additional CH_2 group changes from one compound to the next. However, for all compounds having more than five carbon atoms in the chain, there is a regular increase of 5.77 kcal. for each CH_2 group added. This means that the terminal groups exert an appreciable influence upon the change of heat of formation for each CH_2 group added, only when the additional CH_2 groups are close to the terminal group. For higher homologues, the increase in heat of formation from each additional CH_2 group is the same for all three series. The heats of formation may be calcu-

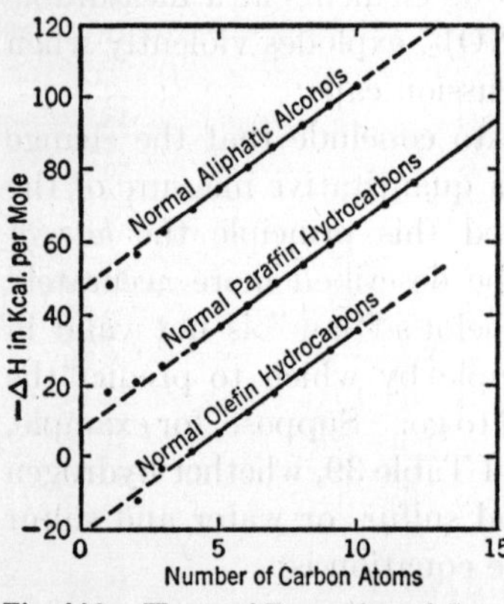

Fig. 110. Heats of Formation of Compounds of Homologous Series.

lated by means of the following equations, derived by Rossini for the three series:

$$\text{Normal } C_nH_{2n+2}\ (n > 5) : \Delta H = -\ 7.91 - 5.77\,n$$
$$\text{Normal } C_nH_{2n}\ (n > 5) : \Delta H = 21.90 - 5.77\,n$$
$$\text{Normal } C_nH_{2n+1}OH\ (n > 5) : \Delta H = -\ 46.71 - 5.77\,n$$

These relationships may be used to calculate heats of formation of higher homologues in these series.

TABLE 40

HEATS OF FORMATION OF GASEOUS COMPOUNDS OF DIFFERENT HOMOLOGOUS SERIES, AT 25° C.

Compound		$-\Delta H$ (Kcal.)
Name	Formula	
Normal Paraffin Hydrocarbons		
Methane	CH_4	18.29
Ethane	C_2H_6	21.04
Propane	C_3H_8	26.05
n-Butane	C_4H_{10}	31.45
n-Pentane	C_5H_{12}	36.89
n-Hexane	C_6H_{14}	42.53
n-Heptane	C_7H_{16}	48.30
n-Octane	C_8H_{18}	54.07
n-Nonane	C_9H_{20}	59.84
n-Decane	$C_{10}H_{22}$	65.61
Normal Olefin Hydrocarbons		
Ethene	$CH_2{=}CH_2$	− 11.70
Propene	$CH_3CH{=}CH_2$	− 3.58
n-Butene-1	$C_2H_5CH{=}CH_2$	1.43
n-Pentene-1	$C_3H_7CH{=}CH_2$	7.09
n-Hexene-1	$C_4H_9CH{=}CH_2$	12.74
n-Heptene-1	$C_5H_{11}CH{=}CH_2$	18.51
n-Octene-1	$C_6H_{13}CH{=}CH_2$	24.28
n-Nonene-1	$C_7H_{15}CH{=}CH_2$	30.06
n-Decene-1	$C_8H_{17}CH{=}CH_2$	35.83
Normal Aliphatic Alcohols		
Methanol	CH_3OH	48.50
Ethanol	CH_3CH_2OH	57.07
n-Propanol	$C_2H_5CH_2OH$	63.42
n-Butanol	$C_3H_7CH_2OH$	69.49
n-Pentanol	$C_4H_9CH_2OH$	75.41
n-Hexanol	$C_5H_{11}CH_2OH$	81.33
n-Heptanol	$C_6H_{13}CH_2OH$	87.10
n-Octanol	$C_7H_{15}CH_2OH$	92.87
n-Nonanol	$C_8H_{17}CH_2OH$	98.64
n-Decanol	$C_9H_{19}CH_2OH$	104.41

Rossini, *B. of Standards J. Res.*, **13**, 21, 189 (1924).
Rossini and Knowlton, *ibid.*, **19**, 339 (1937).

The Change of ΔH with Temperature. So far we have considered the changes in heat content accompanying various isothermal chemical and physical processes. In general, the heat of reaction changes with temperature. This fact was discovered experimentally and explained theoretically by the French physical chemist, C. C. Person, in 1851. The theory was worked out independently, and in greater detail, by G. R. Kirchhoff, the German physicist, in 1858. The ***Person-Kirchhoff relationship*** *states that the change in the heat of reaction with temperature equals the difference between the heat capacities of the products and the factors in the reaction.* This relationship is derived by considering the series of changes illustrated in Figure 111. In this diagram, the heat content of the system H is plotted as ordinate against the absolute temperature T. If the reaction is carried out isothermally at a temperature T, the change in heat content ΔH_T is represented by the line AB. When the products are heated to a temperature $T + dT$, the system is brought to the point C. The increase in heat content is

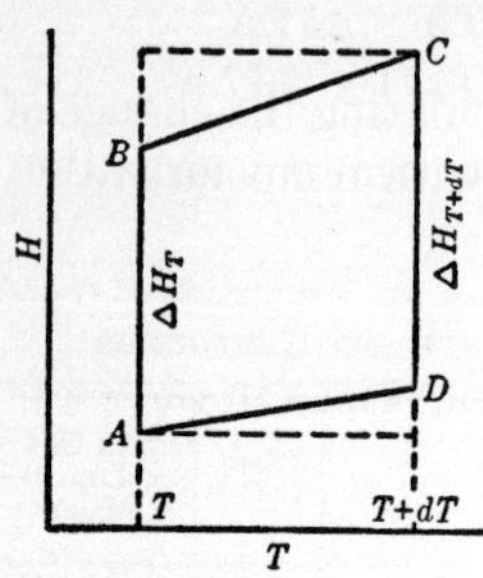

Fig. 111. Illustrating the Person-Kirchhoff Law.

$$\Delta H = C_p'' \, dT$$

where C_p'' is the heat capacity of the products.

The same change from A to C can be brought about by another route; heating the reactants along AD from T to $T + dT$ and then allowing the reaction to proceed isothermally at the higher temperature, with a change in heat content ΔH_{T+dT}, from D to C. Since these two processes begin and end at the same points, the total heat change must be the same. Equating the changes in heat content in the two processes gives:

$$\Delta H_T + C_p''dT = C_p'dT + \Delta H_{T+dT}$$

or

$$\Delta H_{T+dT} - \Delta H_T = (C_p'' - C_p')dT$$

The left-hand side of the equation is the change in ΔH corresponding to the temperature interval dT. The term $(C_p'' - C_p') = \Delta C_p$, hence we may write:

$$\frac{d\Delta H}{dT} = \Delta C_p = C_p'' - C_p'$$

Another derivation of this equation is given on page 623. If the difference in heat capacity may be considered constant over a range of temperature, this equation may be integrated to give:

$$\Delta H_{T''} - \Delta H_{T'} = \Delta C_p(T'' - T')$$

The data in Table 41 will be useful in calculating the change of the heats of a number of common reactions with temperature.

TABLE 41

THE MOLAR HEAT CAPACITIES OF SOME ELEMENTS AND COMPOUNDS

SUBSTANCE	TEMP. (° C.)	C_p IN CAL. × DEG.$^{-1}$ × MOLE^{-1}	SUBSTANCE	TEMP. (° C.)	C_p IN CAL. × DEG.$^{-1}$ × MOLE^{-1}
Aluminum, Al	25	5.83	Hydrogen, H_2	25	6.96
Diamond, C	25	1.48	Oxygen, O_2	25	7.01
Copper, Cu	25	5.85	Nitrogen, N_2	25	6.99
Iron, Fe	25	6.00	Carbon monoxide, CO	25	7.03
Sulfur, S	25	5.5	Carbon dioxide, CO_2	15	8.75
Aluminum oxide, Al_2O_3	0	17.8	Methane, CH_4	15	8.47
Cupric oxide, CuO	0	10.0	Ethylene, C_2H_4	15	10.07
Cupric sulfide, CuS	0	12.3	Ethane, C_2H_6	15	11.60
Ferric oxide, Fe_2O_3	0	23.6	Urea, $(NH_2)_2CO$	25	22.4
Iron pyrites, FeS_2	25	14.8	Glycine, $CH_2(NH_2)COOH$	25	23.9

I.C.T., **V**, 80, 95–101 for all but last two, which are taken from Parks, Huffman, and Barmore, *J. Am. Chem. Soc.*, **55**, 2733 (1933).

The Calorific Value of Foods. The energy required for bodily work is furnished by the oxidation of foods, either directly or indirectly, in the body. A convenient comparison of different foods therefore is furnished by their **calorific value** — the number of calories liberated by the combustion of a gram of each. These values can be calculated from heats of combustion determined with a calorimetric bomb.

There are three main types of food — carbohydrates, fats, and proteins. Carbohydrates consist of the simple sugars and of all substances which can be hydrolyzed to yield simple sugars. Thus glucose and fructose are simple hexoses, with the empirical formula $C_6H_{12}O_6$. Sucrose, $C_{12}H_{22}O_{11}$, is classed as a disaccharide because upon hydrolysis it yields the monosaccharides glucose and fructose. Plants store most of their carbohydrate material as starch, $(C_6H_{10}O_5)_x$, a polymer of unknown complexity. A similar substance, glycogen, $(C_6H_{10}O_5)_y$, sometimes called "animal starch," is the form in which carbohydrates are stored by animals, chiefly in the liver. Since almost all carbohydrates contain hydrogen and oxygen in the atomic proportion of 2 : 1, we might expect that the heat which they liberate on combustion to CO_2 and H_2O would be approximately the same as that liberated by the combustion of the amount of carbon which they contain. Actually, the heats are about twenty per cent higher, as we can see by comparing the heat of combustion of sucrose with that of the 12 gram atoms of carbon it contains. This is because in diamond each carbon atom is held to its *four* nearest neighbors by strong covalent bonds, while in carbohydrates each carbon atom is held to *two* neighboring carbon atoms, except for the terminal ones, which are held to only one each. Less energy is absorbed in breaking the bonds in a carbohydrate, hence more heat is liberated on combustion.

Fats are esters of the trihydric alcohol, glycerol, and various long-chain aliphatic acids, the most important of which is stearic acid, $CH_3(CH_2)_{16}COOH$. Stearin, or glyceryl tristearate, $C_3H_5(C_{18}H_{35}O_2)_3$ is a typical solid fat. Because of the larger percentage of hydrogen and smaller percentage of oxygen, fats furnish more heat on combustion than carbohydrates do. In fact, their average calorific value is over twice as large.

The third class of foods, proteins, chiefly consist of amino acid residues linked together through the elimination of water between the carboxyl group of one and the amino group of another. Thus the amino acids are the unit building blocks of protein material in the same way that monosaccharides are the units of complex carbohydrates. Typical proteins contain about 53 per cent carbon, 7 per cent hydrogen, 23 per cent oxygen, 16 per cent nitrogen, and 1 per cent sulfur. Some proteins, such as casein, contain about 0.8 per cent of phosphorus, while others, like hemoglobin, contain 0.3 per cent of iron. The complete oxidation of carbohydrates and fats in the body yields carbon dioxide and water — the same products obtained in the bomb calorimeter; hence the same quantity of heat is liberated. The chief difference between the combustion of proteins in the bomb and their metabolism in the body is that the former is more complete. The products of combustion are carbon dioxide, water, and nitrogen, while the process of metabolism yields no free nitrogen, but urea and other nitrogenous substances which have an appreciable calorific value, averaging about 1.3 kcal. per g. We must remember also that not all the food which is consumed is digested. About 2 per cent of the carbohydrates, 5 per cent of the fats, and 8 per cent of the proteins leave the body without being utilized.

Taking this factor into consideration, Table 42 gives a résumé of the average calorific value of different kinds of food.

TABLE 42

Calorific Value (Kcal./G.) of Different Types of Food

Material	Calorific Value		Per Cent Absorbed	Physiological Calorific Value
	Combustion	Metabolism		
Carbohydrates	4.1	4.1	98	4
Fats	9.45	9.45	95	9
Proteins	5.65	4.35	92	4

Sherman, *Chemistry of Food and Nutrition*, pp. 167–168.

These values, plus an analysis of foodstuffs for the percentage of carbohydrate, fat, and protein which they contain, allow us to calculate the fuel value of food in nutrition. For example, the average composition of milk is 5.0 per cent carbohydrate, 4.0 per cent fat, and 3.3 per cent protein, hence the nutritional fuel value will be:

Carbohydrate	$0.05 \times 4 = 0.20$	
Fat	$0.04 \times 9 = 0.36$	
Protein	$0.33 \times 4 = 0.13$	
Total	0.69	kcal./g.

Similarly eggs, containing no carbohydrate, 10.5 per cent fat, and 13.4 per cent protein, have a nutritional fuel value of 1.48 kcal./g.

In comparing foods, it is convenient to know the amounts which have the same physiological fuel value. A convenient standard is the amount of the material which furnishes 100 kcal. For milk this quantity would be $100 \div 0.69 = 145$ g., and for eggs, $100 \div 1.48 = 68$ g. In Table 43 we have listed the portions of a few foods which yield 100 kcal. These values are taken from Sherman's authoritative book, *Chemistry of Food and Nutrition*, to which the reader is referred for further information on this subject.

The large differences in 100-kcal. portions are due chiefly to the difference in water content, which is particularly large in the case of milk and fresh vegetables, and negligible in the case of dried beans. The differences between various kinds of meat are due principally to the difference in fat content. The habits of the

TABLE 43

100-Kcal. Portions of Food Material Based on the Factors Carbohydrate and Protein, 4; Fat, 9

Food Material (Edible Portion)	Weight of Portion		Kcal. Furnished by:		
	Grams	Ounces	Carbohydrates	Fats	Protein
Beef, free from visible fat	86	3.0	0	20	80
Beef, round steak . . .	64	2.3	0	45	55
Ham, fat	19	0.7	0	89	11
Salmon	49	1.7	0	57	43
Eggs	67	2.3	0	64	36
Milk	145	5.1	29	52	19
Butter	14	0.5	0	99.5	0.5
Bread, white	38	1.3	81	5	14
Sugar	25	0.9	100	0	0
Beans, dried	29	1.0	69	26	5
Corn, green or canned .	99	3.2	78	10	12
Lettuce	523	18.4	61	14	25
Potatoes	120	4.2	88	1	11
Spinach	418	14.7	54	11	35
Peanuts	18	0.6	18	63	19
Olive oil	11	0.4	0	100	0

individual make a great deal of difference in the calorific value of his diet. Often the fat is discarded, yet as Sherman says, "If a pound of steak consists of 14 ounces of clear lean, and 2 ounces of clear fat, and the fat is not eaten, at least half of the total fuel value of the pound of steak is lost."

Dietary studies have showed that an average man, weighing 70 kg. (154 pounds) and leading a sedentary professional life, requires 2000 to 2250 kcal. per day in his diet. There are several other ways of determining the food requirements, the most direct of which is the respiration calorimeter developed largely by Benedict. One form of this "human calorimeter" consists of a small room, 4×7 feet and $6\frac{1}{2}$ feet high, in which the subject can live for days at a time. The air in the calorimeter is circulated as shown in Figure 112. The carbon dioxide and water vapor are absorbed from the exhaust air, while a known quantity of oxygen is introduced to make up for that consumed in metabolism.

The ventilating air enters and leaves at the temperature of the calorimeter. The whole chamber is insulated from the outside by a series of walls, with dead air spaces between, shown in Figure 113, which illustrates a compact "chair calorimeter." The heat liberated in the calorimeter is carried away by a current of cold water circulating through a copper coil near the ceiling. It is determined from a measurement of the rate of flow of the water and the difference in its temperature as it enters and leaves the coil. Considerable heat also is carried away by the water vapor exhaled by the subject. This heat is calculated from the quantity of water absorbed in the ventilating system. A series of thermels between the walls of the calorimeter and the outer shields indicate any difference in temperature, which is regulated so as to cancel heat losses during an experiment.

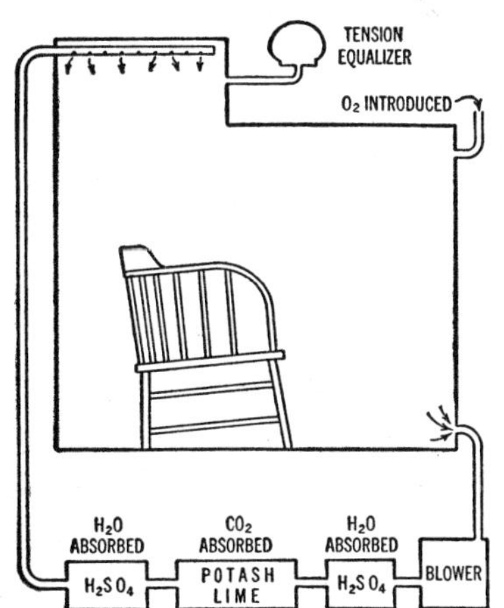

Fig. 112. Ventilating System in Benedict's Respiration Calorimeter.

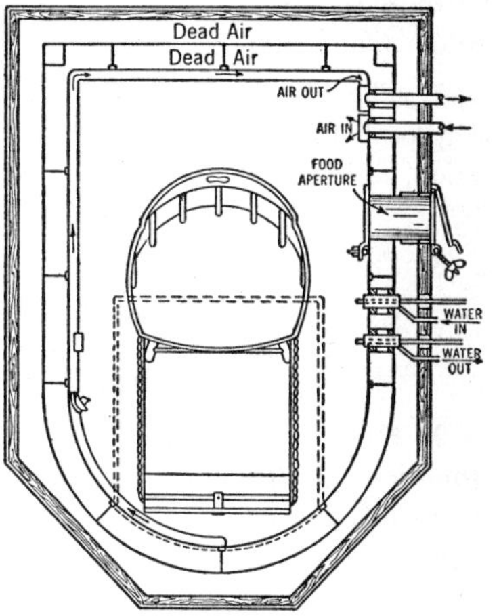

Fig. 113. Benedict's Chair Calorimeter.

Results of a large number of calorimetric experiments agree with the values calculated from dietary studies and calorific values, to about $\frac{1}{4}$ per cent, which is well within experimental error for such experiments. This shows that the source of animal heat is the metabolism of food in the body and that the law of conservation of energy holds here as in the case of inanimate nature.

PROBLEMS AND EXERCISES

1. If 100.00 g. of water, contained in a copper calorimeter weighing 150 g., is heated from 20 to 30° C., how much heat does it receive (*a*) in defined standard calories? (*b*) in mean calories? (*c*) in joules?

2. If 500 g. of benzene at 50.13° C. is poured into 400 g. of carbon tetrachloride, contained in a 200 g. aluminum calorimeter at 23.42°, calculate the final temperature of the system, assuming no heat of mixing and no change of heat capacity with temperature.

3. Calculate approximately the heat of vaporization of the following substances at the boiling point: (*a*) benzene, C_6H_6 (b.p. 80° C.); (*b*) aniline (b.p. 184° C.)

4. How many calories are required to melt 50 g. of ice at 0°, heat the water to 100°, and there vaporize it?

5. If a 10 g. piece of ice, at 0° C. is dropped into 100 g. of water contained in a 50 g. aluminum calorimeter at 25°, what will be the final temperature of the mixture?

6. Estimate the heat of fusion of 1 g. (*a*) of iron (m.p. 1535° C.); (*b*) of sodium (m.p. 97.5° C.).

7. Plot the logarithm of the vapor pressure of water against the reciprocal of the absolute temperature, calculate the molar heat of vaporization, and compare with the experimental value given in Table 34 (page 200).

8. From the data of Table 36, calculate the heats of the following:

$$CaCl_2 \cdot 2\,H_2O + 4\,H_2O \longrightarrow CaCl_2 \cdot 6\,H_2O$$
$$CaCl_2 \cdot 4\,H_2O + aq \longrightarrow CaCl_2 \cdot aq$$
$$NaOH \cdot 25\,H_2O + aq \longrightarrow NaOH \cdot aq$$

9. Using the necessary heats of combustion, calculate the heat of formation, at 18° C., of (*a*) ethane, (*b*) glycerol, (*c*) urea, (*d*) glycine, (*e*) cystine.

10. Calculate the heats of the following reactions:

(*a*) $CuO + H_2 \longrightarrow Cu + H_2O$ (l)
(*b*) $4\,AsH_3 + 3\,O_2 \longrightarrow 4\,As + 6\,H_2O$ (g)
(*c*) $2\,Al + 3\,CuO \longrightarrow Al_2O_3 + 3\,Cu$
(*d*) $4\,FeS_2 + 11\,O_2 \longrightarrow 2\,Fe_2O_3 + 8\,SO_2$

11. Calculate the heats of the following reactions:

H_2O (g) + C $\longrightarrow$ H_2 (g) + CO (g) (water-gas reaction)
CO (g) + $2\,H_2$ (g) $\longrightarrow$ CH_3OH (g) (methanol synthesis)
CH_3OH (g) + CO (g) $\longrightarrow$ CH_3COOH (g) (acetic acid synthesis)

In the last reaction, assume that the heat of vaporization of acetic acid at 18° C. is the same as that at the boiling point, given in Table 34 on page 200.

12. Calculate the heat of hydrolysis of ethyl acetate.

13. (*a*) Calculate the heat of the reaction:

$$C_2H_4\,(g) + H_2 \longrightarrow C_2H_6\,(g)$$

at 18° C.

(*b*) Assuming that the heat capacities of factors and products are constant over a range of temperature, calculate the heat of reaction at 82° C. and compare with Kistiakowsky's results in Table 38 (page 211).

14. From the heats of combustion at 18°, calculate the heat of formation of diethyl ether at 18° and then, by the Person-Kirchhoff relationship, at 100° C.

15. Use Rossini's formulas to calculate the heats of formation of (*a*) *n*-nonane, (*b*) *n*-decanol, (*c*) *n*-heptene-1.

16. Calculate the heat of fusion of ice at − 10° C., assuming that the heat capacities of water and ice are constant from the freezing point to − 10° C.

17. Compare the calorific value in kcal./g. of methanol and ethanol.

18. Calculate the physiological calorific value of two carbohydrates.

19. Calculate the physiological calorific value of glyceryl tributyrate.

20. Calculate the physiological calorific values of valine, glutamic acid, and leucine.

21. Calculate the heats of the following reactions:

(*a*) $CH_3CH(NH_2)COOH\ (s) + 3\ O_2 \longrightarrow 3\ CO_2\ (g) + 2\ H_2O\ (g) + NH_3\ (g)$

(*b*) $2\ NH_3\ (g) + CO_2\ (g) \longrightarrow (NH_2)_2CO\ (s) + H_2O\ (l)$

(*c*) $2(CH_3)_2CHCH_2CH(NH_2)COOH + 15\ O_2 \longrightarrow 11\ CO_2 + (NH_2)_2CO + 11\ H_2O\ (l)$

22. Calculate the calorific value of *dl*-alanine and leucine in the reactions (*a*) and (*c*) of the preceding problem.

READING LIST

Douglas McKie and Niels H. deV. Heathcote, *The Discovery of Specific and Latent Heats.* Edward Arnold and Company, London, 1935.

F. Russell Bichowsky and Frederick D. Rossini, *The Thermochemistry of the Chemical Substances.* Reinhold Publishing Corporation, New York, 1936.

Frederick D. Rossini, "Modern Thermochemistry," *Chem. Rev.*, **18,** 233 (1936).

—— "Heats of Formation of Simple Organic Molecules," *Ind. Eng. Chem.*, **29,** 1424 (1937).

Henry C. Sherman, *Chemistry of Food and Nutrition*, 5th ed. The Macmillan Company, New York, 1937.

CHAPTER 9

SOLUTIONS OF NONELECTROLYTES

A ***solution*** may be defined as *a homogeneous mixture of two or more substances.* The solutions with which we are chiefly concerned in the study of physical chemistry are made up of only two components, one of which, the **solute,** is said to be dissolved in the other, the **solvent.** The terms *solute* and *solvent* do not signify any essential difference in nature or in function between the two components. A mixture of alcohol and water, for example, may be regarded as a solution of alcohol in water or as a solution of water in alcohol. Generally, the component present in relatively large amount is called the *solvent* and the less abundant component the *solute.*

Types of Solutions. The three most familiar types of solutions are *solid in liquid, liquid in liquid,* and *gas in liquid.* A solid also may act as solvent and dissolve another solid, a liquid, or a gas. Some alloys, like those of silver and gold, are *solid solutions.* Salt pairs, such as cesium chloride and rubidium chloride, sometimes form solid solutions. A solid solution may be formed if the two components are alike in crystal lattice and in the dimensions of their unit cells. Solid paraffin, which contains liquid as well as solid hydrocarbons, may be regarded as the solution of a liquid in a solid. An example of a gas dissolved in a solid is the solution of hydrogen in palladium.

Whatever the solvent and solute, the process of solution involves a complete mixing of the molecules of one substance with the molecules of the other. Each substance is *molecularly dispersed* in the other. In general, solid and liquid substances which are most similar chemically will dissolve most readily in one another. This useful generalization that "like dissolves like" was a familiar rule to the alchemists.

In the discussion of the general properties of solutions, we shall confine ourselves chiefly to aqueous solutions, since water is the most important medium for chemical reactions, especially those which take place in plant and animal organisms. Solutions in other solvents such as liquid ammonia, acetic acid, and acetamide, which have been extensively studied, are generally comparable with aqueous solutions and obey the same general laws.

Solubility

The **solubility** *of a substance in a given solvent is the concentration of the saturated solution, i.e., the concentration of the solution in equilibrium with the undissolved phase, at a given temperature and, in the case of gases, at a given partial pressure.* The determination of solubility therefore involves only the analysis of the saturated solution. In the case of a solid solute, the concentration may be determined by evaporating the solution to dryness and weighing the solid residue. If the solid is highly insoluble, the concentration may be found from electrical conductance or electromotive force data (see pages 395 and 421).

Concentration Units. The concentration of a solution may be expressed in various ways, all of which involve the quantity of solute and the quantity of solvent or of solution. The various methods may be summarized in two groups:

A. Weight of solute in a given volume of solution.

(1) Grams of solute per liter of solution.

(2) Moles of solute per liter of solution: Molarity, *M*. The number of moles is found by dividing the weight in grams by the weight of 1 mole. The number of moles of solute in 1 liter of solution is the *molarity* of the solution.

(3) Gram equivalents of solute per liter of solution: Normality, *N*. The number of gram equivalents of solute in 1 liter of solution is called the *normality* of the solution. This way of expressing concentration is most useful in quantitative analysis.

B. Weight of solute in a given weight of solution or solvent.

(1) Per cent by weight. The per cent by weight is the number of grams of solute in 100 grams of the solution. Thus, a 6 per cent solution of sodium chloride in water is a solution of 6 grams of sodium chloride in 94 grams of water.

(2) Grams of solute in 1000 grams of solvent.

(3) Moles of solute in 1000 grams of solvent: Molality, *m*. The number of moles of solute in 1000 grams of solvent is called the *molality* of the solution.

(4) Mole fraction. The *mole fraction* is the number of moles of one component of a solution divided by the total number of moles of all the components present. For example, if we have 0.642 mole of sucrose in 1000 grams, or $\frac{1000}{18.016} = 55.51$ moles of water, the total number of moles of sucrose and water will be 56.15. The mole fraction of sucrose will be $\frac{0.642}{56.15}$, or 0.0114 and the mole fraction of water will be 1.0000 − 0.0114, or 0.9886. More generally, if a solution contains n_A moles of component A, n_B moles of component B, etc., the mole fraction of component A, designated by x_A, will be given by:

$$x_A = \frac{n_A}{n_A + n_B + n_C + \cdots}$$

The mole fractions are the relative numbers of molecules of each of the constituents, and are particularly significant and important in physicochemical relationships.

(5) Mole per cent. The *mole per cent* of a component of a given solution is the number of moles of the component in 100 moles of the solution. It is 100 times the mole fraction.

The concentration units in the second group which are referred solely to *weight*, have two definite advantages over those in the first group which involve *volume:* (1) when substances are mixed to form a solution their *weights* are additive, while *volumes* are not; (2) weight concentrations are independent of the temperature.

TABLE 44

SOLUBILITY OF GASES IN WATER

Gas	Solubility *	
	Ml. per Liter of Water	G. per Liter of Water
Ammonia	1,176,000	895
Hydrogen chloride	517,000	842
Sulfur dioxide	79,790	228.3
Chlorine	4,613	14.6
Hydrogen sulfide	4,670	7.07
Carbon dioxide	1,713	3.35
Nitric oxide	74	0.098
Oxygen	49	0.070
Carbon monoxide	35	0.044
Nitrogen	23	0.029
Hydrogen	22	0.002

* At 0° C. and 760 mm. pressure. Data mostly from Landolt-Börnstein, *Tabellen*, 5th ed., 1923, pp. 762 *et seq.*

The Solubility of Gases in Liquids. Hydrogen chloride, nitrogen dioxide, and ammonia are *very soluble* in water; chlorine, hydrogen sulfide, and carbon dioxide may be termed *moderately soluble;* hydrogen, oxygen, and argon are only *slightly soluble;* possibly the least soluble of all gases is krypton. The most soluble gases react chemically with the water. This is illustrated by the first six of the gases listed in Table 44.

The Effect of Pressure on the Solubility of Gases. The solubility of a gas increases when its partial pressure is increased. The relation is expressed by **Henry's law,** formulated in 1803, which states: *The weight of gas dissolved in a given quantity of solvent is proportional to the partial pressure of the gas.* The generalization may be expressed mathematically, thus:

$$\frac{w}{v} = kp$$

where v is the volume of the solvent, w the weight of the gas, p its partial pressure, and k a constant characteristic of the gas.

Since $\frac{w}{v}$ is the weight of gas dissolved in unit volume of solution, we may designate it as concentration C_2, and since, as a corollary to Boyle's law, the concentration in the gas phase C_1 is proportional to the pressure of the gas p, we may write:

$$C_1 = k^1 p$$

Substituting in the first equation we obtain:

$$C_2 = \frac{k}{k^1} C_1 \qquad \text{or} \qquad \frac{C_2}{C_1} = K$$

Restated in terms of concentration, **Henry's law** is: *The ratio between the concentrations of a gaseous substance in solution and in the gas phase is the same at all partial pressures.*

Data which illustrate Henry's law are given in Table 45 and are plotted in Figure 114.

Henry's law applies to slightly soluble gases even at low temperatures and up to about 5 atmospheres pressure; in the case of moderately soluble gases like carbon dioxide, it applies better at higher temperatures. It is not confined to aqueous solutions, but the values of the constants are different for different solvents. It does not apply if the gas reacts chemically with the solvent or if it dissociates or associates when it dissolves.

TABLE 45

HENRY'S LAW: CHANGE OF SOLUBILITY OF A GAS WITH PRESSURE

OXYGEN IN WATER AT 25° C. *			HYDROGEN SULFIDE IN ANILINE AT 22° C. **		
Pressure of Oxygen, Mm.	Solubility G. per L.	$k=\frac{w}{p}\times 10^7$	Pressure of H_2S, Mm.	Solubility G. per L.	$k=\frac{w}{p}\times 100$
174.7	0.0095	543	102	2.74	2.68
240.7	0.0128	531	199	5.32	2.67
300.3	0.0160	533	390	10.6	2.72
349.0	0.0184	527	579	15.8	2.73
396.1	0.0210	530	874	24.0	2.75
440.5	0.0233	529	1160	31.6	2.72
577.7	0.0303	525			
639.7	0.0337	527			
741.1	0.0393	530			

* J. L. R. Morgan and A. H. Richardson, *J. Phys. Chem.*, **34**, 2356 (1930).
** W. D. Bancroft and B. C. Belden, *J. Phys. Chem.*, **34**, 2123 (1930).

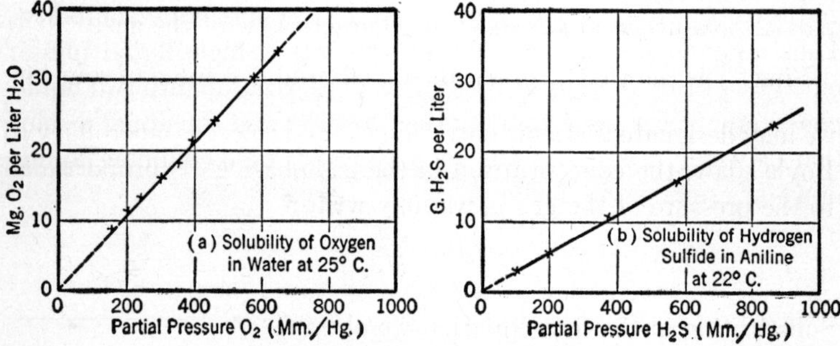

Fig. 114. Plots Illustrating Henry's Law.

The Effect of Temperature on the Solubility of Gases. Most gases become considerably less soluble as the temperature is raised. The extent of the change in the case of several common gases is illustrated by the data in Table 46. Such gases may be expelled

TABLE 46

SOLUBILITY OF GASES AT VARIOUS TEMPERATURES

(Grams Gas per Liter Water)

TEMP. (° C.)	H_2	O_2	CO_2	NH_3
0	0.0019	0.0695	3.35	900
30	0.0015	0.0360	1.25	400
60	0.0012	0.0227	0.58	—
90	0.0005	0.0079	—	—

almost completely by boiling or by passing steam through the solution. As each bubble of steam rises through the solution, gas molecules diffuse into it. Thus the steam carries out the gas molecules and eventually reduces the concentration of dissolved gas virtually to zero. Even ammonia, which reacts with water, may be removed by boiling. However, this is not true for hydrogen chloride and the other hydrogen halides (see page 241).

The Solubility of Liquids in Liquids. Some liquids mix with one another in all proportions and are said to be **consolute.** This is true of fused salts, fused metals, of ethanol or glycerol and water, and of some organic liquid pairs. When two such substances are mixed, the molecules quickly disperse and form a single homogeneous liquid phase. Other liquid pairs are quite insoluble and after being shaken together quickly separate into two liquid phases, one floating on the other. This happens, for example, with water and nitrobenzene. Other liquids again show moderate solubility. Thus water shaken with a little ether gives a single liquid phase; but the addition of more ether may cause separation into two liquid phases, the lower a solution of ether in water and the upper a solution of water in ether. The solubilities of some common liquids in water are given in Table 47.

TABLE 47

SOLUBILITY OF SOME LIQUIDS IN WATER (20° C.)

LIQUID	PER CENT SOLUTE IN SATURATED SOLUTION
Aniline	3.49
Bromine	3.41
Butanol-1	20.1
Carbon disulfide	0.21
Carbon tetrachloride	0.08
Chloroform	0.80
Diethyl ether	6.98
Ethanol	miscible
Ethyl acetate	7.94
Glycerol	miscible
Nitrobenzene	0.19

Consolute Temperatures. The solubility of a liquid in water usually increases with rise in temperature. Often a temperature is reached at which the two liquids become completely miscible; this is called the **consolute temperature** or **critical solution temperature.** As an illustration we will take the system *phenol-water*, which has been studied very carefully. If a small quantity of phenol [1] is shaken with water, it dissolves. At 20° C., if more than 8.36 g. of phenol per 100 g. of solution are added, the mixture separates into two layers, the lower a saturated solution of water in phenol, the upper a saturated solution of phenol in water. As the temperature is raised, the solubility of each substance in the other increases. Finally, at 65.85° C., the two components become completely miscible and one homogeneous liquid phase results. This is the *consolute temperature* of the system.

Hill and Malisoff [2] have determined the compositions of the two layers at various temperatures. Their results are given in Table 48 and are plotted in Figure 115.

TABLE 48

MUTUAL SOLUBILITY OF WATER AND PHENOL

TEMPERATURE ° C.	WT. PER CENT PHENOL IN UPPER LAYER	WT. PER CENT PHENOL IN LOWER LAYER
20	8.4	72.2
30	9.2	69.9
40	9.6	66.8
50	11.8	62.6
55	13.8	59.2
60	16.8	55.1
65	23.9	45.8
65.85	34.0	

The curve AC gives the concentrations of phenol in the upper layer, *i.e.*, the solubilities of phenol in water, at various temperatures, and the curve BC the concentrations of phenol in the lower layer, *i.e.*, the solubilities of water in phenol. This diagram indicates whether one or two phases will result when given weights of water and phenol are mixed at a given temperature. If the per cent of phenol corresponds to a point under the curve, there will be two phases, if to a point outside the curve, there will be a single phase. At the point C, which corre-

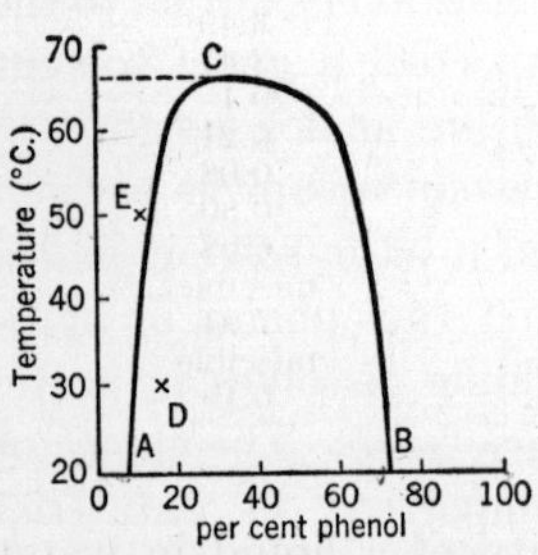

Fig. 115. Phenol-Water Solubility.

[1] Pure phenol is a solid, melting at 43° C. The solution in it of a very small quantity of water lowers the freezing point below room temperature and this moist phenol may be regarded as one member of the liquid pair.

[2] *J. Am. Chem. Soc.*, **48**, 918 (1926).

sponds to 65.85° C. and 34.0 per cent phenol, the two solubility curves meet; hence 65.85° C. is the *consolute temperature.*

Systems like phenol-water, which show an increase in mutual solubility with rising temperature and eventually become consolute, are said to have an **upper consolute temperature.** In some cases the mutual solubility *decreases* with rising temperature. A system of this type is *triethylamine-water;* complete miscibility occurs below 18.5° C., which is the **lower consolute temperature.** The system *nicotine-water* shows complete miscibility above 210° C. and below 60° C., thus having both an *upper* and a *lower consolute temperature.* The upper consolute temperatures of certain common liquid mixtures, such as *ethanol-carbon disulfide,* are below room temperature; thus carbon disulfide and ethanol separate into two layers below 14.4° C.

The Solubility of Solids in Liquids. The solubility of solids in water or any other liquid may be expressed as the number of grams of solute that will saturate 1 liter of the solvent at the given temperature. Knowing the density of the solvent, the weight of solvent may be found and hence the solubility may be expressed as *molality, mole fraction,* or *mole per cent.*

We are not yet in a position to predict with certainty from any specific characteristic of a substance whether or not it will be readily soluble in water or any other solvent. Substances which are soluble in water may be insoluble in ethanol or ether; those which are soluble in ether may be insoluble in ethanol; and so on. It is certain, however, that solubility depends upon the properties of both substances and that the process of solution is mutual to the solvent and the solute. As would be expected, a given solvent usually dissolves readily substances which are analogous to it in composition and structure; for example, gasoline dissolves paraffin wax. Also, an acid substance dissolves in a basic solvent and a basic substance dissolves in an acid solvent; thus phenol or pyrogallol dissolves readily in pyridine, guanidine dissolves in acetic acid, and diphenylamine dissolves in sulfuric acid. The choice of solvents for extractions is extremely important in industrial chemistry and many new solvents have been developed, *e.g.*, methyl cellosolve, $HOH_2C \cdot CH_2OCH_3$. Since this contains two **functional groups** (—OH, characteristic of water and an alcohol, and —C · O · C—, characteristic of an ether), it combines to a large extent the solvent properties of all three types of substances.

The Effect of Temperature on the Solubility of Solids. The solubility of a solid usually is increased by a rise in temperature, although in some cases it is decreased. The change depends upon the **principle of Le Chatelier** (see page 307). *If a substance dissolves with evolution of heat, its solubility will decrease with rising temperature; if it dissolves with absorption of heat, its solubility will increase with rising temperature.* In order to apply this rule, we must know the heat liberated or absorbed when the substance is dissolved in the *nearly saturated solution.* This may be quite different from the heat change when the substance is dissolved in pure water, unless its solubility is very low. The principle therefore is immediately applicable only to such slightly soluble compounds as calcium sulfate, calcium hydroxide, and silver chloride.

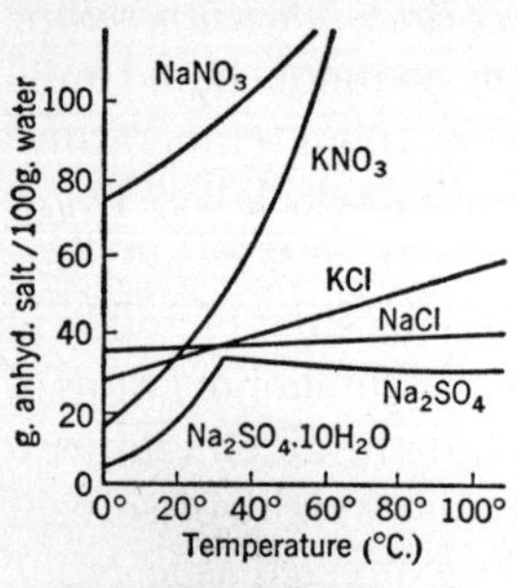

Fig. 116. Solubility of Certain Salts.

In Figure 116 the change in solubility with changing temperature is shown for some salts. Most of the curves are smooth, but some, like that for sodium sulfate, show a break, which indicates that the solid phase is different for the two parts of the curve.

In the case of sodium sulfate, the solid phase up to 32.383° C. is $Na_2SO_4 \cdot 10\,H_2O$; above that temperature it is Na_2SO_4; transition occurs at this temperature from one solid phase to the other, thus:

$$Na_2SO_4 \cdot 10\,H_2O \rightleftharpoons Na_2SO_4 + 10\,H_2O$$

From this it is obvious that the solubility of a substance will depend upon its state of hydration (more generally, of *solvation*) when it is in contact with the saturated solution.

Properties of Solutions

The specific physical properties of a solution differ markedly from those of the solvent. We shall consider in some detail the effects of solid and liquid solutes upon the *vapor pressure,* the *freezing point,* the *boiling point,* and the *osmotic pressure.*

The Ideal Solution. In studying gases, we defined the **ideal gas,** which real gases approach in their behavior as their pressures are reduced toward zero and with which they may be compared. In dealing with solutions, likewise it is profitable to compare real solutions with an **ideal solution** with the following properties: (1) There is no change in volume when the solution is formed from its components. (2) There is no heat effect when the components are mixed. (3) The vapor pressure of each component is equal to the vapor pressure of the pure substance multiplied by its mole fraction in the solution. In general, only very dilute solutions behave *ideally*. The deviations in additivity of volumes in some nearly ideal solutions are indicated by the data in Table 49.

TABLE 49

CHANGE IN VOLUME ON MIXING OF LIQUIDS

LIQUID A	LIQUID B	TOTAL VOLUME WHEN 50.00 ML. OF A ARE MIXED WITH 50.00 ML. OF B
Chlorobenzene	Bromobenzene	100.00
Benzene	Toluene	100.16
Benzene	Carbon tetrachloride	99.85
Hexane	Octane	99.97
Ethyl benzene	Toluene	99.97
Ethanol	Water	96.72

The Derivation of Raoult's Law. **Raoult's law,** enunciated in 1888,[1] relates the vapor pressure of the ideal solution to the concentration. It may be derived as follows: The vapor pressure of a component of a solution is the pressure exerted by the gaseous molecules of the substance in equilibrium with the solution. The pressure of a gas is proportional to the concentration. Since we have:

$$\text{(Substance in gas phase)} \rightleftharpoons \text{(Substance in solution)}$$

it follows that the concentration in the gas phase is proportional to that in the solution, and hence the vapor pressure of the substance is proportional to the number of molecules of the substance present in unit volume of solution. Thus we may write:

$$p_{\text{A}} = kx_{\text{A}}$$

[1] *Zeit. physik. Chem.*, **2**, 353 (1888). François Marie Raoult, 1830–1901, born at Fournes, France, obtained his doctorate in physical sciences at the University of Paris in 1863. In 1867 he was appointed Chargé du Cours de Chimie at the University of Grenoble, and three years later was promoted to the professorship of chemistry there. Although he is best known for his outstanding work on vapor pressure and for the establishment of the fundamentally important law which bears his name, his work in cryoscopy also received international recognition because of its high precision. Many honors came to him, including election as *Commandeur de la Légion d'Honneur*. It was said of him in a memorial address, "La vie de M. Raoult se résume dans un seul mot: le travail." For a portrait of Raoult, see Plate I, facing page 4.

where p_A is the vapor pressure of the substance A, and x_A is its mole fraction in the solution. If $x_A = 1$, *i.e.*, if we are dealing with the pure substance A, then $p_A = k = p^0_A$, the vapor pressure of the pure substance at the given temperature. Substituting this value for k in the previous equation gives:

$$p_A = p^0_A x_A$$

This means that *the vapor pressure due to a component of a solution is equal to the vapor pressure of the pure substance at the given temperature, multiplied by its mole fraction in the solution.* This is one way of stating **Raoult's law.** It will be met in other forms in the subsequent discussion. In general, the more dilute the solution, the more nearly is Raoult's law obeyed.

The Properties of Solutions of Liquids in Liquids: Liquid Pairs. *A system composed of two liquid components usually is called a* ***liquid pair.*** The vapor pressures of such liquid pairs determine their boiling points and their behavior on distillation. The purification of substances by distillation, and the extremely important processes of *fractional distillation* and *steam distillation* obviously depend upon this property. Before discussing actual liquid pairs it is worth while to consider the *ideal solution, i.e.*, the *ideal liquid pair.*

Vapor Pressure and Distillation of the Ideal Solution. If both components A and B of an ideal binary solution are volatile, we may apply Raoult's law to the two components, thus:

$$p_A = p^0_A x_A \qquad \text{and} \qquad p_B = p^0_B x_B$$

The total vapor pressure p will be:

$$p = p_A + p_B = p^0_A x_A + p^0_B x_B$$

Since the vapor pressures are proportional to the mole fractions of the two components in the gas phase, the composition of this phase will be:

$$x'_A = \frac{p_A}{p_A + p_B} \qquad x'_B = \frac{p_B}{p_A + p_B}$$

The relative concentration of either constituent, *e.g.*, A, in the two phases therefore will be:

$$\frac{x'_A}{x_A} = \frac{1}{x_A + \dfrac{p^0_B}{p^0_A} x_B}$$

If $p^0_A = p^0_B$, this ratio will be unity, since in the liquid phase $x_A + x_B = 1$. If $p^0_A > p^0_B$, the concentration of A will be *greater* in the gas phase, and if $p^0_A < p^0_B$, it will be less.

To take a specific example, let us assume that at the given temperature the pure components A and B have vapor pressures of 100 and 50 mm./Hg, respectively, and that the mole fraction of A is 0.80, so that the mole fraction of B is 0.20. Then for the solution:

$p_A = 0.80 \times 100 = 80$ mm./Hg and $p_B = 0.20 \times 50 = 10$ mm./Hg

The total pressure will be:

$$p = p_A + p_B = 90 \text{ mm./Hg}$$

The composition of the vapor phase in this case then is:

$$x'_A = \tfrac{80}{90}, \text{ or } 0.889 \qquad \text{and} \qquad x'_B = \tfrac{10}{90}, \text{ or } 0.111$$

Thus a solution containing 80 mole per cent of A and 20 mole per cent of B is in equilibrium with a vapor containing 88.9 mole per cent of A and 11.1 mole per cent of B. The component A, with the higher vapor pressure, is relatively more concentrated in the vapor phase than in the liquid phase.

If the compositions of the vapor phase for various mixtures of the same two components are calculated and plotted against the total vapor pressures, they yield a vapor-pressure diagram for an ideal liquid pair like that shown in Figure 117. Here the abscissas

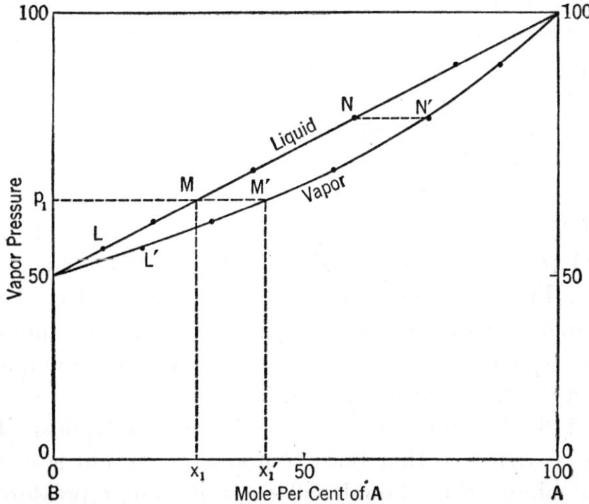

Fig. 117. Vapor-Pressure Diagram for an Ideal Liquid Pair.

represent the composition of both the liquid and the vapor phases and the ordinates the total vapor pressure of the liquid. The curve labeled *vapor* gives the composition of the vapor in equilibrium with the solution having the vapor pressure corresponding to the ordinate. For example, the liquid with composition x_1 and vapor pressure p_1, represented by the point M, is in equilibrium with vapor of composition x'_1; the liquid with composition and vapor pressure represented by the point N is in equilibrium with vapor represented by the point N', and so on. Since the mixture is an *ideal solution* of two liquids, the vapor pressures are additive and the vapor-pressure–composition curve is a straight line, shown as LMN in the diagram. The composition of the vapor in equilibrium with various mixtures is given by a curve $L'M'N'$, falling below the liquid vapor-pressure–composition curve.

This diagram shows that the vapor in equilibrium with the ideal solution of two liquids is richer in the more volatile component than is the solution; hence, *the two components could be separated by fractional distillation.*

Vapor Pressures of Liquid Pairs. Only very dilute solutions or those in which the components are nearly identical in chemical nature behave ideally. In most cases, liquid pairs deviate from Raoult's law. The deviations may be either positive or negative, *i.e.*, the vapor pressure may be either greater or less than that calculated. If both components show positive deviations, the total vapor pressure will be greater than that calculated and the curve passes through a maximum. If the components show negative deviations, the total vapor pressure will be less than that calculated and the curve usually goes through a minimum.

Typical vapor pressure curves for liquid pairs are shown in Figure 118. In each of these diagrams the broken lines represent the partial pressures of the components and the dotted lines the calculated partial pressures. Figure 118 (*a*) represents a nearly ideal pair; Figure 118 (*b*) shows a system with positive deviation and a vapor pressure curve passing through a maximum; and Figure 118 (*c*) shows a system with negative deviation and a vapor pressure curve passing through a minimum.

Figure 118 (*d*) represents a pair of immiscible liquids. If such a system is stirred so that both components present a surface to the vapor phase, each liquid will exert its vapor pressure independently of the other component. The total pressure then

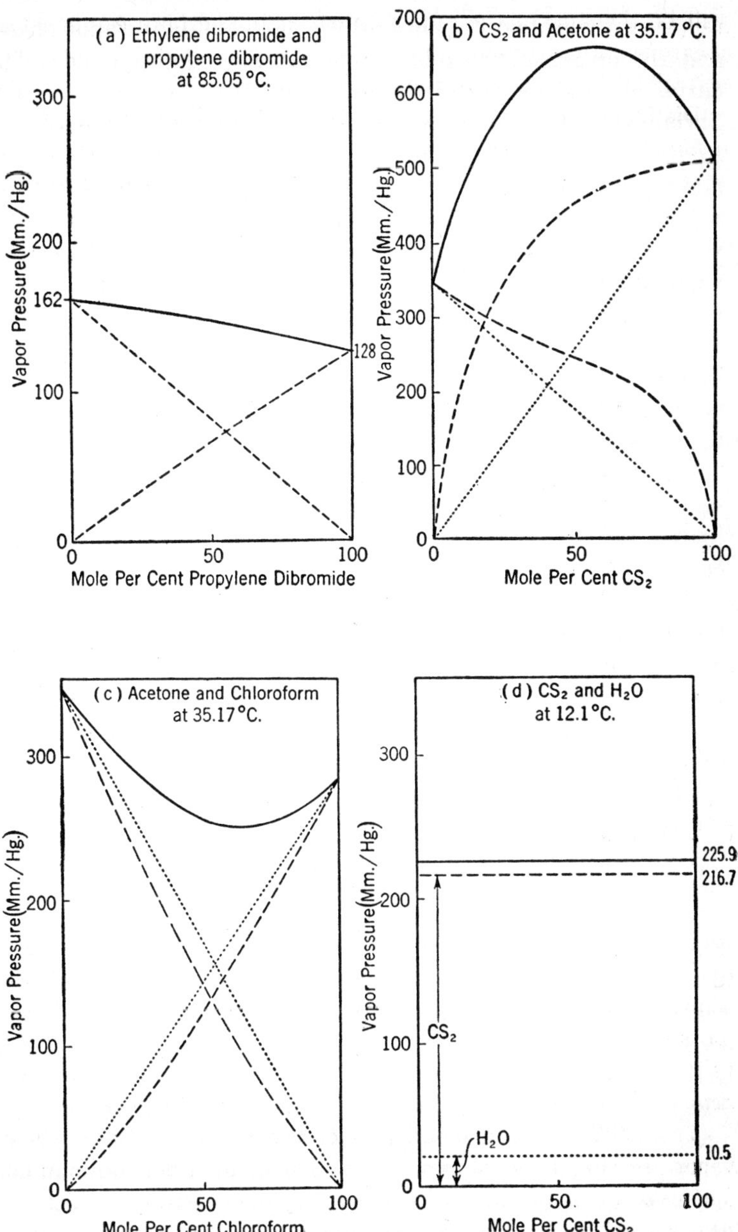

Fig. 118. Vapor Pressures of Liquid Pairs.

will be the sum of the vapor pressures of the pure components, regardless of the proportions in which they are mixed. This gives a straight line parallel to the composition axis.

Distillation of Liquid Pairs. *The **boiling point** of a liquid is defined as the temperature at which the vapor pressure of the liquid is equal to the pressure of the atmosphere.* Corresponding to each

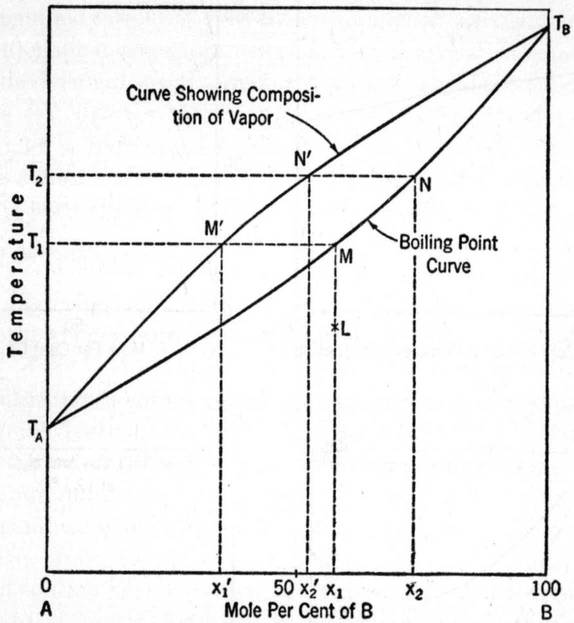

Fig. 119. Boiling-Point Diagram for a Liquid Pair Whose Vapor Curve Shows Neither a Maximum nor a Minimum.

type of *vapor pressure diagram* we may construct a *boiling point diagram* which explains what occurs during distillation of the solution. In the vapor pressure diagram the vapor pressure is plotted against the composition *at constant temperature,* whereas in the boiling point diagram the temperature of boiling is plotted against the composition *at constant* (*e.g.*, *atmospheric*) *pressure.*

(1) Distillation of a liquid pair of two miscible liquids whose vapor-pressure curve shows neither a maximum nor a minimum. This type includes the *ideal solution* and many solutions which are nearly ideal, such as benzene-ethylene dichloride, benzene-carbon disulfide, water-acetone, chlorobenzene-bromobenzene, chloroform-carbon tetrachloride, oxygen-nitrogen. The boiling-point diagram for such a system is shown in Figure 119.

Consider what occurs when such a liquid pair is distilled. If we heat a solution of composition x_1 from a temperature represented by the point L, the vapor pressure rises until, at the point M, it equals the pressure of the atmosphere and boiling begins. The composition of the vapor first distilling off is x'_1 and the temperature of boiling T_1; the vapor is richer in A, the lower boiling constituent, than was the original solution. Since, as boiling proceeds, the residue becomes increasingly richer in B, the higher-boiling constituent, the temperature of boiling rises (*e.g.*, to T_2) and the composition of the residue gradually changes from x_1 to x_2, while that of the distillate changes from x'_1 to x'_2. Thus from a solution with the initial concentration x_1 we obtain a distillate of composition approximately $\frac{x'_1 + x'_2}{2}$, and, at the same time, a residual solution of composition x_2. The distillation has effected a partial separation of A and B; repeated distillation effects an almost complete separation of the two components. Each *fraction* collected between suitable temperature limits is redistilled, and with each *fractionation* the separation of the two components becomes more nearly complete. The process of *fractional distillation* is much used in industry to separate liquids from one another and also to obtain liquid products with boiling point limits suitable for particular purposes. The fractionation of crude petroleum to obtain petroleum ether, gasoline, kerosene, and various lubricating oils, is an important process of this kind.

(2) Distillation of a liquid pair whose vapor-pressure curve shows a maximum. Since the vapor-pressure curve shows a maximum, the boiling-point curve for such a solution will pass through a minimum. The behavior on distillation of a solution of this type may be predicted from the boiling-point diagram shown in Figure 120.

If a solution of composition and temperature represented by the point L is heated, it begins to boil at M, the solution of initial composition x_1 giving a distillate of composition x'_1. As the boiling proceeds the temperature rises from T_1 to T_2, and during this interval distillates of compositions from x'_1 to x'_2 are obtained. A comparison with Figure 119 shows that fractionation can separate only the component A from the solution of composition x_m, boiling at the minimum point on the curve T_m. In the same way a solution of composition and temperature represented by L_1 begins to boil at Q, the solution with the initial composition y_1 giving vapor of composition y'_1. As distillation proceeds the composition of the vapor changes to y'_2 as that of the residual solution changes to y_2. Fractionation will yield, in this case, pure B and a solution of composition x_m. At the minimum point the vapor pressure curve coincides with the boiling point curve; in other words *the*

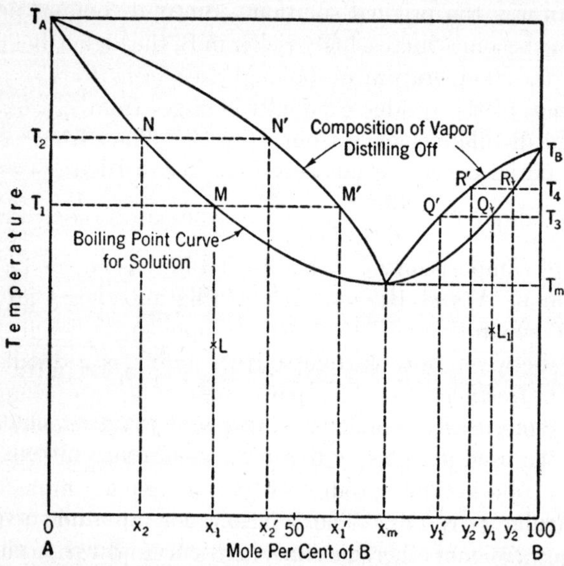

Fig. 120. Boiling-Point Diagram for a Liquid Pair Whose Vapor-Pressure Curve Shows a Maximum.

composition of the vapor distilling off is the same as the composition of the residual liquid. A solution of this composition will distil without change in composition or temperature and constitutes a **minimum constant-boiling solution.**

The liquid pair *water-ethanol* is a particularly interesting and important example of this type of system. The boiling point of pure ethanol is 78.39° C.; the constant-boiling solution, which contains 95.59 per cent of ethanol, boils at 78.15° C. This small difference in boiling temperatures accounts for the impossibility of obtaining ethanol more concentrated than 95.59 per cent by fractionation of a more dilute solution if the distillation is carried out at atmospheric pressure. However, in this as in other similar cases, the composition of the constant-boiling solution changes with the external pressure. If the pressure is kept sufficiently low, fractionation may be accomplished and pure ethanol obtained. Data illustrating the change of composition of the constant-boiling solution with changing pressure are given for the ethanol-water system in Table 50.

TABLE 50

EFFECT OF CHANGING PRESSURE ON THE COMPOSITION OF CONSTANT-BOILING ETHANOL-WATER SOLUTIONS

PRESSURE IN MM./HG.	BOILING POINTS ° C.		PER CENT ETHANOL IN CONSTANT-BOILING SOLUTION
	Ethanol	Constant-Boiling Solution	
1450	95.50	95.35	95.27
1075	87.26	87.03	95.33
760	78.39	78.13	95.59
200	47.97	47.95	97.30
130	39.35	39.34	98.75
100	34.20	34.20	99.46
75	29.35	None formed	100.00

J. Wade and R. W. Merriman, *J. Chem. Soc.*, **99**, 997 (1911).

Other systems of this kind are acetic acid-pyridine, chloroform-acetone, benzene-ethanol, chloroform-methanol, nitrous oxide-ethane.

(3) Distillation of a liquid pair whose vapor-pressure curve shows a minimum. Since the vapor-pressure curve shows a minimum, the boiling-point curve for the system will pass through a maximum. The vapor-pressure diagram for a system of this kind is shown in Figure 118 (*c*); the corresponding boiling-point diagram is shown in Figure 121.

Reasoning analogous to that in connection with Figure 120 will lead to the conclusion that the distillation of a solution containing x_1 mole per cent of B will yield a constant boiling solution of composition x_m and a distillate with a smaller proportion of B. Similarly, distillation of a solution of composition y_1 will yield a constant boiling solution of composition x_m and a distillate richer in B.

One of the most interesting and important liquid pairs of this type is hydrogen chloride and water. When a solution of hydrochloric acid is distilled, both water and acid distil off, the proportions depending largely on whether the concentration of acid is above or below that of the solution with minimum vapor pressure. In either case the boiling temperature rises and eventually becomes constant. The composition of the distillate becomes equal to that of the residual solution and remains so as the distillation

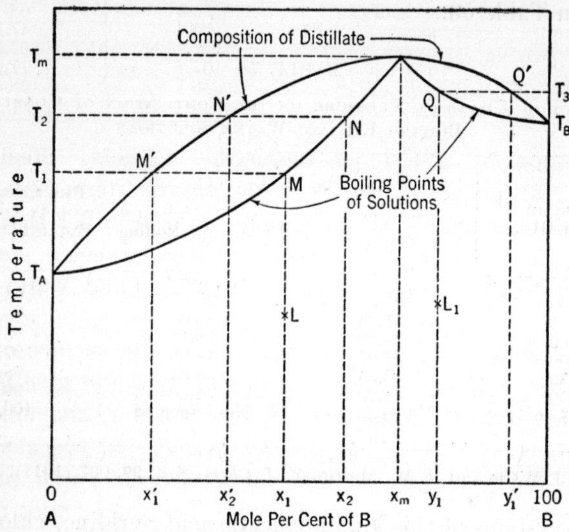

Fig. 121. Distillation of a Liquid Pair Whose Vapor-Pressure Curve Shows a Minimum.

proceeds further. At a pressure of 760 mm./Hg the constant-boiling solution contains 20.221 per cent hydrochloric acid and has a boiling point of 108.584° C. The composition of this constant-boiling solution is so definite and the solution so readily obtained that it serves as a convenient primary standard in acidimetry. The change in composition of the constant-boiling solution with pressure is shown in Table 51.

TABLE 51

Composition of Constant-Boiling Hydrochloric Acid Solution

Pressure in Mm./Hg.	**770**	**760**	**750**	**740**	**730**
Per Cent HCl	20.197	20.221	20.245	20.269	20.293

Foulk and Hollingsworth, *J. Am. Chem. Soc.*, **45**, 1227 (1923).

Other liquid pairs of this type with their compositions and boiling points are listed in Table 52.

TABLE 52

LIQUID PAIRS HAVING MAXIMUM BOILING POINTS

LIQUID A	LIQUID B	B. P. (° C.) AT 760 MM.	PER CENT OF B IN CONSTANT-BOILING SOLUTION
Water	Nitric acid	120.5	68
Water	Hydrogen bromide	126	47.5
Water	Hydrogen iodide	127	57.0
Water	Formic acid	107.1	77.9
Water	Sulfuric acid	338	98.3

Distillation of a Pair of Immiscible Liquids: Steam Distillation. Although no liquids are *completely* immiscible, many pairs of liquids are so nearly insoluble in each other that for all practical purposes they may be considered immiscible. Examples are water-nitrobenzene, water-bromobenzene, and water-chlorobenzene.

Nitrobenzene carefully introduced below the surface of water in a suitable container will form a lower layer and give no odor. Only the water will vaporize. When, however, the mixture is shaken so that both liquids present surfaces to the gas phase, they will both vaporize to the extent of their vapor pressures at the temperature of the experiment. The total vapor pressure will be the sum of the vapor pressures of the two liquids. The attempt to distil the two-layer system of the two liquids causes violent bumping which can be prevented only by thorough agitation. As the temperature rises, the partial pressures of the two components increase, and boiling begins when their sum equals the atmospheric pressure. The distillate, throughout the distillation, contains the two components in the ratio of their vapor pressures at the temperature of distillation. The principle is best explained with reference to the most important process of this type, *viz., steam distillation.*

Steam distillation is a valuable process in the purification of organic substances. Very frequently in organic syntheses the isolation of the main product requires its separation from several by-products, usually by distillation. Direct distillation of a complex mixture often causes some decomposition, which may be avoided by applying steam distillation at a lower temperature. The process is carried out using an apparatus such as that shown in Figure 122.

The steam generated in flask *A* passes into the mixture in flask *B*, containing nitrobenzene. At first the steam raises the temperature of the contents of flask *B* and much of it condenses. Then, as each bubble of steam rises through the liquid it becomes saturated with the nitrobenzene vapor which diffuses into it. As the

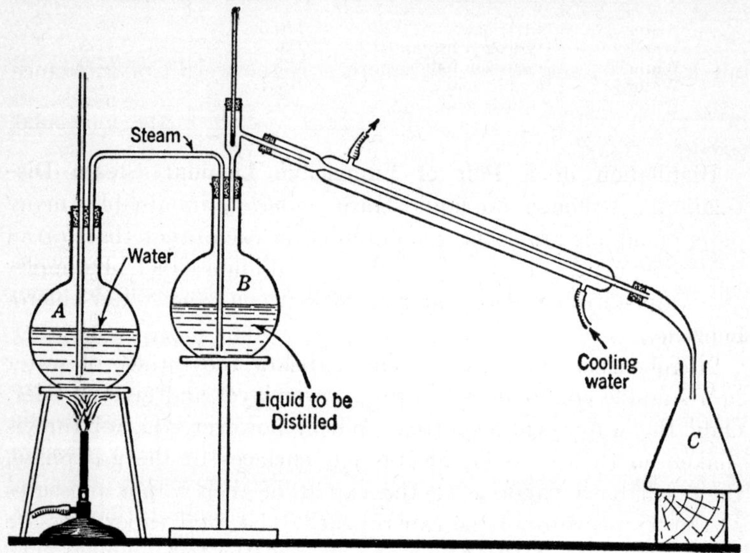

Fig. 122. Apparatus for Steam Distillation.

distillation proceeds, the air is gradually driven out of the flask *B*, and the space above the liquid is filled with a mixture of water and nitrobenzene vapors, in the proportion of the vapor pressures of the two liquids. When the total vapor pressure equals the atmospheric pressure, the mixed vapors pass into the condenser *C* and are collected as the distillate. Obviously, the temperature of distillation will be lower than 100° C. In this case it is 99.3° C., where the vapor pressure of water is 740 mm., that of nitrobenzene is 20 mm., and both together equal atmospheric pressure.

The process of steam distillation is not limited to immiscible liquid pairs but is found very useful in the preparation of such substances as aniline and phenol, which are moderately soluble in water even at room temperature.

Molecular Weights from Steam Distillation Data. The vapor pressure of a liquid is proportional to the number of moles in a given volume of the vapor phase. Hence, if we represent by p_A

and p_B the vapor pressures of water and liquid B at a given temperature, and by n_A and n_B the number of moles of the two substances in a given volume of the vapor phase:

$$\frac{p_A}{p_B} = \frac{n_A}{n_B}$$

but n_A is $\frac{w_A}{M_A}$, and n_B is $\frac{w_B}{M_B}$, where w is the weight of substance in a given volume of the vapor phase and M is the molecular weight. Hence,

$$\frac{p_A}{p_B} = \frac{w_A M_B}{w_B M_A}$$

The relative weights of the two components of the vapor phase will be the same as their relative weights in the distillate, from which we can determine the value of $\frac{w_A}{w_B}$. The vapor pressure of water, p_A at the temperature of distillation, may be taken from vapor pressure tables. Subtracting this from the barometric pressure P at the time of the experiment gives the vapor pressure of the other liquid p_B. Knowing the molecular weight of water, we can calculate that of the other liquid by substitution in the equation:

$$M_B = M_A \frac{w_B p_A}{w_A(P - p_A)}$$

This method of determining molecular weights is simple, and applicable to liquids with high boiling points, which cannot be vaporized readily. However, the accuracy with which the molecular weight is determined by this method decreases with decreasing vapor pressure of B.

The Properties of Solutions of Solids in Liquids. When a solid is dissolved in a liquid, it lowers the vapor pressure and the freezing point, raises the boiling point, and causes osmotic pressure. These effects, dependent chiefly upon the number of particles of solute in a given quantity of solvent and not upon their nature, are called the *colligative properties* of the solution. All of the last three effects may be considered to be the *result* of the lowering of the vapor pressure. Hence, we can see why vapor pressure plays such an important role in the physical chemistry of solutions. We shall confine our discussion to water as solvent.

The relationships among the three colligative properties are shown diagrammatically in Figure 123. The precise relationship and the connection of the molal depression and molal elevation constants with the heat of fusion and heat of vaporization, respectively, will be discussed in the chapter on thermodynamics (see page 636).

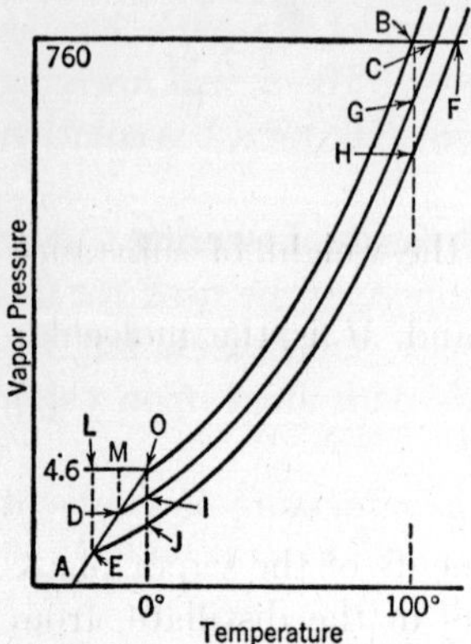

Fig. 123. Vapor-Pressure Curves for Water and Solutions (Schematic).

Lowering of the Vapor Pressure by a Solid Solute. The vapor pressure of the solid is negligible, and that of the solvent is given by Raoult's law (see page 234), thus:

$$p_A = p^0_A x_A$$

The lowering of the vapor pressure, therefore, will be:

$$\begin{aligned}\Delta p &= p^0_A - p^0_A x_A \\ &= p^0_A(1 - x_A) \\ &= p^0_A x_B\end{aligned}$$

or

$$\frac{\Delta p}{p^0_A} = x_B$$

If the number of moles of solute is n_2 and of solvent n_1, we can write:

$$\frac{\Delta p}{p^0_A} = \frac{n_2}{n_1 + n_2}$$

The expression $\frac{\Delta p}{p^0_A}$ is called the *relative vapor pressure lowering.*

A numerical example will show the way in which Raoult's law may be applied. Let us calculate the relative lowering of the vapor pressure due to dissolving 0.50 mole of urea in 1000 g. of water. The solution contains 0.50 mole in $\frac{1000}{18.016}$ or 55.51 moles of water. Hence $n_2 = 0.50$ and $n_1 = 55.51$. Substituting these values, we have:

$$\frac{\Delta p}{p^0_A} = \frac{0.50}{55.51 + 0.50} = 0.0089$$

For *dilute* solutions n_2 is negligible compared to n_1, as the preceding equation shows, so that we can write for the relative vapor pressure lowering:

$$\frac{\Delta p}{p^0{}_A} = \frac{n_2}{n_1} = \frac{m}{55.51} = 0.018016\, m$$

This is the most useful mathematical form of Raoult's law as applied to *dilute* aqueous solutions of solids. The actual lowering of the vapor pressure is small, only 0.31 mm./Hg for a 1 m solution at 20° C.

Molecular Weights from the Vapor-Pressure Lowering. Any one of the colligative properties of solutions may be used for determining the molecular weights of soluble substances, but because of experimental difficulties, methods dependent upon vapor pressure lowering have been little used.

Raoult's law for the lowering of the vapor pressure of a solvent by a solid solute may be stated thus:

$$\frac{p^0 - p}{p^0} = \frac{n_2}{n_1 + n_2} = \frac{\frac{w_2}{M_2}}{\frac{w_1}{M_1} + \frac{w_2}{M_2}}$$

where w_1 and w_2 are the weights of solvent and solute, the molecular weights of which are M_1 and M_2. Then the above expression can be solved for M_2 to yield:

$$M_2 = \frac{w_2}{w_1} \times \frac{M_1 p}{p^0 - p}$$

Knowing M_1 and determining the other terms experimentally, we may find M_2, the molecular weight of the solute.

Molecular weights can be determined with an accuracy of 1 per cent by a simple method based upon the measurement of the lowering of the vapor pressure.[1] A sample of the solution is weighed into a crucible and placed in a brass container with a second crucible containing a solution of a standard substance, *e.g.*, potassium chloride. The container is evacuated to hasten diffusion of the water vapor. When equilibrium has been reached, the solutions will have the same vapor pressure. The weight of potassium chloride taken and the weight of the residual solution give its concentration. Since the vapor pressures of potassium chloride solutions have been determined accurately, the vapor pressure of this residual solution is known. The concentration of the other solution is also found from the weight of substance taken and that of the residual solution. Thus knowing the vapor pressure of the water p^0, we have all

[1] Mason and Gardner, *J. Chem. Ed.*, **13**, 188 (1936).

the data necessary for calculating the molecular weight of the solid. The above **isopiestic method** of determining vapor pressures of solutions may be made very precise.

The Depression of the Freezing Point. Two methods of determining freezing points are applicable to solutions: (1) the *equilibrium method,* and (2) the *cooling* (or *heating*) *curve method.*

(1) The equilibrium method. If a *pure liquid* is partially frozen, so that both solid and liquid are present, and placed in a tube surrounded by a jacket at nearly the same temperature, its freezing point may be determined with a thermometer which, for accurate work, should be of the Beckmann (differential) type, graduated in fiftieths or hundredths of a degree and properly standardized. To find the freezing point of an *aqueous solution,* it is first cooled, then transferred to a tube or thermos flask to which is added chipped ice which has been dried with filter paper. A thermometer is inserted and the temperature is read accurately after it has become constant. Since ice may melt or separate in attaining equilibrium in the system, the concentration of the equilibrium solution usually will not be precisely that taken initially. It must be determined by a suitable chemical or physical analytical method.

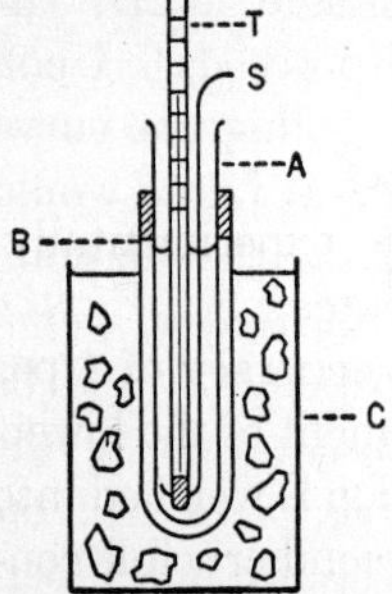

Fig. 124. Freezing-Point Apparatus.

(2) The cooling-curve method. Although not highly accurate this method is convenient when a sufficiently large quantity of solution is available and may also be used at high temperatures. The apparatus used for aqueous solutions may have the form shown in Figure 124. Enough of the liquid is put into the tube *A* to cover completely the bulb of the thermometer *T*. The liquid is thoroughly agitated by means of the stirrer *S*, made of heavy nichrome wire or of glass. The vessel *C* contains a freezing mixture of ice and salt. The tube *A* is not immersed directly in the freezing mixture in *C* but is insulated by an air gap between it and the larger tube *B* which is surrounded by the freezing mixture. This prevents too rapid cooling of the liquid. Beginning at a temperature several degrees above zero, temperature readings are taken at regular intervals, *e.g.*, every 30 seconds, as the liquid cools. We shall suppose that readings are taken until the whole mass has become solid.

If the temperature readings are plotted against the time, the **cooling curves** for water and for the solution of a solid such as urea will have the forms shown in Figure 125.

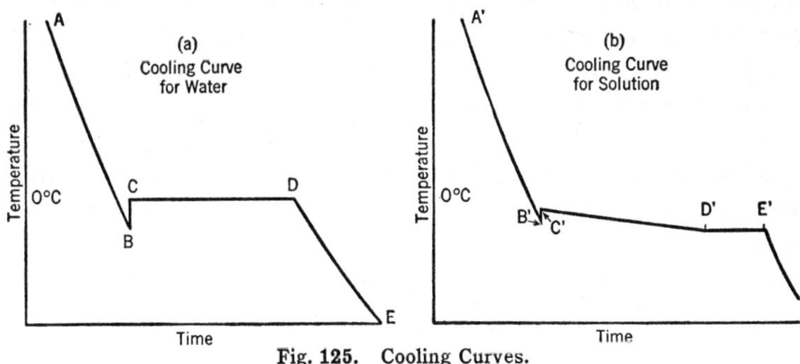

Fig. 125. Cooling Curves.

In the case of pure water there is some supercooling, the temperature dropping below the freezing point before solid begins to form; then when ice begins to separate, at B, the temperature rises rapidly to C, that is, to 0° C., and remains constant until all of the water has frozen. When solidification is complete at D, the temperature again drops as cooling of the ice proceeds. Upon warming the solid at the same rate as the former cooling, the curve could be retraced from E to C; melting would begin at D and would be complete slightly beyond C. The point C on the diagram represents the *freezing point*, and the point D the *melting point*. For water or any other pure substance the two points would lie on a horizontal line and therefore would represent exactly the same temperature. In other words, *the freezing point and the melting point of a pure substance are identical.* The rise in temperature from B to C is due to the evolution of the latent heat of fusion as the ice separates.

The cooling curve for a solution parallels that for water until the solid begins to separate. When the solid phase, ice, begins to form at B', the temperature rises to C' but does not quite reach the true freezing point of the solution. This is because the separation of ice leaves the solution somewhat more concentrated than it was initially. For this reason the supercooling of the solution should be prevented as completely as possible by vigorous stirring. As the curve shows, the temperature drops gradually from C' as ice separates, thus rendering the solution increasingly more concentrated. At a point D' the solution becomes saturated, and solid solute crystallizes out, with the ice and solute in a constant proportion known as a **eutectic mixture** (see page 602). The curve becomes horizontal and continues so until solidification is complete at E'. The temperature then drops, indicating cooling of the solid.

By carefully producing the curve $D'C'$ to cut the curve $A'B'$ the accuracy of the freezing point determination may be increased. It is important to observe in Figure 125 that the freezing point C' of the solution is lower than the freezing point C of the water. The difference between these two temperatures is the *depression of the freezing point* ΔT_f of the solvent water by the solute.

If the solid were heated to retrace the curve, melting would start at E', which is *below* the freezing point of the solution. In other words, *the freezing point and the melting point of such a solution are different.* This holds true for practically all solutions except eutectic mixtures.

Freezing Point as a Test for Purity. For a pure substance, the freezing point is the same as the melting point, whereas for most solutions it is different. One method of testing the purity of a substance is to test its freezing and melting points. If the two are not identical, *i.e.*, if the temperature drops as solid separates or rises as the solid melts, then the material is not a pure substance. A much-used criterion of the purity of organic compounds is the constancy of the freezing point.

Freezing-Point Depression and Concentration. The greater the concentration of the solution, the lower will be the freezing point and therefore the greater will be the freezing-point depression.

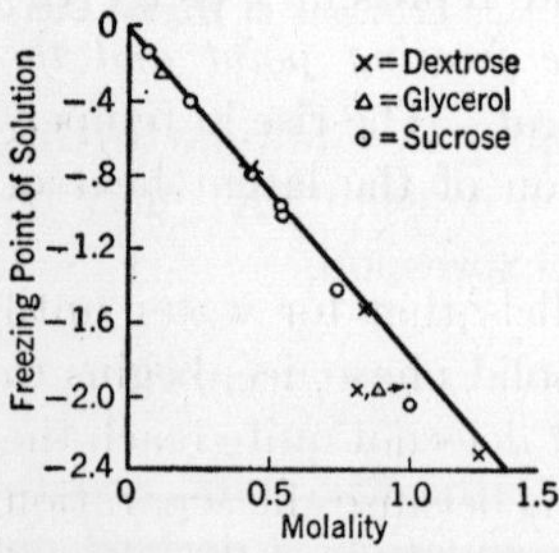

Fig. 126. Freezing-Point Depression and Molal Concentration.

Raoult, in 1882, first pointed out the relationship illustrated in Figure 126, that *the depression of the freezing point by an undissociated solute in dilute solution is proportional to the molal concentration of the solution.* This may be put in mathematical form, thus:

$$\Delta T_f = K_f m$$

where ΔT_f is the observed depression, m the molal concentration of the solution, and K_f is a constant, characteristic of the solvent, known as the **molal depression con-**

stant. For water it has the value 1.86. The values for some other useful solvents are shown in Table 53.

TABLE 53

MOLAL DEPRESSION CONSTANTS FOR VARIOUS SOLVENTS

SOLVENT	F. P., °C.	K_f	SOLVENT	F. P., °C.	K_f
Diethyl ether	−116	1.79	Acetic acid	16.6	3.90
Chloroform	−63	4.67	Phenol	43	7.27
Aniline	−6	5.87	Diphenyl	69	8.2
Water	0.0	1.86	Acetamide	82	3.63
Benzene	5.5	5.12	Camphor	178	37.7

Since the depression of the freezing point of water, or any other solvent, is not exactly a linear function of the concentration when the concentration is *high*, the value for K_f may only be determined accurately with solutes of known molecular weights in solutions at concentrations of 0.5 m or less. Data which illustrate the deviations from direct proportionality at higher concentrations are plotted in Figure 127. Notice that the true value of the molal depression constant can be determined by extrapolating these curves to zero molality, where they all converge at 1.86. In addition to this method of evaluation, the molal depression constant, K_f, may be calculated from the heat of fusion by the expression,

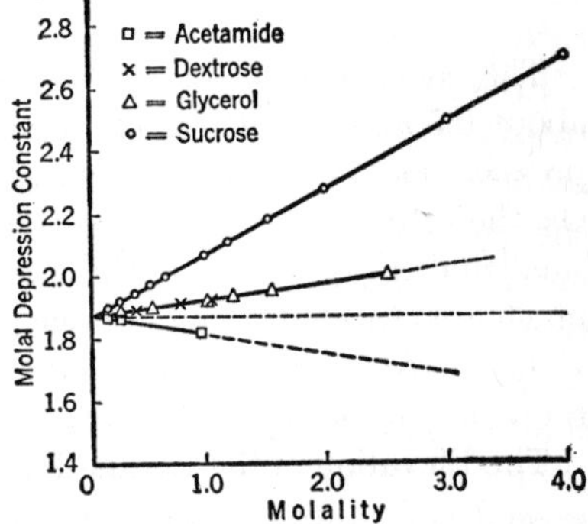

Fig. 127. Divergence of K_f for Water from 1.86 in Various Solutions at Higher Concentrations.

$$K_f = \frac{RT^2}{L_f}$$

where R is the gas constant, T the absolute freezing point, and L_f the heat of fusion in cal. per mole. This equation is derived on page 638.

Liquid solutes, like solids, lower the freezing points of solvents and, when the solution is dilute, obey the proportionality law:

$$\Delta T_f = K_f m$$

Molecular Weights by the Cryoscopic Method. The cryoscopic method, based upon the determination of the depression of the freezing point, is used to find the molecular weights of those substances which do not readily vaporize without decomposition. Water or some other substance of known molal depression constant can be used as solvent. The method is limited, however, to substances which are not ionized in the solvent used.

If g grams of solute are dissolved in w grams of solvent, then the molality

$$m = \frac{g}{M} \times \frac{1000}{w}$$

Hence

$$\Delta T_f = \frac{g}{M} \times \frac{1000}{w} \times K_f$$

and

$$M = g \times \frac{1000\, K_f}{w \Delta T_f}$$

The concentration of the solution should not be greater than about 0.5 m, since at higher concentrations the freezing-point depression does not usually obey the proportionality law, $\Delta T_f = K_f m$. On the other hand, if the solution is too dilute, the depression is small and the accuracy of the method is diminished. Camphor is much used in identifying organic substances. Because of the high value for K_f, the freezing-point depression is relatively large and the accuracy of the determination thereby increased.

The Elevation of the Boiling Point. *The **boiling point** of a liquid is the temperature at which the vapor pressure of the liquid becomes equal to the external pressure, usually the pressure of 1 atmosphere.* Since a nonvolatile solute lowers the vapor pressure of the solvent and contributes no vapor pressure of its own, the solution of such a solute must reach a temperature higher than the boiling point of the pure solvent before its vapor pressure would reach 760 mm./Hg. Thus *a nonvolatile solute invariably raises the boiling point of any solvent.*

The Determination of the Boiling Point. The boiling point of a pure substance is determined very easily. It only is necessary to distil the liquid using a distilling column and placing the thermometer just below the side tube of the column, where the superheating of the vapor is at a minimum.

The accurate determination of the boiling point of a *solution* is a matter of greater difficulty. Conditions of the experiment must be such that true equilibrium is established between the liquid and the vapor of the solvent. Merely distilling, or boiling under a reflux condenser cannot give an accurate result, since some of the solvent is not actually present in the solution and so the concentration is not known. A form of boiling-point apparatus which has been found satisfactory is illustrated in Figure 128. Since gentle boiling suffices, no appreciable amount of solvent actually is held up in the condenser. Superheating must also be prevented as far as possible. Bubbles of vapor formed at the bottom of the tube force the liquid through the inverted funnel and up the tubes, from the tips of which it sprays out over the thermometer, which thus is bathed with the solution at the temperature of the surrounding vapor.

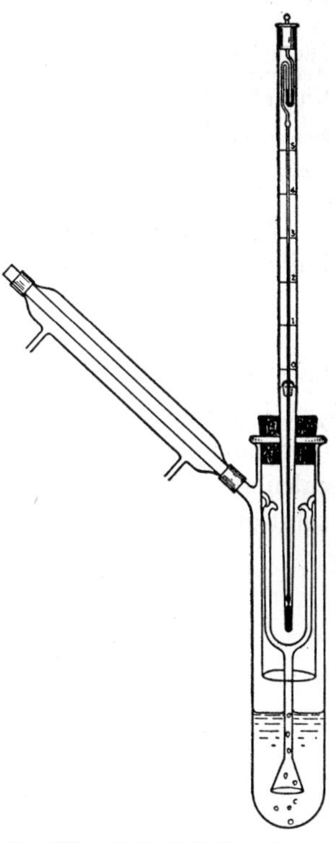

Fig. 128. Cottrell Boiling-Point Apparatus.

Boiling Point Elevation and Concentration. The lowering of the vapor pressure of a solvent by a nonvolatile solute is proportional to the molal concentration of the solution (see page 247). In order to bring the solution to the boiling point it must be heated to a higher temperature in order to make up for the diminution in vapor pressure. . Hence, the elevation of the boiling point should be proportional to the lowering of the vapor pressure and to the molal concentration of the solution. The relation is, in fact, an accurate one for dilute solutions. The mathematical expression takes the same form as that for the depression of the freezing point and may be stated thus:

$$\Delta T_b = K_b m$$

where ΔT_b is the elevation of the boiling point, and K_b is a constant characteristic of the solvent, called the **molal elevation constant.** For water it has the value 0.52. The values for some other solvents are given in Table 54.

TABLE 54

Molal Elevation Constants for Various Solvents

Solvent	B. P., °C	K_b	Solvent	B. P., °C	K_b
Diethyl ether	34.6	2.16	Water	100.0	0.52
Acetone	56.5	1.73	Acetic acid	118.1	3.07
Chloroform	61.2	3.88	Phenol	181.4	3.60
Carbon tetrachloride .	76.8	4.88	Diphenyl	254.9	7.06
Benzene	80.1	2.57	Benzil	347	10.0

The simple proportionality law relating the elevation of the boiling point and the concentration,

$$\Delta T_b = K_b m$$

holds quite accurately when m is small, that is, when the solution is fairly dilute, but at higher concentrations the experimentally determined values of ΔT_b usually deviate considerably from the calculated values, as illustrated in Figure 129 where data for sucrose solutions are plotted.

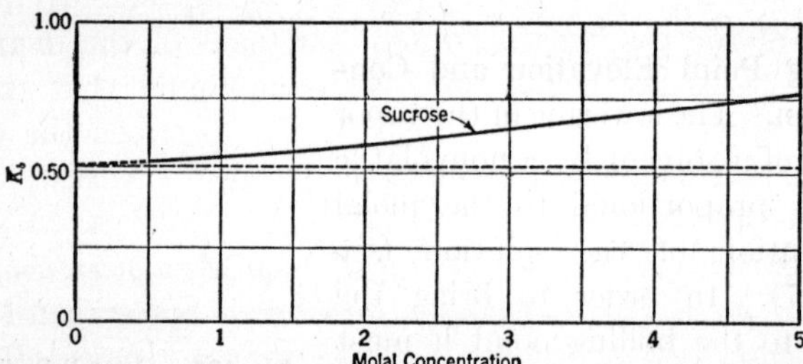

Fig. 129. Molal Elevations of the Boiling Point for Aqueous Sucrose Solutions.

Molecular Weights by the Ebullioscopic Method. The ebullioscopic method, based upon a determination of the elevation of the boiling point, can be used for solutes which are nonvolatile and undissociated, although it is somewhat less accurate than the cryoscopic method and is employed less frequently.

A known weight of the solute is dissolved in a known weight of the solvent, and the boiling point of the solution is found. Since the solution must be dilute enough for the proportionality law to hold, the boiling point must be determined to 0.001° C., usually with a Beckmann thermometer. Since a change of pressure of 1 mm./Hg alters the boiling point (of water) about 0.03° C., the boiling points of the solvent and of the solution are determined in rapid succession. The most serious sources of error are superheating of the liquid and the change in concentration by loss of solvent. Since the publication of the original boiling point elevation method by Beckmann in 1889, many attempts have been made to modify the apparatus so as to minimize these errors. The Cottrell apparatus shown in Figure 128 on page 253 is one of the most satisfactory.

The equation for the molecular weight, analogous to that which we derived for the freezing point depression (page 252) is:

$$M = g \times \frac{1000}{w} \times \frac{K_b}{\Delta T_b}$$

The Distribution Law. The *distribution law* expresses the relation between the concentrations of a given substance in two different phases in equilibrium with each other. The law applies to equilibrium between a gas and its solution in any solvent and to equilibrium between solutions of a substance in two solvents which are not completely miscible. *Henry's law*, published first in 1803, relating the solubility of a gas in a given solvent to the pressure of the gas, was a limited statement of the distribution law. In 1872, Berthelot and Jungfleisch found that the same principle applied to the *partition* of iodine between the two immiscible solvents carbon disulfide and water. Nernst, in 1891, formulated the law in general terms.

The **distribution law** may be stated thus: *At a given temperature a substance present in two phases in equilibrium is distributed between the two phases in a definite ratio of concentrations, provided it is not different chemically in the two phases.* The law may be expressed mathematically, thus:

$$\frac{C_2}{C_1} = K_d$$

where C_1 and C_2 are the concentrations of the substance in the two phases, and K_d is the **distribution constant.** The constant is characteristic of the given system at a given temperature.

Derivation of the Distribution Law. If a volatile substance is shaken with a system of two immiscible liquids, A and B, it will dissolve and distribute itself between the two phases. If the solute obeys Henry's law in both phases, its concentrations will be given by the equations:

$$C_1 = k_1 p \text{ (in A)} \qquad \text{and} \qquad C_2 = k_2 p \text{ (in B)}$$

Here p is the vapor pressure in the gas phase in equilibrium with *both* A and B, hence, dividing the second equation by the first gives:

$$\frac{C_2}{C_1} = \frac{k_2}{k_1} = K_d$$

Since any substance is volatile to some extent, this derivation actually holds for the distribution of any substance the vapor of which obeys Henry's law. *The* ***distribution constant*** *K_d is the ratio of the solubilities in the two solvents.*

Applications of the Distribution Law. (1) Distribution between gas phase and liquid phase. The distribution law applied to such a case is merely a restatement of Henry's law. For a system composed of a gas in equilibrium with its solution in a given solvent at a given temperature, the expression

$$\frac{C_2}{C_1} = K_d$$

means that the concentration of a gas in the solution phase bears a constant ratio to its concentration in the gas phase.

(2) Distribution between two liquid phases. The application of the distribution law to the distribution, or partition, of a solute between two immiscible solvents is of special importance. In the familiar qualitative test for the halogens, their aqueous solutions are shaken with chloroform, carbon disulfide, or carbon tetrachloride, and the color of the nonaqueous solution is characteristic of the element. If carbon tetrachloride, which is immiscible with water, is used and the two are shaken and then allowed to stand, they form a two-layer system with the denser carbon tetrachloride layer beneath. Since the halogens are more soluble in carbon tetrachloride than in water, they are transferred chiefly to the carbon tetrachloride layer during the shaking. An aqueous solution of iodine, for example, is almost decolorized while the carbon tetrachloride layer becomes a deep purple.

The distribution of the iodine, determined by its relative solubilities in the two solvents, is given by the equation:

$$\frac{C_2}{C_1} = K_d$$

where C_1 is the concentration in the aqueous layer and C_2 the concentration in the carbon tetrachloride layer. The value for K_d

at 20° C. is 85. Data illustrating the application of the law are given in Table 55. The concentrations of succinic acid are expressed as mole per cent. The total concentration in the aqueous phase is corrected for the small ionization of the acid to give the concentration of *undissociated acid* here tabulated. The concentrations of iodine are given as grams per 1000 ml. of solvent. In each case C_1 refers to the *water*.

TABLE 55

DISTRIBUTION OF A SOLUTE BETWEEN TWO IMMISCIBLE SOLVENTS

Succinic Acid in Diethyl Ether and Water at 20° C.			Iodine in Carbon Disulfide and Water at 18° C.		
C_1	C_2	K_d	C_1	C_2	K_d
0.2025	0.1535	0.76	0.041	17.4	420
0.431	0.319	0.74	0.032	12.9	400
0.495	0.366	0.74	0.016	6.6	410
0.629	0.465	0.74	0.010	4.1	410
0.936	0.686	0.74	0.0017	0.76	440

Values for the *distribution constants*, K_d, for two of the halogens between some common solvents and water are shown in Table 56.

TABLE 56

DISTRIBUTION CONSTANTS FOR TWO HALOGENS BETWEEN OTHER SOLVENTS AND WATER AT 20° C.

Solute	Other Solvent	Molal Solubility in Other Solvent	K_d
Bromine	Carbon disulfide	—	78
Iodine	Carbon disulfide	0.0611	420
Iodine	Chloroform	0.0233	109
Iodine	Carbon tetrachloride	0.0116	85

(3) Association of the solute. The distribution law may be applied to determine the **degree of association** of a solute which is normal in one solvent and associated in another solvent immiscible with the first. As an illustration let us take the case of benzoic acid, which is not associated or appreciably dissociated in aqueous solutions of moderate dilution, but is associated in solution in benzene. When the acid is shaken with a system of these two solvents, the equilibrium may be expressed by the simple equation:

$$\underset{\text{(in water)}}{n\, C_6H_5COOH} \rightleftharpoons \underset{\text{(in benzene)}}{(C_6H_5COOH)_n}$$

For this the equilibrium constant, which also is the distribution constant, is:

$$K_d = K_e = \frac{C_{(C_6H_5COOH)_n}}{C^n_{C_6H_5COOH}} = \frac{C_2}{C_1^n}$$

Hence

$$C_1^n = \frac{C_2}{K_d}$$

and

$$n = \frac{\log C_2 - \log K_d}{\log C_1}$$

The concentration of benzoic acid in each phase can be determined by titration with a standard basic solution. In the above expression the *quantity* of acid may be expressed as grams, gram equivalents, or moles, and the numerical value of the constant K_d will depend upon the concentration unit used. In Table 57 are given data which show the applicability of the above expression for n to the distribution of benzoic acid between water and benzene. By substituting in this expression two sets of concentrations, C_1 and C_2, we obtain two equations which can be solved for n. In this case we have used the data marked with an asterisk in Table 57 from which the *degree of association* n is found to be 2.01. Evidently, the benzoic acid is associated in benzene to form $(C_6H_5COOH)_2$. Upon this assumption the values of K_d at different concentrations are calculated and found to have the nearly constant values given in column 4 with the average value 69.26.

TABLE 57

ASSOCIATION OF BENZOIC ACID IN BENZENE AT 10° C.

C_1 (IN WATER)	C_2 (IN BENZENE)	n	K_d
0.0429	0.1149	2	62.4
0.0562	0.2380	2	75.3
0.0823*	0.4726*	2	69.8
0.1124*	0.8843*	2	70.0
0.1780	2.1777	2	68.7
0.2430	4.0544	2	68.7
0.2817	5.4851	2	69.1

* Data from which n and K_d were initially calculated as described above.

By application of the distribution law the degrees of association of various substances have been determined. Thus lithium chloride is almost entirely $(LiCl)_2$ in amyl alcohol (pentanol) solution; acetic acid and monochloroacetic acid are associated in benzene, chloroform, carbon tetrachloride, and other solvents.

PROBLEMS AND EXERCISES

1. Express in (1) molality, (2) molarity, and (3) mole per cent:
(*a*) Concentrated H_2SO_4, d = 1.84 g./ml., 98.3 per cent acid;
(*b*) Constant-boiling HNO_3, d = 1.42 g./ml., 68 per cent acid;
(*c*) Constant-boiling HCl, d = 1.106 g./ml., 20.22 per cent acid.

2. Find the mole fraction of each component of a mixture containing 2.546 g. NaCl, 3.670 g. K_2SO_4, 0.442 g. KCl, and 0.666 g. Na_2SO_4.

3. Find the mole per cent of each constituent of an aqueous solution which is 1.64 per cent NaCl and 6.33 per cent NaOH by weight.

4. What will be the mole fraction of nitric acid in the solution resulting when 50 g. of 1 *m* solution of nitric acid are mixed with 50 g. of 0.50 *m* barium hydroxide?

5. The solubility of acetylene in water at 20° C. is 0.117 g. per 100 ml. when the partial pressure of the gas is 743 mm. Compute the solubilities at the following partial pressures: (1) 560 mm.; (2) 458 mm.; (3) 276 mm.; (4) 840 mm. Make a theoretical plot of Henry's law; determine the same values from the graph and compare the two sets of results.

6. Assuming Henry's law and the simple gas laws, show that the volume of a gas which will dissolve in a given quantity of liquid at a given temperature is *independent* of the partial pressure of the gas.

7. In successive experiments 5, 10, and 20 g. of phenol are shaken with 100 g. of water, first at 20° C. and then at 60° C. Plot the data of Table 48 in a curve like that of Figure 115, and determine (*a*) in each case whether a one- or two-layer system will form; (*b*) if a two-layer system forms, what the temperature will be at which it would change to a one-layer system; (*c*) If a two-layer system forms, what will be the weights of phenol and of water in each layer.

8. Given an ideal liquid pair, A and B, with vapor pressures at 50° C. of 200 and 300 mm., respectively, calculate the total vapor pressures of solutions in which the mole fractions of A are 0.20, 0.40, 0.50, 0.60, and 0.80. Draw the vapor pressure diagram like that shown in Figure 117.

9. Calculate the weight of (1) methanol, CH_3OH, (2) ethylene glycol, $(CH_2OH)_2$, and (3) glycerol, $C_3H_5(OH)_3$, which, when dissolved in 2 liters of water, would just prevent the formation of ice at 10° F.

10. At a pressure of 760 mm., monochlorobenzene, C_6H_5Cl, distils with steam at a temperature of 91.4° C., at which the vapor pressure of pure water is 554 mm. Calculate the mole per cent of each component in the distillate.

11. A solution of 4.00 g. of an unknown substance in 200 g. of benzene is found to freeze at 4.82° C.; the benzene freezes at 5.49° C. Calculate the molecular weight of the substance.

12. The solution of 1.01 g. of a substance in 60 g. of acetic acid freezes at 16.05° C. Pure acetic acid freezes at 16.60° and boils at 118.09° C. At what temperature would the solution boil? What is the molecular weight of the substance?

13. Using the data of Table 45, on page 228, to determine the solubility of oxygen, calculate the freezing point of water saturated with oxygen at 25° C., when the pressure of oxygen is 760 mm.

14. Monochlorobenzene, C_6H_5Cl, and monobromobenzene, C_6H_5Br, form a nearly ideal liquid pair. Calculate the composition of a solution which boils at 140° C. and a pressure of one atmosphere, if the vapor pressures of the pure substances are 940 and 496 mm. respectively at this temperature.

15. If the vapor pressure of water at 20° C. is 17.535 mm., find the vapor pressure of a 12.00 per cent solution of urea, $CO(NH_2)_2$.

16. Ether, $C_4H_{10}O$, at 20° C. has a vapor pressure of 442 mm. and a solution of 6.12 g. of benzoic acid, C_6H_5COOH, in 47.7 g. of ether has a vapor pressure of 410 mm. at the same temperature. Find the molecular weight of the benzoic acid from these data.

17. Ether boils at 34.604° C. A solution made by dissolving 0.909 g. of resorcinol, $C_6H_4(OH)_2$, in 70.6 ml. of ether, measured at 25° C., boils at 34.944° C. Find the molecular weight of resorcinol. The density of ether at 25° C. is 0.713 g./ml.

18. In an experiment a solution of 2.181 g. of camphor, $C_{10}H_{16}O$, in 96.18 g. of acetone, $(CH_3)_2CO$, is found to boil at 56.73° C. Acetone is found to boil at 56.48° C. Assuming the molecular weight for camphor, compute the molal elevation constant for acetone.

READING LIST

S. Glasstone, *Textbook of Physical Chemistry.* D. Van Nostrand Company, New York, 1940. Pp. 615–641, 683–732.

W. B. Meldrum and F. T. Gucker, Jr., *Introduction to Theoretical Chemistry.* American Book Co., New York, 1936. Pp. 80–100. Includes a more elementary discussion of vapor pressure lowering.

"Symposium on Non-Aqueous Solutions," *Chem. Rev.*, **8**, 167–335 (1931). Papers dealing with solutions in hydrogen sulfide, ammonia, hydrogen fluoride, and acetic acid, by W. V. Evans, A. W. Davidson, N. F. Hall, J. H. Simons, and J. A. Wilkinson.

J. H. Hildebrand, *Solubility of Non-Electrolytes*, 2d ed. Reinhold Publishing Corporation, New York, 1936.

W. Swietosławski, *Ebulliometry — the Physical Chemistry of Distillation.* Chemical Publishing Company, New York, 1937. Chapter 1 describes apparatus for boiling determining point elevation, with many illustrations.

CHAPTER 10

OSMOSIS AND OSMOTIC PRESSURE

Osmosis and *osmotic pressure* are of interest in physical chemistry because of their relation to other phenomena in solution and of especial interest in physiological chemistry because of their bearing upon tissue structure and life processes. To some extent the phenomenon of *osmosis* parallels that of *diffusion*, and a brief discussion of the latter subject may enable us to understand the former more clearly.

Diffusion. A gas introduced into a container distributes itself quickly and uniformly throughout the available space. The rapid motion of its molecules, only slightly hindered by other molecules in its environment, renders its diffusion rapid. The lighter the gas molecule and the higher the temperature, the greater is the rate of diffusion.

The diffusion of a substance in a liquid medium also depends upon kinetic motion, but the greater density of the medium and the much shorter free path of the particles of both solute and solvent slows down the diffusion rate. Graham investigated the subject quantitatively in 1851. He put a solution in an unstoppered bottle, which he carefully immersed in water, as shown in Figure 130, and after a suitable time took samples from different levels and analyzed them. This was done at various temperatures and with various initial concentrations of the solution. His results showed that the rate of diffusion of the solute depends upon its nature, the temperature, and the concentration of the solution. The rate of diffusion also depends upon the nature of the solvent. For example, iodine diffuses more

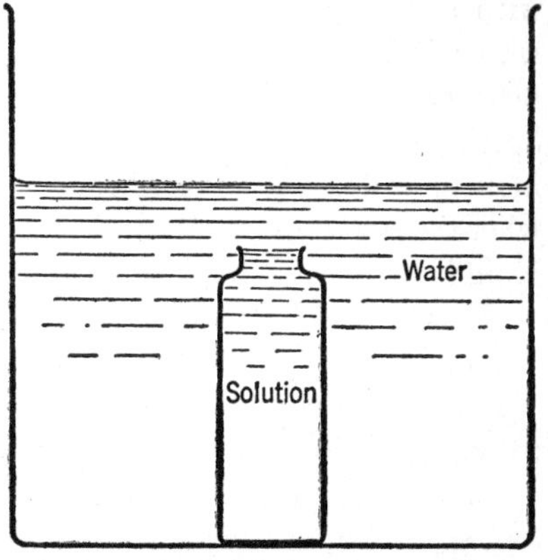

Fig. 130. Graham's Experiment to Show Diffusion of Solute.

rapidly in carbon disulfide than it does in benzene, and gold diffuses more rapidly in tin than in lead.

The slow rate of diffusion of a solute in water may be demonstrated readily. If a concentrated solution of cupric chloride is run into a cylinder of water so as to form a layer at the bottom, the diffusion is shown by the upward spreading of the blue color. Weeks may elapse before the blue color reaches the top of the cylinder.

If the bottle containing the solution (Fig. 130) is covered with a membrane of parchment paper tied tightly around its neck, experiment shows that the diffusion of a solute like cupric chloride is not greatly retarded. The parchment paper is permeable to the solute as well as to the water, and so cupric and chloride ions as well as water molecules migrate through it. Sugar and other un-ionized solutes, likewise, will diffuse through it.

Diffusion involves not only the migration of solute particles, which may be observed as in the experiment illustrated in Figure 130, but also the migration of solvent molecules. *Osmosis,* which we shall now discuss, involves migration of solvent molecules only.

Osmosis. As long ago as 1748 the French Abbé Nollet, professor of physics in Paris, observed that when a bladder was filled with a strong solution of alcohol, tightly tied, and immersed in water it became greatly extended. Water permeated into the bladder, but alcohol could not pass out. In the same way, if the bottle in Figure 130 is closed by tying a bladder tightly over the mouth, water will pass through the membrane into the bottle, whereas sugar or a salt will not readily pass out. Thus, as in Nollet's experiment, the bladder becomes distended. *Such a membrane, which will permit the passage of one component of a solution and not of the other, is called a* ***semipermeable membrane.***

Even more completely semipermeable membranes are prepared by precipitation of cupric ferrocyanide or of silicates of the heavy metals. If a drop of cupric sulfate solution is introduced into a dilute potassium ferrocyanide solution from the end of a capillary dropper, it becomes surrounded by a film or membrane of cupric ferrocyanide. This is permeable to neither of the two solutes but is permeable to water, which diffuses through the membrane from the more dilute into the more concentrated solution until the pressure ruptures the membrane. A similar mechanism explains the "chemical flower garden." When crystals of various salts of the heavy metals, such as manganous, cobaltous, and cupric sulfates and ferric nitrate, are put into a solution of sodium silicate of density about 1.1 g. per ml., they cause growths of the colored silicates of the metals. The growth is due to the successive formation and rupturing of "cells," which are drops of the solution of the salt, *e.g.*, cupric sulfate, surrounded with a semipermeable membrane of the corresponding silicate, in this case cupric silicate.

Osmosis may be studied better by using a cell prepared as follows: A porous earthenware cylinder is filled with cupric sulfate solution and immersed in a solution of potassium ferrocyanide. Both solutes diffuse into the pores of the cylinder, and when the cupric ions and the ferrocyanide ions meet, they react to give the familiar chocolate-brown precipitate of cupric ferrocyanide. This forms a gelatinous film across each pore, and so builds up a strong semipermeable membrane. If the cell is now filled with sugar solution, a stopper carrying a long glass tube of small bore inserted, and the cell immersed in water, the level of the solution in the glass tube will rise continuously, perhaps to a height of several feet, as the water permeates the membrane. The same effect may be observed using a simpler cell. A carrot, or other root vegetable, is bored out, filled with sugar solution, and fitted with a rubber stopper and glass tube. When the carrot is immersed in water, osmosis takes place, and the level of the solution in the tube rises to a height of 10 feet or more in the course of 24 hours.

On the basis of such effects we may formulate the following definition: ***Osmosis*** *is the permeation of a semipermeable membrane by one component of a solution in the direction which tends to equalize the solute concentrations on both sides of the membrane.* Water is usually the component of solutions which permeates the membrane. As this definition implies, osmosis will take place not only when the cell containing a solution is immersed in water but also when it is immersed in a more dilute solution.

Osmotic Pressure. In the experiments just described, the "head" of solution within the tube constitutes a hydrostatic pressure, and the maximum height of the aqueous column for the given solution is a measure of the *osmotic pressure* of the solution in the cell. A more accurate measure of the osmotic pressure of the *original solution* is, however, the pressure that just prevents the passage of water through the membrane into the solution. We may state, then, as a practical definition, that *the* ***osmotic pressure*** *of a solution is the least pressure which must be applied to the surface of the solution to prevent the passage of solvent through a semipermeable membrane into the solution, when the membrane surrounding the solution is immersed in the pure solvent.*

The Measurement of Osmotic Pressure. In 1866 Moritz Traube, professor of chemistry at Breslau, constructed an osmotic cell by precipitating cupric ferrocyanide in the walls of a porous cup. Although his observations of osmosis were only qualitative, most later work is based upon the precipitated membrane which he introduced. Four methods of measurement will be considered briefly.

(*a*) **The method of Pfeffer.** In 1887 the botanist Wilhelm Pfeffer used for quantitative measurements cells made by the method of Traube. His results, although not highly accurate, were a notable contribution to physical chemistry, since they were the basis upon which van't Hoff established several important generalizations, and they also pointed the way for further research on osmotic pressure. Some of his results for sugar solutions of various concentrations at different temperatures are given in Tables 58 and 59.

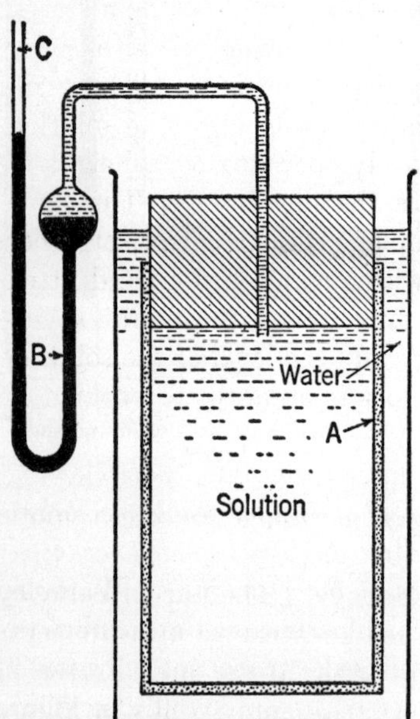

Fig. 131. Pfeffer's Apparatus.

Pfeffer's apparatus is shown diagrammatically in Figure 131. *A* is a porous cup carrying a membrane of cupric ferrocyanide, which was formed by filling the cup with potassium ferrocyanide solution and immersing in cupric sulfate solution, thus permitting the two solutions to diffuse into the pores, where precipitation took place. The cell is filled with the solution of which the osmotic pressure is to be measured, and immersed in water. As the water enters the solution, the pressure developed is measured with the manometer *B*; eventually this pressure becomes constant and measures the osmotic pressure of the solution.

(*b*) **The method of Morse and Frazer.** H. N. Morse and J. C. W. Frazer, professors of chemistry at the Johns Hopkins University, improved upon Pfeffer's cell and measured the osmotic pressures of solutions of various sugars and related compounds over a wide range of concentrations and temperatures. The cell used by the Johns Hopkins group is illustrated diagrammatically in Figure 132. With the aid of the electric current the cupric ferrocyanide membrane is formed near the outside of the porous cylinder *D*, which is firmly attached to the metal plug *F*. Through this plug passes the glass tube *G*, where the water is forced in. The solution is contained in a bronze cylinder *H*. The whole apparatus is thermostated at the desired temperature. A suitable manometer, which is a mercury column for low pressures or an electrical resistance gage for high pressures, is attached at *E*. The maximum pressure which it records is taken as the osmotic pressure of the solution.

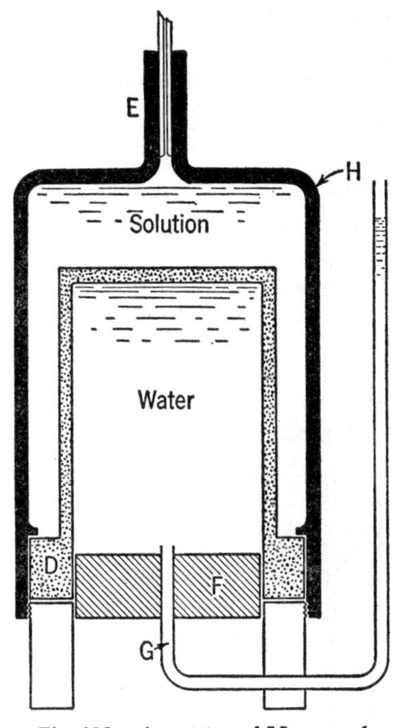

Fig. 132. Apparatus of Morse and Frazer.

(*c*) **The method of Berkeley and Hartley.** The Earl of Berkeley and E. G. J. Hartley, in England, made extensive measurements of osmotic pressures simultaneously with Morse and Frazer in America. Their osmotic cell is shown diagrammatically in Figure 133. Instead of determining the pressure developed in the cell by the passage of water into it, they applied pressure within the cell, gradually increasing it until the flow of water, initially inwards, was reversed in direction. The pressure at the point of reversal is, of course, the osmotic pressure of the solution. The measurements made by both groups of workers were of high precision and of much greater accuracy than Pfeffer's.

In their apparatus the cupric ferrocyanide membrane is deposited, with the aid of the electric current, near the outside surface of the porcelain tube J. The tube is firmly clamped in position in the gun-metal casing K, into which the solution is introduced. The porcelain tube J is filled with water and connected with an open, fine-bore gage tube L, which indicates sensitively the direction of flow of water through the membrane. By means of the capillary tube M connection is made with the pump by which the pressure is applied to the solution, and with the manometer for measuring the applied pressure. The whole apparatus is thermostated at the desired temperature.

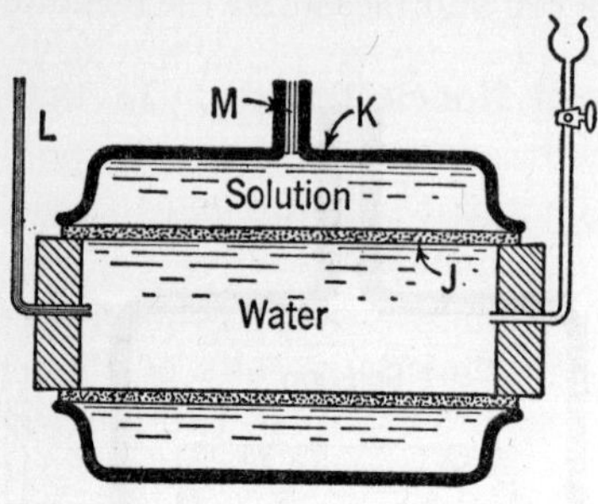

Fig. 133. Apparatus of Berkeley and Hartley.

(*d*) **The porous disk method.** Still another method for measuring osmotic pressure is the *porous disk method,* first used by Townsend in 1928 at the suggestion of J. C. W. Frazer. The apparatus is illustrated in Figure 134. The determination depends upon the adjustment of tension on the solvent just sufficient to counterbalance the difference in vapor pressures of the solvent and the solution. The method has been found especially useful in the case of nonaqueous solutions. The semipermeable membrane in this method is the air-solution interface. The solution is put in the bulb R so that the level is below the top of the tube S, which contains the water. The disk T, made of fine glass powder sintered with clay, is permeable to the liquid, but its pores are so fine that the capillary attraction exceeds the osmotic pressure to be measured. The air over solvent and solution is removed by a pump at P. The transfer of vapor from solvent to solution, or solution to solvent, is controlled

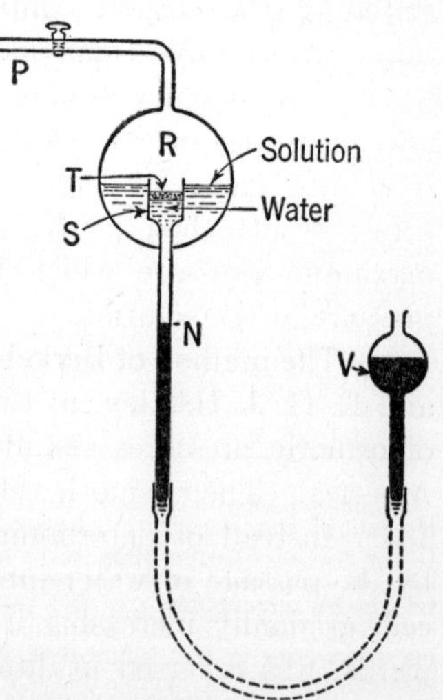

Fig. 134. Porous Disk Apparatus.

by adjusting the tension by raising or lowering the mercury bulb V. The osmotic pressure is equal to the tension applied to the solvent at N and is the difference in mercury levels plus the height of the solvent column in S.

Osmotic Pressures of Solutions of Nonelectrolytes. In 1887, the famous Dutch chemist, van't Hoff,[1] showed how osmotic pressure is related to the lowering of the vapor pressure and to other colligative properties of solutions, and demonstrated that a close analogy exists between the behavior of substances in solution and in the gaseous state. Using the experimental results of Pfeffer as a basis for his deductions, he called attention[2] to two remarkable relationships:

First, *the osmotic pressure of a dilute solution of a nonelectrolyte is directly proportional to the concentration C or inversely proportional to the volume V containing a given weight of solute, when the temperature remains constant.* Expressed mathematically, this is:

$$\pi = k_1C \quad \text{or} \quad \pi V = k_1 \quad \text{(temperature constant)}$$

where π is the osmotic pressure. This relationship, which is analogous to Boyle's law for gases, was pointed out by van't Hoff in these words: "The following table [Table 58] contains Pfeffer's determinations of the osmotic pressure P in sugar solutions of concentration C at room temperature (13.2 to 16.1°):

TABLE 58

A Comparison of Osmotic Pressure and Concentration of Sucrose

Concentration (C) (Per Cent)	Osmotic Pressure (P) (Mm./Hg.)	$\frac{P}{C}$
1	535	535
2	1016	508
2.74	1518	554
4	2082	521
6	3075	513

[1] Jacobus Henricus van't Hoff (1852–1911) was born in Rotterdam, Holland. He taught chemistry at Utrecht and later for many years was a professor at the University of Amsterdam. His early interest was in organic chemistry, particularly in connection with optical activity, which he explained on the basis of the tetrahedral arrangement of the valences of carbon. Later he turned to physical chemistry, for which his proficiency in mathematics fitted him. In addition to his discoveries in the realm of solutions he carried through a comprehensive and masterful study of chemical dynamics and equilibrium. In 1896 he was called to a research professorship at the University of Berlin "with the right, but without the obligation, of teaching." He remained there for the rest of his life. For a portrait of van't Hoff, see frontispiece.

[2] J. H. van't Hoff, *Zeit. physik. Chem.*, **1**, 481 (1887), translated into English as "The Role of Osmotic Pressure in the Analogy between Solutions and Gases," *Alembic Club Reprint* No. 19.

The approximately constant quotients $\frac{P}{C}$ point to an actual proportionality between pressure and concentration."

Second, *the osmotic pressure of a dilute solution of given concentration varies directly as the absolute temperature.* This may be expressed mathematically thus:

$$\pi = k_2T \text{ (concentration or volume constant)}$$

This corresponds to Charles's law for gases. For this relationship van't Hoff found proof when he compared Pfeffer's observed values for the osmotic pressures of a 1 per cent solution of sugar at various temperatures with the pressures calculated for a gas of the same molar concentration at the same temperatures. His figures are given in Table 59.

TABLE 59

THE CHANGE OF OSMOTIC PRESSURE WITH TEMPERATURE COMPARED WITH THE CALCULATED GAS PRESSURE

TEMPERATURE ° C.	OSMOTIC PRESSURE (ATM.)	CALCULATED GAS PRESSURE (ATM.)
6.8	0.664	0.665
13.7	0.691	0.681
14.2	0.671	0.682
15.5	0.684	0.686
22	0.721	0.701
32	0.716	0.725
36	0.740	0.735

The agreement is satisfactory, considering the rather large experimental error of Pfeffer's measurements.

Since $\pi = \frac{k_1}{V}$ when T is constant

and $\pi = k_2T$ when V is constant,

reasoning like that applied in combining Boyle's and Charles's laws, on page 76, shows that:

$\pi V = kT$ when V and T vary

The latter has the same form as the combined equation for the gas laws,

$$PV = RT$$

The analogy becomes still more apparent when we find that k is approximately equal to 1.99 calories per degree per mole, when V

liters of solution contain 1 mole of solute. Since this is the numerical value of R, van't Hoff's equation for the osmotic pressure of a dilute solution containing 1 mole of solute, finally becomes:

$$\pi V = RT$$

This equation may be applied to calculate roughly the osmotic pressure of a given solution, and such calculated values give some idea of the magnitude of the pressure set up. For example, if 1 mole of glucose or any other nonelectrolyte is present in 22.4 liters of solution at 0° C., the osmotic pressure calculated from this equation will be 1 atmosphere; if 1 mole is present in 1 liter of solution the osmotic pressure would be 22.4 atmospheres, or over 300 pounds per square inch.

Van't Hoff expressed the laws of osmotic pressure for dilute solutions in terms of volume concentrations, that is, *molarity*. Morse and other later workers in the field found that the laws hold more satisfactorily and to higher concentrations if the *molality* is used. In other words, it is preferable to represent the osmotic pressure of a dilute solution containing 1 mole of solute by the equation:

$$\pi = mRT$$

where m is the molality. This equation allows for the volume occupied by the solute molecules themselves, much as the van der Waals' equation corrects for the volume occupied by the molecules of a gas. Some of the more accurate modern values for

TABLE 60

OSMOTIC PRESSURES OF SUCROSE SOLUTIONS, IN ATMOSPHERES

MOLAL CONCENTRATION	TEMPERATURE ° C.				
	0 (Calculated)	0	10	20	50
0.1	2.24	2.48	2.52	2.61	2.66
0.2	4.48	4.76	4.93	5.11	5.32
0.3	6.72	7.14	7.39	7.67	8.04
0.4	8.97	9.52	9.87	10.22	10.81
0.5	11.21	12.00	12.40	12.86	13.62
0.6	13.45	14.50	14.98	15.52	16.46
0.7	15.69	17.03	17.65	18.20	19.37
0.8	17.93	19.65	20.34	21.09	22.31
0.9	20.17	22.32	23.09	23.93	25.35
1.0	22.41	25.05	25.92	26.87	28.46

Data of Morse and co-workers from *I.C.T.*, IV, 429.

the osmotic pressures of dilute solutions at various temperatures are given in Table 60 along with values at 0° C., calculated from the preceding equation.

The Mechanism of Osmosis. Van't Hoff made the important generalization that *the osmotic pressure of a dilute solution depends upon the number of dissolved particles per unit volume rather than upon their nature.* That is, osmotic pressure is a colligative property of a solution. His work left unanswered, however, two important questions: (1) How does a semipermeable membrane exercise its selective action in allowing solvent molecules to pass through while excluding solute particles? (2) What is the cause of osmotic pressure?

Several theories have been suggested as to the manner in which the water or other solvent passes through a semipermeable membrane. Every such case of osmosis may be regarded as a transfer of solvent from a region of higher to a region of lower *escaping tendency.*

(1) The molecular sieve theory. This theory originated with Traube. It pictures the membrane as a sieve through which the water molecules can pass while the large molecules of a solute like sugar are stopped. There are relatively more water molecules on the water side of the membrane than on the solution side, where they are partly replaced by solute molecules; hence, more water molecules pass into the osmotic cell than out of it. In consequence, the level of solution rises. This theory still may be applied in the case of colloid sols but for true solutions it seems less plausible than others.

(2) The vapor pressure theory. The vapor pressure is a direct measure of the *escaping tendency* of the water or other solvent, hence this theory furnishes a satisfactory explanation of many cases of osmosis. The theory assumes that the semipermeable membrane is composed of a series of capillary openings, too small to admit liquid, but large enough for vapor to pass from the water on one side of the membrane and from the solution on the other. The vapor pressure of the water is greater than that of the solution, so that the vapor phase in equilibrium with the water is more than saturated with respect to the solution. Consequently, the vapor condenses into the solution and causes a slow distillation from the water to the solution, thus raising the solution level.

(3) The membrane solution theory. This theory postulates that the water or other solvent is soluble in the material of the semipermeable membrane, whereas the solute is not. Thus water forms a solid solution in a cupric ferrocyanide membrane. The solid solution that is in equilibrium with the water is supersaturated with respect to the solution within the cell. Consequently, the water goes out of solution in the membrane, adding itself to the solution in the cell and thus causing the level of the latter to rise.

The *membrane solution theory* receives some support from two simple experiments: (*a*) If a cylinder containing oxygen is capped with a piece of thin rubber, covered with a layer of water, and then surrounded with an atmosphere of ammonia, the total pressure within the cylinder increases because the ammonia dissolves in the water, passes through the rubber, and vaporizes into the oxygen where its partial pressure is low. (*b*) If a little water is shaken with ether in a cylinder and allowed to stand so that a layer of ether floats on a thin layer of water, and if chloroform is then introduced carefully beneath the water layer, the water layer is slowly pushed up. The ether dissolves in the water and passes into the chloroform in which it is much more soluble.

This theory postulates that the solvent goes from a region of higher to a region of lower escaping tendency through the medium of solution rather than through that of vapor as in the vapor pressure theory.

The Cause of Osmotic Pressure. No completely satisfactory explanation of the *cause* of osmotic pressure has yet been offered. Some have attempted to explain the pressure as due to the bombardment of the membrane by solute particles; others have focused attention upon the solvent rather than upon the solute and have attributed the pressure to the tendency of the solvent to pass through the membrane into the cell.

Van't Hoff discovered that the osmotic pressure of a dilute solution was numerically equal to that which the same amount of substance would exert if it were a gas occupying the same volume at the same temperature. This apparent analogy led him to a somewhat guarded suggestion. In 1892 he wrote: "Once again we have the equally futile question, what then exerts the osmotic pressure? Really, as already emphasized, I am concerned only with its magnitude; and since it has been found to be equal to the gas pressure, one is inclined to think that the mechanism of its production is similar to that found in the case of gas pressure. Let him, however, who is led astray by this view, simply leave the question of mechanism alone altogether." What van't Hoff offered merely as a plausible suggestion was accepted and amplified by others, but with results that were not entirely satisfactory.

The other view, that osmotic pressure is due to the tendency of the solvent molecules to pass through the membrane into the cell, is more widely held at present. According to it, the osmotic pressure is the pressure of the solvent on the *outside* of the membrane in excess of the pressure inside. Thus the pressure that must be applied inside the cell just to prevent passage of the solvent into the cell is a measure of the osmotic pressure. The excess pressure outside supposedly is due to the fact that more molecules of solvent can bombard a given area of the membrane than is possible inside where solute particles interfere.

Some light is thrown on the picture by a consideration of the vapor pressure relations between solvent and solution. Suppose we put under the same bell jar two beakers, one containing a pure solvent and the other containing a solution of a nonvolatile substance in the same solvent. The vapor pressure of the solution will be lower than that of the pure solvent, so that vapor will tend to leave the surface of the pure solvent and to condense upon that of the solution. The pure solvent will distil over into the solution, tending to equalize the vapor pressures. The distillation could be prevented, however, if the vapor pressure of the solution could be raised or that of the solvent lowered. We have seen on page 149 that a change in temperature will cause a change in vapor pressure. It is also true that a change in *pressure* will cause a change in vapor pressure (see page 634). *An increase in the total pressure on a substance will increase its vapor pressure.* Hence, in the case we are considering, we could increase the vapor pressure of the solution by increasing the pressure upon it. By applying sufficient pressure we could make the vapor pressure of the solution equal to, or even greater than, that of the pure solvent. In order to do this without changing the vapor pressure of the pure solvent, we would have to apply pressure to the solution alone by means of a piston which is impervious to the solution, but which is freely permeable to the vapor of the solvent. The apparatus for such an imaginary experiment is illustrated in Figure 135. The excess pressure which we would have to apply to the solution in order to raise its vapor pressure until it is equal to that of the solvent, would be exactly the same as the osmotic pressure. When the two vapor pressures are equal, there is no further tendency for the solvent to pass into the solution; a state of equilibrium exists.

The osmotic pressure must not be confused with the difference between the vapor pressure of the solvent and that of the solution. The osmotic pressure is of the order of hundreds of atmospheres for a solution the vapor pressure of which, as calculated by Raoult's law, is only a few millimeters less than that of the pure solvent.

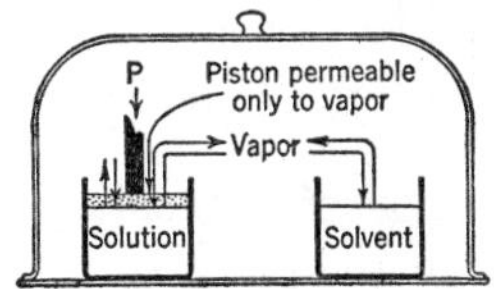

Fig. 135. Illustrating the Relation between Vapor Pressure and Osmotic Pressure.

In the porous disk method, the excess of pressure on the solution as compared to that on the pure solvent is brought about by *reducing* the pressure upon the solvent. The method is limited to dilute solutions because the tension cannot be as much as an atmosphere before the column of solvent breaks.

The change in vapor pressure affords another definition of osmotic pressure which we may state thus: *The* ***osmotic pressure*** *of a given solution is the excess pressure which must be applied to it in order to increase the vapor pressure of the solution until it equals that of the pure solvent.* Obviously, this concept of osmotic pressure involves no assumption as to the nature of the membrane or the mechanism of osmosis, and is very general in its application. Although we have discussed the relation on the basis of vapor pressure, the theory is not limited to a membrane made up of capillary openings. The vapor pressure is simply the most convenient way of visualizing and measuring the escaping tendency of the solvent molecules — their tendency to pass out of the liquid phase.

Relation of Osmotic Pressure to Freezing Point Depression. Osmotic pressure finds frequent application in biological and physiological studies. Where the quantity of material is small, the direct measurement of osmotic pressure is difficult, and usually it is calculated from a determination of the closely related depression of the freezing point. Both the osmotic pressure and the freezing point depression of dilute solutions vary with the molal concentration so that the osmotic pressure must be proportional to the freezing point depression, thus:

$$\frac{\pi_1}{\pi_2} = \frac{\Delta_1 T_f}{\Delta_2 T_f}$$

For approximate calculations, a 1 molal solution of a nonelectrolyte may be assumed to freeze at $-1.86°$ C. and to have an osmotic pressure of 22.41 atmospheres at 0° C. Hence, the osmotic pressure of a given solution, in atmospheres, may be found approximately from the depression of the freezing point, ΔT_f, by the expression:

$$\frac{\pi}{22.41} = \frac{\Delta T_f}{1.86} \qquad \text{or} \qquad \pi = 12.1\ \Delta T_f$$

Role of Osmosis and Osmotic Pressure in Physiology. Osmosis and osmotic pressure occupy an important place in the physiology of plants and animals. Although the study has been handicapped by the delicate nature of many of the membranes and by the necessity of working with cells and organs removed from the living organism, many interesting facts and relationships have been established. Only a few of these can be dealt with here.

(1) The plant and animal are both composed of millions of individual cells, each surrounded by a cell wall, which functions as a more or less perfect semipermeable membrane. Water and solutes of low complexity pass through such membranes into the cell where they may be synthesized into the more complex substances of which plant and animal tissues are composed and to which the cell wall is not permeable. Thus the simple substances absorbed by the plant from the soil and from the air, and the simple substances resulting from digestion in the animal body, are transformed into the more permanent structural tissue.

(2) The effect of immersing plant cells in media containing different concentrations of solutes was demonstrated very nicely by the Dutch botanist de Vries.[1] He used cells extracted from the epidermis of the leaf of the *Tradescantia discolor*, which contain a blue pigment and are readily observed under the microscope. Some of his observations, using various solutions, are illustrated in Figure 136. The contents of the cell, in this case the cell sap, is an aqueous solution of glucose, potassium malate, and inorganic salts, of about 2.5 per cent total concentration. At room temperature it has an osmotic pressure of about 5 atmospheres.

In the normal cell, illustrated by Figure 136 (*a*), as it occurs in the plant, the membrane is distended to fill completely the framework of the cell. In this case the cell is said to have normal **turgor** or **tonicity**; *i.e.*, the stretching force on the cell wall is normal. The

[1] *Zeit. phys. Chem.*, **2**, 415 (1889).

appearance of the cell is unchanged if it is immersed in a solution having the same osmotic pressure as the contents of the cell, *hence such a solution is said to be* **isotonic** *with the contents of the cell.*

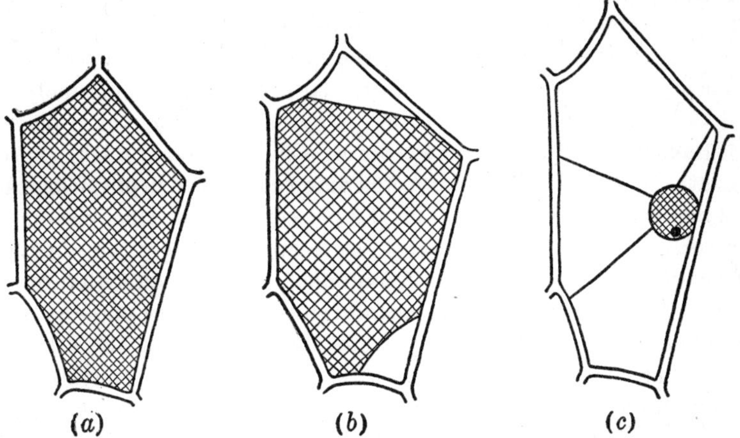

Fig. 136. Behavior of Plant Cells in Solutions of Various Concentrations.

Figure 136 (*b*) shows what happens when the cell is immersed in a 0.22 *M* sucrose solution. This solution is more concentrated than the cell contents, hence *has a higher osmotic pressure and is said to be* ***hypertonic*** *with respect to the cell contents.* Water passes out of the cell and it shrinks. *This osmosis out of a biological cell into water or a more dilute solution, causing a shrinkage of the cell, is known as* ***plasmolysis.*** Figure 136 (*c*) illustrates the very strong plasmolysis that takes place when the cell is immersed in 1 *M* potassium nitrate solution. The cell sheath, or membrane, is completely torn away from the supporting cellulose framework and only the cytoplasm remains.

(3) Experiments with red blood cells yield particularly interesting results. These cells, unlike the plant cells discussed above, have no rigid support for the semipermeable membrane. They consist merely of a thin, elastic envelope, through which water and certain simple solutes readily pass. When the blood cells are put into water or a dilute solution, water passes into the cells. The external liquid *has a lower osmotic pressure than the cell contents, and is said to be* ***hypotonic*** *with respect to the cell contents.* Whenever blood cells are put into a hypotonic environment, they become distended and very soon burst, the hemoglobin coloring the water red. *This*

process of breakage due to osmosis into the cell is called **laking.** When the blood cells are put into solutions which are hypertonic to the contents of the cells, water passes out of the cells, *i.e.*, *plasmolysis* takes place; the cells shrink and settle out of suspension.

These effects show why any fluid injected into the blood must be isotonic with the blood *plasma*, the liquid content of the cell. If the injected fluid is *hypertonic* with respect to the blood, plasmolysis takes place; if the injected fluid is *hypotonic*, laking takes place. Either effect, in the blood stream of a living person, might cause death. Consequently, all injected material is given in **physiological saline solution,** which contains 0.9 per cent of salt, chiefly sodium chloride, and has an osmotic pressure approximately the same as that of blood. Even a slight hypotonicity of the blood with respect to the contents of the cells is harmful since it opens the pores by distending the cells and thus permits diffusion out of the cells of material which does not ordinarily pass through the membrane. *This abnormal escape of cell contents, particularly hemoglobin, is known as* **hemolysis.**

(4) The blood of different mammals differs somewhat in osmotic pressure. The average freezing point of mammalian blood is about $-0.59°$ C., corresponding to an osmotic pressure of about 7.1 atmospheres at 0° C., or 8.1 atmospheres at blood heat, 37° C. Human blood contains about 2.2 per cent solids and 97.8 per cent water, and has an average osmotic pressure of about 7.7 atmospheres at body temperature. The average osmotic pressures of the blood of various mammals are listed in Table 61.

TABLE 61

OSMOTIC PRESSURE OF MAMMALIAN BLOOD AT BODY TEMPERATURE

MAMMAL	π (ATM.)	MAMMAL	π (ATM.)
Man	7.7	Rabbit	8.1
Horse	7.7	Sheep	8.5
Dog	7.8	Pig	8.5
Ox	7.9	Cat	8.8

The osmotic pressure of human blood does not remain altogether constant. It varies slightly in a given individual during the day. Early in the morning it may be as low as 7.2 atmospheres, while in midafternoon, after a heavy lunch, it may rise to 8.0 atmospheres. Such a daily variation is to be expected since the blood is the fluid which transports nourishment to the tissues and removes waste products. The blood receives amino acids, sugars, and other products of digestion from the digestive tract, and waste products from the tissues, while water, urea, and various other substances are given up or altered into less soluble materials. It is, in fact, remarkable that the variation in osmotic pressure is so slight. The kidneys are the main control organs. If they are diseased, the osmotic pressure of the blood rises and shows a daily variation wider than normal, thus disturbing the whole metabolism.

The blood of cold-blooded animals is not like that of the mammals, which remains nearly constant even under the most extreme environmental conditions. The blood of fish and other cold-blooded marine animals is practically isotonic with sea water, which freezes at − 2.3° and therefore has an osmotic pressure about four times as great as the blood of mammals. The blood of a cold-blooded animal, such as a fish, tends to adjust itself until its osmotic pressure approximates that of its environment. The adaptation is not always successful, however, and many salt-water fish do not long survive a transfer to fresh water, because of excessive dilution of their body fluids.

PROBLEMS AND EXERCISES

1. Calculate (1) the osmotic pressure at 20° C., (2) the freezing point, and (3) the boiling point of:

(*a*) a solution made by dissolving 26.46 g. of dextrose, $C_6H_{12}O_6$, in 2 kg. of water

(*b*) a 2.76 per cent solution of sucrose, $C_{12}H_{22}O_{11}$, in water

(*c*) a solution containing 301 g. of sucrose in 1 liter of solution of density 1.113 g./ml.

(*d*) a solution containing 2.12 per cent dextrose, 3.41 per cent sucrose, and 1.70 per cent levulose

(*e*) a solution obtained by mixing 100 g. of a 3.4 per cent solution of urea, $CO(NH_2)_2$, with 100 g. of a 1.6 per cent solution of sucrose.

2. Calculate approximately the freezing points of the mammalian bloods listed in Table 61, and the osmotic pressure of sea water at body temperature.

3. According to Pfeffer's results, the osmotic pressure of a solution of 4.06 g. of sugar in 100 ml. of solution was 2.74 atmospheres at 14° C. The density of the solution was 1.08 g./ml. Calculate the molecular weight of the sugar.

4. What weight of dextrose must be added to 100 g. of a 0.6 per cent solution of cane sugar to give a solution isotonic with physiological saline solution, *i.e.*, with blood?

5. The osmotic pressure of a 1 per cent solution of urea in water is 3.73 atmospheres at 10° C. Calculate (1) the freezing point of the solution and (2) the molecular weight of urea.

6. Using the data given in Table 60, page 269, examine the relation $\pi/c = k$, at 50° C.

7. Using the data in the same table, plot the graph showing the variation of osmotic pressure with concentration at (*a*) 0° C.; (*b*) 50° C.

8. Using the data in the same table plot the osmotic pressure against the absolute temperature for a solution of 1 molal concentration. Comment on the correspondence of this curve with that for the relation $\pi = kT$. What is the osmotic pressure at blood temperature?

9. Using several sets of values from the same table, test the applicability of the expression $\pi = mRT$, where m is the molality.

READING LIST

A. Findlay, *Osmotic Pressure*, 2d ed. Longmans, Green & Company, London, 1919. An excellent summary of the earlier development of the subject, including the work of Berkeley and Hartley and of Morse and Frazer.

A. Findlay, *Physical Chemistry for Students of Medicine*, 2d ed. Longmans, Green & Company, London, 1931. Pp. 32–62; two chapters on diffusion and osmotic pressure.

J. A. N. Friend, *Textbook of Physical Chemistry*. 2 v. J. B. Lippincott Company, Philadelphia, 1933–1935. Vol. I, pp. 380–393.

S. Glasstone, *Textbook of Physical Chemistry*. D. Van Nostrand Company, New York, 1940. Pp. 641–664.

H. C. Jones, *The Modern Theory of Solutions*, Harper & Brothers, New York, 1899. Papers (in English translation) by Pfeffer, van't Hoff, Raoult, and Arrhenius.

CHAPTER 11

REACTION KINETICS

The term **reaction kinetics,** or **chemical kinetics,** refers broadly to the velocity of chemical reactions, the extent to which they go before reaching equilibrium, and the way in which the reaction rates and the equilibrium proportions are influenced by such factors as temperature, pressure, catalysts, and the absorption of radiant energy. Research in this field of chemistry has been carried on with a two-fold purpose: (1) to gain some insight into the *mechanism* of chemical reactions, and (2) to obtain as complete data as possible on the rates of specific reactions under changing conditions, in order to compute the quantity of a given product obtainable from a given set of reagents in a given time, without the necessity of further experiment. Although the ultimate goal has not yet been attained, this research has established certain principles regarding reactions in general. The study of *reaction kinetics* is not only interesting in pure physical chemistry but also is important in other sciences involving chemical systems and in industry.

Reaction Velocity

Many chemical reactions take place so rapidly that the quantitative measurement of their rates is quite impossible. Familiar examples are found among ionic reactions involving the formation of precipitates, ordinary combustions, and the many reactions which take place with "explosive violence." Other reactions, especially some of those involving organic substances, are so slow that no change is observable even after several weeks. Between these extremes are reactions proceeding with measurable speeds, with which we are primarily concerned in the study of reaction kinetics. Of course, some reactions which are too slow for measurement under ordinary conditions may be accelerated by raising the temperature or by other means, and so made to take place with measurable velocity.

The definition of *reaction velocity* is very similar to that of velocity of motion. *Fundamentally, the* **velocity** *of a chemical reaction is* *expressed as the change in the quantity of the reactant in unit time.* Most experiments on reaction kinetics are carried out at constant volume, so that the quantity of each reactant is proportional to its *concentration.* Hence *it is customary to express the* **velocity** *of a chemical reaction as the change in concentration of the reactant in unit time.* Since the concentration ordinarily is expressed in moles per liter, and the time in seconds or minutes, the reaction velocity is expressed as change in molarity per second or per minute.

Experimental Methods of Measuring Reaction Velocity. The study of reaction kinetics depends upon the experimental determination of reaction velocities, by either direct or indirect means, depending upon the nature of the reaction.

The most direct method is chemical analysis for one constituent of the reacting system at suitable time intervals. For example, in studying the decomposition of hydrogen peroxide into water and oxygen, a measured volume may be removed at a known time, diluted, acidified with dilute sulfuric acid, and titrated with standard potassium permanganate solution to determine its content of hydrogen peroxide. In all such methods, the analysis must give the concentration of the reacting mixture *at the moment the sample is taken.* To prevent change in concentration, the analysis is carried out rapidly or the reaction in the sample is "frozen," either by dilution or by rapid cooling, or by adding the analytical reagent in excess and determining the excess by a back titration.

The change in pressure which frequently accompanies gaseous reactions may be used to follow their progress. Some reactions also may be followed by collecting and measuring evolved gas. Thus the decomposition of hydrogen peroxide may be studied by collecting the evolved oxygen in a eudiometer, which is read at suitable time intervals. When gas is evolved from a solution, however, the solubility of the gas causes an error, and supersaturation may vitiate the results, unless it is eliminated by vigorous stirring.

Often a reaction may be followed by the progressive change in some physical property of the reacting system. For example, the *inversion* of sucrose may be studied by means of a polarimeter which measures the angle of rotation of plane polarized light passing through the solution. The reaction is:

$$\underset{\text{sucrose}}{C_{12}H_{22}O_{11}} + H_2O \longrightarrow \underset{\text{dextrose}}{C_6H_{12}O_6} + \underset{\text{levulose}}{C_6H_{12}O_6}$$

Since the angle of rotation of the light beam goes through zero and changes sign during this reaction, the process is called *inversion* and the equimolar mixture of dextrose and levulose is called *invert sugar*. The progress of the reaction is followed by the polarimeter without disturbing the reacting system.

If one of the reactants is colored, the change of color, compared with that of standard solutions, may furnish a measure of the reaction rate. Thus, the rate of combination of bright yellow camphorquinone and hydrocyanic acid to form a colorless cyanhydrin is measured readily by comparison with color standards.

Electrical conductance also may be used to follow the course of a reaction, when the conductance of the products is different from that of the reagents. This method is applicable in studying the rate of saponification[1] of esters with bases. In the case of ethyl acetate, the reaction is described by the equation:

$$CH_3COOC_2H_5 + OH^- \longrightarrow C_2H_5OH + CH_3COO^-$$

The ethanol and ethyl acetate are nonelectrolytes, and the conductance due to the cation remains practically constant, so that any change in conductance during the reaction is due to the replacement of the fast hydroxyl ion by the slow acetate ion. Thus the course of the reaction may be followed by the change in conductance without disturbing the reacting mixture. Studies of this type have shown that the rates of esterification are greater, the simpler the ester. Methyl acetate, for example, saponifies more rapidly than does methyl propionate, and this in turn more rapidly than ethyl propionate.

Influence of Conditions upon Reaction Velocity. The factors which most generally influence the speed of chemical reactions are (1) concentration or pressure, (2) temperature, (3) the presence of catalysts, and (4) exposure to radiant energy.

Influence of Concentration upon Reaction Velocity. In 1850, Wilhelmy studied the rate of inversion of sucrose in the presence of acids and found that the speed of inversion is proportional to the concentration of sucrose in the solution, provided that the concentration of the acid and the temperature remain the same. He noted that as the inversion progresses and the concentration of sucrose decreases, the reaction becomes slower. In 1867, the

[1] The term *saponification* was originally applied to the preparation of a *soap* from a fat, which is an ester, and a strong base. The term is now applied to the action of any strong base with an ester.

influence of the quantity or concentration of a reactant on the rate of reaction was concisely summarized by two Norwegian chemists, Guldberg and Waage, in a generalization which became known as **the law of mass action,** or, better, **the law of concentration effect.** This law, one of the most fundamental generalizations referring to chemical reactions, may be stated thus: *The rate of a simple chemical reaction is directly proportional to the concentration of each reactant, raised to a power equal to the number of molecules of the reactant in the equation for the actual reaction.*

Thus if a substance A is decomposing according to the equation:

$$A \longrightarrow \cdots$$

the rate of change will be given by:

$$r = k[A]$$

where the square brackets denote concentration. For a reaction of the type:

$$A + B \longrightarrow \cdots$$

since $\qquad r = k_1[A]$, when [B] is constant

and $\qquad r = k_2[B]$, when [A] is constant

it follows that

$$r = k[A][B] \text{ when [A] and [B] both vary.}$$

For a simple reaction of the general type:

$$aA + bB + cC + \cdots \longrightarrow \cdots$$

the rate of the reaction will be given by the expression:

$$r = k[A]^a[B]^b[C]^c \cdots$$

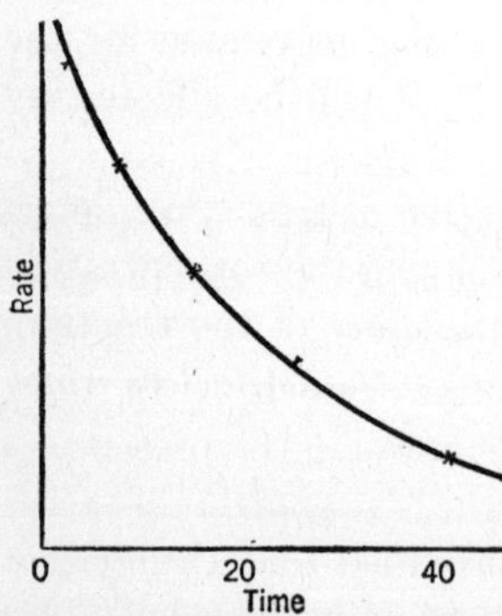

Fig. 137. Change of Reaction Rate with Time (Diminishing Concentration).

The data given in Table 62 for the decomposition of hydrogen peroxide (in the presence of a catalyst) and the curve in Figure 137 show that this reaction rate decreases progressively with diminishing concentration of the reactants. The calculation of the rate, therefore, calls for more precise mathematical treatment than merely dividing the total change by the total time as was done to obtain the values in column 4 of Table 62.

TABLE 62

CHANGE OF REACTION RATE WITH CONCENTRATION

TIME (MINUTES)	H_2O_2 REMAINING (ML. $KMnO_4$)	H_2O_2 CHANGED (ML. $KMnO_4$)	RATE OF CHANGE (ML. $KMnO_4$ PER MINUTE)
0	46.1	0.0	—
5	37.1	9.0	1.80
10	29.8	16.3	1.46
20	19.6	26.5	1.02
30	12.3	33.8	0.73
50	5.0	41.1	0.37

By taking the time intervals so short that the change in concentration is negligibly small, we can express the rate by the differential ratio $\frac{dx}{dt}$, where dx is the infinitesimal change in concentration of the reactant during the infinitesimal interval of time dt. When the concentration of the reactant is *increasing* with time, the rate is *positive*, $+\frac{dx}{dt}$; when it is *decreasing*, the rate is negative, $-\frac{dx}{dt}$.

Molecularity and Order of Reaction. The ordinary balanced chemical equation for a reaction, which we shall call the **stoichiometric equation,** ordinarily does not tell us the **mechanism** of the reaction. If we know the equation for the mechanism of a reaction, we can classify the reaction as **unimolecular** if only one molecule reacts, **bimolecular** if two molecules react, **termolecular** if three react, and so on. We can also write the expression for the rate of each type of reaction, and show how it will be affected by the concentration of each reactant.

Actually, our problem is exactly the reverse of this. We determine the effect upon reaction velocity of varying the concentration of the different reactants, and thus find the *order* of the reaction. *The* ***order of a reaction*** *is the number of concentration factors which enter into the equation for the rate.* Thus if:

$$r = k[A]^2 \quad \text{or} \quad r = k[A][B] \quad \text{or} \quad r = k[B]^2$$

the reaction is *second order,* since the product of *two* concentration factors is involved in each case. In the first case, the reaction is "second order with respect to A," in the third case "second order with respect to B," and in the second case it is *first* order with respect to either A or B alone, but second order for the whole reaction. The order of a reaction generally is not the same as the **molecularity,** *i.e.*, the number of molecules represented in the equation, but from the order of a reaction under known conditions we can try to *infer* its mechanism and hence its molecularity.

Zero Order Reactions. Reactions of which the speeds are independent of the concentration of reactant, *i.e.*, which proceed at the same rate *regardless of the concentration,* are called *zero order* reactions. The rate expression for a reaction of this type is:

$$-\frac{d[\mathrm{A}]}{dt} = k_0$$

A reaction may be of zero order when some outside source of energy, such as the light which induces a photochemical reaction, is the determining factor.

First Order Reactions. If, at various time intervals during a reaction in which the single reactant, A, is changing at constant volume, the observed reaction rate is given by the expression:

$$-\frac{d[\mathrm{A}]}{dt} = k_1[\mathrm{A}]$$

then the reaction is of the *first order.* Here k_1 is the **velocity constant,** characteristic of the reaction at a given temperature. By putting $[\mathrm{A}] = 1$ we see that k_1 is the rate of reaction when the concentration is unity.

By the process of *integration* between the limits of two definite concentrations, $[\mathrm{A}]_1$ and $[\mathrm{A}]_2$, we may convert this equation from the differential to the finite form, and by changing from natural to common logarithms, we obtain the expression:

$$\log \frac{[\mathrm{A}]_1}{[\mathrm{A}]_2} = \frac{k_1(t_2 - t_1)}{2.303}$$

where t_2 and t_1 are the times after the beginning of the reaction at which the concentrations of the reacting substance are $[\mathrm{A}]_2$ and $[\mathrm{A}]_1$, respectively. If the initial concentration $[\mathrm{A}]_0$ is determined, then t_1 is zero and $[\mathrm{A}]_1$ is $[\mathrm{A}]_0$, and the expression may be written:

$$\log \frac{[\mathrm{A}]_0}{[\mathrm{A}]} = \frac{k_1 t}{2.303}$$

where $[\mathrm{A}]$ is the concentration at the time t.

Examples of First Order Reactions. Several *first order reactions* have been studied:

(1) Radioactive disintegration. The disintegration of a radioactive element is first order. In the change,

$$Ra \longrightarrow Rn + \alpha \text{ particle} + 2\,\epsilon$$

the velocity of the change can be followed by measuring the intensity of radiation, provided the radioactive product, Rn, is removed continuously. If I_0 is the initial radioactivity and I the radioactivity at the end of t hours, this equation holds:

$$\log \frac{I_0}{I} = \frac{k_1 t}{2.303}$$

The velocity of this change is independent of the temperature.

(2) The decomposition of hydrogen peroxide. The stoichiometric equation for the decomposition is,

$$2\,H_2O_2 \longrightarrow 2\,H_2O + O_2$$

but it is a first order reaction, as shown by the data of Harned[1] given in Table 63. The decomposition is catalyzed by iodide ion, by ferric ion, and by the enzyme *catalase*, any of which composes with the hydrogen peroxide solution a homogeneous system. In this table, the change of concentration in t minutes is denoted by x, and the concentration at the end of time t by $(a - x)$, where a is the initial concentration. Using these symbols, the first order equation becomes:

$$k_1 = \frac{2.303}{t} \log \frac{a}{a - x}$$

TABLE 63

DECOMPOSITION OF HYDROGEN PEROXIDE IN 0.02 M KI AT 25° C.

t (MINUTES)	x	$a - x$	k_1
0	0.00	57.90	—
5	7.50	50.40	0.02775
10	14.00	43.90	0.02768
25	28.80	29.10	0.02752
45	41.20	16.70	0.02763
65	48.30	9.60	0.02764
Infinity	57.90 $= a$	0	—

The constancy of k_1 shows conclusively that the reaction is of the first order with respect to H_2O_2.

[1] *J. Am. Chem. Soc.*, **40**, 1461 (1918).

(3) The decomposition of nitrogen pentoxide. Nitrogen pentoxide, N_2O_5, a solid with high vapor pressure which sublimes readily, decomposes in the gas phase according to the stoichiometric equation:

$$2\,N_2O_5 \longrightarrow 4\,NO_2 + O_2$$

Daniels and Johnston[1] followed the reaction by measuring the increase in pressure as the decomposition went on. Making a suitable correction for the decrease in pressure caused by the equilibrium,

$$4\,NO_2 \rightleftharpoons 2\,N_2O_4$$

they found that the decomposition of nitrogen pentoxide in the gas phase was first order. The decomposition in inert solvents, such as carbon tetrachloride and chloroform, is also first order, although the velocity constant differs for the different solvents.

(4) The inversion of sucrose. Bimolecular reactions will be first order whenever the concentration of one reactant is so large compared to that of the other that its change during the reaction is negligible. Its concentration would appear, then, as a constant in the second order equation, *i.e.*, the rate follows the first order equation.

A well-known example of this type of reaction is the inversion of sucrose in the presence of an enzyme or of hydrogen ion,

$$\underset{\text{sucrose}}{C_{12}H_{22}O_{11}} + H_2O \longrightarrow \underset{\text{dextrose}}{C_6H_{12}O_6} + \underset{\text{levulose}}{C_6H_{12}O_6}$$

As already mentioned on page 280, this reaction is followed by the change in angle of rotation of plane polarized light. If α_0 is the initial angle of rotation, α_t the angle after t hours, and α_f the angle at the end of the reaction, the velocity constant is given by the first order equation put in the form:

$$k_1 = \frac{2.303}{t}\log\frac{(\alpha_0 - \alpha_f)}{(\alpha_t - \alpha_f)}$$

The data in Table 64 show the constancy of k_1 when calculated by this equation.

Second Order Reactions. When there are *two* molecules reacting as represented by the equation,

$$A + B \longrightarrow \cdots$$

[1] *J. Am. Chem. Soc.*, **43**, 53 (1921).

TABLE 64

VELOCITY OF INVERSION OF SUCROSE

t (HOURS)	$\alpha_t°$	k_1	t (HOURS)	$\alpha_t°$	k_1
0	78.00	—	42	2.30	0.0342
2	71.00	0.0343	48	− 1.96	0.0340
4	65.10	0.0366	61	− 9.00	0.0342
12	44.60	0.0342	86	− 15.80	0.0341
18	32.40	0.0348	95	− 17.25	0.0342
24	22.45	0.0344	Infinity	− 21.15 = α_f	—

At 30° C. 28.750 g. formic acid as catalyst in 250 ml. Data recalculated from Rosanoff, Clark, and Sibley, *J. Am. Chem. Soc.*, **33,** 1911 (1911).

the reaction is *bimolecular.* The rate expression at constant volume is:

$$-\frac{d[\mathrm{A}]}{dt} = -\frac{d[\mathrm{B}]}{dt} = k_2[\mathrm{A}] \times [\mathrm{B}]$$

A reaction which follows this equation is *second order.*

If the two molecules are identical,

$$2\,\mathrm{A} \longrightarrow \cdots$$

the rate expression becomes:

$$-\frac{d[\mathrm{A}]}{dt} = k_2[\mathrm{A}]^2$$

Integration of the differential rate equations between times *0* and t, corresponding to concentration changes from $[\mathrm{A}]_0$ and $[\mathrm{B}]_0$ to [A] and [B], respectively, gives the expressions:

$$\frac{2.303}{[\mathrm{A}]_0 - [\mathrm{B}]_0} \log \frac{[\mathrm{B}]_0 \times [\mathrm{A}]}{[\mathrm{A}]_0 \times [\mathrm{B}]} = k_2t$$

and

$$\frac{[\mathrm{A}]_0 - [\mathrm{A}]}{[\mathrm{A}]_0 \times [\mathrm{A}]} = k_2t$$

Examples of Second Order Reactions. Most of the simple homogeneous reactions which have been studied are of the *second order.*

(1) The saponification of ethyl acetate. This reaction, which may be represented by the stoichiometric equation,

$$CH_3COOC_2H_5 + OH^- \longrightarrow C_2H_5OH + CH_3COO^-$$

has been studied carefully. The velocity constant is the same for all strong bases, indicating that hydroxyl ion is one of the reactants. Using the conductance method to follow the course of the reaction, Walker obtained the results given in Table 65. The solution was 0.01 *M* with respect to both ester and base at the beginning of this experiment, so that the *second order* constant is given by:

$$k_2 = \frac{1}{t}\frac{[A]_0 - [A]}{[A]_0 \times [A]}$$

where [A] represents the concentration of either ester or base.

TABLE 65

Saponification of Ethyl Acetate at 25° C.

Time (Minutes)	$[A]_0 - [A]$ (Moles/Liter)	k_2
0	0	—
5	0.00245	6.49
9	0.00367	6.44
13	0.00459	6.53
20	0.00566	6.52
33	0.00680	6.44
Infinity	$0.01000 = [A]_0$	—

Walker, *Proc. Roy. Soc.*, **A 78,** 157 (1906).

(2) Other reactions. These include reactions between alkyl halides, *e.g.*, C_2H_5I, and sodium phenate, C_6H_5ONa, or sodium benzylate, $C_6H_5CH_2ONa$; also a number of reactions involving gases, such as the decomposition of hydrogen iodide and nitrogen dioxide.

Third Order Reactions. When three molecules react according to the equation,

$$A + B + C \longrightarrow \cdots$$

the reaction is termolecular. The expression for the rate of such a reaction at constant volume, in its most general form, is:

$$-\frac{d[A]}{dt} = -\frac{d[B]}{dt} = -\frac{d[C]}{dt} = k_3[A] \times [B] \times [C]$$

Reactions which obey this equation are of the **third order.** Such reactions, involving simultaneous collision of three molecules, are rare, and the occurrence of reactions of still higher orders has not been definitely established.

Among the few known third order reactions are the gas-phase oxidations of nitric oxide with oxygen, chlorine, and bromine. The mechanism of these reactions probably involves the simultaneous collision of two molecules of nitric oxide with one of the other gas, according to one of the equations:

$$2\,NO + O_2 \longrightarrow 2\,NO_2$$
$$2\,NO + Cl_2 \longrightarrow 2\,NOCl$$
$$2\,NO + Br_2 \longrightarrow 2\,NOBr$$

Determination of the Order of a Reaction. Various methods have been developed for determining the *order* of a given reaction.

(1) Trial method. The most direct method is to obtain data on the concentrations at various times, substitute them successively into the expressions for the various orders, and find which equation gives the most nearly constant value for k.

(2) Graphical method. A second method, called the *graphical method*, is to determine what function of the concentration, plotted against the time, gives a straight line. If the initial concentrations of the reactants are equal, and the value of each at any moment is called C, a straight line is obtained: (*a*) for a first order reaction, if $\log C$ is plotted against time; (*b*) for a second order reaction, if $\frac{1}{C}$ is plotted against time; and (*c*) for a third order reaction if $\frac{1}{C^2}$ is plotted against time. If the initial concentrations are not equal, in the case of a second order reaction, a straight line is obtained if $\log \frac{[A]}{[B]}$ is plotted against time.

(3) Half-period method. A third method, applicable when the various reactants are present in equivalent concentrations, is to determine the **half-period,** which may be defined as *the time required for half of the reactant initially present to react.*

The *half-period* for a first order reaction may be derived as follows: The rate expression for a first order reaction is:

$$\log \frac{[A]_0}{[A]} = \frac{k_1 t}{2.303}$$

and if $[A]_h = \frac{1}{2}[A]_0$ and t is put equal to t_h,

$$t_h = \frac{2.303 \log 2}{k_1} = \frac{0.693}{k_1}$$

Since $\frac{[A]_0}{[A]_h}$ is always equal to 2, the half-period for a first order reaction is independent of the initial concentration.

Similarly, the half-period for a second order reaction, when $[A]_0 = [B]_0$, is found to be:

$$t_h = \frac{1}{k_2[A]_0}$$

For a third order reaction, when $[A]_0 = [B]_0 = [C]_0$:

$$t_h = \frac{1}{k_3[A]_0^2}$$

Thus the order of a reaction may be found from the half-period for various initial concentrations, $[A]_0$. If the given reaction is first order, the half-period will be independent of the initial concentration; if it is second order, the half-period will be proportional to $\frac{1}{[A]_0}$; if it is third order, the half-period will be proportional to $\frac{1}{[A]_0^2}$; if nth order, it will be proportional to $\frac{1}{[A]_0^{n-1}}$ provided n is greater than 0.

Influence of Temperature on Reaction Velocity. If the same substances at the same concentrations are allowed to react at different temperatures, the rates of reaction are found to be quite different, usually increasing at higher temperatures. Different reactions are, however, affected to different degrees. Thus, methyl acetate is hydrolyzed by sodium hydroxide solution 1.82 times as rapidly at 35° C. as at 25° C., while sucrose is hydrolyzed by dilute hydrochloric acid 4.13 times as fast at 35° C. as at 25° C. These figures are given by Rice and Urey,[1] who conclude that: "These two examples represent the normal limits of the variation, and it is only very rarely that a homogeneous reaction has a temperature coefficient greater than that obtaining in the hydrolysis of cane sugar (sucrose), or less than that in the corresponding reaction with methyl acetate." It is useful to remember that as a general rule *a rise in temperature of 10° C. doubles or triples the speed of a reaction.* Data which illustrate the effect of temperature rise in the case of several reactions are given in Table 66.

The half-period for the decomposition of nitrogen pentoxide at various temperatures has been calculated by Daniels.[2] Some of the results obtained are shown in Table 67.

[1] H. S. Taylor, *A Treatise on Physical Chemistry*. D. Van Nostrand Co., New York, 1930. Second edition. II, p. 970.

[2] F. Daniels, *Chemical Kinetics*. Cornell University Press, Ithaca, N. Y., 1938, p. 19.

TABLE 66

EFFECT OF TEMPERATURE ON REACTION VELOCITY

Reaction	Order	Temperature, ° C.	k
$CO(CH_2COOH)_2 \longrightarrow CO(CH_3)_2 + 2\ CO_2$ (in aqueous solution)	First	0 10 20	2.46×10^{-5} 10.8×10^{-5} 47.5×10^{-5}
$CH_3I + C_2H_5ONa \longrightarrow C_2H_5OCH_3 + NaI$ (in ethanol solution)	Second	0 6 12	5.60×10^{-5} 11.8×10^{-5} 24.5×10^{-5}
$2\ FeCl_3 + SnCl_2 \longrightarrow 2\ FeCl_2 + SnCl_4$ (in aqueous solution)	Third	0 12 21	5.08×10^{-2} 31.5×10^{-2} 87.5×10^{-2}

Moelwyn-Hughes, *The Kinetics of Reaction in Solution.* Oxford University Press, Oxford, 1933.

TABLE 67

EFFECT OF TEMPERATURE ON THE DECOMPOSITION OF N_2O_5

Temperature, ° C.	k_1	Half-Period	
− 100	2.7×10^{-18}	8.4×10^{12} years	2.7×10^{21} sec.
− 50	2.7×10^{-11}	830 years	2.6×10^{10} sec.
− 25	7.3×10^{-9}	5 years	1.6×10^{8} sec.
0	7.3×10^{-7}	11 days	9.5×10^{5} sec.
50	8.7×10^{-4}	13 minutes	7.8×10^{2} sec.
100	0.15	4.6 seconds	4.6 sec.
200	1.6×10^{2}	3.9×10^{-4} sec.	3.9×10^{-4} sec.
300	3.1×10^{4}	3.9×10^{-6} sec.	3.9×10^{-6} sec.

The data given in Table 67 show that a reaction which takes place instantaneously at a high temperature may not proceed at an appreciable rate at a low temperature.

Unlike the usual case, the reaction of nitric oxide with oxygen, chlorine, or bromine has a *negative* temperature coefficient, the

TABLE 68

VELOCITY CONSTANT FOR THE OXIDATION OF NITRIC OXIDE AT VARIOUS TEMPERATURES

Temperature, ° A.	$k_3 \times 10^{-9}$	Temperature, ° A.	$k_3 \times 10^{-9}$
80.1	41.8	228.1	10.1
90.1	40.1	293.1	7.38
143.1	20.2	323.6	6.62
163.1	16.6	363.1	4.51

Kassel, *Kinetics of Homogeneous Gas Reactions*, The Chemical Catalog Co., New York, 1932, p. 167.

value of k_3 decreasing with rising temperature. This is shown by the data in Table 68 for the reaction of nitric oxide with oxygen.

The Arrhenius Equation. In 1889 Arrhenius pointed out a useful empirical relationship between reaction velocity and temperature. The **Arrhenius equation** may be stated in the forms

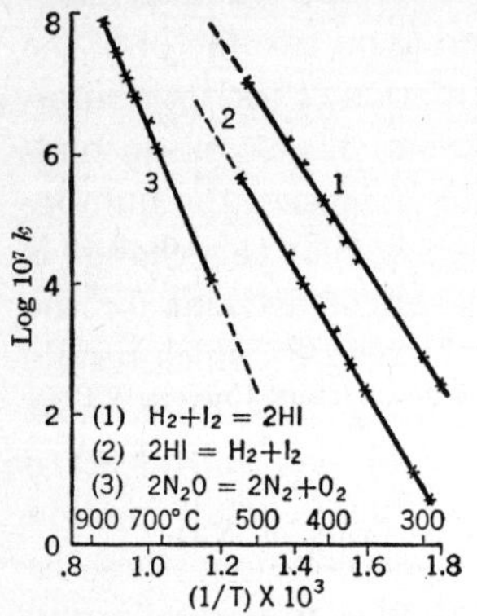

Fig. 138. Change of Velocity Constant with Temperature.

$$\ln k = B - \frac{A}{RT} \qquad \text{or} \qquad k = B'e^{-\frac{A}{RT}}$$

where A and B or B', are constants characteristic of the reaction, R is the gas constant, and T is the absolute temperature. The logarithmic form of the equation represents a straight line, if $\ln k$ or $\log k$ is plotted against $\frac{1}{T}$, and its applicability may be tested by such plots. Data for several reactions plotted in this way in Figure 138 show that the Arrhenius equation is obeyed over a considerable temperature range.

The slope is equal to $-\frac{A}{RT}\cdot$ Even if the plot of $\ln k$ against the reciprocal of the temperature shows a curvature, differentiation shows that,

$$\frac{d \ln k}{d\left(\frac{1}{T}\right)} = -\frac{A}{RT}$$

so that the tangent at any point is equal to $-\frac{A}{RT}\cdot$

Substituting experimental values of the rate constant, k' and k'' at the temperatures T' and T'', into the logarithmic form of the Arrhenius equation, and subtracting these two equations, we can eliminate B and obtain:

$$\ln \frac{k'}{k''} = \frac{A}{R}\left[\frac{1}{T''} - \frac{1}{T'}\right]$$

which, on changing to common logarithms and substituting the value for R, 1.987 calories per degree, becomes:

$$\log \frac{k'}{k''} = \frac{A}{4.576}\left[\frac{1}{T''} - \frac{1}{T'}\right]$$

From values for k determined at two temperatures, we can solve for A, and thus calculate the velocity constant k at any other temperature.

Activated Molecules. If we make the reasonable assumption that a chemical reaction takes place only when the reacting molecules collide, the rate of reaction will depend upon two factors: the number of collisions per second, and the fraction of the total number of collisions which result in chemical reaction. A rise in temperature speeds up the molecules and hence increases the number of collisions per second; but calculations show that this change is only a few per cent for a 10° rise, which cannot account for the *doubling* of the average velocity of chemical reactions which results from this temperature rise. Most of the change, therefore, must be due to an increase in the fraction of the collisions which lead to chemical reaction. Arrhenius assumed that only a small fraction of the molecules were capable of reacting upon collision; these he termed *active molecules.* He assumed that the active molecules differ chemically from the inactive ones. If they are formed *endothermically,* their number must increase with rising temperature, according to Le Chatelier's principle. The constant A in the Arrhenius equation must have the dimensions of RT, *i.e., energy,* since $\ln k$ is a pure number and B and $\frac{A}{RT}$ also must be pure numbers. Arrhenius called A the **energy of activation** and interpreted it as the energy required to form the *active* from the *normal* molecule.

At present we accept the general ideas of Arrhenius' theory and think of the activated molecules as those which have a greater *energy content* than the average molecules. Only those molecules with sufficient energy will react when they collide; the others will rebound without reacting. The number of active molecules at different temperatures can be calculated from an extension of the kinetic theory. According to the kinetic theory frequent collisions give the molecules of a gas a very wide range of energies, the distribution of which is shown diagrammatically in Figure 139. The ordinates represent the per cent of the molecules having velocities corresponding within a narrow range to the values represented by the abscissas. One curve represents the distribution at a temperature of 300° A., and the other the distribution at a higher temperature, 600° A. The area between each curve and the horizontal axis represents the total number of molecules, which, of course, is constant. However, the number of molecules having energies greater than a certain amount, for example, those to the right of the line *CD* in the diagram, increases *very greatly* with a

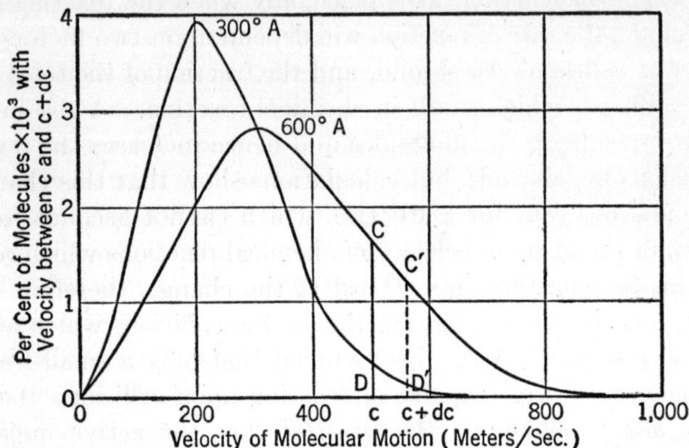

Fig. 139. Distribution of Energy among Molecules at Different Temperatures.

small rise in temperature. Thus, if the line *CD* represents the minimum energy which the molecules must have in order to react, the area to the right of *CD* represents the number of *active molecules* and the proportion of these active molecules evidently increases very rapidly with rise of temperature.

The **energy of activation** may be defined as *the average excess energy of the active molecules*, or "*the average energy of all the molecules that react minus the average energy of all the molecules.*" [1] The greater the number of molecules which possess this excess energy, the greater will be the speed of the reaction. Also, the smaller the energy of activation, the greater will be the number of molecules with sufficient energy to react, and the greater the speed of reaction.

The Mechanism of Reactions. The mechanism of bimolecular reactions, which usually are second order, can be described briefly thus: When a molecule of one substance collides with a molecule of the other and their energies are insufficient to bring about reaction, they rebound after collision. If their combined available energy is equal to or greater than the energy of activation, they

[1] F. Daniels, *Chemical Kinetics*. Cornell University Press, Ithaca, N. Y., 1938, p. 19.

will react. Some energy will be dissipated, given off as heat to other reactant molecules or to the walls of the containing vessel.

Termolecular reactions, which usually are third order, may be assumed to proceed in a similar manner, except that in this case three molecules with sufficient energy must collide simultaneously.

The mechanism of a unimolecular reaction, which usually is first order, also is explained on the collision hypothesis. Molecules acquire, by collision, sufficient energy to react. After an interval of time, the length of which depends upon the vibration frequency of the molecule, the energy becomes distributed among the molecular vibrational and rotational motions and reaches the valence bond which must be broken before reaction will occur. When the energy has become distributed, the bond breaks and the molecule decomposes. However, if the activated molecule collides with another molecule or with the wall of the container before it decomposes, it may lose a part of its energy and thus become deactivated. Thus, there is no direct dependence of reaction rate upon collision frequency, *i.e.*, upon pressure. The rate of a unimolecular reaction is independent of collision frequency except when the pressure is low and the rate of deactivation is diminished. A chain-reaction mechanism may also be applied to account for the properties of unimolecular reacting systems.

Complex Reactions. The reaction which follows a single course, with no interfering reactions, is the exception and not the rule. Most reactions are complex, rendering the interpretation of rate data difficult. A reaction may be complicated by *side reactions, consecutive reactions, chain reactions*, and *reversible reactions.*

Side reactions may be illustrated by the decomposition of hydroxylamine in aqueous solution, which occurs according to two different stoichiometric equations:

$$3\ NH_2OH \longrightarrow NH_3 + N_2 + 3\ H_2O$$
$$4\ NH_2OH \longrightarrow 2\ NH_3 + N_2O + 3\ H_2O$$

Another example is the chlorination of benzene, which occurs chiefly according to the two following stoichiometric equations:

$$C_6H_6 + Cl_2 \longrightarrow C_6H_5Cl + HCl$$
$$C_6H_6 + 3\ Cl_2 \longrightarrow C_6H_3Cl_3 + 3\ HCl$$

Consecutive reactions are typified by the hydrolysis of esters of dibasic acids. For example, diethyl oxalate reacts with dilute basic solutions in two steps, thus:

$$\begin{array}{l}COOC_2H_5\\ |\\ COOC_2H_5\end{array} + OH^- \longrightarrow \begin{array}{l}COO^-\\ |\\ COOC_2H_5\end{array} + C_2H_5OH$$

$$\begin{array}{l}COO^-\\ |\\ COOC_2H_5\end{array} + OH^- \longrightarrow \begin{array}{l}COO^-\\ |\\ COO^-\end{array} + C_2H_5OH$$

Before the first reaction has gone to completion, the second begins. The disintegration of radioactive elements is an excellent example of consecutive reactions. The study of the rate of a particular disintegration is complicated by the fact that its products themselves are disintegrating to form other radioactive elements.

If a side reaction is slow compared to the main reaction, the speed of the latter frequently may be determined without quantitative determination of the products of the side reaction. Also, in the case of *consecutive reactions,* if all of the reactions but one are rapid, the rate of that one may be found by analyzing for a product of the final reaction.

Chain reactions. The concept of a *chain reaction* is useful in picturing the mechanism of certain reactions. *A* ***chain reaction*** *is a reaction which occurs in several steps, the reactants in all the steps being composed of the same elements, and each step after the first taking place as the result of the preceding step.* Two types of chain reactions are recognized although they are not always distinguished clearly.

In *energy chains,* the energy from an exothermic reaction is passed on by the molecules of the products to activate the molecules of the reagents, instead of merely increasing the velocity of all the molecules. In *substance chains,* the chain is carried on by the formation of particularly reactive substances, such as *free radicals* or *atoms.* In photochemical reactions, promoted by exposure of the reacting system to light, the energy of activation is obtained by absorption of the light energy, and a chain reaction is thus inaugurated.

One of the best-known examples of a chain reaction is that between hydrogen and chlorine. This reaction can be initiated by the absorption of light of suitable wave length, by bombardment with α particles, or by absorption of energy in some other form. Since about a million times as many molecules react as could be activated directly by the energy absorbed, a chain mechanism probably is involved.

If the reaction proceeds by a *substance chain*, it may be represented thus:

$$Cl_2 + \text{light} \longrightarrow 2\,Cl$$
$$Cl + H_2 \longrightarrow HCl + H$$
$$H + Cl_2 \longrightarrow HCl + Cl$$

and so on. If this chain is not broken, an infinite number of molecules could react, once the first reaction has taken place even to an infinitesimal extent. However, the chain may be broken by the three-body collision of two H atoms, two Cl atoms, or one of each, *with another molecule which can take up the excess energy*.

If there is an *energy chain* involved, the step reactions may be represented thus:

$$Cl_2 + \text{light} \longrightarrow Cl_2^*$$
$$Cl_2^* + H_2 \longrightarrow HCl + HCl^*$$
$$HCl^* + Cl_2 \longrightarrow HCl + Cl_2^*$$

and so on. Here the asterisk (*) indicates activated molecules. This chain may be broken by collision of the activated molecules with normal molecules.

A chain reaction also may be initiated by mixing the reactants with a small amount of a reactive substance. Thus, sodium vapor introduced into a mixture of hydrogen and chlorine initiates a reaction chain, thus:

$$Na + Cl_2 \longrightarrow NaCl + Cl$$
$$Cl + H_2 \longrightarrow HCl + H$$

and so on. There is spectroscopic evidence to support the idea that the reaction of chlorine and methane, initiated by sodium vapor, may be a chain reaction involving *free radicals*, thus:

$$Na + Cl_2 \longrightarrow NaCl + Cl$$
$$Cl + CH_4 \longrightarrow HCl + CH_3$$
$$CH_3 + Cl_2 \longrightarrow CH_3Cl + Cl$$

and so on.

Reversible Reactions and Equilibrium

Reversible Reactions. So far we have not considered the most common type of reactions, where the products of a reaction may themselves react to re-form the reagents. Only when the forward reaction is much faster than the reverse reaction are we justified in ignoring the latter in velocity measurements. Even in such a case, as the reaction nears completion, the speed of the forward reaction will be so small that the speed of the reverse reaction becomes considerable.

Usually the speeds of the forward and reverse reactions are comparable so that rate measurements may be made only at the beginning of the reaction, when the reagents are in great excess over the products and the rate of the reverse reaction is negligible in comparison with that of the forward reaction. In such a case the measured velocity constant progressively decreases as the reaction proceeds. Reversibility can, of course, be eliminated as a complicating factor in rate measurements if one of the products is removed as fast as it is formed, *e.g.*, if a slightly soluble gas or solid is formed in a reaction in solution.

Equilibrium in Reversible Reactions. *A reaction is said to be* ***reversible*** *when it may proceed to a considerable extent in either direction.* Obviously, the reaction cannot go to completion in either direction if it is carried out *in a closed system*, that is, if none of the reactants is removed in any way. There are many familiar examples: Hydrogen reacts with iodine at 400° C. to form hydrogen iodide; hydrogen iodide decomposes at 400° C. into hydrogen and iodine; but regardless of which are taken as reagents, the reaction does not go to completion but slows down, and apparently stops, with all three reactants still present. Similarly at 600° C. nitrogen and hydrogen unite to form ammonia; under the same conditions, ammonia decomposes into nitrogen and hydrogen; the reaction apparently comes to a halt with all the reactants present.

In a reversible reaction, such as those mentioned, equilibrium is considered to be not *static*, but *dynamic*. The forward reaction slows down, in accordance with the principle of the law of concentration effect, as the concentrations of the reagents decrease; and the reverse reaction accelerates as the concentrations of the products increase. As the process goes on, the two rates become more nearly the same, and *eventually become equal.* The system is then said to be in a state of *equilibrium. When a reversible reaction is in* ***equilibrium,*** *the rate of the forward reaction is equal to the rate of the reverse reaction and there is no subsequent change in the proportions of reactants.* A reversible reaction is represented by an equation with double arrows, thus:

$$H_2 + I_2 \rightleftharpoons 2\,HI$$
$$N_2 + 3\,H_2 \rightleftharpoons 2\,NH_3$$
$$CH_3COOH + C_2H_5OH \rightleftharpoons CH_3COOC_2H_5 + H_2O$$

The Equilibrium Constant. Consider the case where the forward and reverse reactions are both bimolecular. The reaction may be represented by the equilibrium equation:

$$A + B \rightleftharpoons C + D$$

The second order equation for the forward reaction gives the rate:

$$-\frac{d[A]}{dt} = -\frac{d[B]}{dt} = k_2[A][B]$$

For the reverse reaction:

$$-\frac{d[C]}{dt} = -\frac{d[D]}{dt} = k_2'[C][D]$$

When equilibrium has been reached the two rates are equal and so we may write:

$$k_2[A][B] = k_2'[C][D]$$

and

$$\frac{k_2}{k_2'} = \frac{[C][D]}{[A][B]} = K_c$$

The quantity K_c is known as the **equilibrium constant.** The subscript $_c$ indicates that it is calculated from *concentrations.* If the reactants are *gases* and their relative quantities are expressed as *partial pressures,* the equilibrium constant is,

$$K_p = \frac{p_C p_D}{p_A p_B}$$

where p_A is the partial pressure of the gaseous reactant A, p_B of B, and so on. Notice that it is conventional to write the concentrations or partial pressures of the products in the numerator of the equilibrium constant expression, and those of the reagents in the denominator.

For an equilibrium involving any number of reactants and

products, if the mechanism of the reaction can be represented by the simple equation:

$$aA + bB + \cdots \rightleftharpoons cC + dD + \cdots$$

a line of reasoning similar to that outlined above will allow us to derive the equation for the equilibrium constant:

$$K_c = \frac{[C]^c[D]^d \cdots}{[A]^a[B]^b \cdots}$$

In case the mechanism of the reaction is more complicated, we can still derive the same expression for the equilibrium constant on the assumption that each step in the actual mechanism is individually reversible. If the same general reaction involves gases, we may express the equilibrium constant in terms of partial pressures, thus:

$$K_p = \frac{p_C{}^c \times p_D{}^d \times \cdots}{p_A{}^a \times p_B{}^b \times \cdots}$$

Although we can use either K_c or K_p in dealing with gaseous reactions, the two will be numerically equal only if there is no change in volume during the reaction; hence we must specify clearly which constant is given in any particular case. K_c and K_p are true constants, independent of pressure, only if we are

TABLE 69

SOME EQUILIBRIUM CONSTANTS

REACTION	EQUILIBRIUM EXPRESSION *	K	t (° C.)
$N_2 + 3\,H_2 \rightleftharpoons 2\,NH_3$	$\frac{p^2_{NH_3}}{p_{N_2}p^3_{H_2}}$	4.7×10^{-7}	700
$N_2 + O_2 \rightleftharpoons 2\,NO$	$\frac{p^2_{NO}}{p_{N_2}p_{O_2}}$	.0123	3927
$CO_2 + C \rightleftharpoons 2\,CO$	$\frac{p^2_{CO}}{p_{CO_2}}$	1235	800
$H_2 + I_2 \rightleftharpoons 2\,HI$	$\frac{p^2_{HI}}{p_{H_2}p_{I_2}}$	50.4	454
$H \cdot C_2H_3O_2 + C_2H_5OH \rightleftharpoons C_2H_5 \cdot C_2H_3O_2 + H_2O$	$\frac{[C_2H_5 \cdot C_2H_3O_2][H_2O]}{[H \cdot C_2H_3O_2][C_2H_5OH]}$	4.05	8

* In any reaction the concentration of a *solid* may be regarded as constant, corresponding to its vapor pressure at that temperature. This value is included in K_p and does not appear in the equilibrium expression, which contains only the partial pressures of the *gases*.

dealing with *ideal gases*, but they are nearly enough constant for practical purposes with real gases at moderate pressures.

In Table 69 are given values for the equilibrium constants for several reactions at specified temperatures.

The equilibrium constant is very useful because its value does not depend upon the proportions of reactants taken. Regardless of how much or how little of each initially enters into the reaction, the equilibrium invariably adjusts itself so that the equilibrium constant K is the same. This fact is brought out by the data given in Table 70 for the reaction, $H_2 + I_2 \rightleftharpoons 2\,HI$.

TABLE 70

EQUILIBRIUM CONSTANT FOR FORMATION OF HI (444° C.)

$[H_2]$	$[I_2]$	$[HI]$	K_c
.0268	.0002	.0177	59
.0099	.0020	.0328	54
.00321	.0078	.0337	45
.0017	.0114	.0315	50
.0003	.0242	.0202	56
			Av. 53

M. Bodenstein, *Zeit. physik. Chem.*, **22**, 16 (1897).

From the equilibrium constant we can calculate the partial pressures (or concentrations) of products which will result if we bring together certain known concentrations of reactants. The calculations are sometimes complicated, but a fairly simple example will illustrate the method:

What will be the final concentration of HI if hydrogen and iodine are brought together at 0.01 mole per liter, if $K_c = 53$? According to the equation, $H_2 + I_2 \rightleftharpoons 2\,HI$, *2 moles* of HI are formed from *1 mole* of H_2 and *1 mole* of I_2. $[H_2] = [I_2]$ at all times, since the two concentrations were equal at the start and the gases are used up at the same rate. The concentration of either substance at any time is equal to the initial concentration minus the amount used up in making HI, which is $\frac{1}{2}[HI]$, therefore at any time:

$$[H_2] = [I_2] = (0.01 - \tfrac{1}{2}[HI])$$

The *final* concentration of HI is obtained by substitution in the equilibrium expression:

$$\frac{[HI]^2}{[H_2][I_2]} = 53$$

which gives us

$$\frac{[HI]^2}{(0.01 - \frac{1}{2}[HI])^2} = 53$$

or, taking roots and clearing,

$$[HI] = 7.28\,(0.01 - \tfrac{1}{2}[HI])$$

whence

$$[HI] = 0.0157 \text{ mole/liter}$$

Change of Equilibrium Constant with Temperature. An important relationship is obtained when the Arrhenius equations for the forward and reverse reactions are differentiated with respect to T, giving:

$$\frac{d\ln k}{dT} = \frac{A}{RT^2} \qquad \text{and} \qquad \frac{d\ln k'}{dT} = \frac{A'}{RT^2}$$

Subtracting these two equations, we obtain:

$$\frac{d\ln k - d\ln k'}{dT} = \frac{d\ln \frac{k}{k'}}{dT} = \frac{d\ln K_p}{dT} = \frac{A - A'}{RT^2}$$

Another important relation, derived thermodynamically by van't Hoff (see page 645), gives the change in the logarithm of the equilibrium constant with temperature in terms of heat of reaction. This is known as the **van't Hoff equation** and may be stated thus:

$$\frac{d\ln K_p}{dT} = \frac{\Delta H^0}{RT^2}$$

where ΔH^0 is the standard heat of reaction in the forward direction, *i.e.*, when the reaction proceeds from left to right. A comparison of this reaction and the preceding one shows that

$$\Delta H^0 = A - A'$$

In other words, the heat absorbed when the reactants in their standard states are transformed into the products in their standard states is equal to the energy absorbed in activating the reactants, minus that absorbed in activating the products of the reaction.

If ΔH^0 is independent of temperature, we can integrate this equation to obtain:

$$\ln K_p = C - \frac{\Delta H^0}{RT} \quad \text{or} \quad \log \frac{K_p'}{K_p''} = \frac{0.4343 \times \Delta H^0}{R}\left[\frac{1}{T'} - \frac{1}{T''}\right]$$

Either of these equations describes the change of K_p with temperature with considerable accuracy, unless the temperature range is too large. Obviously, if we know K_p at one temperature and ΔH^0, we can calculate K_p at any other temperature; or if we know K_p at two temperatures we can use the equation to calculate its value at any other temperature, and also to calculate the standard heat of reaction, ΔH^0. The use of the equation is illustrated in Figure 140, where we have plotted Bodenstein's values of $\ln K_p$ against $\frac{1000}{T}$ for the reaction:

$$H_2 + I_2 \rightleftharpoons 2\,HI$$

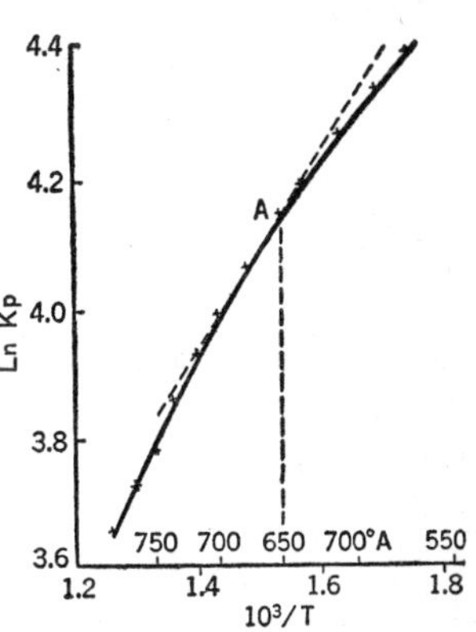

Fig. 140. Change of K_p with Temperature.

The Free Energy Change in a Chemical Reaction. As we saw on page 213, Berthelot advanced the idea that the *heat of a reaction* was a measure of the driving force of the reaction, *i.e.*, of its tendency to proceed. This idea did not prove correct. An accurate measure of the driving force of a chemical reaction is given, however, by the so-called *free energy change*, ΔF. The *decrease* in free energy, $-\Delta F$, is the maximum work which can be derived from a chemical reaction proceeding at constant pressure, as shown on page 629. One very convenient way to calculate the free energy change is from the equilibrium constant, which, as we have seen, is a measure of the extent to which a reversible reaction goes in either direction. If we are dealing with *ideal gases*, starting with the reactants each at a pressure of one atmosphere and ending with the products each at atmospheric pressure, the change in the standard free energy of the system during the reaction, ΔF^0 is given by the equation:

$$\Delta F^0 = -RT \ln K_p$$

This equation may be applied to real gases at moderate pressures. A rigorous equation, taking into account the deviations of real gases from ideal behavior, is discussed on page 645.

A *decrease* of the free energy of a system during a reaction, corresponding to a *liberation* of energy, indicates a tendency for the reaction to take place. *The magnitude of the free energy decrease is a quantitative measure of the driving force of the reaction.* One of the most important results of equilibrium measurements is the knowledge of free energy changes which they yield. In the following table are given the free energy changes accompanying a few representative reactions.

TABLE 71

THE FREE ENERGY CHANGES OF CERTAIN REACTIONS AT 25° C.

Reaction				ΔF^0 *in Kcal.*
$\frac{1}{2}$ H_2 (g)	+ $\frac{1}{2}$ Cl_2 (g)	$\longrightarrow$	HCl (g)	− 22.69
$\frac{1}{2}$ H_2 (g)	+ $\frac{1}{2}$ Br_2 (g)	$\longrightarrow$	HBr (g)	− 12.54
H_2 (g)	+ $\frac{1}{2}$ O_2 (g)	$\longrightarrow$	H_2O (l)	− 56.56
H_2 (g)	+ S (rhombic)	$\longrightarrow$	H_2S (g)	− 7.84
C (graphite)	+ 2 H_2 (g)	$\longrightarrow$	CH_4 (g)	− 12.80
C (graphite)		$\longrightarrow$	C (diamond)	+ .39
$\frac{1}{2}$ N_2	+ $\frac{3}{2}$ H_2	$\longrightarrow$	NH_3 (g)	− 3.91
$\frac{1}{2}$ N_2	+ $\frac{1}{2}$ O_2	$\longrightarrow$	NO (g)	+ 20.85
$\frac{1}{2}$ N_2	+ O_2	$\longrightarrow$	NO_2 (g)	+ 11.92
NH_4NO_3 (solution)		$\longrightarrow$	2 H_2O (g) + N_2 + $\frac{1}{2}$ O_2	− 63.6

From Lewis and Randall, *Thermodynamics*, pp. 607, 608.

Free energy changes, like heat changes, are additive for different reactions. Thus we can calculate the free energy changes for a large variety of substances, as the following example will illustrate. Let us calculate the free energy change in the reaction:

$$NO + \tfrac{1}{2} O_2 \longrightarrow NO_2$$

From Table 71 we take the free energies of formation of NO_2 and NO and write:

$$NO \longrightarrow \tfrac{1}{2} N_2 + \tfrac{1}{2} O_2 - 20.85 \text{ kcal.}$$
$$\tfrac{1}{2} N_2 + O_2 \longrightarrow NO_2 + 11.92 \text{ kcal.}$$

Adding these equations and rearranging terms gives:

$$NO + \tfrac{1}{2} O_2 \longrightarrow NO_2 - 8.93 \text{ kcal.}$$

Since the formation of NO_2 from NO involves a free energy decrease, $\Delta F = -$ 8.93 kcal., we therefore conclude that the reaction would go in this direction at 25° C.

Free energy values are extremely important in indicating the *stability* or *instability* of different substances. Those which are formed with a large *decrease* of free energy (ΔF a large *negative* value) are stable. Those formed with a large *increase* of free energy are unstable. Thus from Table 71 we see that at room temperature water, methane, and ammonia are stable, while nitric oxide, nitrogen dioxide, and ammonium nitrate (even in solution) are unstable.

Free energy values indicate whether or not a given reaction may take place; *i.e.*, what the conditions would be *at equilibrium.* Unfortunately these values tell us nothing of the *rate* — the length of time required to reach equilibrium. Thus hydrogen and chlorine will unite to form hydrogen chloride with a great liberation of energy, but the reaction is negligibly slow at room temperature unless suitably catalyzed. In this particular case a flash of light from a magnesium ribbon will cause an explosive combination. Similarly the diamond is less stable thermodynamically than graphite at atmospheric pressure, but the rate of change is so slow that a diamond ring still may be considered a safe investment.

Influence of Conditions upon Equilibrium

In discussing the influence of conditions upon reversible reactions, we must consider two separate results: (*a*) the influence of conditions on the *time required to attain equilibrium,* and (*b*) the influence of conditions upon the *proportions of reactants present* when equilibrium has been attained. In industrial operation both of these have very direct bearing upon the success of a process from an economic point of view. The various conditions and their effects will be discussed briefly in turn.

Influence of Conditions upon the Time for Attainment of Equilibrium. (1) Influence of a catalyst. A substance which acts catalytically upon a given reversible reaction affects equally the forward and the reverse reactions. Consequently, the time for reaching equilibrium is lessened. This effect, like that of temperature change, is of great industrial interest.

(2) Influence of temperature change. Since a rise in temperature accelerates both the forward and reverse reactions, we can easily see that the higher the temperature the shorter will be the time required for reaching equilibrium. The magnitude of this effect may be judged from the data given in Table 72 for the combination of nitrogen and oxygen to form nitric oxide as in the arc process for nitrogen fixation.

TABLE 72

Time for the Formation of One Half of the Equilibrium Concentration of Nitric Oxide

Temperature, ° A.	1000	1500	1900	2100	2500	2900
Time	82 yrs.	30 hrs	2 min.	5 sec.	.01 sec.	.00004 sec.

(3) **Influence of concentration.** Upon this point we have little information. Most experimental studies have been confined to solutions. Thus E. Cohen and his collaborators found that a pressure of 1500 atmospheres *decreased* the velocity constant for the hydrolysis of cane sugar 26 per cent and *increased* the velocity constant for the hydrolysis of ethyl acetate by 37.4 per cent. Compared with a change of 10° in temperature, a change of 1000 atmospheres in pressure therefore seems to have little effect on the rates of chemical reactions.

Influence of Conditions upon Proportions at Equilibrium. (1) **Influence of catalyst.** The presence of a catalyst has *no influence on the proportions present at equilibrium, i.e.*, on the value of the equilibrium constant. It is true that in various industrial processes a catalyst increases the yield of desired products, but this simply is because it speeds up the reaction so that it produces more of the product in a given time or an appreciable yield at a lower temperature. Any other result than this would be contrary to the laws of thermodynamics and would imply *perpetual motion.*

(2) **Influence of temperature.** The influence of temperature is extremely important. A change of 100° may cause a tenfold change in the value of the equilibrium constant, as we have already seen on page 290.

(3) **Influence of concentration.** An increase in the proportion of one reactant in a reversible reaction at equilibrium will bring about a change in the amounts of the other reactants. This result may be deduced from the equilibrium constant expression corresponding to the reaction under consideration. For example, in the reaction:

$$2\,SO_2 + O_2 \rightleftharpoons 2\,SO_3$$

for which

$$K_c = \frac{[SO_3]^2}{[SO_2]^2[O_2]}$$

if the concentration of oxygen be increased, more sulfur trioxide will form in order that the value of K_c may remain the same. This means that in any equilibrium if the concentration, or proportion, of one of the reactants be increased the equilibrium will shift in the opposite direction.

Instead of increasing the concentration, or partial pressure, of one reactant, the pressure on the entire system may be increased. The effect of this is to bring about a shift in the equilibrium in the direction attended by a *decrease in volume.* Thus the equilibrium yield of ammonia in the Haber process at 400° C. is increased from 0.4 per cent at 1 atmosphere to 79.8 per cent at 1000 atmospheres.

If a reaction takes place without change in volume, as in the case of the arc process:

$$N_2 + O_2 \rightleftharpoons 2\,NO$$

the per cent yield of the product is unaffected by the total pressure.

The Principle of Le Chatelier. A most interesting and useful principle which makes possible the prediction of equilibrium shifts due to changes in conditions is the **principle of Le Chatelier,**[1] which may be stated thus: *If a physico-chemical system is in equilibrium, a change in any of the factors, such as temperature, pressure, and concentration, which determine the conditions of equilibrium will cause the equilibrium to shift in such a way as to nullify the effect of this change.* This is really a statement in words of the principles which were expressed mathematically in the equations:

$$K_c = \frac{[C]^c[D]^d}{[A]^a[B]^b}$$

$$\ln K_p = C - \frac{\Delta H}{RT}$$

and

$$\frac{d\ln K_p}{dT} = \frac{\Delta H}{RT^2}$$

[1] Henri Le Chatelier was born in Paris in 1850. In 1883 he became professor in the Collège de France and later professor at the Sorbonne. In 1887 he received the degree of Doctor of Physical and Chemical Science and in the same year became professor of industrial chemistry at the École des Mines. Two years later he returned to the Collège de France and in 1907 became professor of general chemistry at the University of Paris. Here he directed the researches of more than one hundred candidates for the doctorate. He is best known for his work on dynamic equilibrium, particularly for the establishment of the *principle* which bears his name. His work on thermometry, metallurgy, and explosives also was important. He was active in the national life of France, and for his achievements in this field, as well as for those in science, was the recipient of many honors. He died in 1936, in his 86th year. For a portrait of Le Chatelier, see Plate VI, facing page 308.

Upon this basis the effects dealt with in the foregoing discussion may be predicted as follows:

(1) If the reaction is *exothermic, e.g.:*

$$2\ H_2 + O_2 \rightleftharpoons 2\ H_2O - 115.7 \text{ kcal.}$$

the application of heat, *i.e.*, the raising of the temperature from outside, would cause the equilibrium to shift in the direction that would tend to *lower* the temperature (nullify the effect of the alteration), and so the tendency to decompose would be greater the higher the temperature. This is stated concisely in the second equation above, which is this case becomes:

$$\ln K_p = C + \frac{115{,}800}{1.987\ T}$$
$$= C + \frac{58{,}280}{T}$$

As T *increases*, $\ln K_p$ *decreases* and hence the partial pressure of steam is lower and the partial pressures of hydrogen and oxygen are higher at high temperatures. This conclusion is borne out by the experimental data given in Table 73.

TABLE 73

THE EFFECT OF TEMPERATURE ON THE DECOMPOSITION OF STEAM

Temperature (° C.)	1300	1500	1705	2155	2257	2300
H_2O decomposed (per cent)	.0027	.02	.102	1.18	1.77	2.60

These data show that the combination of hydrogen and oxygen, explosive at the ignition temperature of about 600° C., becomes distinctly less spectacular at high temperatures.

(2) If the reaction is *endothermic* it is favored by a rise in temperature. A case in point is the combination of nitrogen and oxygen in the arc process:

$$N_2 + O_2 \rightleftharpoons 2\ NO + 43.0 \text{ kcal.}$$

Raising the temperature causes the equilibrium to shift in the direction attended by an absorption of heat since this has a tendency to lower the temperature. The data of Table 74 show this effect.

Plate VI. HENRI LE CHATELIER

(*For biographical note see page 307.*)

TABLE 74

THE EFFECT OF TEMPERATURE ON THE COMBINATION OF N_2 AND O_2

Temperature (° A.)	2033	2580	2675	3000	3200	3500
NO formed (per cent)	0.82	2.62	2.86	4.52	5.51	7.23

Data of Nernst, from Curtis, *Fixed Nitrogen*, p. 145. New York, The Chemical Catalog Co., 1932.

(3) An increase in the total pressure (at constant temperature) causes the equilibrium to shift in the direction attended by a decrease in volume. According to the principle of Le Chatelier if the pressure be increased, the equilibrium will shift in the direction which will tend to diminish the pressure, *i.e.*, to decrease the volume occupied by the reacting system. This is illustrated by the data for the Haber process in Table 76, page 312. If there is no volume change as the reaction takes place, then a change of pressure should cause no shift in the equilibrium. This has been found to be the case.

Applications to Industrial Processes. It is not difficult to realize how these principles may be brought to bear upon numerous industrial processes as well as upon those of purely scientific interest. Given raw materials, the industrial chemist is concerned primarily with turning out the desired product in sufficient amount at smallest cost. Consequently he must work out the conditions under which his reaction will give best results — a compromise between high yield and rapid production. The conditions may be established by the method of "trial and error," but usually it is vastly more economical when the establishment of conditions is guided by predictions based on chemical principles. An apt illustration of the necessity in industrial work of an understanding of chemical equilibria and the thermodynamic principles we have discussed is given by the following quotation from Le Chatelier,[1] who wrote in 1888:

> These investigations of a rather theoretical sort are capable of much more immediate practical application than one would be inclined to believe. Indeed the phenomena of chemical equilibrium play a capital role in all operations of industrial chemistry. . . .

[1] Quoted by Lewis and Randall, *Thermodynamics*. The McGraw-Hill Book Co., New York (1923), pp. 2–3, from *Ann. mines* [8] **13,** 157 (1888).

It is known that in the blast furnace the reduction of iron oxide is produced by carbon monoxide, according to the reaction

$$Fe_2O_3 + 3\,CO = 2\,Fe + 3\,CO_2$$

but the gas leaving the chimney contains a considerable proportion of carbon monoxide, which thus carries away an important quantity of unutilized heat. Because this incomplete reaction was thought to be due to an insufficiently prolonged contact between carbon monoxide and the iron ore, the dimensions of the furnaces have been increased. In England they have been made as high as thirty meters. But the proportion of carbon monoxide escaping has not diminished, thus demonstrating, by an experiment costing several hundred thousand francs, that the reduction of iron oxide by carbon monoxide is a limited reaction. Acquaintance with the laws of chemical equilibrium would have permitted the same conclusion to be reached more rapidly and far more economically.

In order to realize the line of attack of the industrial chemist, let us put ourselves in his place to work out one such problem, the fixation of nitrogen by combination with oxygen, subsequent oxidation of the nitric oxide to nitrogen dioxide, and absorption of this in water or a basic solution to form nitrate. A study of the system yields the following facts: The reaction of nitrogen with oxygen to form nitric oxide, which is too slow for practical application at temperatures below 2500° C., is reversible and endothermic:

$$N_2 + O_2 \rightleftharpoons 2\,NO + 43.0 \text{ kcal.}$$

The yield therefore will be increased by a rise in temperature; the higher the temperature the better the yield. To form the product at a rate that might make the process industrially profitable also would require a high temperature. Since there is no volume change when nitrogen and oxygen unite, there can be no advantage in carrying out the process under increased pressure.

To meet these requirements, the oxygen-nitrogen mixture is passed through the electric arc, the maximum practically attainable temperature of which reaches about 3500° C. Under these conditions, the yield of nitric oxide would be at a maximum, but another effect might diminish the final yield. If the gas mixture were allowed to pass through a zone becoming progressively cooler, the equilibrium would shift considerably in the exothermic direction; *i.e.*, the nitric oxide would decompose. To avoid this, the gas mixture must be cooled as rapidly as possible. This is achieved in part by using the "flaming arc," spread out into a thin disk by the application of a magnetic field, so that the mixture passes through a thin and sharply defined heating zone, beyond which it cools rapidly.

The next step in the process is to oxidize the nitric oxide to nitrogen dioxide:

$$2\,NO + O_2 \longrightarrow 2\,NO_2$$

This from our experience in elementary chemistry we know to take place spontaneously and rapidly and with noticeable warming when the two gases come in contact. But what happens at room temperature may not happen at higher temperatures. In the reversible exothermic process:

$$2\,NO + O_2 \rightleftharpoons 2\,NO_2 - 28.1 \text{ kcal.}$$

an elevated temperature would favor the decomposition of the nitrogen dioxide because the decomposition takes place with absorption of heat. Data which show this shift in equilibrium are given in Table 75.

TABLE 75

DECOMPOSITION OF NO_2 AT DIFFERENT TEMPERATURES

Temperature (° C.)	**630**	**494**	**279**	**184**
NO_2 decomposed (per cent) . .	99.0	56.5	13.0	5.0

Consequently the gas mixture must be cooled nearly to room temperature before even approximately complete oxidation of the nitric oxide can be expected.

As another example, let us consider more briefly the Haber process for the synthesis of ammonia. The equation indicating the reaction and thermal effect involved is:

$$N_2 + 3\,H_2 \rightleftharpoons 2\,NH_3 - 21.9 \text{ kcal.}$$

Since the reaction is exothermic, a rise in temperature would cause a shift in equilibrium from right to left, *i.e.*, would favor the decomposition of ammonia rather than its synthesis. Actually the proportion of ammonia in equilibrium at ordinary temperatures is probably very nearly 100 per cent of the theoretical yield; and at high temperatures, say 1000° C., the yield is vanishingly small; ammonia can be decomposed almost completely by passing it through a tube containing a red-hot wire. A low temperature then is advisable; but at room temperature the reaction is so slow that no detectable combination takes place. By the use of a catalyst the reaction may be speeded up to give a fair yield at moderately low temperatures. A temperature of about 400–500° C. is actually used, which is a compromise between a high yield and a lower yield rapidly obtained.

Another factor is important here. The formation of ammonia is accompanied by a 50 per cent decrease in volume, consequently the equilibrium proportion of ammonia will be greater the higher the pressure. The pressure in the Claude modification of the process is nearly 1000 atmospheres or 14,000 lbs. per sq. in. The data of Table 76 indicate the effect of pressure increase upon the equilibrium proportions in this system.

TABLE 76

THE EFFECT OF PRESSURE ON THE YIELD OF NH_3 AT 400° C.

Pressure (atm.)	1	10	30	50	100	200	500	1000
NH_3 formed (per cent)	0.4	3.8	10.0	15.0	25.8	35.0	50.5	79.8

PROBLEMS AND EXERCISES

1. In what *units* is k expressed in (a) the equation for a reaction of the *first order?* (b) the equation for a reaction of the *second order?*

2. Calculate the velocity constant for the hydrolysis of methyl acetate in the presence of hydrochloric acid, which is a first order reaction, from the following data: Vol. of base required to titrate 2 ml. of initial solution = 26.60 ml.; vol. of base required to titrate 2 ml. of solution after 3 hours = 29.32 ml.; vol. required for 2 ml. at end of reaction = 42.03 ml. The reaction is:

$$CH_3COOCH_3 + H_2O \longrightarrow CH_3COOH + CH_3OH$$

3. Calculate the energy of activation in calories per mole for the decomposition of nitrogen pentoxide, given that the velocity constant k_1 is 3.46×10^{-5} at 25° C., and 4.98×10^{-4} at 45° C.

4. For each of the following sets of data plot $\log C$, $1/C$, and $1/C^2$, respectively, against t, and hence deduce the *order* of the reaction:

(a) The decomposition of N_2O_5:

t in sec.	0	184	526	867	1877
C in moles/liter	2.33	2.08	1.67	1.36	0.72

(b) The saponification of ethyl acetate:

t in min.	0	5	9	13	20	33
C in moles of base/liter	0.01000	0.00755	0.00633	0.00541	0.00434	0.00320

5. Using the data in Table 66 on page 291, calculate the activation energy for each of the reactions there given.

6. The thermal decomposition of acetone is a *first order* reaction in which the half-period at 600° C. is 80 sec. How long would it take (*a*) for $\frac{1}{10}$ of the acetone to decompose? (*b*) for $\frac{1}{5}$ of the acetone to decompose?

7. Calculate the half-period for the saponification of ethyl acetate at 25° C., if the initial concentrations of ester and of base are both 0.0100 mole/liter and the velocity constant, when time is expressed in *minutes*, is 6.49, as given by the expression for a *second order* reaction.

8. Calculate the velocity constant for the inversion of sucrose from the data given in Table 64, on page 287, for 4 hours and for 61 hours.

9. From the data of Table 71 on page 304, calculate the free energy changes in the reactions:

(*a*) $HCl + \frac{1}{2} Br_2 \longrightarrow HBr + \frac{1}{2} Cl_2$

(*b*) $2\,NH_3 + \frac{5}{2} O_2 \longrightarrow 2\,NO + 3\,H_2O$

In which direction will each of these reactions proceed?

10. The equilibrium constant for the reaction $2\,NO \rightleftharpoons N_2O_4$ has the following values:

T	273.0	291.3	322.9	346.6	372.8
K_p	65.0	13.8	1.25	0.296	0.075

(*a*) Test the applicability of the equation $\ln K_p = \text{constant} - \frac{\Delta H^0}{RT}$ by plotting the values of $\log K_p$ against $1/T$.

(*b*) Calculate: (1) the value of K_p at 25° C.; (2) the heat of reaction.

READING LIST

W. B. Meldrum and F. T. Gucker, Jr., *Introduction to Theoretical Chemistry.* American Book Company, New York, 1936. On pp. 161–187 will be found a more elementary treatment of the subject of *reaction kinetics and equilibrium.*

F. Daniels, *Chemical Kinetics.* Cornell Univ. Press, Ithaca, N. Y., 1938.

S. Glasstone, *Textbook of Physical Chemistry.* D. Van Nostrand Company, New York, 1940. Pp. 1024–1103; 1130–1168.

C. N. Hinshelwood, *The Kinetics of Chemical Change.* Oxford University Press, New York, 1940.

H. S. Taylor, ed., *Treatise on Physical Chemistry,* 2d ed. D. Van Nostrand Company, New York, 1931. Pp. 949–1102.

"Symposium on the Kinetics of Homogeneous Gas Reactions," *Chemical Reviews,* **10,** 1–264 (1932). Papers by F. Daniels, L. S. Kassel, H. Ramsperger, B. Lewis, G. B. Kistiakowsky, H. Eyring, O. K. Rice, F. O. Rice, W. C. Bray, V. K. LaMer, M. and M. L. Kilpatrick, G. Scatchard, and E. A. Moelwyn-Hughes.

CHAPTER 12

THE IONIC THEORY

The *ionic theory* was published in 1887 by Svante Arrhenius under the title "On the Dissociation of Substances Dissolved in Water."[1] Its main accomplishment was to bring the colligative properties of aqueous solutions into direct relationship with the electrolytic properties. Also it served to systematize many empirical facts concerning inorganic and analytical chemistry. The critical examination of the theory as applied to aqueous solutions and its extension to nonaqueous solutions have been one of the main fields of research in physical chemistry during the past fifty years. As a result of this research the theory has been modified in several important respects.

Summary of Facts Regarding Solutions. The ionic theory was intended to explain certain facts concerning the properties of solutions.[2] Prior to the enunciation of the theory, investigations of solutions were carried on along three main lines, largely independent of one another: (1) chemical reactions; (2) electrochemical properties; (3) colligative properties.

(1) Chemical reactions. Reactions involving inorganic substances in solution were known to be very rapid; in contrast, those between organic substances were often very slow. When two solutions containing salts were mixed without production of a precipitate, evaporation of the solution might give all four possible salts. Also, the study of precipitation reactions by Williamson, in 1850, indicated that there was a continual "change of radicals" in solution, a mechanism suggesting the modern idea of equilibrium in such systems.

(2) Electrochemical properties. By 1887 the electrochemical properties of solutions had been studied extensively. The decomposition of water by Nicholson and Carlisle in 1800 soon was followed by Davy's preparation of sodium and potassium by electrolysis of their fused hydroxides and Berzelius' electrolysis

[1] "Über die Dissociation der in Wasser gelosten Stoffe." *Zeit. physik. Chem.*, **1**, 631 (1887).

[2] For a more detailed discussion see Meldrum and Gucker, *Introduction to Theoretical Chemistry*, pp. 190–203.

of various salt solutions. In 1833 Michael Faraday established the quantitative laws of electrolysis that bear his name and coined many of the terms still in use, such as *ion*, *anode*, *cathode*, *anion*, and *cation*. The "grand chain" theory regarding the mechanism of electrolysis advanced by Grotthuss in 1805, was modified by Clausius in 1857. He concluded that the dissociation of molecules into ions could not be *caused* by the electric current and postulated that ions were already present in the solution of an electrolyte. Hittorf, in 1853, showed that different ions traveled with different speeds. He developed a method for determining these relative speeds, and hence the transference number of each ion, *i.e.*, the fraction of the total current which it carried. Kohlrausch measured quantitatively the *conductances* of solutions, using the Wheatstone bridge. From his results he concluded that the ions in a solution moved independently of one another, each kind of ion with a characteristic velocity, or *mobility*.

Thus it will be seen that much was known regarding the existence and behavior of ions and the process of electrolysis prior to the time of Arrhenius.

(3) Colligative properties. Early work on the freezing points and boiling points of aqueous solutions showed that equimolar solutions of similar salts had nearly the same freezing point. Thus, equimolar KCl, KOH, and KNO_3 solutions froze at the same temperature. Likewise, equimolar Na_2SO_4, K_2SO_4, and $(NH_4)_2SO_4$ solutions froze at the same temperature, which, however, was lower than that of the former group. Beginning a systematic study in 1881, Raoult showed that for "normal" solutes (*i.e.*, nonelectrolytes) the *depression of the freezing point*, the *elevation of the boiling point*, and the *lowering of the vapor pressure are each proportional to the molal concentration.* He established the values for the molecular depression constant K_f and the molecular elevation constant K_b for water as solvent. The freezing point depressions, the boiling point elevations, and the vapor pressure lowerings were, in general, greater for electrolytes than for normal solutes.

In 1885 van't Hoff correlated these properties with the *osmotic pressure*, which he showed was proportional to the vapor pressure lowering and, hence, to the freezing point depression. He also showed that the osmotic pressure of a given solution was nearly equal numerically to the pressure the same quantity of substance would exert as a gas at the same temperature, *i.e.*, that an expression similar to the gas laws equation, $PV = RT$, applied to the osmotic pressure of a solution. Since the properties of gases could be explained on the basis of the number of particles in a given volume as postulated by the kinetic theory, he concluded that the properties of solutions could be explained on a similar basis. This led him to the important generalization: The *freezing point depression, boiling point elevation, vapor pressure lowering, and osmotic pressure are each proportional to the number of solute particles in a given volume of solution.* Obviously, "abnormal" solutes, *i.e.*, salts, bases, and acids, in some manner yielded more than the "normal" number of solute particles when dissolved in water.

The Arrhenius Theory. It remained for Arrhenius to correlate the colligative properties of solutions of acids, bases, and salts with their electrochemical properties. This was the fundamental accomplishment of the *theory of electrolytic dissociation.* We need not discuss in detail the postulates of the *Arrhenius theory* or, as it is sometimes called, the *classical theory of ionization*, but will present the *ionic theory* of today with emphasis on some of the more outstanding modifications of the original theory.

The Ionic Theory. We may summarize the main postulates of the modern ionic theory as follows:

(1) In aqueous solution, salts, bases, and acids yield two kinds of particles, called *ions*, one carrying a positive electric charge, the other a negative electric charge. The number of unit charges on an ion, representing the number of electrons lost or gained by the neutral atom, corresponds to the valence of the ion.

(2) The ions are produced mainly in two ways: (*a*) by the dissociation of ions already present in the solid electrolyte,[1] *e.g.*,

$$\underline{K^+Cl^-} \longrightarrow K^+ + Cl^-$$
$$\underline{Na^+OH^-} \longrightarrow Na^+ + OH^-$$

(*b*) by reaction of the solute with water, *e.g.*,

$$HCl + H_2O \longrightarrow H_3O^+ + Cl^-$$
$$HC_2H_3O_2 + H_2O \rightleftharpoons H_3O^+ + C_2H_3O_2^-$$

In most cases *strong* electrolytes are completely ionized at all concentrations; *weak* electrolytes are partially ionized at finite concentrations and completely ionized only at infinite dilution.

[1] A solid substance is represented by an underlined formula, *e.g.*, $\underline{K^+Cl^-}$.

(3) When an electric current is passed through the solution of an electrolyte, the positively charged ion, the *cation*, moves towards the negatively charged *cathode*, and the negatively charged ion, the *anion*, moves towards the positively charged *anode*. The movement of the ions through the solution constitutes the *electric current*, which thus is made up of a positive current towards the cathode and a negative current towards the anode. By discharge of cations at the cathode and of anions at the anode, neutral molecules are obtained, due to gain or loss of electrons.[1]

(4) The ions act like molecules in depressing the freezing point, raising the boiling point, lowering the vapor pressure of the solvent water, and in establishing the osmotic pressure of a solution. Thus a substance yielding two ions per molecule has about twice the effect of a "normal" solute, and one yielding three ions per molecule about three times the effect. However, the ions do not act as independently of one another as molecules do; their effects are modified by *interionic forces.*

(5) The properties of electrolytes in solution are the properties of the ions. In aqueous solution, acidic properties are ascribed to hydrogen ion, H_3O^+, basic properties to hydroxyl ion, OH^-, and the properties of salts to the ions corresponding to the salt, except when the ions react with the ions of water, *i.e.*, *hydrolyze*. The reactions between electrolytes are reactions of the ions.[2]

Complete Dissociation of Salts and Bases. Those salts and bases which are classed as *strong electrolytes* are electrovalent compounds and are assumed to be *completely dissociated* in aqueous solution. Some of the reasons for this assumption are:

(1) When salts and strong bases are fused, they conduct electricity as well as their 1 molar solutions. This means that they are ionized in the liquid state. It may be assumed that the ions present in the crystal are rigidly held by crystal forces; when these forces are overcome, *i.e.*, when the substance is melted, the ions are free to move and thus carry the electric current. In contrast, fused weak electrolytes, like mercuric chloride and acetic acid, are practically nonconductors.

[1] For a discussion of electrode reactions see Meldrum and Gucker, *loc cit.*, pp. 341–362.

[2] *Neutralization* is discussed on page 322; for other reactions see Meldrum and Gucker, *loc cit.*, pp. 216–254; Meldrum, Flosdorf, and Daggett, *Semimicro Qualitative Analysis.* American Book Co., New York, 1939, pp. 94–152, 281–323.

(2) X-ray studies of crystals of salts and strong bases have furnished evidence that the units of the structure of such substances in the solid state are *ions* and not *molecules*. In the sodium chloride crystal, for example, shown diagrammatically in Figure 141, the sodium and chloride ions are not in any way associated *in pairs*. On the contrary, each sodium ion is surrounded by six equidistant chloride ions, and each chloride ion is surrounded by six equidistant sodium ions. The valence forces of each ion in the interior of the crystal are equally distributed among the ions of the other element that surround it. There is, therefore, no such thing as a *molecule* of sodium chloride in the solid state. Similar lattice structures exist in the case of other salts and bases.

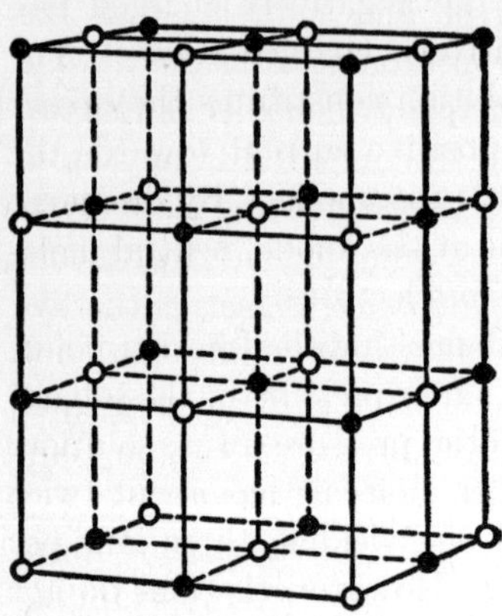

Fig. 141. Structure of NaCl Crystal.

(3) In the formation of a salt from a metal and a halogen, the electric current indicating the transfer of electrons from the metal to the halogen may easily be demonstrated. This means that the metal becomes charged positively, the halogen negatively.

In view of the foregoing and other less direct evidence we are justified in concluding that salts and bases are ionized in the solid state and that when they dissolve in water the ions composing them merely separate. Accordingly, the equation

$$\underline{NaCl} \longrightarrow Na^+ + Cl^-$$

represents the *dissociation of ions*, not the *formation of ions*. It would be more precise to write:

$$\underline{Na^+Cl^-} \longrightarrow Na^+ + Cl^-$$

but this method of representing dissociation is little used.

The Nature of the Hydrogen Ion. The Arrhenius theory of ionization postulated that the substance common to all acids in aqueous solution was the hydrogen ion, H^+. The importance of hydrogen ion in many branches of science has increased with the years and the literature on the subject has grown to vast dimensions. In recent years ideas regarding its nature have undergone a notable change.

There is much evidence, both direct and indirect, that the *hydrogen ion* is not the *proton* but the proton combined with one or more molecules of water. Some of this evidence is as follows:

(1) The proton, H^+, is extremely small compared to any atom or to any other ion. Consequently, its velocity during electrolysis should be vastly greater than that of any other ion. Experiments show that the hydrogen ion moves about twice as fast as the hydroxyl ion and five times as fast as the chloride ion under the same conditions, but the naked proton should move at an even greater velocity. Hence, the hydrogen ion probably is the proton combined with at least one molecule of water.

(2) Perchloric acid has been prepared in the crystalline form, corresponding to the composition $HClO_4 \cdot H_2O$. X-ray examination has shown that the crystal lattice is composed of $H(H_2O)$ and ClO_4 clusters, which are probably ionic, since perchloric acid is a strong acid. The dissociation is probably the same as for a salt, thus:

$$H_3OClO_4 \longrightarrow H_3O^+ + ClO_4^-$$

The structure of the monohydrated acid crystal is similar to that of the ammonium salt, NH_4ClO_4, which is probably ionic, and this suggests a close similarity between the hydrogen ion, H_3O^+, and the ammonium ion, NH_4^+.

(3) The existence of a monohydrated hydrogen ion in solutions in liquid sulfur dioxide has been demonstrated. Liquid sulfur dioxide, like other covalent substances, is nonconducting. Neither water nor hydrogen bromide alone forms a conducting solution when dissolved in sulfur dioxide. However, a solution of both water and hydrogen bromide in sulfur dioxide is an excellent conductor. When the solution is electrolyzed, bromine is liberated at the anode, showing the presence of bromide ions, and hydrogen is evolved at the cathode. Also, the solution near the cathode gains one molecule of water for each hydrogen ion deposited at the cathode. This suggests that the hydrogen ion was combined with one molecule of water, *i.e.*, $H(H_2O)^+$. Hence the changes at the electrodes during electrolysis may be represented thus:

At the anode:

$$2\,Br^- \longrightarrow Br_2 + 2\,\epsilon$$

At the cathode:

$$2\,H_3O^+ + 2\,\epsilon \longrightarrow H_2\uparrow + 2\,H_2O$$

(4) Evidence that the proton is hydrated in aqueous solution has been obtained by Dole [1] from the study of the glass electrode. His results indicated that "as the hydrogen ion migrates through the glass it carries exactly one molecule of water along with it."

In view of such evidence from different lines of investigation, there seems little doubt that the hydrogen ion in aqueous solution is H_3O^+. Other ions, like K^+, Li^+, Cl^-, and SO_4^{--}, doubtless are hydrated also, but combination is much less stable and the type of hydration involved in these cases is comparable rather with the hydration of NH_4^+ or the further hydration of H_3O^+. The similarity in structures of these last two ions is evident if we compare the mode of their formation by the reaction of H^+ with ammonia and with water, thus:

$$\mathrm{H:\overset{..}{\underset{..}{N}}:H} + \mathrm{H^+} \longrightarrow \left[\mathrm{H:\overset{H}{\underset{H}{N}}:H}\right]^+ \qquad \mathrm{:\overset{..}{\underset{..}{O}}:H} + \mathrm{H^+} \longrightarrow \left[\mathrm{H:\overset{..}{\underset{H}{O}}:H}\right]^+$$

(In the diagram the lower H is bonded below N and below O in the reactants.)

The naming of the ion, H_3O^+, has been a matter of some controversy. Among the names suggested have been *oxonium*, *hydroxonium*, and *hydronium*.[2] However, there seems to be little reason to alter the name of the ion at all. Chemists have erroneously believed that the hydrogen ion in aqueous solution was H^+; accumulated evidence indicates that it is, instead, H_3O^+. But it is the same ion whose properties, effects, and reactions have been studied from the earliest days of the ionic theory. Consequently, we shall continue to call it the *hydrogen ion*, differentiating it from H^+ by calling the latter the *proton*.

The Ionization of Acids. Anhydrous acids, unlike salts and bases, are not ionized in the pure state. The study of dipole moments has indicated that they are predominantly covalent in structure, in contrast to salts and bases which are electrovalent. This conclusion is in accord with the fact that they are poor conductors in the liquid state. Liquid hydrogen chloride, hydrogen bromide, and acetic acid, for example, are practically nonconductors; sulfuric acid shows a minimum conductance when the

[1] *J. Am. Chem. Soc.*, **54**, 2120, 3095 (1932).
[2] See the report by H. N. Alyea, *J. Chem. Ed.*, **16**, 535 (1939).

ratio of water to sulfur trioxide is 1 : 1 as in the anhydrous acid; nitric acid shows a diminishing conductance as it approaches 100 per cent concentration. Nevertheless, some acids are strong electrolytes in aqueous solution.

The mechanism of ionization of an acid is essentially different from that of a salt or a base. It cannot be the mere separation of ions since ions are not present in the pure substance, but involves *reaction with the water* to form H_3O^+ and another ion. Thus, the ionization of typical acids, some of them strong and probably completely ionized in fairly dilute solution, others weak, and some dibasic and tribasic acids ionizing *in stages*, may be represented as follows:

$$HCl + H_2O \longrightarrow H_3O^+ + Cl^-$$
$$HNO_3 + H_2O \longrightarrow H_3O^+ + NO_3^-$$
$$HC_2H_3O_2 + H_2O \rightleftharpoons H_3O^+ + C_2H_3O_2^-$$
$$H_2SO_4 + H_2O \longrightarrow H_3O^+ + HSO_4^-$$
$$HSO_4^- + H_2O \rightleftharpoons H_3O^+ + SO_4^{--}$$
$$H_3PO_4 + H_2O \rightleftharpoons H_3O^+ + H_2PO_4^-$$
$$H_2PO_4^- + H_2O \rightleftharpoons H_3O^+ + HPO_4^{--}$$
$$HPO_4^{--} + H_2O \rightleftharpoons H_3O^+ + PO_4^{---}$$

The electrovalent compounds $H_3O^+Cl^-$, $H_3O^+NO_3^-$, and $H_3O^+HSO_4^-$, corresponding to the ions produced from HCl, HNO_3, and H_2SO_4 with water, unlike the compound $H_3O^+ClO_4^-$, perchloric acid monohydrate, mentioned on page 319, have not been isolated.

Action of Ammonia as a Base. The action of ammonia with an acid solution is probably a direct reaction with the hydrogen ion, thus:

$$NH_3 + H_3O^+ \rightleftharpoons NH_4^+ + H_2O$$

With water, ammonia gives a weakly basic solution due to the reaction:

$$NH_3 + H_2O \rightleftharpoons NH_4^+ + OH^-$$

Conductance measurements show that about 1 per cent of the ammonia is in the form of ammonium ion; the other 99 per cent probably is present as ammonia; there is no evidence either definitely for or definitely against the existence of NH_4OH as a molecular species.

Neutralization. According to the ionic theory the reaction of an acid with a base is the reaction of hydrogen ion with hydroxyl ion, thus:

$$H_3O^+ + OH^- \longrightarrow 2\,H_2O$$

If this is correct, then the heat evolved when a gram equivalent of any strong acid is neutralized by a base in dilute solution, should always be the same. This has been found to be the case. The heats of neutralization of various acids and bases at different concentrations have been determined very accurately by T. W. Richards[1] and his co-workers.[2] In the case of strong acids and strong bases, the heats of neutralization, although not equal at higher concentrations, diminish and converge as the concentration becomes less and as the heat of dilution becomes smaller. In the case of the weak acetic acid, the heat of neutralization *increases* as the concentration decreases. The most striking result of this important series of investigations was that when the curves for the heats of neutralization of strong acids with strong bases, on the one hand, and that for the heat of neutralization of acetic acid with a strong base, on the other, were extrapolated to the zero concentration axis, they coincided at the value of 13.64 kcal. in all cases. The heat of neutralization of 1 gram equivalent of hydrogen ion by hydroxyl ion is, therefore, 13.64 kcal., *i.e.*,

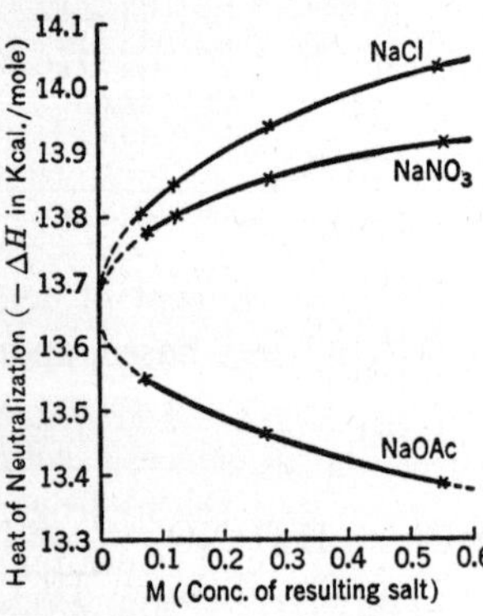

Fig. 142. Heats of Neutralization at Different Concentrations.

$$H_3O^+ + OH^- \longrightarrow 2\,H_2O - 13.64\text{ kcal.}$$

[1] Theodore William Richards was born in Germantown, Pennsylvania, in 1868. After graduating from Haverford College at the age of seventeen, he went to Harvard and there received his doctor's degree three years later. He spent two years studying in Europe, then returned to Harvard, where he remained as a teacher of chemistry until his death in 1928. Richards was a brilliant and versatile experimenter and carried on research in a number of fields. Although perhaps best known for his work on the revision of atomic weights for which he developed many new and improved forms of apparatus and finer analytical technique, he made contributions of fundamental importance also in the fields of thermochemistry and thermodynamics, the ionization theory, the compressibility and other properties of the atom, and electrochemistry. His scientific work was presented in more than three hundred publications, which are evidence of the fine scientific imagination, lucid and logical reasoning, and experimental skill of the author, and which brought him recognition all over the world. In 1914 he was awarded the Nobel prize in chemistry, the first American to be so honored. His portrait faces page 324.

[2] Richards and Gucker, *J. Am. Chem. Soc.*, **51,** 712 (1929); Richards and Hall, *ibid.*, **51,** 731 (1929); Richards and Mair, *ibid.*, **51,** 737 (1929).

The curves by which this result was deduced are shown in Figure 142. The experimental results from which these curves were drawn are given in part in Table 77.

TABLE 77

HEATS OF NEUTRALIZATION AT VARIOUS CONCENTRATIONS OF REACTANTS

MOLES WATER PER MOLE OF REAGENT	MOLES WATER PER MOLE OF PRODUCT	HEATS OF NEUTRALIZATION, $-\Delta H$ IN KCAL.		
		$NaOH + HCl$	$NaOH + HNO_3$	$NaOH + H \cdot C_2H_3O_2$
25 + 25	51	14.250	14.025	——
50 + 50	101	14.017	13.893	13.381
100 + 100	201	13.915	13.842	13.464
200 + 200	401	13.845	13.795	13.515
400 + 400	801	13.785	13.760	13.544
800 + 800	1601	——	——	13.557
∞ + ∞	∞	*13.64* *	*13.64* *	*13.64* *

* Values extrapolated to infinite dilution.

The Lowry-Brønsted Acid-Base Concept. The concept of acid and base current among chemists until recently was based upon the theory of Arrhenius. According to this theory, in terms of the more modern concept of the hydrogen ion, an *acid* is a compound of hydrogen which reacts with water so that the hydrogen becomes hydrogen ion, H_3O^+; a *base* is a compound containing hydroxyl which dissociates, giving hydroxyl ion, OH^-. The action of an acid with a base is represented by the equation,

$$H_3O^+ + OH^- \longrightarrow 2\,H_2O$$

and the ionization of water by the reverse equation. This acid-base theory applies only to aqueous systems since water alone can ionize exclusively into hydrogen and hydroxyl ions.

In 1923 T. M. Lowry and J. N. Brønsted independently put forward a concept of acids and bases that applies to nonaqueous solvents as well as to water.[1]

According to the Lowry-Brønsted theory, *an* ***acid*** *is a substance, in either the molecular or the ionic state, which is capable of giving up a proton,* and *a* ***base*** *is a substance, in either the molecular or the ionic state, which is capable of taking on a proton.* An acid-base

[1] Lowry, *J. Chem. Soc.*, **123,** 848 (1923); Brønsted, *Rec. trav. chim.*, **42,** 718 (1923); *Chem. Rev.*, **5,** 284 (1928); Bjerrum, *Chem. Rev.*, **16,** 287 (1935). For a brief review of several proposed acid-base theories which are so broad that they would permit classification of nearly all reactions as acid-base reactions, see Hall, *J. Chem. Ed.*, **17,** 124 (1940).

reaction, then, is one which involves the *transfer* of a proton from an acid to a base. An acid and a base may be defined by the fundamental equation:

$$\textit{acid} \rightleftharpoons \textit{base} + \textit{proton}$$

Thus, acetic acid is an acid because it gives up a proton; acetate ion is a base because it takes on a proton:

$$HC_2H_3O_2 \rightleftharpoons C_2H_3O_2^- + H^+$$

Also, hydrogen chloride is an acid, and chloride ion is a base:

$$HCl \rightleftharpoons Cl^- + H^+$$

Hydroxyl ion, OH^-, is a base because it takes on a proton, and obviously the corresponding acid is water, H_2O:

$$OH^- + H^+ \rightleftharpoons H_2O$$

Water is not only an acid; it is also a base since it may take up a proton, thus:

$$H_2O + H^+ \rightleftharpoons H_3O^+$$

A list of some of the more common acids and bases arranged according to this concept is given in Table 78.

TABLE 78

LIST OF ACIDS AND THEIR CORRESPONDING BASES
(ACCORDING TO THE LOWRY-BRØNSTED THEORY)

ACID	$\rightleftharpoons$	BASE	+ PROTON	ACID	$\rightleftharpoons$	BASE	+ PROTON
H_2O	$\rightleftharpoons$	OH^-	$+ H^+$	HNO_3	$\rightleftharpoons$	NO_3^-	$+ H^+$
H_3O^+	$\rightleftharpoons$	H_2O	$+ H^+$	H_2SO_4	$\rightleftharpoons$	HSO_4^-	$+ H^+$
NH_4^+	$\rightleftharpoons$	NH_3	$+ H^+$	HSO_4^-	$\rightleftharpoons$	SO_4^{--}	$+ H^+$
$HC_2H_3O_2$	$\rightleftharpoons$	$C_2H_3O_2^-$	$+ H^+$	H_2CO_3	$\rightleftharpoons$	HCO_3^-	$+ H^+$
HCl	$\rightleftharpoons$	Cl^-	$+ H^+$	HCO_3^-	$\rightleftharpoons$	CO_3^{--}	$+ H^+$

As we have already seen, the proton, *i.e.*, H^+, cannot exist free in a solution; hence, an acid can give up a proton only if some base is present to take it on. Therefore, *two* acids and *two* bases must take part in every reaction involving a proton, according to the equation:

$$\textit{acid}_1 + \textit{base}_2 \rightleftharpoons \textit{base}_1 + \textit{acid}_2$$

facing page 324 *Byrd Studio*

Plate VII. THEODORE WILLIAM RICHARDS

(*For biographical note see page 322.*)

where *base*$_1$ is the base corresponding to *acid*$_1$, and *acid*$_2$ is the acid corresponding to *base*$_2$. For example:

$$HCl + OH^- \rightleftharpoons Cl^- + H_2O$$
$$H_3O^+ + OH^- \rightleftharpoons H_2O + H_2O$$
$$HC_2H_3O_2 + NH_3 \rightleftharpoons C_2H_3O_2^- + NH_4^+$$
$$H_2O + NH_3 \rightleftharpoons OH^- + NH_4^+$$
$$HCO_3^- + OH^- \rightleftharpoons CO_3^{--} + H_2O$$

The *strength* of an acid is the quantitative measure of its tendency to lose protons; the *strength* of a base is a measure of its tendency to take them on. The stronger the acid is, the weaker will be the corresponding base. For example, HCl is a strong acid; Cl^- is a weak base. $HC_2H_3O_2$ is a rather weak acid; $C_2H_3O_2^-$ is a fairly strong base. HCO_3^- is a weak acid; CO_3^{--} is a strong base. H_2O is a weak acid; OH^- is a strong base. When equivalent concentrations of acid and base are used, the reaction will take place spontaneously to form the weaker acid and weaker base. For example, the following reactions take place spontaneously to virtual completion:

$$HCl + OH^- \longrightarrow Cl^- + H_2O$$
$$H_3O^+ + OH^- \longrightarrow 2\,H_2O$$
$$HNO_3 + NH_3 \longrightarrow NO_3^- + NH_4^+$$

The Lowry-Brønsted theory has been applied successfully to various phases of solution chemistry. It serves particularly well in the explanation of homogeneous catalysis, for which Brønsted developed it (see page 562). It involves a definition of *base* quite different from that of Arrhenius but otherwise is readily reconciled with many of the older tenets.

Factors Which Influence Ionization. We have seen already how the extent of ionization in solution depends upon the nature of the solute, whether it is held together by electrovalent or by covalent bonds. The amount of ionization also depends upon the *concentration* of the solution, in the case of a weak electrolyte, and upon the nature of the solvent and the size of the ions of the solute.

(1) *The nature of the solvent* affects ionization to a very marked degree. Certain substances, like hydrogen chloride, do not, in the pure state, resemble salts. They are inherently much less polar. Thus the hydrogen chloride molecule volatilizes at a low temperature, while salts are all hard to volatilize. A study of the change of the dielectric constant of gaseous hydrogen chloride with temper-

ature shows that the electrons are held somewhat nearer to the chlorine than to the hydrogen, so that the gaseous molecule is slightly polar; but it shows no tendency to decompose into hydrogen ions and chloride ions. Dry liquid hydrogen chloride is not a conductor of electricity. However, the presence of even a trace of moisture will make the substance conducting. In dilute solution in water we have every evidence for nearly complete dissociation. Here then the ionization is due to the influence of the solvent in which hydrogen chloride is dissolved. This fact is further emphasized by the difference in the properties of solutions of hydrogen chloride in water and in other solvents such as benzene. In these other solvents the conductance is very much less, and there is practically no ionization.

The extent of ionization of any particular substance depends, therefore, to a large extent upon the nature of the solvent. One factor is undoubtedly the *chemical reaction* between the solvent and the solute. The energy of *solvation* (in water, *hydration*) is sometimes very large and tends to drag the solute into solution.

(2) Another important effect of the solvent is that it weakens the electrical force of attraction between the ions which are immersed in it and thus assists ionization. This effect is measured quantitatively by the *dielectric constant* D of the solvent. The ***dielectric constant*** *may be defined as the capacity of a medium to affect the force exerted between electrical charges immersed in the medium.* It can be defined mathematically in terms of Coulomb's law thus:

$$D = \frac{qq'}{Fr^2}$$

where q and q' are the charges on the particles, F is the force between them, and r is their distance apart. The standard of dielectric constant values is a vacuum, the dielectric constant of which is unity. That of air is practically unity, while that of some liquids is much higher. When we say that the dielectric constant of water is 78.6, we mean that the force required to separate two oppositely charged particles is $\frac{1}{78.6}$ of that required to effect the same separation in a vacuum or in air. This is apparent if we put Coulomb's law in the more usual form:

$$F = \frac{qq'}{Dr^2}$$

The force between the two charges is inversely proportional to the dielectric constant of the medium if other things are the same. The dielectric constant of a vacuum and of air is unity, while that of benzene is 2 and that of water is 78.6 at 25° C. If we consider two ions the same distance apart in air and in water as indicated in Figure 143, we see that the force between them will be only 0.0127 times as great in water as in air (Fig. 143).

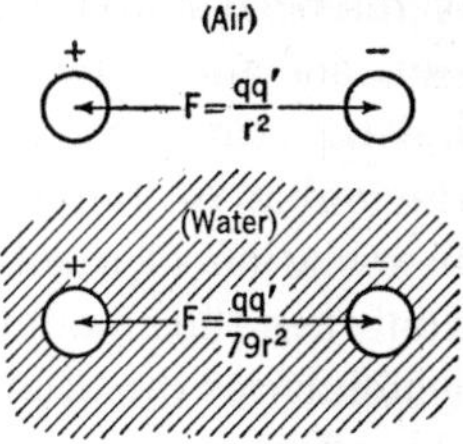

Fig. 143. Coulomb's Law.

Hence, as J. J. Thomson pointed out in 1893 and W. Nernst in 1894, if other things are equal, *substances which possess a high dielectric constant should be good ionizing media.* Nernst cites the facts given in Table 79 to show that this rule is at least qualitatively correct.

TABLE 79

THE RELATION BETWEEN THE DIELECTRIC CONSTANT AND THE IONIZING POWER OF DIFFERENT MEDIA

SOLVENT	DIELECTRIC CONSTANT	ELECTROLYTIC DISSOCIATION OF SOLUTE
Low vacuum	1.0	None at normal temperature
Benzene	2.3	Extremely small but measurable conductivity indicates a trace of dissociation
Ether	4.1	Noticeable conductivity of the dissolved electrolyte
Ethanol	25	Moderately strong dissociation
Formic acid	62	Strong dissociation of dissolved salts
Water	80	Very strong dissociation
Hydrocyanic acid	96	Very strong dissociation

The data on which this table is based are taken from Nernst, *Theoretical Chemistry*, 6th ed.

Many others have studied the dissociation of electrolytes in different solvents to test the **Thomson-Nernst rule** cited above. Walden studied a single solute, tetraethylammonium iodide, in fifty different solvents with dielectric constants ranging from 8 to 80. He found that the change in ionization was indeed striking, as is shown in Figure 144, where we have plotted his most complete series of

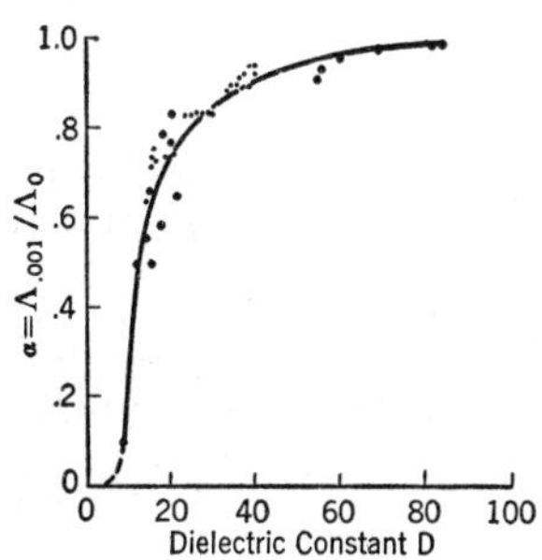

Fig. 144. Change of α with D for Tetraethylammonium Iodide at 25° C.

measurements. The abscissa represents the dielectric constant of the medium, and the ordinate represents the apparent degree of dissociation, α, in a one-thousandth molar solution. The results show a qualitative agreement with the Thomson-Nernst rule, but the scattering of the points shows that other factors — besides the value of the dielectric constant — influence the degree of dissociation of a substance in different solvents. One of these is doubtless the amount of solvation of the solute. The way in which it influences dissociation can best be understood when we consider the effect of the size of the ions upon the energy required to separate them.

(3) Another factor which influences the ionization of an electrolyte is the *mean ionic diameter* of the ions or, more exactly, the closest distance to which the positive and negative ions can approach. This distance is designated by a in Figure 145. Now if we assume that the charge of the ion is located at its center, we can show from Coulomb's law that the *energy*[1] E required to separate completely two charges q and q' from an initial distance a is:

$$E = \frac{qq'}{aD}$$

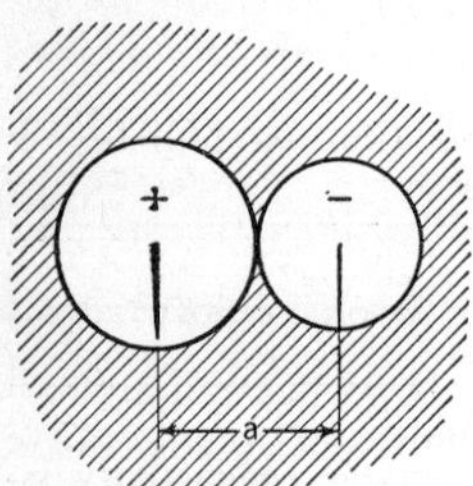

Fig. 145. Effect of Ion Size.

Hence, other things being equal, the dissociation energy is inversely proportional to the distance a between the centers of the ions. Salts with large ions will therefore tend to be more completely dissociated than those with small ions.

If an ion is hydrated in solution and surrounded by a firmly held shell of the solvent, the distance a may be appreciably larger than the ionic radius in the crystal lattice, although it is usually of the same order of magnitude, 10^{-7} to 10^{-8} cm. The difference in the effective ionic radius due to different solvation in the various solvents may account for many of the differences in apparent degree of dissociation in different solvents of nearly the same dielectric constant, which as we have pointed out are shown in Figure 144.

[1] Energy = force × distance. In moving one charge from r to $r + dr$, the energy $= \frac{qq'dr}{Dr^2}$. If we move the charge from distance $r = a$ to $r = \infty$, the energy $= \frac{qq'}{D}\int_a^\infty \frac{dr}{r^2}$, which upon integration gives the equation above.

Within the last few years Kraus and Fuoss[1] have carried out an experimental and theoretical study of the effect of the dielectric constant of the solvent and the size of the ions of the solute upon its dissociation. While we cannot describe here their experimental methods and their theoretical treatment, we shall state some of the conclusions which they reached. The molecules of any liquid are in continual motion due to the thermal energy they possess. When the solvent molecules collide with the molecules of a dissolved electrolyte, they may cause them to dissociate into ions, provided the energy of dissociation is not too great in comparison with the thermal energy, which has the value RT, where R is the gas constant and T the absolute temperature. If the dielectric constant of the solvent is low and the ionic diameter of the ions is small, the energy of dissociation will be large, and collisions of the solvent molecules at ordinary temperature will cause but little dissociation. Under these circumstances the solute will be a weak electrolyte. On the other hand, if the dielectric constant of the solvent is large and the ions of the solute are also large, the energy of dissociation will be small, and the collisions of the solvent molecules will cause a large amount of dissociation. The electrolyte under these conditions will be highly ionized in solution. By studying a single electrolyte in a series of solvents with varying dielectric constants, it is possible to study the effect of changing dielectric constant alone, provided the solvation of the electrolyte does not change greatly. As a solvent, Kraus and Fuoss used mixtures of water, with a dielectric constant of 78.6, and dioxane, with a dielectric constant of 2.2. Different mixtures gave values of the dielectric constant varying between these limits. As a solute they used tetraisoamylammonium nitrate, which they found behaved like a strong electrolyte in the solutions of high dielectric constant and like a weak electrolyte in solutions of low dielectric constant. From a study of the conductance ratio in solvent mixtures of different dielectric constants, they determined the degree

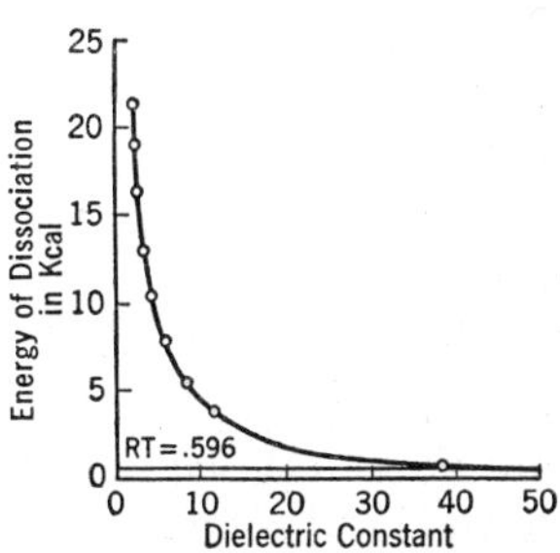

Fig. 146. Change of Energy of Dissociation of Tetraisoamylammonium Nitrate with Dielectric Constant at 25° C.

[1] Kraus and Fuoss, *J. Am. Chem. Soc.*, **55**, 21 (1933); **55**, 476 (1933); **55**, 1019 (1933); **55**, 2387 (1933). A number of later articles have continued this investigation.

of dissociation and also the energy of dissociation, which we have plotted in Figure 146. As this plot shows, the energy of dissociation is high when the dielectric constant is low, but decreases and becomes very small when the dielectric constant becomes even half as great as that of water. When the dielectric constant is 2.4, the energy of dissociation is large, 20,000 calories. When the dielectric constant becomes as large as 43.6, the energy of dissociation has decreased to the thermal energy of the solvent molecules, 596 calories at 25°. In such a solution, the solute is nearly completely dissociated; for, once the ions are separated, the thermal motion of the solvent molecules is enough to prevent their recombination to any great extent. We shall return to this question in Chapter 13 dealing with "Ionic Equilibria."

Ionic Concentration and Activity

Colligative Properties of Dilute Solutions. In 1885 van't Hoff had shown that the osmotic pressure of dilute solutions containing 1 mole of any normal solute in V liters was given by an equation analogous to that of the ideal gas law, namely:

$$\pi V = RT$$

Solutions of electrolytes always showed a *greater* osmotic pressure than that calculated from this equation, and van't Hoff suggested the more general equation:

$$\pi V = iRT$$

where the factor i for electrolytes is greater than one, and changes with the concentration.

The ***van't Hoff factor i*** *measures the departure of a given solute from the laws of the ideal dilute solution.* It may be interpreted as the ratio of the *effective concentration* of the solute to its molal concentration. One mole of an acid, base, salt, or other solute has an effect on the colligative properties of the solution equal to i moles of the ideal solute.

Since the osmotic pressure and the depression of the freezing point are proportional, the same factor may be used to express the divergence of the depression of the freezing point from that of the ideal solution, thus:

$$\Delta T_f = imK_f$$

In an aqueous solution the observed depression ΔT_f is given by the equation:

$$\Delta T_f = 1.86\, im$$

For the ideal solution of a nonelectrolyte, $i = 1$, and the freezing point curve *in dilute solution* is a straight line with the slope 1.86. Figure 147 shows the values of i at different concentrations for a number of nonelectrolytes and electrolytes, based on modern data. At concentrations below 1 m the value of i for all of the nonelectrolytes approaches 1, the value for the ideal solution, while sodium chloride, calcium chloride, and ferric chloride approach 2, 3, and 4 respectively. Since the colligative properties are proportional to the *concentration* of the solution, this indicates that sodium chloride, calcium chloride, and ferric chloride in dilute solution furnish respectively 2, 3, and 4 times as many particles as a normal substance of the same concentration.

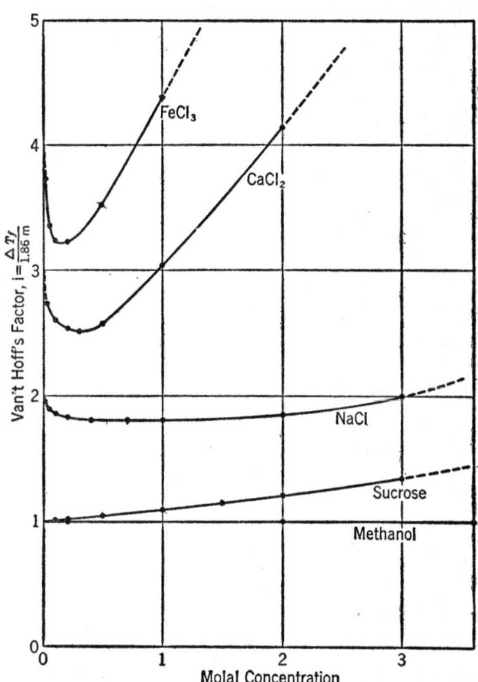

Fig. 147. Values of van't Hoff's Factor i for Various Solutes.

Degree of Dissociation, α. Arrhenius assumed that the van't Hoff factor i indicated the dissociation of an electrolyte in a solution and used it to determine the degree of dissociation, α. For one mole of a nonelectrolyte, i equals 1. In the case of an electrolyte, i is greater than 1. If α is the degree of dissociation of an electrolyte yielding two ions per molecule, we shall have:

$$i = 1 + (2 - 1)\alpha$$

and for an electrolyte giving ν ions,

$$i = 1 + (\nu - 1)\alpha$$

Rearranging this expression and solving for α, gives:

$$\alpha_v = \frac{i - 1}{\nu - 1}$$

Thus defined, α_v is called the ***van't Hoff coefficient.***

The value of α found from the freezing point depression is an approximate measure of the degree of ionization of a weak electrolyte as solute, but it does not have this meaning in the case of a strong electrolyte. To find α for a weak electrolyte, the freezing point of the pure solvent and then the freezing point of the solution is determined with a Beckmann thermometer or platinum resistance thermometer; the difference is ΔT_f. For the highest sensitivity, a multiple thermel is used to read directly the difference between the freezing points of the solvent and solution. In either case, i is found from the expression:

$$\Delta T_f = imK_f$$

Even before the work of van't Hoff, Arrhenius had used another method of determining the degree of dissociation, based upon conductance measurements. *If one equivalent weight of a solute is dissolved in a solvent to give a solution of concentration c, the conductance of this solution, between parallel plates 1 cm. apart, is called the* ***equivalent conductance*** *of the solution* (see page 385). Arrhenius assumed that the **conductance ratio,** $\frac{\Lambda_c}{\Lambda_0}$, where Λ_c is the equivalent conductance of a given solution at a given concentration and Λ_0 is the equivalent conductance at infinite dilution, was a true measure of the **degree of dissociation,** *i.e., the fraction of the total number of solute molecules which are dissociated.* Later work has shown that although the method applies satisfactorily in the case of weak electrolytes, it does not apply to strong electrolytes (see page 390 *et seq.*).

Ionic Concentration. The molar concentration of a given ion in the solution of a weak uni-univalent electrolyte, such as acetic acid, may be obtained by multiplying the molar concentration of the solution by the degree of ionization. For example, the concentration of hydrogen or of acetate ion in 0.1 M acetic acid solution, for which α is 0.0134, would be 0.1×0.0134, or 0.00134 mole per liter. The total concentration of the solution then would be the sum of the undissociated acid concentration and the concentrations of the two ions, *i.e.*, $(0.1 - 0.00134) + 2 \times 0.00134$, or 0.100134 mole per liter. The colligative properties of the solution should correspond to this concentration. In the case of dilute solutions of *weak* electrolytes this direct calculation yields results which correspond closely to the properties of the solution, but this is not true of solutions of *strong* electrolytes. To deal satisfactorily with strong electrolytes even in dilute solution, another concept must be introduced, *viz.*, the *activity*.

Activity and Activity Coefficients. Arrhenius held that either the van't Hoff coefficient, $\alpha_v = (i - 1)/(\nu - 1)$, or the conductance ratio, $\alpha_\Lambda = \Lambda_c/\Lambda_0$, was a true measure of the degree of dissociation of an electrolyte. However, it has since been shown that the conductance ratio and the van't Hoff coefficient are not numerically the same, especially at higher concentrations. This is evident from the two curves in Figure 148, where the two factors are plotted against the square root of the molarity. At zero concentration both are unity, corresponding to complete dissociation. Up to about 0.1 *M* the van't Hoff coefficient is *slightly less* than the conductance ratio, and beyond this concentration the divergence becomes greater. The conductance ratio decreases regularly to 0.43 at 4.5 *M*, while the van't Hoff coefficient passes through a minimum of about 0.81 at 0.7 *M* and then increases to 1.15 at 4.5 *M*. Thus, according to Arrhenius' assumption, sodium chloride is 43 per cent dissociated according to one method, and 115 per cent dissociated according to the other. Evidently the van't Hoff coefficient, at least, cannot indicate the true degree of dissociation. Although the conductance ratio decreases regularly with increasing concentration and is never greater than 1, evidence resulting from the study of transference numbers, discussed on page 391, proves that it too cannot give the *true* degree of dissociation.

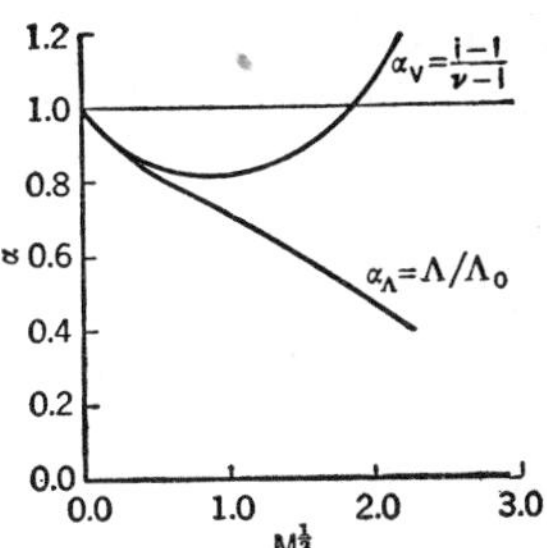

Fig. 148. Van't Hoff Coefficient and Conductance Ratio for NaCl at 0° C.

Since neither the conductance ratio nor the van't Hoff coefficient could be regarded as a satisfactory criterion of the behavior of strong electrolytes, some different basis was sought. G. N. Lewis[1] suggested the concept of **activity,** which has come into general application. *The* ***activity,*** ***a,*** *represents the effective concentration of a substance as evaluated by its behavior in solution.* It is related to the molal concentration of the electrolyte by a factor gamma, γ, called the mean **activity coefficient,** thus:

$$\gamma = \frac{a}{m}$$

so that we may define the ***activity coefficient*** *as the number by which the molal concentration must be multiplied to obtain the activity.* A more rigorous definition of *activity* will be found on page 643. The method of determining γ which is most generally applicable depends upon the measurement of the electromotive force of suitable galvanic cells. This is discussed on page 425 *et seq.*

The mean activity coefficients of a number of representative electrolytes of different valence types are given in Table 80. The change in activity coefficient with changing concentration is shown graphically in Figures 149 and 150, where the activity coeffi-

TABLE 80

MEAN ACTIVITY COEFFICIENTS OF REPRESENTATIVE ELECTROLYTES AT ROUND CONCENTRATIONS (25° C.)

m	0.00	0.01	0.05	0.10	0.50	1.00	1.50	2.00	3.00	4.00	16
KCl	1.000	0.899	0.815	0.764	0.644	0.597	0.576	0.569	0.571	0.581	
NaCl	1.000	0.903	0.821	0.778	0.678	0.656	0.659	0.670	0.714	0.779	
LiCl	1.000	0.901	0.819	0.779	0.725	0.757	0.819	0.919	1.174	1.554	
HCl	1.000	0.904	0.829	0.796	0.757	0.810	0.903	1.019	1.320	1.762	43.2
$BaCl_2$	1.000	0.723	0.554	0.495	0.395	0.398					
$SrCl_2$	1.000	0.729	0.571	0.512	0.427	0.449	0.526	0.638	1.083		
$CaCl_2$	1.000	0.732	0.582	0.528	0.510	0.725	1.065	1.555	3.385		
Na_2SO_4	1.000	0.721	0.514	0.435	0.267	0.206	0.172	0.152			
H_2SO_4	1.000	0.617	0.397	0.313	0.178	0.150		0.147	0.166	0.203	1.40
$La(NO_3)_3$	1.000	0.57	0.391	0.326							

Abridged from Harned, "The Electrochemistry of Solutions" (Chap. XII, p. 772, of Taylor, *A Treatise on Physical Chemistry*, 2d ed. Courtesy of D. Van Nostrand Company, Inc.), except the last entry for HCl and the data for H_2SO_4, which are taken from Lewis and Randall, *Thermodynamics*, pp. 336 and 357 respectively.

[1] Gilbert Newton Lewis is professor of chemistry at the University of California. Born in Weymouth, Mass., in 1875, he received both his bachelor's and doctor's degrees at Harvard. In 1907 he joined the staff of the Massachusetts Institute of Technology, where he remained until his appointment as Professor of Chemistry and Dean of the College of Chemistry at the University of California in 1912. Although perhaps best known for his outstanding contributions in the field of thermodynamics, he has carried on researches in many other branches of physical chemistry, including solutions of electrolytes, atomic structure, and electromotive force. For portrait of Lewis, see Plate II, facing page 116.

cients taken from Table 80 are plotted as ordinates against the square root of the molality taken as abscissa. The initial slope is the same for all electrolytes of the same valence type, and is

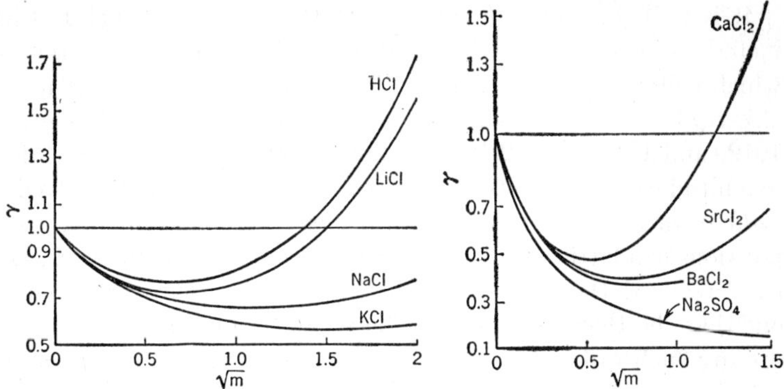

Fig. 149. Activity Coefficients of Some 1–1 Electrolytes at 25° C.

Fig. 150. Activity Coefficients of Some 2–1 Electrolytes at 25° C.

steeper for electrolytes of higher valence type. However, at all appreciable concentrations there are very marked differences even among such similar electrolytes as KCl, NaCl, and LiCl. The curves for γ and the van't Hoff coefficient are somewhat similar. The two quantities are not equal but are related mathematically.

The Debye-Hückel Theory of Interionic Attraction. For solutions less dilute than 0.25 *M*, Arrhenius found good agreement, within the limits of his experimental error, between the van't Hoff coefficient, $\alpha_v = (i - 1)/(\nu - 1)$, and the conductance ratio, $\alpha_\Lambda = \Lambda_c/\Lambda_0$, for various strong electrolytes, and hence he assumed that either of the α's represented the degree of dissociation of the electrolyte and that there existed an equilibrium between the ions and the undissociated molecules. For a uni-univalent electrolyte like KNO_3 in 0.1 *N* solution, α by either method was found to be about 84 per cent. As early as 1908, A. A. Noyes[1] concluded that such strong electrolytes are *100 per cent dissociated* and he summarized evidence supporting this conclusion. This view

[1] Arthur Amos Noyes, 1866–1936, was a distinguished American physical chemist, who for many years was professor at the Massachusetts Institute of Technology, and later at the California Institute of Technology. He was noted for his work in analytical chemistry as well as in the fields of solution chemistry and thermodynamics. See Plate XIII, facing page 500.

has been fully substantiated by later work. But if the electrolyte is completely dissociated, what is the reason for the discrepancy between the *ionic concentration* and the *activity?* What is the physical significance of the *activity?*

It is probable that the decrease in the activity coefficient with increasing concentration for solutions of moderate concentrations which is illustrated in Figures 149 and 150 is due to a change in the electrical energy acting between the separated ions. Milner, in 1912, and Ghosh, in 1918, attempted to compute the numerical magnitude of the electrical effects. Ghosh's theory involved a *static* arrangement in which the ions, though occupying fixed positions in a lattice, were farther apart than in the crystal. P. Debye[1] realized the fallacies in this simplified picture and pointed out that the thermal energy of the solvent molecules would break up any such ordered lattice structure. Further study led to the very important theory that bears the name of the joint authors, the *Debye-Hückel theory.* The physical basis for this theory may be explained simply; the mathematical details, which are somewhat involved, may be found elsewhere.

The question which Debye and Hückel sought to answer was: *How do the electrical charges on the ions affect the activity of the ions as the concentration of the solution changes?* If the solution of an electrolyte were magnified so that the individual particles could be observed, they would be found to be in rapid thermal motion. Each individual ion, either cation or anion, is surrounded by an *ion atmosphere* composed of all the other ions in the solution.

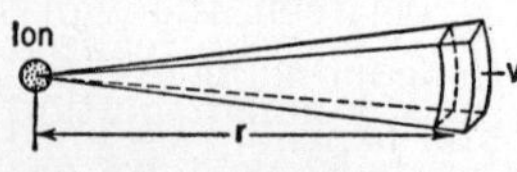

Fig. 151. Illustrating "Ion Atmosphere."

If a small volume v of this ion atmosphere is observed from a given ion, as illustrated in Figure 151, both cations and anions would be seen to wander through this space. However, on the average, due to the influence of the chosen ion, the space would be occupied more frequently by an oppositely charged ion. Because of this, when the solution is diluted, *energy is absorbed in order to separate the ions.* This electrical energy accounts for the difference in behavior between a dilute solution of ions and a dilute solution of a nonelectrolyte with the same number of solute particles in a

[1] Peter Debye, born in Holland in 1884, is one of the most famous physical chemists of today. Formerly at the University at Zurich, later at Leipzig and then at Berlin, he is now Head of the Chemistry Department at Cornell University. He received the Nobel Prize in Chemistry in 1936. See Plate XV, facing page 564.

given volume of solution. The concentration of the electrolytic solution *appears to be less* than that of the nonelectrolytic solution, *i.e.*, the *activity* of the electrolytic solute is *less* than the activity of the nonelectrolytic solute. Because of this effect, the calculated activity coefficient is less than unity and decreases as the concentration increases. In dilute solutions the activity coefficient agrees with the calculated value.

Since all of the colligative properties of a solution are related mathematically to the activity, the effect of the *ion atmosphere* can be calculated from any one of them. For example, in the case of an ideal solute, the osmotic pressure is proportional to the concentration and, as van't Hoff pointed out, is numerically equal to the pressure which the same quantity of the substance would exert as a gas at the same temperature. In the case of an electrolytic solution, *if there were no interionic attraction*, i would equal ν, the total number of ions formed. Actually, the value of i is always *less* than ν, because the interionic attraction *opposes* the dilution of the solution and acts against the normal osmotic pressure. For example, in a solution of NaCl we would expect $i = 2$, if the solution were completely dissociated and the ions behaved like uncharged molecules. Actually because of interionic forces, we find i is less than 2 for this solute.

The Debye-Hückel theory furnishes a rather simple mathematical expression which applies satisfactorily to explain interionic-attraction effects *in very dilute solutions*. But, although much important experimental work has been done, the behavior of more concentrated solutions has not yet been explained. The difficulty of dealing with concentrated solutions may be realized when we consider that the *solute molecules* in a 1 molal solution at 0° C. are packed together as closely as the molecules of a gas under 22.4 atmospheres pressure.

Some of the "limiting laws" of the **Debye-Hückel theory,** which assume that the ions are simply point charges and which apply to real solutions only up to a concentration of about 0.01 molal, can be stated briefly as follows: (1) The *logarithm of the activity coefficient* decreases proportionally to the square root of the concentration. (2) The *equivalent conductance* decreases proportionally to the square root of the concentration. The first of these laws will be discussed briefly in the following section; the second on page 391 *et seq.*

The activity coefficient. The logarithm of the activity coefficient should be a linear function of the square root of the concentration, thus:

$$\log \gamma = -K_1 z_1 z_2 \sqrt{\mu}$$

where the factor K_1 is calculated from natural constants, the dielectric constant of the solvent, and the absolute temperature. At 25° C. it is 0.505. The factors z_1 and z_2 are the charges on the ions of the electrolyte, and μ is the ionic strength of the solution. The **ionic strength** is the same as the molality for uni-univalent electrolytes and is, in general, equal to one half the sum Σ of the stoichiometric concentration m of each ion multiplied by the square of its valence, thus:

$$\mu = \tfrac{1}{2} \sum_i m_i z_i^2$$

Thus a solution m molal in sodium sulfate contains $2\,m$ sodium ions, each with a charge $z_1 = 1$, and m sulfate ions, each with a charge $z_2 = 2$. Therefore:

$$\mu = \tfrac{1}{2}\,\Sigma(2\,m \times 1^2 + m \times 2^2) = 3\,m \qquad \text{and} \qquad \frac{\mu}{m} = 3$$

The values of the *valence product*, $z_1 z_2$, the slope factor, $K_1 z_1 z_2$, and the ratio between the ionic strength and the concentration, $\frac{\mu}{m}$, are given in Table 81 for several types of electrolytes.

TABLE 81

VALUES OF $z_1 z_2$, $K_1 z_1 z_2$ AND $\frac{\mu}{m}$ FOR VARIOUS VALENCE TYPES

SALT	VALENCE TYPE	$z_1 z_2$	$K_1 z_1 z_2$	$\frac{\mu}{m}$
KCl	1–1	1	0.505	1
Na_2SO_4	2–1	2	1.010	3
$BaCl_2$	1–2	2	1.010	3
$K_3Fe(CN)_6$ . . .	3–1	3	1.515	6
$La(NO_3)_3$	1–3	3	1.515	6

A knowledge of the ionic strength enables us to compare solutions containing several electrolytes. Thus, each of the following solutions would have the ionic strength $\mu = 0.1$: 0.1 m NaCl; 0.05 m KCl + 0.05 m HCl; 0.033 m Na_2SO_4; 0.01 m $La(NO_3)_3$ + 0.01 m $BaCl_2$ + 0.01 m NaCl.

According to the Debye-Hückel theory, the decrease in the activity coefficient of an electrolyte in very dilute solution should be greater, the higher its valence type and the greater the ionic strength of the solution. That the former prediction is at least qualitatively correct is evidenced by the curves for the activity coefficients for various electrolytes in Figures 149 and 150 on page 335. In most cases, however, the activity coefficient goes through a minimum at a concentration between 0.5 and 1.5 *m*, and increases in more concentrated solutions as shown in these figures. In 16 *m* hydrochloric acid solution, the activity coefficient is 43.2. This general increase in the activity coefficients at higher concentrations must be due to forces other than the simple interionic attraction forces, and no theory has been developed to calculate the complete course of these curves, although an enormous amount of experimental work has been carried out in determining activity coefficients.

The constant, K_1, in the equation for γ, has in the denominator the absolute temperature and the dielectric constant, each raised to the $\frac{3}{2}$ power. Therefore, the theory predicts that $\log \gamma$ should be inversely proportional to these two as variables, and as the minus sign in the equation indicates, it should decrease. Noyes and Baxter compared the rates of decrease of γ in water, with a dielectric constant of 78.7, and in ethanol, with a dielectric constant of 24.6, and found that the predicted sixfold steeper slope in the case of the ethanol agreed with the observed values. Although the theory does not apply so well for solutions of electrolytes in liquids of low dielectric constant (*e.g.*, benzene, dielectric constant 2) at room temperature, a better agreement between the experimental and the predicted values is obtained at higher temperatures.

The fundamental postulates of the Debye-Hückel interionic attraction theory seem well established, since the theory successfully accounts for nearly all the properties of very dilute solutions of strong electrolytes. It may also be extended to deal with weak electrolytes at somewhat higher concentrations and to enable us to predict under what circumstances a substance will behave as a strong electrolyte and under what conditions we may expect it to be a weak electrolyte. Unfortunately, the theory cannot deal with even moderately concentrated solutions. Why do the activity coefficients usually pass through a minimum and then *increase* in more concentrated solutions? Why do the equivalent conductances no longer obey the simple law in concentrated solutions? We do not yet have any satisfactory answer to these questions. Perhaps some day a complete and comprehensive theory of electrolytic solutions will be evolved, embracing all concentrations of strong and weak electrolytes. At present the very incompleteness of our theories makes the subject especially fascinating.

PROBLEMS AND EXERCISES

1. A solution of 0.1499 g. of potassium nitrate in 30.00 g. of water freezes at $-0.1739°$ C. (*a*) Find the van't Hoff factor *i*. (*b*) Find the degree of dissociation according to the Arrhenius theory. (*c*) At what temperature would you expect this solution to boil?

2. Show how the general equation $i = 1 + (\nu - 1)\alpha$ applies in the case of (*a*) HCl, (*b*) $BaCl_2$, and (*c*) $La_2(SO_4)_3$.

3. Solutions of the following electrolytes freeze at the temperatures indicated. In each case calculate *i* and the van't Hoff coefficient which is equal to α according to the Arrhenius theory. (*a*) 0.2 *m* $Pb(NO_3)_2$, f.p. $= -0.712°$ C.; (*b*) 0.7 *m* HNO_3, f.p. $= -2.46°$ C.; (*c*) 1.0 *m* $FeCl_3$, f.p. $= -8.18°$ C.

4. The solubility of picric acid, $C_6H_2(NO_2)_3OH$, at 20° C. is 1.23 g. per 100 ml. water. Assuming 23.4 per cent dissociation at this concentration, find the approximate hydrogen ion concentration in the saturated solution.

5. Find the hydrogen ion concentration in a 0.5 *M* solution of formic acid, given that α is 0.021. What would be the freezing point of this solution? What would be the value of the van't Hoff factor *i*?

6. Summarize the postulates of the Arrhenius theory and briefly indicate the modifications which have been made in them.

READING LIST

W. B. Meldrum and F. T. Gucker, Jr., *Introduction to Theoretical Chemistry*. American Book Company, New York, 1936. Pp. 190–206. The ionic theory is discussed mainly from the historical point of view.

H. C. Jones, *The Modern Theory of Solution*. Harper and Bros., New York, 1899. This contains a translation of Arrhenius' paper.

H. J. M. Creighton and W. A. Koehler, *Principles and Applications of Electrochemistry*. John Wiley and Sons, New York, Vol. 1, 3d ed., 1935, pp. 315–346 deal with "activity" and related topics.

"A Symposium on Electrolytes," *Chem. Rev.*, **13,** 1–139 (1933). Papers by V. K. LaMer, G. Scatchard, D. A. MacInnes, L. P. Hammett, T. F. Young, F. T. Gucker, Jr., and others.

CHAPTER 13

IONIC EQUILIBRIA

One postulate of the Arrhenius theory was that in a solution an equilibrium exists between the molecular and the ionic forms of the electrolyte. Although such an assumption is no longer tenable for strong electrolytes, it is extremely useful in the case of weak electrolytes, particularly acids, bases, and water, and in the case of slightly soluble electrovalent compounds. We shall derive the expressions for the *ionization constant of a weak acid*, the *ion product of water*, the *solubility product of slightly soluble substances*, and the *hydrolysis constant* for salts.

Any chemical system in equilibrium at a given temperature is characterized by an *equilibrium constant*, K_c. If the reagents and products all were *ideal solutes*, the equilibrium constant could be expressed in terms of their *concentrations:*

$$K_c = \frac{[C]^c[D]^d \cdots}{[A]^a[B]^b \cdots} \qquad \text{(classical equilibrium constant)}$$

Since this is not the case in ionic equilibria, the constant can be expressed rigorously only in terms of the *activities:*

$$K = \frac{a_C{}^c \times a_D{}^d \times \cdots}{a_A{}^a \times a_B{}^b \times \cdots} \qquad \text{(activity equilibrium constant)}$$

The Ionization Constant for a Weak Acid K_a. For a weak acid HA, the ionization process may be represented thus:

$$HA + H_2O \rightleftharpoons H_3O^+ + A^-$$

The activity equilibrium constant for this reaction is given by the expression:

$$K = \frac{a_{H_3O^+} \times a_{A^-}}{a_{H_2O} \times a_{HA}}$$

The activity of the water in dilute aqueous solution is practically constant and equal to its concentration, which in pure water is $\frac{1000}{18.0}$ or 55.5 molar. Replacing the activity of the water by k, the equilibrium constant expression may be written:

$$K = \frac{a_{H_3O^+} \times a_{A^-}}{k\, a_{HA}}$$

or

$$K \times k = K_a = \frac{a_{H_3O^+} \times a_{A^-}}{a_{HA}}$$

where K_a is called the *ionization constant* for the acid.

For weak acids in solutions which do not contain many other ions, we may replace activities by concentrations and write:

$$K_a = \frac{[H_3O^+][A^-]}{[HA]}$$

where the concentrations of molecules and of ions are expressed in molarity.

The Ionization Constant for a Weak Base, K_b. Weak bases may be divided into two classes: first, those that ionize directly into OH^- and a cation, which we may represent generally by B^+; second, those that ionize by reaction with water, taking on a proton and producing OH^-. The latter class includes ammonia and aniline, methylamine, urea, and other substituted ammonias.

The general equilibrium equation for the former is:

$$BOH \rightleftharpoons B^+ + OH^-$$

the expression for the equilibrium constant, which is also that for the basic ionization constant, is:

$$K_b = \frac{a_{B^+} \times a_{OH^-}}{a_{BOH}}$$

or, in terms of concentrations:

$$K_b = \frac{[B^+][OH^-]}{[BOH]}$$

We may consider the equation and the constant for ammonia as representative of the second group. Ammonia is assumed to ionize by reaction with water, thus:

$$NH_3 + H_2O \rightleftharpoons NH_4^+ + OH^-$$

The expression for the concentration equilibrium constant is:

$$K_c = \frac{[NH_4^+][OH^-]}{[H_2O][NH_3]}$$

As in the case of the acetic acid above, the $[H_2O]$ may be considered a constant, k. The expression then becomes:

$$K_c \times k = K_b = \frac{[NH_4^+][OH^-]}{[NH_3]}$$

Applications of the Ionization Constant. The ionization constants of acids and bases are useful because they give so much information, in very concise form. From the numerical value of the constant at a given temperature we can calculate the degree of ionization and the ionic concentrations. Ionization constants also are useful for comparing the strengths of weak acids and weak bases.

Calculation of the Degree of Ionization. The expression for the ionization constant may be put in the form:

$$K_a = \frac{\alpha c \times \alpha c}{(1 - \alpha)c} = \frac{\alpha^2 c}{(1 - \alpha)}$$

This equation is known as **Ostwald's dilution law** after Wilhelm Ostwald, professor of physical chemistry at the University of Leipzig, who first derived this expression connecting the degree of ionization α with the concentration c of the electrolyte or with its reciprocal, the *dilution* V.

In the case of weak acids or weak bases in all but the most dilute solutions, α is very much less than unity, so that we can neglect the α in the denominator of the equation above and write as an approximate equation:

$$K_a = \alpha^2 c$$

and similarly for a weak base:

$$K_b = \alpha^2 c$$

The complete equation may be rearranged to give:

$$\alpha^2 c + K_a \alpha - K_a = 0$$

The general solution of an algebraic equation of the form,

$$ax^2 + bx + c = 0$$

is,

$$x = \frac{-b \pm \sqrt{b^2 - 4ac}}{2a}$$

Hence for the above equation, since α can only be positive,

$$\alpha = \frac{-K_a + \sqrt{K_a^2 + 4cK_a}}{2c}$$

An example will explain how these equations evaluating α are applied to find *ionic concentration* and *degree of ionization.* Given that K_a for acetic acid at 25° C. is 1.81×10^{-5}, what will be the concentration of hydrogen ion and what will be the degree of ionization of the acid in 0.5 M solution?

We have,

$$[H_3O^+] = [C_2H_3O_2^-] = 0.5\ \alpha \text{ mole per liter}$$

Therefore,

$$K_a = 1.81 \times 10^{-5} = \frac{0.5\ \alpha \times 0.5\ \alpha}{(1 - \alpha) \times 0.5}$$

or

$$0.25\ \alpha^2 + 0.905 \times 10^{-5}\ \alpha - 0.905 \times 10^{-5} = 0$$

which, on solving as a quadratic equation by the formula given above, yields

$$\alpha = 0.0060 \quad \text{or} \quad 0.60 \text{ per cent}$$

For most purposes it is sufficiently accurate to use the approximate form of Ostwald's dilution law, which in this case is:

$$K_a = 1.81 \times 10^{-5} = \frac{0.5\ \alpha \times 0.5\ \alpha}{0.5} = 0.5\ \alpha^2$$

and

$$\alpha = \sqrt{\frac{1.81 \times 10^{-5}}{0.5}} = 0.0060$$

Calculation of Ionic Concentration. If the acid is weak and the solution is not too dilute, we may set the un-ionized acid concentration equal to the total solute concentration. In general,

$$[H_3O^+] = [A^-] = \sqrt{K_a c}$$

and the error in using this equation will be only 1 per cent if the concentration of the acid is 10^4 times the ionization constant. In the case of 0.5 *m* acetic acid, for example, we have:

$$[H_3O^+] = [C_2H_3O_2^-] = \sqrt{1.78 \times 10^{-5} \times 0.5}$$
$$= 0.0030 \text{ mole per liter}$$

The Ionization of Dibasic and Polybasic Acids. Acids containing more than one ionizable hydrogen atom invariably ionize *in steps, i.e.*, the secondary ionization is less than the primary, and, in the case of a tribasic acid, the tertiary is less than the secondary. Thus, in the case of carbonic acid, there are two steps:

Primary ionization:

$$H_2CO_3 + H_2O \rightleftharpoons H_3O^+ + HCO_3^-$$

Secondary ionization:

$$HCO_3^- + H_2O \rightleftharpoons H_3O^+ + CO_3^{--}$$

For phosphoric acid, there are the three steps:

Primary ionization:

$$H_3PO_4 + H_2O \rightleftharpoons H_3O^+ + H_2PO_4^-$$

Secondary ionization:

$$H_2PO_4^- + H_2O \rightleftharpoons H_3O^+ + HPO_4^{--}$$

Tertiary ionization:

$$HPO_4^{--} + H_2O \rightleftharpoons H_3O^+ + PO_4^{---}$$

Each of these equilibria is complete in itself, and for each a characteristic ionization constant may be written. These, with their numerical values, are as follows:

Primary:

$$K_a' = [H_3O^+] \times \frac{[H_2PO_4^-]}{[H_3PO_4]} = 1.2 \times 10^{-2}$$

Secondary:

$$K_a'' = [H_3O^+] \times \frac{[HPO_4^{--}]}{[H_2PO_4^-]} = 6.9 \times 10^{-8}$$

Tertiary:

$$K_a''' = [H_3O^+] \times \frac{[PO_4^{---}]}{[HPO_4^{--}]} = 1.7 \times 10^{-12}$$

Unless the solution is very dilute, the hydrogen ion concentration in a solution of phosphoric acid is due almost entirely to the *primary* ionization. The phosphate ion concentration is very low, as may readily be calculated. If we multiply together the equations for the three ionization constants and also multiply the constants themselves, we obtain the expression for the **total** or **over-all ionization constant:**

$$\frac{[H_3O^+]^3[PO_4^{---}]}{[H_3PO_4]} = 1.4 \times 10^{-21}$$

The concentration of the un-ionized phosphoric acid, $[H_3PO_4]$, is computed from the value for K_a' for the primary ionization and found to be approximately 0.070 mole per liter for a 0.1 *M* solution, that of H_3O^+ being approximately 0.029 mole per liter. Substituting these values in the expression just given, we obtain:

$$\frac{(0.027)^3 \times [PO_4^{---}]}{0.073} = 1.4 \times 10^{-21}$$

so that the concentration of phosphate ion, $[PO_4^{---}]$, has the very low value 3.8×10^{-18} mole per liter. In a similar way, the concentrations of $H_2PO_4^-$ and HPO_4^{--} may also be calculated.

Acid Salts of Weak Polybasic Acids. In the solution of an acid salt of a weak polybasic acid in water, the equilibria set up are:

$$BHA \longrightarrow B^+ + HA^-$$
$$HA^- + H_2O \rightleftharpoons H_3O^+ + A^{--}$$
$$HA^- + H_3O^+ \rightleftharpoons H_2O + H_2A$$

We shall consider the first reaction to be complete. The ionization constants for the second and third reactions are:

$$\frac{[H_3O^+][A^{--}]}{[HA^-]} = K_a''$$

and

$$\frac{[H_3O^+][HA^-]}{[H_2A]} = K_a'$$

If the acid salt ion were simply a monobasic acid, the $[H_3O^+]$ and the $[A^{--}]$ produced in the second reaction would be equal. However, some of the H_3O^+ resulting from this ionization is used up in forming the acid according to the third equation. The total concentration of A^{--} is equal to the concentration of hydrogen ion *plus* that of the acid:

$$[A^{--}] = [H_3O^+] + [H_2A]$$

Substituting into this equation the values of $[A^{--}]$ and $[H_2A]$ respectively from the two preceding equations and setting $[HA^-] = c$, the total acid salt concentration, gives, after rearrangement of terms, the desired equation for the hydrogen ion concentration:

$$[H_3O^+] = \sqrt{\frac{K_a'K_a''c}{K_a' + c}}$$

At moderate salt concentrations, if the first ionization constant is small (1 per cent or less) compared with c, it may be disregarded and we have the very simple relationship:

$$[H_3O^+] = \sqrt{K_a'K_a''} = \sqrt{K}$$

where K is the *total* ionization constant of the acid. Notice that in this case, unlike the others mentioned above, the $[H_3O^+]$ is *independent of concentration,* as long as $c \geqq 100\ K_a'$.

To take a numerical example, if we want to calculate the hydrogen ion concentration in 0.05 M $NaHCO_3$, for which $K_a' = 4.5 \times 10^{-7}$ and $K_a'' = 5.6 \times 10^{-11}$, we can safely use the approximate equation, since K_a' equals 0.001 per cent of c, hence:

$$[H_3O^+] = \sqrt{4.5 \times 10^{-7} \times 5.6 \times 10^{-11}} = 5.0 \times 10^{-9}\ M$$

The ionization constants for some weak acids and weak bases are given in Tables 82 and 83. The values given are from various sources. They refer strictly to the *activity ionization constant* but they may be used with *concentrations* to give results which can be considered approximately correct.

TABLE 82

IONIZATION CONSTANTS OF WEAK ACIDS

ACID	FORMULA	K_a'	K_a''	K_a'''
Inorganic				
Arsenic	H_3AsO_4	5.0×10^{-3}	4.0×10^{-5}	6.0×10^{-10}
Boric	H_3BO_3	6.0×10^{-10}	—	—
Carbonic	H_2CO_3	4.5×10^{-7}	5.6×10^{-11}	—
Hydrocyanic	HCN	1.3×10^{-9}	—	—
Hydrofluoric	HF	6.9×10^{-4}	—	—
Hydrogen sulfide	H_2S	9.1×10^{-8}	1.0×10^{-15}	—
Hypochlorous	$HOCl$	6.7×10^{-10}	—	—
Nitrous	HNO_2	4.6×10^{-4}	—	—
Phosphoric	H_3PO_4	1.2×10^{-2}	6.9×10^{-8}	1.7×10^{-12}
Sulfurous	H_2SO_3	1.7×10^{-2}	5.0×10^{-6}	—
Organic				
Acetic	CH_3COOH	1.8×10^{-5}	—	—
Benzoic	C_6H_5COOH	5.7×10^{-4}	—	—
Citric	$HOC(CH_2)_2(COOH)_3$	8.2×10^{-4}	4.1×10^{-5}	3.2×10^{-6}
Formic	$HCOOH$	2.1×10^{-4}	—	—
Glycollic	$HOCH_2COOH$	1.5×10^{-4}	—	—
Lactic	$CH_3CHOHCOOH$	1.4×10^{-4}	—	—
Oxalic	$(COOH)_2$	3.8×10^{-2}	3.0×10^{-5}	—
Phenol	C_6H_5OH	1.3×10^{-10}	—	—
Phthalic	$C_6H_4(COOH)_2$	1.3×10^{-3}	3.9×10^{-6}	—
Salicylic	$C_6H_4(OH)(COOH)$	1.1×10^{-3}	1.0×10^{-13}	—

TABLE 83

IONIZATION CONSTANTS OF WEAK BASES

BASE	FORMULA	K_b
Ammonia	NH_3	1.8×10^{-5}
Aniline	$C_6H_5NH_2$	4.6×10^{-10}
Hydrazine	NH_2NH_2	3.0×10^{-6}
Pyridine	C_5H_5N	1.2×10^{-9}
Quinoline	C_9H_7N	3.2×10^{-10}
Methylaniline	$C_6H_5NHCH_3$	7.0×10^{-9}
Dimethylaniline	$C_6H_5N(CH_3)_2$	2.4×10^{-10}
Methylamine	CH_3NH_2	4.0×10^{-4}
Dimethylamine	$(CH_3)_2NH$	5.0×10^{-4}
Trimethylamine	$(CH_3)_3N$	6.0×10^{-5}
Ethylamine	$C_2H_5NH_2$	5.6×10^{-4}
Diethylamine	$(C_2H_5)_2NH$	1.2×10^{-3}
Triethylamine	$(C_2H_5)_3N$	6.4×10^{-4}

Dielectric Constant, Ion Size, and Dissociation Constant. We have seen on page 327 that the extent of ionization and the dissociation of polar compounds in solution depends upon the nature of the solvent, and particularly upon its dielectric constant, and upon the size of the ions of the solute. Kraus and Fuoss, to whose work we referred before, have shown that there is no such thing as a strong or weak electrolyte *per se* but that the degree of dissociation depends largely upon the dielectric constant of the solvent and the size of the ions.

They studied solutions of tetraisoamylammonium nitrate, $[(C_5H_{11})_4N]NO_3$, in mixtures of dioxane and water, in which they could vary the dielectric constant from 2.2 to 78.6. They measured the conductances of solutions and hence determined the conductance ratios at different concentrations of solute in different mixtures of the two solvents. They corrected for the interionic-attraction forces and calculated the "true" degrees of dissociation and hence the dissociation constants in various solvent mixtures. They found that the dissociation constant varied enormously with the dielectric constant, as their theoretical equations had predicted. For example, when the dielectric constant increased from 2.38 to 11.9, the dissociation constant (measuring the degree of dissociation for solutions of equal concentration) increased from 2×10^{-16} to 9×10^{-4}. In the former case, the electrolyte is dissociated less than is pure water at room temperature; and in the latter case, it is dissociated somewhat more than acetic acid in water at the same temperature and concentration. When the dielectric constant reached 43.6, measurements of conductance, corrected for interionic attraction, indicated *complete dissociation.*

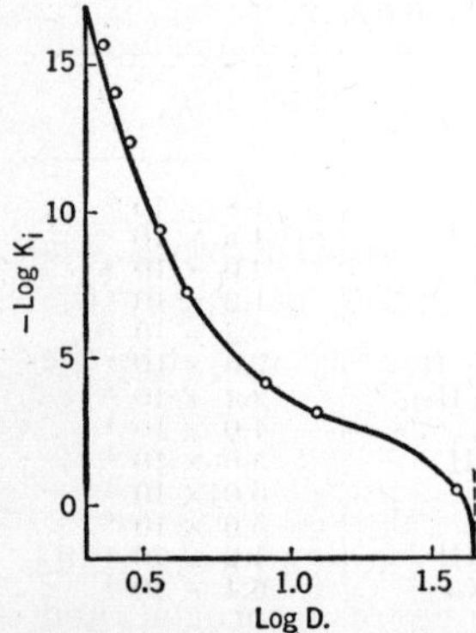

Fig. 152. Change of Dissociation Constant with Dielectric Constant.

The results obtained by Kraus and Fuoss are shown graphically in Figure 152, where the negative logarithm of the dissociation constant of the electrolyte is plotted as ordinate against the logarithm of the dielectric constant as abscissa. The line is the graph of their theoretical equation, while the points represent experimental values. These experimenters concluded that if the ions are small and the dielectric constant of the solvent is low, the dissociation constant will also be small; this conclusion is verified by their experimental results. For any salt there will be a critical value of the dielectric constant of the solvent above which dissociation will be complete. A salt made up of *larger* ions than those composing tetraisoamylammonium nitrate, for which they find a mean ionic diameter of 6.4×10^{-8} cm., will be completely dissociated in a solvent of *lower* dielectric constant than the critical value cited above, 43.6; one made up of *smaller* ions would be completely dissociated only if the dielectric constant is *higher* than this. They calculate for water at 25° C. a critical ionic diameter of 3.5×10^{-8} cm., which is in agreement with experimental conductance data.

The Ion Product for Water. Although water usually is classed as a nonconductor, the purest water ever obtained was found to have a slight, though measurable, conductance (see p. 395). This conductance indicates the ionization of water itself. According to the modern ionic theory, the ionization may be written:

$$2\,H_2O \rightleftharpoons H_3O^+ + OH^-$$

The secondary ionization,

$$H_2O + OH^- \rightleftharpoons H_3O^+ + O^{--}$$

must be negligibly slight.

The equilibrium constant for the ionization of water is:

$$K = \frac{a_{H_3O^+} \times a_{OH^-}}{a^2_{H_2O}}$$

The proportion of ionized water is so small that we may consider its activity as a constant, k, and so obtain the expression:

$$a_{H_3O^+} \times a_{OH^-} = K \times k^2 = K_w$$

The product of the concentrations of the two ions, therefore, is a constant, which is called the *ion-product constant*, or simply the **ion product, K_w,** for water. In dilute solutions we may use the *concentrations* and write:

$$K_w = [H_3O^+][OH^-]$$

The ion product for water holds constant in dilute aqueous solutions; although the relative concentrations of hydrogen and hydroxyl ion may be altered, their *product* always remains the same.

The value of K_w has been determined from measurements of electrical conductance and of the electromotive force of acid-base cells, and also from studies of the catalytic effect of the hydrogen ion. The value at 25° C. found by these various methods is 1.01×10^{-14}. In pure water the concentrations of hydrogen ion and hydroxyl ion are equal since the ionization of 1 mole of water produces 1 mole of each ion. Consequently, at 25° C.:

$$[H_3O^+] = [OH^-] = \sqrt{1 \times 10^{-14}} = 1 \times 10^{-7} \text{ mole per liter.}$$

The ion product, K_w, changes with the temperature as shown in Table 84; the corresponding changes in the concentrations of hydrogen ion and hydroxyl ion at the neutral point are also shown.

TABLE 84

Ion Product for Water at Various Temperatures

Temperature ° C.	Ion Product $K_w \times 10^{14}$	$[H_3O^+]$ and $[OH^-]$ at Neutral Point (Mole per Liter) $\times 10^7$
0	0.13	0.36
18	0.59	0.77
25	1.01	1.0
50	5.6	2.4
100	48	6.9
218	461	21.5

From the ion-product expression and the value of the constant at the given temperature, we may calculate the hydrogen ion concentration in the solution of a base or the hydroxyl ion concentration in the solution of an acid. For example, what is the hydroxyl ion concentration in 0.01 *M* hydrochloric acid solution at 25° C.? Substituting in the ion-product expression the hydrogen ion concentration, which may be taken as 0.01 mole per liter, we obtain:

$$0.01 \times [OH^-] = 1 \times 10^{-14}$$

so that

$$[OH^-] = \frac{1 \times 10^{-14}}{0.01} = 1 \times 10^{-12} \text{ mole per liter}$$

What is the hydrogen ion concentration in 0.02 *M* sodium hydroxide at 50° C.? Here we have,

$$[H_3O^+] \times 0.02 = 5.6 \times 10^{-14}$$

or

$$[H_3O^+] = \frac{5.6 \times 10^{-14}}{0.02} = 2.8 \times 10^{-12} \text{ mole per liter}$$

The *p*H Acidity Scale. The hydrogen ion concentrations of aqueous solutions which are met in scientific work vary over a remarkably wide range. For one purpose a concentration of 1 molar may be desirable; for another a concentration about that of water, 10^{-7} molar, may be more useful; and for a third, a basic solution in which the hydrogen ion concentration is as low as 10^{-14} molar may be required. In all such cases the hydrogen ion concentration may be a significant factor in the process concerned. It is, for example, an extremely important factor in the regulation of life processes. In order to simplify its expression, the Danish biochemist, Sørensen,[1] in 1909, suggested the ***p*H scale,** which has come into wide use.

*The **p**H of a solution is the negative exponent of the hydrogen ion concentration,*[2] thus:

$$pH = \log \frac{1}{[H_3O^+]} = -\log [H_3O^+]$$

or

$$[H_3O^+] = 10^{-pH}$$

If the $[H_3O^+]$ is 1×10^{-5} mole per liter, the pH of the solution is $-\log 10^{-5}$ or 5. Conversely, if a solution has a pH of 9, then we have:

$$9 = -\log [H_3O^+] = \log \frac{1}{[H_3O^+]} \qquad \text{or} \qquad [H_3O^+] = 10^{-9}$$

The symbol ***p*OH** is used to indicate the alkalinity of a solution. It is related to the hydroxyl ion concentration by the expression:

$$pOH = \log \frac{1}{[OH^-]} = -\log [OH^-]$$

At 25° C., as we have seen:

$$[H_3O^+] \times [OH^-] = 10^{-14}$$

Hence:

$$\log [H_3O^+] + \log [OH^-] = -14$$

or

$$-\log [H_3O^+] - \log [OH^-] = 14$$

or

$$pH + pOH = 14$$

In a neutral solution at 25° C., $p\text{H} = p\text{OH} = 7$. If the pH is less than 7, the solution is acid; if the pH is greater than 7, it is basic.

[1] Søren Peter Lauritz Sørensen was born in 1868 on the Danish island of Zeeland. After a brilliant career at the University of Copenhagen he took his doctorate in 1899. In 1901 he succeeded Kjeldahl as Director of the Chemical Section of the Carlsberg Laboratory at Copenhagen. His early work was in the inorganic and analytical field, but later he turned to biochemistry in which he has made many valuable contributions. He is best known as the "father of pH." For portrait, see Plate VIII, facing page 372.

[2] This may be regarded as a *preliminary* definition. See page 442 for a more practical definition based on e.m.f. measurements with the hydrogen electrode.

The pH of a solution in which the hydrogen ion concentration is 3×10^{-4} mole per liter, may be found thus:

$$p\text{H} = -\log(3 \times 10^{-4}) = -\log 3 + \log 10^4 = -0.48 + 4 = 3.52$$

In the same solution:

$$p\text{OH} = 14 - p\text{H} = 10.48$$

The relations among pH, pOH, and the hydrogen ion concentration are illustrated further in Table 85.

TABLE 85

HYDROGEN ION CONCENTRATION, pH AND pOH, AT 25° C.

HYDROGEN ION CONCENTRATION MOLE PER LITER		pH	pOH	
1	10^{0}	0	14	Acid
0.1	10^{-1}	1	13	Acid
0.0001	10^{-4}	4	10	Acid
$0.0_{6}1$ *	10^{-7}	7	7	Neutral
$0.0_{10}1$	10^{-11}	11	3	Basic
$0.0_{13}1$	10^{-14}	14	0	Basic

* The subscript indicates the number of zeros between the decimal point and the first significant figure.

The Ionization of Ampholytes. Hydroxides of many elements, like chromium, zinc, aluminum, arsenic, etc., are amphoteric in character, reacting with both hydrogen and hydroxyl ions. Both acid and basic properties also are shown by many organic substances, including amino acids, peptides, and proteins, which are important biologically. *Such substances are called* ***ampholytes.*** The ionization of ampholytes at first was formulated as the dissociation of *neutral molecules,* thus:

$$\text{A} + \text{H}_2\text{O} \rightleftharpoons \text{H}_3\text{O}^+ + \text{A}^- \qquad \text{(acid ionization)}$$

and

$$\text{A} \rightleftharpoons \text{A}^+ + \text{OH}^- \qquad \text{(basic ionization)}$$

According to this formulation, the ionization constants would be:

$$k_a = \frac{a_{\text{H}_3\text{O}^+} \times a_{\text{A}^-}}{a_\text{A}} \quad \text{and} \quad k_b = \frac{a_{\text{A}^+} \times a_{\text{OH}^-}}{a_\text{A}}$$

However, these constants proved to be of the order of 10^{-9} or 10^{-10} for k_a and 10^{-11} or 10^{-12} for K_b — much smaller than the values of 10^{-5} for acetic acid and for ammonia, which closely resemble the acid and basic groups in amino acids.

In 1916, E. Q. Adams and, in 1923, Niels Bjerrum showed that a more reasonable formulation of the ionization of the amino acids and peptides was to assume that they exist in solutions chiefly as **hybrid ions.** Thus glycine, usually written H_2NCH_2COOH, is now thought to exist in aqueous solution, and also in the solid state, chiefly as the hybrid ion $^{+}H_3NCH_2COO^{-}$, with a high dipole moment, which explains the fact that the dielectric constant of its solutions is much larger even than that of water. When an acid is added to glycine, the neutralization reaction is written:

$$^{+}H_3NCH_2COO^{-} + H_3O^{+} \rightleftharpoons {}^{+}H_3NCH_2COOH + H_2O$$

while the reaction with a base is:

$$^{+}H_3NCH_2COO^{-} + OH^{-} \rightleftharpoons H_2NCH_2COO^{-} + H_2O$$

In general, if the un-ionized ampholyte is designated A, the hybrid ion $^{+}A^{-}$, the cation ^{+}A and the anion A^{-}, the acid ionization is:

$$^{+}A + H_2O \rightleftharpoons {}^{+}A^{-} + H_3O^{+}$$

corresponding to which the acid ionization constant is:

$$K_a = \frac{a_{H_3O^+} \times a_{^+A^-}}{a_{A^+}}$$

Similarly, the basic ionization is:

$$A^{-} \rightleftharpoons {}^{+}A^{-} + OH^{-}$$

and the basic ionization constant is:

$$K_b = \frac{a_{^+A^-} \times a_{OH^-}}{a_{A^-}}$$

Values of these constants for certain ampholytes, on the hybrid-ion mechanism, are given in Table 86. The reader should realize, however, that ionization constants for ampholytes often are given, with no clear statement as to their meaning, on the old *neutral-molecule* theory. The relationship between the constants K_a and K_b of the hybrid-ion formulation, and k_a and k_b of the neutral-molecule theory may be found by multiplying $K_a \times k_b$:

$$K_a k_b = \frac{a_{H_3O^+} \times a_{^+A^-}}{a_{A^+}} \times \frac{a_{A^+} \times a_{OH^-}}{a_A}$$

Since A on the old theory and $^{+}A^{-}$ on the new each represent the *undissociated* molecule, the terms a_A and $a_{^+A^-}$ cancel, and

$$K_a k_b = a_{H_3O^+} \times a_{OH^-} = K_w$$

Hence:

$$K_a = \frac{K_w}{k_b}$$

Similar calculations show that

$$K_b = \frac{K_w}{k_a}$$

TABLE 86

IONIZATION CONSTANTS AT 25° C. FOR SOME SIMPLE AMPHOLYTES, WITH THE FORMULA $^{+}H_3N{\cdot}CH(R){\cdot}COO^{-}$

AMINO ACID	R GROUP	K_a	K_b
Glycine	$-H$	4.47×10^{-3}	6.00×10^{-5}
Alanine	$-CH_3$	4.57×10^{-3}	7.41×10^{-5}
Valine	$-CH(CH_3)_2$	5.18×10^{-3}	5.24×10^{-5}
Leucine	$-CH_2 \cdot CH(CH_3)_2$	4.70×10^{-3}	5.55×10^{-5}
Isoleucine	$-CH(CH_3)C_2H_5$	4.81×10^{-3}	5.73×10^{-5}
Norleucine	$-CH_2 \cdot (CH_2)_3CH_3$	4.63×10^{-3}	6.83×10^{-5}

C. L. A. Schmidt, *Chemistry of the Amino Acids and Proteins.*

The Hydrolysis of Salts. When a salt is formed from an acid and base, one or both of which are weak, it will hydrolyze in water. The resulting solution is either basic or acid depending upon whether the acid or the base is the weaker. The effect is due to the reaction of an ion of the salt with an ion of water to form the weak electrolyte. Thus a solution of sodium acetate, made from the strong sodium hydroxide and the weak acetic acid, has a basic reaction; a solution of ammonium chloride, made from the weak base, ammonia, and the strong hydrochloric acid, has an acid reaction. The basic reaction of sodium acetate is explained by the following equations:

$$NaC_2H_3O_2 \longrightarrow Na^+ + C_2H_3O_2^-$$
$$+$$
$$2\,H_2O \rightleftharpoons OH^- + H_3O^+$$
$$\downarrow\uparrow$$
$$\longrightarrow HC_2H_3O_2 + H_2O$$

The net effect is that the H_3O^+ is partly removed from the solution by combination with $C_2H_3O_2^-$, and this leaves the OH^- in excess over the H_3O^+; hence the solution is basic. The ammonium chloride likewise reacts with the water, thus:

$$NH_4Cl \longrightarrow NH_4^+ + Cl^-$$
$$+$$
$$2\,H_2O \rightleftharpoons OH^- + H_3O^+$$
$$\downarrow\uparrow$$
$$\longrightarrow NH_3 + H_2O$$

In this case OH^- is removed by reaction with NH_4^+, and so H_3O^+ is in excess over the OH^-; hence the solution is acid.

If the salt is made from a weak acid and a weak base, both ions of the salt will be partially removed by reaction with the ions of water and the resulting solution will be acid, basic, or neutral depending upon the *relative* strengths of the acid and base involved. Ammonia and acetic acid are ionized to almost the same degree and hence the salt made from them, ammonium acetate, is almost neutral. The reaction of this salt with water may be represented thus:

$$
\begin{array}{ccccc}
NH_4C_2H_3O_2 \longrightarrow & NH_4^+ & + & C_2H_3O_2^- & \\
 & + & & + & \\
2\,H_2O \rightleftharpoons & OH^- & + & H_3O^+ & \\
 & \updownarrow & & \updownarrow & \\
NH_3 + H_2O \leftarrow & & & & \rightarrow HC_2H_3O_2 + H_2O
\end{array}
$$

Utilizing the ionization constants for the acid and base concerned in a hydrolytic reaction and the ion product for water, we may put these effects on a quantitative basis and calculate the hydrogen and hydroxyl ion concentrations in the solutions of salts.

Salt of a Weak Base and a Strong Acid. The hydrolysis of the salt, BA, made from a weak base, BOH, and a strong acid, HA, may be represented by the following equilibrium diagram:

$$
\begin{array}{ccc}
BA \longrightarrow & B^+ + A^- & \\
 & + & \\
2\,H_2O \rightleftharpoons & OH^- + H_3O^+ & \\
 & \updownarrow & \\
 & BOH &
\end{array}
$$

The salt and the acid are so highly ionized that we need not consider their undissociated molecules. In other words, *we assume they are completely ionized.* The important equilibria are those between water and its ions and between the weak base and its ions, for which the following equilibrium constant equations hold simultaneously:

$$[H_3O^+][OH^-] = K_w$$

$$\frac{[B^+][OH^-]}{[BOH]} = K_b$$

The equation for the whole equilibrium may be written:

$$B^+ + A^- + 2\,H_2O \rightleftharpoons BOH + H_3O^+ + A^-$$

Since A^- does not enter into the reaction, it may be dropped from the equation. The equilibrium is completely represented by:

$$B^+ + 2\,H_2O \rightleftharpoons BOH + H_3O^+$$

The equilibrium constant for this reaction is:

$$\frac{[BOH][H_3O^+]}{[H_2O]^2[B^+]} = K_c$$

Since the value of $[H_2O]$ is constant in a dilute aqueous solution, we may write:

$$\frac{[BOH][H_3O^+]}{[B^+]} = K_c \times k = K_h$$

K_h is known as the **hydrolysis constant.** Multiplying numerator and denominator by $[OH^-]$ gives:

$$[H_3O^+][OH^-] \cdot \frac{[BOH]}{[B^+][OH^-]} = K_h$$

The first term on the left is K_w and the second is the reciprocal of the ionization constant for the base, K_b, hence the hydrolysis constant for the hydrolysis of a salt of a weak base and a strong acid is given by the equation:

$$K_h = \frac{K_w}{K_b} = \frac{[BOH][H_3O^+]}{[B^+]}$$

We can now proceed to calculate the hydrogen ion concentration resulting from the hydrolysis. The equation, $B^+ + 2H_2O \rightleftharpoons BOH + H_3O^+$, shows that the hydrolytic reaction forms BOH and H_3O^+ *in equal concentrations*. For each mole of BOH there is also formed one mole of H_3O^+. In every case which we shall consider, the $[H_3O^+]$ formed by the hydrolysis is so much larger than that in pure water that we may write:

$$[BOH] = [H_3O^+]$$

Substituting this value for [BOH] in the expression for K_h and rearranging, gives

$$[H_3O^+]^2 = \frac{[B^+]K_w}{K_b} = [B^+]K_h$$

or

$$[H_3O^+] = \sqrt{\frac{[B^+]K_w}{K_b}} = \sqrt{[B^+]K_h}$$

Now if the degree of hydrolysis is *small*, little of the B^+ will be tied up as the hydroxide, BOH, and so the concentration of B^+ will be very nearly equal to the concentration of the original salt, which we shall call c. Hence the equation may be written simply:

$$[H_3O^+] = \sqrt{\frac{cK_w}{K_b}} = \sqrt{cK_h}$$

This equation can be stated very conveniently in logarithmic form, introducing pH. Taking the logarithm of each side and changing signs throughout gives:

$$-\log [H_3O^+] = -\tfrac{1}{2}\log c - \tfrac{1}{2}\log K_w + \tfrac{1}{2}\log K_b$$

Now $-\log [H_3O^+] = p$H. Similarly the values $-\log K_w$ and $-\log K_b$, the **ionization exponents** of water and the base, are often designated respectively by $\boldsymbol{pK_w}$ and $\boldsymbol{pK_b}$. The equation then becomes:

$$pH = \tfrac{1}{2}\,pK_w - \tfrac{1}{2}\,pK_b - \tfrac{1}{2}\log c$$

In case the salt is *largely hydrolyzed*, the $[B^+]$ will be considerably *less* than the original salt concentration c. In fact, it will be equal to the original concentration *minus* the amount of base formed, or:

$$[B^+] = c - [BOH] = c - [H_3O^+]$$

Substituting this value of $[B^+]$ in the equation $[H_3O^+]^2 = [B^+]K_h$ gives the more general equation:

$$[H_3O^+]^2 = (c - [H_3O^+])K_h$$

This equation may be solved by the general quadratic formula and, since $[H_3O^+]$ is positive, gives the solution:

$$[H_3O^+] = \frac{\sqrt{K_h^2 + 4\,K_hc}}{2} - \frac{K_h}{2}$$

If K_h is very much smaller than c, this reduces to the simpler equation which we derived above:

$$[H_3O^+] = \sqrt{K_hc} = \sqrt{\frac{cK_w}{K_b}}$$

We may define the ***degree of hydrolysis, x,*** as the *fraction of the total salt which is hydrolyzed:*

$$x = \frac{[BOH]}{c} = \frac{[H_3O^+]}{c}$$

Hence, in the case of the salt of a weak base and strong acid such as we have been considering, if the hydrolysis is sufficiently small to justify using the equation,

$$[H_3O^+] = \sqrt{K_h c} = \sqrt{\frac{cK_w}{K_b}}$$

we may write:

$$x = \sqrt{\frac{K_h}{c}} = \sqrt{\frac{K_w}{K_b c}}$$

Notice that the degree of hydrolysis becomes *greater* as the concentration becomes *less*. It is inversely proportional to the *square root* of the concentration.

A numerical example will make these principles clearer. Calculate the hydrolysis constant, pH, and degree of hydrolysis of NH_4Cl in a .001 M solution. In this case, $K_b = 1.8 \times 10^{-5}$ (Table 83, page 347).

$$K_h = \frac{K_w}{K_b} = \frac{10^{-14}}{1.8 \times 10^{-5}} = 5.5_5 \times 10^{-10}$$

$$[H_3O^+] = \sqrt{K_h c} = \sqrt{55._5 \times 10^{-14}} = 7.4 \times 10^{-7}\ M$$

$$pH = 7 - \log 7.4 = 7 - 0.87 = 6.13$$

$$x = \frac{[H_3O^+]}{c} = \frac{7.4 \times 10^{-7}}{.001} = 7.4 \times 10^{-4}$$

The salt therefore is 0.074 per cent hydrolyzed.

Salt of a Weak Acid and a Strong Base. By means of reasoning exactly analogous to that which we have used above, we can show that in this case the equilibrium equation is:

$$A^- + H_2O \rightleftharpoons HA + OH^-$$

The other equations are similar except that K_a takes the place of K_b and $[OH^-]$ takes the place of $[H_3O^+]$, thus:

$$[OH^-] = \sqrt{\frac{cK_w}{K_a}} = \sqrt{cK_h}$$

whence

$$[H_3O^+] = \frac{K_w}{[OH^-]} = \sqrt{\frac{K_a K_w}{c}}$$

and

$$pH = \tfrac{1}{2}\, pK_w + \tfrac{1}{2}\, pK_a + \tfrac{1}{2} \log c$$

Finally, the degree of hydrolysis:

$$x = \frac{[OH^-]}{c} = \sqrt{\frac{K_w}{K_a c}}$$

Here, as before, *the degree of hydrolysis is inversely proportional to the square root of the salt concentration, c.* The student should verify these equations by working out the complete derivations.

To illustrate this case, let us calculate the pH in a 0.1 M solution of Na_2CO_3. For this salt, K_a is the constant for the *secondary* ionization of H_2CO_3 since we are dealing with the equilibrium:

$$CO_3^{--} + H_2O \rightleftharpoons HCO_3^- + OH^-$$

for which

$$K_2 = 5.6 \times 10^{-11}$$

and

$$pK_a = 11 - 0.75 = 10.25$$

Hence

$$pH = 7 + 5.13 - 0.5 = 11.63$$

This shows that the solution is *strongly alkaline.* In this solution, the *degree of hydrolysis* is approximately:

$$x = \sqrt{\frac{K_w}{K_a c}} = \sqrt{\frac{10^{-14}}{5.6 \times 10^{-12}}} = 4.2 \times 10^{-2}$$

The solution is therefore 4.2 per cent hydrolyzed.

Salt of a Weak Acid and a Weak Base. These salts are often very completely hydrolyzed, although the solution will remain nearly neutral if the acid and base are equally weak. The equilibrium equation is:

$$B^+ + A^- + H_2O \rightleftharpoons HA + BOH$$

for which the hydrolysis constant is:

$$\frac{[HA][BOH]}{[B^+][A^-]} = K_h = \frac{K_w}{K_a K_b}$$

If the acid and base are of equal strength, [HA] = [BOH], and if the salt is completely ionized (and only slightly hydrolyzed), $[B^+] = [A^-] = c$.

$$[HA] = [BOH] = c\sqrt{\frac{K_w}{K_a K_b}}$$

In this case, the degree of hydrolysis,

$$x = \frac{[HA]}{c} = \sqrt{\frac{K_w}{K_a K_b}}$$

will be *independent of concentration.* In this respect the salt of a weak acid and a weak base differs from the first two types which we have considered, where the degree of hydrolysis varies inversely as the square root of the concentration c.

If we want to calculate the extent of hydrolysis of such a salt as ethylamine formate, using the last equation above we find:

$$x = \sqrt{\frac{10^{-14}}{5.6 \times 2.1 \times 10^{-8}}} = 2.9 \times 10^{-4}$$

The Hydrolysis of Ampholytes. When an ampholyte is dissolved in water, the equilibria may be represented thus:

$$2\,A \longrightarrow {}^{+}A^{-} + {}^{+}A^{-}$$

$$2\,H_2O \rightleftharpoons H_3O^+ + OH^-$$

$$A^+ + H_2O \;\rightleftharpoons\; (H_3O^+) \qquad (OH^-) \;\rightleftharpoons\; A^-$$

Three equilibrium constants are involved, which in terms of *concentrations* are:

$$K_a = \frac{[H_3O^+][{}^{+}A^{-}]}{[A^+]} \qquad \text{whence} \qquad [A^+] = \frac{[H_3O^+][{}^{+}A^{-}]}{K_a}$$

$$K_w = [H_3O^+][OH^-] \qquad \text{whence} \qquad [OH^-] = \frac{K_w}{[H_3O^+]}$$

$$K_b = \frac{[{}^{+}A^{-}][OH^-]}{[A^-]} \qquad \text{whence} \qquad [A^-] = \frac{[{}^{+}A^{-}][OH^-]}{K_b} = \frac{[{}^{+}A^{-}]K_w}{K_b[H_3O^+]}$$

Since the solution is electrically neutral,

$$[A^+] + [H_3O^+] = [A^-] + [OH^-]$$

Substituting into this equation the values for $[A^+]$, $[A^-]$, and $[OH^-]$ from the preceding equations and solving for the hydrogen ion concentration gives:

$$[H_3O^+] = \sqrt{\frac{K_wK_a([{}^{+}A^{-}] + K_b)}{K_b([{}^{+}A^{-}] + K_a)}}$$

If the hydrolysis is *small*, we may let $[{}^{+}A^{-}] = c$, the total concentration of ampholyte, and solve for the hydrogen ion concentration directly. If the hydrolysis is appreciable, the approximate value of $[H_3O^+]$ obtained as above is used to calculate $[A^+]$ and $[A^-]$, from the three original equilibria. Then the value of $[{}^{+}A^{-}]$, found from the equation

$$c = [{}^{+}A^{-}] + [A^+] + [A^-]$$

is substituted in the preceding equation to give a better value of $[H_3O^+]$. Rarely, a repetition of the process is necessary to give a satisfactory approximation.

As the above equation shows, (1) in a *dilute* solution of an ampholyte, when $[^+A^-]$ is much less than K_a and K_b, the hydrogen ion concentration $[H_3O^+]$ is equal to $\sqrt{K_w}$, as in pure water, while (2) in a *concentrated* solution, when $[^+A^-]$ is much greater than K_b and K_a,

$$[H_3O^+] = \sqrt{\frac{K_wK_a}{K_b}}$$

The Isoelectric Point. As shown on page 548, in a conductance cell an ampholyte usually migrates toward one pole or the other when a direct current is passed through the solution. The direction of motion depends upon the pH of the solution. Thus, in solutions of egg white which have been boiled, the egg protein migrates towards the *cathode* in acid solutions and toward the *anode* in basic solutions. *The value of the* pH *at which the ampholyte does not migrate in either direction is called the* ***isoelectric point*** *for that ampholyte.* At the isoelectric point, the concentrations of the cation A^+ and anion A^- must be equal. If we divide the equation for the acid by that for the basic dissociation constants, expressed in terms of concentrations, and substitute for the value of $[OH^-]$, we find:

$$\frac{K_a}{K_b} = \frac{[H_3O^+]^2}{K_w} \times \frac{[A^-]}{[A^+]} \quad \text{or} \quad [H_3O^+] = \sqrt{\frac{K_wK_a}{K_b} \times \frac{[A^+]}{[A^-]}}$$

At the isoelectric point, the concentrations of anion and cation are equal, and if the hydrogen concentration is denoted by $[H_3O^+]_i$

$$[H_3O^+]_i = \sqrt{\frac{K_aK_w}{K_b}}$$

A consideration of this equation shows that *the isoelectric point for an ampholyte is the same* pH *which is approached by a* ***concentrated*** *solution of the ampholyte.* Thus, Sørensen showed that the pH of a 1.0 M solution of glycine is within 0.001 pH unit of the isoelectric point.

It is possible to prove that the concentration of hybrid ion $[^+A^-]$ is a *maximum* at the isoelectric point, and the sum of $[A^+]$ and $[A^-]$ is a *minimum*.

The logarithmic expression for the isoelectric exponent is:

$$pH_i = \tfrac{1}{2}\,(pK_a + pK_w - pK_b)$$

The Solubility Product Constant, K_s. Chemical reactions involving the formation of precipitates play a predominant role in qualitative and quantitative analysis. Precipitates of inorganic substances may form when the corresponding ions are brought together in solution. Such reactions as the following are familiar:

$$Ag^+ + Cl^- \longrightarrow \underline{AgCl}$$
$$Ba^{++} + SO_4^{--} \longrightarrow \underline{BaSO_4}$$
$$3\,Ca^{++} + 2\,PO_4^{---} \longrightarrow \underline{Ca_3(PO_4)_2}$$

Experimental evidence, such as conductance and electromotive force measurements, as well as direct solubility measurements, show that no such precipitation reaction is complete; a greater or less concentration of each reacting ion always remains in solution. Likewise, when any electrovalent substance is put into water, at least a little of the substance always goes into solution, giving ions. In such a case, the substance is already ionized in the solid state, consequently the equilibrium involves only the solid phase and the ions in solution.

For an electrovalent substance BA, which is only slightly soluble and which yields the ions B^+ and A^-, the equilibrium would be:

$$\underline{BA} \rightleftharpoons B^+ + A^-$$

The expression for the *classical* equilibrium constant is:

$$K = \frac{[B^+][A^-]}{\underline{[BA]}}$$

But the concentration of a solid substance is constant; it is the mass of substance per unit volume, *e.g.*, so many moles per liter. Hence, we may put $\underline{[BA]}$ equal to k. The expression thus becomes:

$$[B^+][A^-] = K \times k = K_s$$

where K_s is the **solubility product.**

A Kinetic Interpretation of the Solubility Product. If a crystal of a slightly soluble salt were so magnified that we could see the individual particles, we should find that the surface consists of the ions arranged in an orderly lattice. Some of these ions at any particular moment would be dissolving from the crystal, while other ions from the solution would be settling upon the crystal lattice in other places. If the solution is *saturated* with respect to the salt, the number of ions leaving the crystal in any time will be exactly the same as the number precipitating upon the lattice. We can easily formulate these conditions mathematically as follows: The number of the B^+ ions leaving the surface of the crystal will be proportional to the area, s_{B^+}, of the crystal face covered by the B^+ ions, while the number of B^+ ions returning to the surface of the crystal will be proportional to the concentration of B^+ ions in the solution and to the portion of the surface upon which they can deposit, which is proportional to the area covered by A^- ions. At equilibrium these two numbers will be equal, and we may write:

$$k_1 s_{B^+} = k_2 s_{A^-}[B^+]$$

An analogous equation holds for the A^- ions, namely:

$$k_3 s_{A^-} = k_4 s_{B^+}[A^-]$$

The constants k_1, k_2, k_3, k_4 are the proportionality factors for the steps mentioned above. If we multiply the first equation by the second and cancel out the identical terms on the two sides, we find:

$$k_1 k_3 = k_2 k_4 [B^+][A^-]$$

Rearranging terms and putting the single constant K_s for the fraction involving the four rate constants gives finally:

$$[B^+][A^-] = \frac{k_1 k_3}{k_2 k_4} = K_s$$

This is exactly the same equation for the solubility product which we derived by the first method.

The principle involved in the solubility product expression may be stated thus: *In a saturated solution of an electrovalent substance of limited solubility, the product of the ionic concentrations, raised to the powers indicated in the stoichiometric equation for the dissociation, is constant at a given temperature.* The concentration of an ion may be altered by adding another electrolyte yielding an ion in common with the solid substance, but the *ion product* remains the same; if the concentration of one ion increases, that of the other decreases correspondingly.

In the general reaction:

$$B_bA_a \rightleftharpoons bB^+ + aA^-$$

the solubility product is:

$$K_s = [B^+]^b[A^-]^a$$

If we represent by s_0 the molar solubility of the solute B_bA_a *in water,* we see that, since 1 mole of solute yields b ions of B and a ions of A, the concentration of B^+ will be bs_0 and that of A^- will be as_0, so that:

$$K_s = (bs_0)^b \times (as_0)^a$$

Hence, if the solubility of the substance is known, the solubility product is readily calculated. A few typical solubility products are given in Table 87.

TABLE 87

SOLUBILITY PRODUCTS FOR VARIOUS SUBSTANCES AT ROOM TEMPERATURE

SUBSTANCE	SOLUBILITY PRODUCT	K_s
AgCl	$[Ag^+][Cl^-]$	2×10^{-10}
$PbCl_2$	$[Pb^{++}][Cl^-]^2$	2×10^{-4}
$BaSO_4$	$[Ba^{++}][SO_4^{--}]$	1×10^{-10}
$CaCO_3$	$[Ca^{++}][CO_3^{--}]$	5×10^{-9}
Ag_2CrO_4	$[Ag^+]^2[CrO_4^{--}]$	2×10^{-12}
$Fe(OH)_3$	$[Fe^{+++}][OH^-]^3$	1×10^{-36}
$MgNH_4PO_4$	$[Mg^{++}][NH_4^+][PO_4^{---}]$	3×10^{-13}

The following example illustrates the calculation of the solubility product from the solubility. The solubility of silver chromate is 0.02623 g. per liter, or 0.000079 mole per liter. The solubility product is:

$$K_s = [Ag^+]^2[CrO_4^{--}] = (2\,s_0)^2 \times (s_0) = 4\,s_0^3$$
$$= 4 \times (7.9 \times 10^{-5})^3 = 2.0 \times 10^{-12}$$

Similarly the solubility of a salt may be calculated from its solubility product. The solubility product for lead sulfide, for example, is 4.2×10^{-28}. For lead sulfide we have:

$$K_s = 4.2 \times 10^{-28} = [Pb^{++}][S^{--}] = s_0 \times s_0$$

Hence if there were no hydrolysis, the solubility in water would be:

$$s_0 = \sqrt{4.2 \times 10^{-28}}$$
$$= 2 \times 10^{-14} \text{ mole per liter}$$

Multiplying this by the gram molecular weight, we obtain:

$$2 \times 10^{-14} \times 239 = 4.8 \times 10^{-12} \text{ gram per liter}$$

The effect of a common ion upon the solubility of a slightly soluble electrolyte may be seen from the following calculation. In determining chloride quantitatively, how much chloride would remain in 100 ml. of the solution when sufficient silver nitrate solution had been added to make the concentration 0.1 M in Ag^+? For AgCl we find from Table 87:

$$K_s = [Ag^+][Cl^-] = 2 \times 10^{-10}$$

Substituting 0.1 for $[Ag^+]$,

$$0.1 \times [Cl^-] = 2 \times 10^{-10}$$

and

$$[Cl^-] = 2 \times 10^{-9} \text{ mole per liter}$$
$$= 7.1 \times 10^{-9} \text{ g. per 100 ml.}$$

Validity of the Solubility Product. The *classical* solubility product principle does not hold quantitatively. The addition of a common ion usually does not cause the solubility to diminish as much as required by the expression, $K_s = [B^+]^b[A^-]^a$; nor is the solubility always unaffected by the pressure in the solution of other substances which furnish no ion in common with the solute. Usually the solubility is *increased* by the addition of a salt with no common ion. *The effect of such an electrolyte on the solubility often is called the* ***salt effect.***

The *salt effect* is illustrated by the curves shown in Figures 153 and 154. The former shows the variation in solubility of thallous

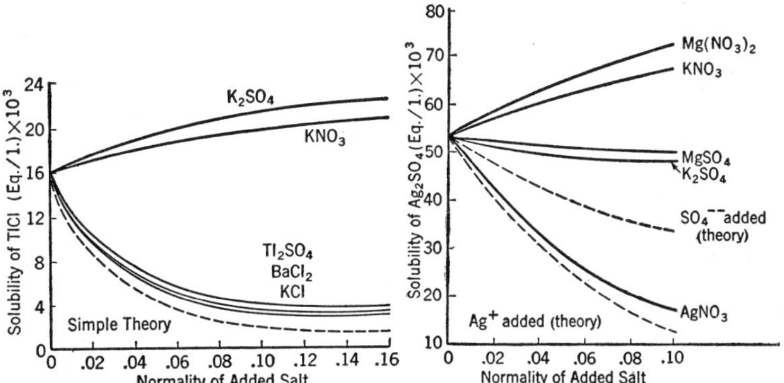

Fig. 153. Influence of Various Salts on the Solubility of TlCl.

Fig. 154. Influence of Various Electrolytes on the Solubility of Ag_2SO_4.

chloride with increasing concentrations of added substances; the latter shows the similar variation in the case of silver sulfate. In the former case the three salts with common ions decrease the solubility somewhat less than the solubility product predicts, while the two salts with no common ion increase the solubility. In the second case excess silver nitrate decreases the solubility somewhat less than the theory predicts, while excess sulfate hardly decreases the solubility at all; KNO_3 and $Mg(NO_3)_2$ markedly increase the solubility of Ag_2SO_4. These effects, inexplicable on the basis of the theory of Arrhenius, can be understood in terms of the Debye-Hückel theory.

The solubility-product expression holds rigorously if *activities* are substituted for *concentrations*. Thus, for the uni-univalent salt, BA, at a given temperature, we have:

$$K_s = a_{B^+} \times a_{A^-}$$

If the slightly soluble salt is in pure water or in a solution containing no common ion, we may substitute γm for a (see p. 334) and thus obtain:

$$K_s = \gamma^2 m^2$$

If we represent the solubility in water by s_0 and that in a solution by s, we may substitute s and s_0 for m and obtain:

$$K_s = \gamma_0{}^2 s_0{}^2 = \gamma^2 s^2$$

and thus:

$$\frac{\gamma_0}{\gamma} = \frac{s}{s_0}$$

This means that the activity coefficient for a slightly soluble uni-univalent salt is inversely proportional to its solubility. The expression may be put in the logarithmic form,

$$\log \gamma_0 - \log \gamma = \log \frac{s}{s_0}$$

This equation is widely used in determining the activity coefficients of slightly soluble salts in dilute solutions. According to the Debye-Hückel theory, as explained on page 338, the activity coefficient should be a linear function of the *ionic strength*, μ, at concentrations approaching zero: $\log \gamma = - K_1 z_1 z_2 \sqrt{\mu}$. If $\log \left(\frac{s}{s_0}\right)$ is plotted against $\sqrt{\mu}$, it will be found to approach a straight line in very dilute solutions. The intersection of this line with the axis of ordinates will correspond to the value of $\log \gamma = 0$; since at zero concentration of salt, $\gamma = 1$. The logarithm of the activity coefficient at any other concentration is simply measured downward from this point as origin. As an illustration of this method, we may take the results of Brønsted, LaMer, and their coworkers, who used insoluble cobaltammine salts, which could be analyzed accurately by titration of the ammonia liberated when the salt is heated with a strong base. Typical results are plotted in Figure 155 which shows the very satisfactory agreement found in most cases. In these experiments the salt under investigation was present in only a small concentration, and the ionic atmosphere was chiefly due to other salts which were added. These figures show that the activity coefficient depends on the *ionic strength of the solution as a whole* and not on the concentration of the particular salt. The Debye-Hückel theory explains the observed *increase* in solubility of a salt when another salt with no common ion is added. Any electrolyte added *increases* the ionic strength (μ). This *decreases* the value of log γ (since $\log \gamma = -K_1 z_1 z_2 \sqrt{\mu}$) and hence more salt must dissolve in order to keep the activity product constant. The Debye-Hückel theory thus explains qualitatively the *positive* deviations from the solubility product principle (Figures 153 and 154, page 365) when salts with *high valence* common ions are added to insoluble salts.

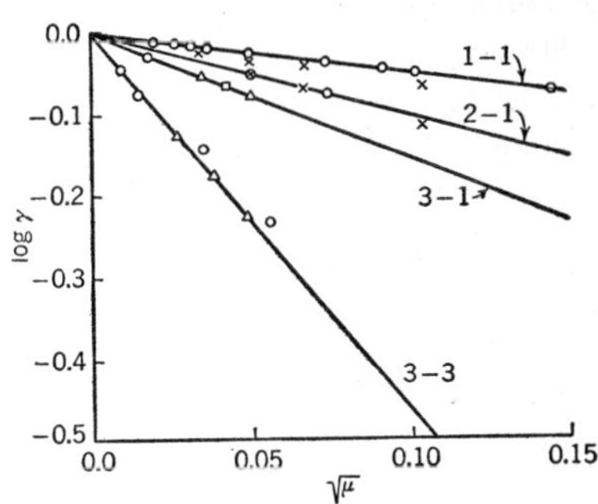

Fig. 155. Test of Debye-Hückel Limiting Law for Salts of Different Valence Types.

PROBLEMS AND EXERCISES

1. Assuming K_w as given in Table 84, page 350, and assuming Avogadro's number, calculate the number of hydrogen ions, at 25° C., in 1 ml. of (*a*) water; (*b*) 0.1 *N* HCl; (*c*) 0.5 *N* KOH.

2. Find the concentration of hydroxyl ion in a solution 0.2 *M* in ammonia and 0.2 *M* in ammonium chloride.

3. Given that the degrees of ionization of salicylic acid and phenol, respectively, are 10.0 per cent and 0.0030 per cent, in 0.10 *N* solution, calculate the ionization constant of each.

4. Given that the *p*H of a solution is (*a*) 3, (*b*) 4.9, (*c*) 8.64, find the hydrogen ion concentration.

5. Using the ionization constants given in Tables 82 and 83, on page 347, find the hydrogen ion concentration and the *p*H of each of the following solutions: (*a*) 0.08 *N* acetic acid; (*b*) 0.16 *M* potassium bioxalate; (*c*) a solution which is 0.2 *N* in formic acid and 0.1 *N* in sodium formate; (*d*) 0.16 *N* sodium dihydrogen phosphate.

6. Calculate the concentrations of $H_2PO_4^-$ and HPO_4^{--} in a 0.1 *M* solution of phosphoric acid.

7. To 400 ml. of 0.2660 *N* lactic acid are added 600 ml. of 0.1000 *N* sodium lactate. Find the hydrogen ion concentration and the *p*H of the resulting solution.

8. Using the solubility products listed in Table 87, page 364, find the solubility in g. per 100 ml. of (*a*) magnesium ammonium phosphate; (*b*) silver chloride; (*c*) lead chloride.

9. Using the values listed in Table 84, page 350, plot the values for the ion product for water against the temperature. Find by interpolation the value for blood heat, 37° C., and hence calculate the *p*H in pure water at this temperature.

10. Plot the values for *p*H in water given in the same table against the temperature and find the *p*H at 37° C. by interpolation. Compare with the result of the calculation in problem 9.

11. Find the *p*H and the *p*OH in 0.01 *N* ammonium hydroxide solution.

12. Using the data of Table 83, page 347, calculate the degree of ionization of a 0.02 *N* solution of each of the following: (*a*) ammonia; (*b*) methylamine; (*c*) dimethylamine.

13. How many grams of solid potassium acetate must be added to 100 ml. of 0.1 *M* acetic acid solution to reduce its *p*H to 3.00?

14. Find the degree of hydrolysis of ammonium acetate at 25° C. in 1 *M* aqueous solution.

15. Write the equilibrium equation for the hydrolysis of a salt of a weak acid and a weak base, and the expressions for the equilibrium constants involved. From these derive an equation for the hydrogen ion concentration in such a solution by a method of reasoning similar to that employed for ampholytes on page 360.

16. Using the equation derived in problem 15, calculate the hydrogen ion concentration and *p*H (*a*) in a 0.1 *M* solution of ammonium nitrite; (*b*) in a 0.01 *M* solution of ammonium benzoate; (*c*) in a 0.05 *M* solution of methylamine lactate.

17. Calculate the *p*H (*a*) in a 0.01 *M* solution of glycine; (*b*) in a 0.1 *M* solution of valine; (*c*) in a 0.05 *M* solution of alanine.

18. Calculate the isoelectric point for glycine, valine, and alanine and compare the values with the *p*H found in problem 17.

READING LIST

L. P. Hammett, *Solutions of Electrolytes*, 2d ed. McGraw-Hill Book Company, New York, 1936. Pp. 24–101.

I. M. Kolthoff, *Indicators*, rev. and enl. by N. H. Furman. John Wiley & Sons, New York, 1926. Chapter II, "Amphoteric Compounds."

C. L. A. Schmidt, *Chemistry of the Amino Acids and Proteins*. Charles C. Thomas, Publisher, Springfield, Ill., 1938. Chapter XI, "Amphoteric Properties of Amino Acids and Proteins."

CHAPTER 14

ELECTROLYTIC CONDUCTANCE

Electrical Units. The flow of electricity through a circuit is like the flow of water through a pipe. In the hydraulic system, a pump forces the water through the pipes. The rate of flow depends upon the pressure exerted by the pump and also upon the mechanical resistance of the pipe, which is less for a short pipe of large diameter than for a long pipe of small diameter. Similarly, the flow of electricity depends upon the electrical pressure or *potential difference* furnished by the generator or battery, and the *electrical resistance* of the whole circuit.

Before discussing the mechanism of conductance, we shall define some of the units used in electrical measurements.

(1) The *quantity of electricity, Q,* is measured in *coulombs.* The definition depends upon Faraday's laws of electrolysis, which will be discussed later (page 372). *The* ***coulomb*** *is defined as the quantity of electricity which will deposit 0.00111800 g. of silver from a solution of silver nitrate, under specified conditions.*

(2) The *rate of flow* or *current, I,* is measured in *amperes. One* ***ampere*** *is a current of one coulomb per second.*

(3) The *electrical resistance, R,* is measured in *ohms. The* ***ohm*** *is defined as the resistance, at 0° C., of a column of mercury weighing 14.4521 g., having a uniform cross section (of about 0.01 sq. cm.) and a length of 106.300 cm.* Mercury makes a good standard of resistance because it can be purified easily and, being a liquid, its resistance is reproducible and not, like that of a solid, dependent upon its previous treatment.

(4) The unit of *electromotive force, E,* is the *volt.* It is defined in terms of the two preceding units. *The* ***volt*** *is the electromotive force required to force a current of one ampere through a resistance of one ohm.*

The relationship between the current, voltage, and resistance in a circuit is expressed by **Ohm's law:**

$$E = IR \qquad \text{or} \qquad I = E/R$$

If we know the value of any two of these quantities in a circuit, we can always calculate the value of the third from Ohm's law.

Classification of Conductors. Conductors of electricity may be divided into two classes. ***Conductors of the first class*** *show no material change as the current passes through them.* Metals belong to this class. They consist of lattices of positive ions, through which the valence electrons flow when a difference of potential is applied. The current consists of the stream of electrons, and there is no motion of the positive ions. In ***conductors of the second class,*** *the passage of the electric current is accompanied by a transfer of matter.* Fused salts and conducting solutions belong to this class, in which the conductors are the ions, which move freely toward the electrodes, where they may be neutralized and liberated. A study of the changes which take place during electrolysis throws a great deal of light upon the nature of the solutions.

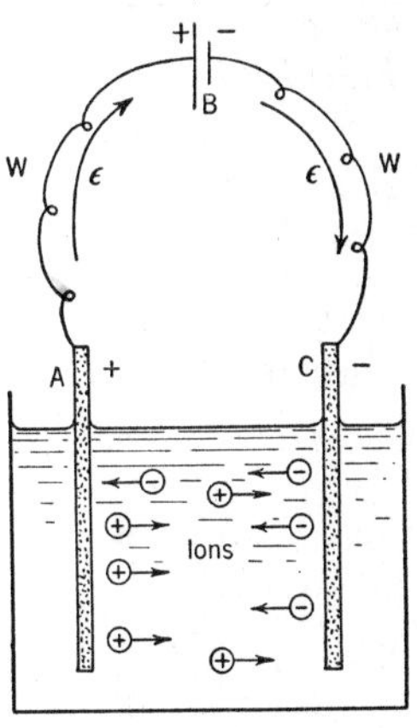

Fig. 156. Typical Electrolytic Circuit.

A typical electrolytic circuit is illustrated in Figure 156. The battery B develops an electromotive force which causes the flow of current through the external circuit. The electrons flow through the wires WW to the cathode C and from the anode A back to the battery. The current through the electrolytic cell is carried by the ions in the solution. The negatively charged **anion** moves toward the positively charged **anode,** and the positively charged **cation** goes toward the negatively charged **cathode.**

In the battery, as will be explained in Chapter 15, chemical energy is changed into electrical energy; while the opposite transformation occurs in the electrolytic cell, where electrical forces bring about chemical changes.

Electrode Reactions. The primary reactions occurring at the electrodes are oxidation and reduction. The former takes place at the anode, and furnishes electrons to it, while the latter is brought about by the electrons taken from the cathode. The reactions are independent of each other, but the same amount of reaction takes place at each electrode. This was first shown by Michael Faraday, the brilliant English chemist and physicist who assisted Sir Humphry Davy at the Royal Institution in London, and later succeeded him as director of the Institution. **Faraday's**

laws of electrolysis, correlating the quantitative changes at the two electrodes, state that:

(1) *The weight of material changed at each electrode is proportional to the quantity of electricity passed through the solution.*

(2) *The weights of material changed at the different electrodes are proportional to the equivalent weights of the substances changed.*

The most careful experiments have shown no exception to Faraday's laws. *The quantity of electricity required to bring about one gram equivalent of chemical change is known as the* ***faraday, F,*** *which is equal to 96,494 coulombs.*

Since the passage of 96,494 coulombs corresponds to the addition of electrons to 1 gram equivalent of a univalent ion, *e.g.* Ag^+, and since 1 gram equivalent of Ag^+ is composed of 6.023×10^{23} silver ions, the charge of each ion and also that of the electron must be $\frac{96,494}{6.023 \times 10^{23}}$ or 1.602×10^{-19} coulomb.

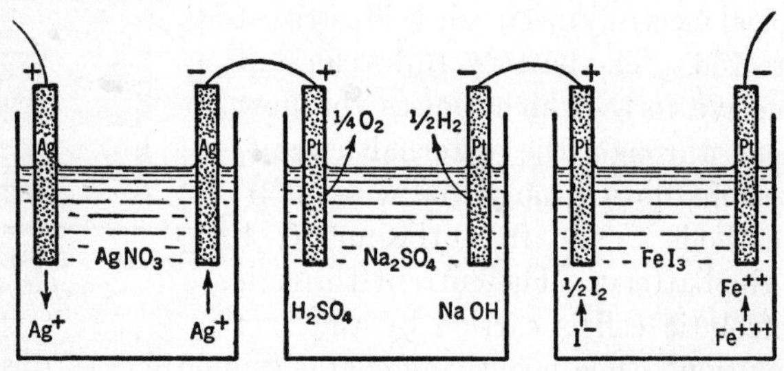

Fig. 157. Electrolysis: Illustrating Faraday's Laws for Various Reactions.

Faraday's laws may be illustrated by means of Figure 157, which shows three electrolytic cells connected in series so that the same quantity of electricity (1 faraday) flows through each. In the first cell, 107.880 g. of silver dissolve from the anode and the same weight deposits on the cathode. The reactions are:

$$\begin{array}{ll} \textit{anode} & \underline{Ag} \longrightarrow Ag^+ + \epsilon \\ \textit{cathode} & Ag^+ + \epsilon \longrightarrow \underline{Ag} \downarrow \end{array}$$

In the second cell, the electrolysis of sodium sulfate does not liberate the constituents of the salt but instead sets free oxygen and hydrogen from the water, according to the reactions:

$$\begin{array}{ll} \textit{anode} & \frac{3}{2} H_2O \longrightarrow H_3O^+ + \frac{1}{4} O_2 \uparrow + \epsilon \\ \textit{cathode} & H_2O + \epsilon \longrightarrow \frac{1}{2} H_2 \uparrow + OH^- \end{array}$$

facing page 372

Plate VIII. SØREN PETER LAURITZ SØRENSEN

(*For biographical note see page 351.*)

The passage of 1 faraday through this cell therefore sets free 8.0000 g. (5.6 l., S.T.P.) of oxygen at the anode and 1.0080 g. (11.2 l., S.T.P.) of hydrogen at the cathode. At the same time, one gram equivalent of hydrogen ion appears at the anode and one gram equivalent weight of hydroxyl ion at the cathode.

In the third cell, 126.92 g. of iodine are liberated at the anode, and at the cathode, assuming that no other change takes place, 55.84 g. of iron are reduced from ferric to ferrous:

$$\textit{anode} \qquad I^- \longrightarrow \tfrac{1}{2} I_2 + \epsilon$$

$$\textit{cathode} \qquad Fe^{+++} + \epsilon \longrightarrow Fe^{++}$$

Coulometers. Any electrolytic process might be used to measure the quantity of electricity flowing in a circuit. In many cases, however, the products of electrolysis depend upon the conditions, and such processes therefore are not suitable for use. For instance, when a solution of a chloride is electrolyzed, oxygen as well as chlorine may be liberated at the anode. The *sum* of the number of equivalents of the two gases will equal the number of faradays passed through the solution, but the quantity of *each* gas would be required to determine the quantity of electricity.

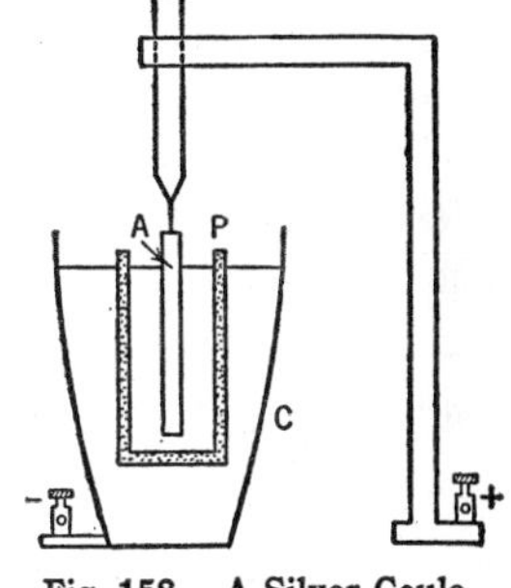

Fig. 158. A Silver Coulometer.

The **silver coulometer** illustrated in Figure 158 is the standard for accurate measurement. It has been studied with great care at the National Bureau of Standards.[1] A large anode *A*, of pure silver, is suspended in a solution of purified silver nitrate contained in a platinum crucible or dish *C*, which serves as cathode. The anode is surrounded by a porous cup *P* to catch any anode mud which would contaminate the deposit of silver. The dish is weighed before and after the experiment and the difference corresponds to the weight of silver deposited. Since 107.880 g. of silver are deposited by 1 faraday or 96,494 coulombs,

$$1 \text{ coulomb} \approx \frac{107.880}{96.494} = 0.00111800 \text{ g. of silver}$$

This furnishes the legal definition of the coulomb.

[1] Rosa and Vinal, *Bull. Bur. of Stand.*, **13,** 479 (1916), give a discussion of possible sources of error and practical specifications for this instrument.

In the **copper coulometer,** two copper electrodes are immersed in a solution of cupric sulfate. The weight of copper deposited on the cathode is a measure of the quantity of electricity. The copper coulometer is somewhat less accurate than the silver coulometer.

The **iodine coulometer** contains a solution of potassium iodide, from which iodine is liberated at the anode. The quantity is determined rapidly by titration with standard thiosulfate solution.

The **gas coulometer** is the simplest but least accurate. Hydrogen and oxygen, liberated by the electrolysis of a solution, are collected together in a gas buret. From the volume of gas evolved, corrected to the dry basis at S.T.P., the number of coulombs may be calculated.

TRANSFERENCE NUMBERS

In ionic solutions the current consists of a stream of cations flowing in one direction and a stream of anions flowing in the opposite direction. If the ions moved at the same rate, each would carry half the current; otherwise they would carry unequal amounts. In only a few salts do the ions move with the same speed; in general, the speeds are different. *The fraction of the total current which each kind of ion carries is called the* ***transference number*** *of the ion in the electrolyte under investigation.* The transference number of the anion, n_a, plus the transference number of the cation, n_c, obviously equals unity:

$$n_a + n_c = 1$$

There are two general methods of measuring transference numbers — the **moving boundary method** and the **Hittorf method.**

The Moving Boundary Method. This method is based upon the fact that a distinct boundary can be established between solutions of two different electrolytes, due to a difference in the colors of the ions or in their refractive indices. When a difference in potential is applied between the ends of a tube containing the solutions, the boundary will move; and if the *faster* ion is ahead, the boundary will remain sharp and distinct and will measure the speed of this ion.

The simplest method of forming the boundary is that devised by Cady and Longsworth and illustrated in Figure 159. A flat button of cadmium is sealed into the bottom of a glass tube, which is filled with hydrochloric acid. If the cadmium is made the anode, it will go into solution and a boundary will form between the hydrochloric acid and the cadmium chloride. A boundary formed thus by the passage of the current is called an **autogenic boundary.** Although both electrolytes are colorless, there is enough difference in refraction between the light hydrochloric acid and the dense cadmium chloride, to give a clear boundary which is easily seen. Moreover, the boundary is stable and remains sharp. The fast-moving hydrogen ions tend to pull away from the slower cadmium ions, but this increases the potential gradient on the latter and keeps them in step. The motion of the boundary is a measure of the transference number of the hydrogen ion, and the cadmium serves as an **indicator ion.**

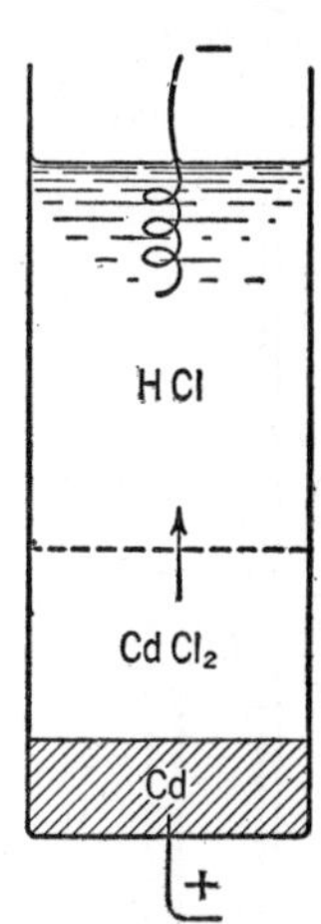

Fig. 159. Method of Cady and Longsworth for Forming an Autogenic Boundary.

In many cases, an autogenic boundary cannot be formed, and two solutions must be brought into contact without mixing. This can be done by means of a special stopcock, but is accomplished more conveniently by the **shearing mechanism** of MacInnes and Brighton. As shown in Figure 160, two circular disks of plate glass are held together by an axial pin. A hole is drilled through each, into which the end of a glass tube is sealed. When the disks are turned, two different solutions in the two tubes are brought into contact smoothly and a **sheared boundary** is formed.

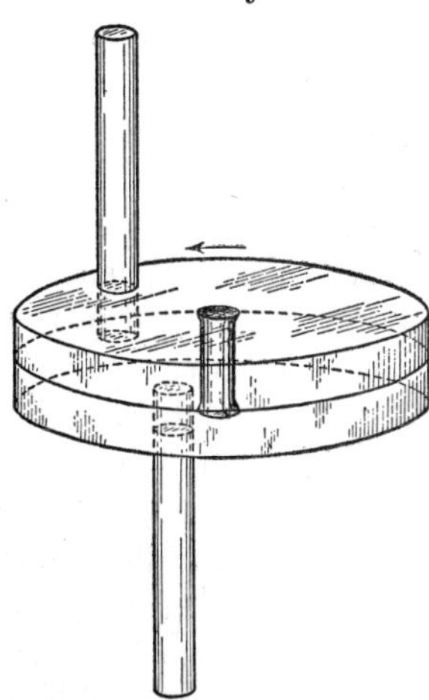

Fig. 160. Method of MacInnes and Brighton for Forming a Sheared Boundary.

The most accurate recent measurements by means of the moving boundary method have been carried out by Longsworth, at the Rockefeller Institute in New York. His apparatus, shown in Figure 161, is applicable to either autogenic or sheared boundaries. Two graduated tubes of different diameter, *A*, *B*, are cemented into the glass disks mounted as shown. The lower disk, *C*, also has a cylindrical recess in which a metal button can be placed, for the formation of an autogenic boundary. The tube *D* carries the electrical connection to this button. In making a measurement by this method, the disks are turned so as to place one of the measuring tubes in line with the metal button and the electrode chamber *F*. The apparatus is filled with solution, and a suitable electrode is put into the chamber *F*. The whole apparatus is then put into a vibration-free thermostat, and the measurements are carried out.

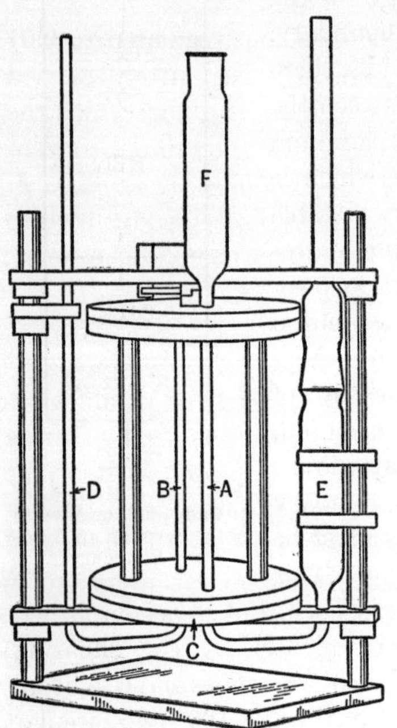

Fig. 161. The Moving Boundary Cell Used by Longsworth. (*J. Am. Chem. Soc.*, **54**, **2742** (**1932**).)

In forming rising sheared boundaries, the upper disks are clamped together with the electrode chamber *F* aligned above one of the measuring tubes. This unit is then put in place so that the measuring tube is not in line with the outlet tube from the electrode chamber *E*. The indicator solution fills the chamber *E* and its tube, while the solution under investigation fills the upper tubes. When the electrodes have been inserted and the apparatus mounted in the thermostat, the current is turned on. A trigger releases a spring, which slowly twists the upper unit on its axis and brings the measuring tube into line with the tube from *E*. The boundary formed at the lower disks then moves up the tube.

If a descending boundary is desired, the bottom disks are clamped together with the measuring tube in line with the outlet from *E*. The solution under investigation fills this part of the apparatus, and the indicator solution fills the chamber *F*. When the trigger is released, the sheared boundary is formed at the upper disks and travels down the tube.

In any case, the transference number is determined readily. It is defined as the fraction of the current carried by the ion under investigation. Thus the transference number of the cation is:

$$n_c = \frac{\text{current carried by cation}}{\text{total current}}$$

The total current I is measured accurately and regulated to 0.01 per cent by an ingenious automatic control. The current carried by the cation is equal to the volume, in liters, through which the boundary sweeps in one second, multiplied by the normal concentration of the salt, N, and the number of coulombs per faraday, F. If the volume V is measured in ml., it must be divided by 1000 to give the volume in liters. The whole expression therefore becomes:

$$n_c = \frac{VNF}{1000\ I}$$

The tube is graduated, over a 10-cm. length, and the volumes between marks are very carefully calibrated with mercury. During an experiment, the boundary is timed as it passes each of the graduations. In one of Longsworth's experiments with 0.02 N sodium chloride and a current of 0.0016001 ampere, the volume of 1.2110 ml. between the first and last graduations was swept out in 3453 seconds, or slightly less than an hour.

The transference number measured thus is subject to two small corrections: (1) the volume effect and (2) the solvent correction. The former is due to the fact that there is a change in volume at the electrode, as the current passes, which moves the whole column of solution. This can be calculated and is made definite by keeping one electrode closed throughout the experiment. It amounts to approximately 0.01 per cent in a 0.01 N solution and increases somewhat with the concentration. The solvent correction takes account of the traces of conducting impurities. It may amount to 0.1 per cent in a 0.01 N solution and decreases with the concentration.

The Hittorf Method. Hittorf, in a series of investigations beginning in 1853, was the first to measure transference numbers accurately. His method, quite different from that which we have just discussed and more tedious in execution, was based upon analysis of the solution around the anode or cathode, after an electrolysis. It is illustrated schematically in Figure 162. Suppose that the tube contains a solution of lithium chloride, electrolyzed between an anode A of silver and a cathode C of silver chloride deposited on a silver or platinum wire. The chloride ions moving to the anode will react with the silver ions formed there to deposit silver chloride. The over-all anode reaction is:

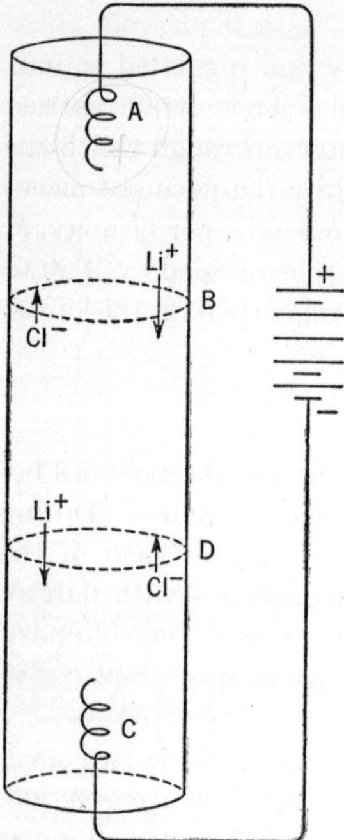

Fig. 162. Hittorf Transference Apparatus (Schematic).

$$\underline{Ag} + Cl^- \longrightarrow \underline{AgCl} \downarrow + \epsilon$$

Lithium ions will move toward the cathode, but they will not deposit there because lithium is too active a metal. Instead, silver ions from the silver chloride will deposit, liberating an equivalent amount of chloride ions. The over-all cathode reaction is:

$$\underline{AgCl} + \epsilon \longrightarrow \underline{Ag} \downarrow + Cl^-$$

If we had studied lithium chloride by the moving boundary method, we would know that the lithium ion carries $\frac{1}{3}$ and the chloride ion $\frac{2}{3}$ of the current. If we perform an experiment until 1 faraday of electricity has passed, one equivalent of chloride ion will be formed at the cathode, and one equivalent of the same ion deposited at the anode. During this time, the current flowing across any plane cross section of the middle of the tube will consist of $\frac{1}{3}$ of an equivalent of lithium ion moving toward the cathode and $\frac{2}{3}$ of an equivalent of chloride ion moving toward the anode. Suppose now that we divide the tube by means of the planes *B*, *D*, far enough from the electrodes so that the section *BD* is not affected by the electrode changes. The section above *B* will be called the **anode compartment,** that between *B* and *D* the **middle compartment,** and that below *D* the **cathode compartment.** During the experiment, the concentration in the middle compartment is unchanged. The changes in the other compartments are as follows:

ANODE COMPARTMENT		CATHODE COMPARTMENT	
Cl^- deposited	1 eq.	Cl^- liberated	1 eq.
Cl^- moved in	$\frac{2}{3}$ eq.	Cl^- moved out	$\frac{2}{3}$ eq.
Cl^- lost	$\frac{1}{3}$ eq.	Cl^- gained	$\frac{1}{3}$ eq.
Li^+ moved out	$\frac{1}{3}$ eq.	Li^+ moved in	$\frac{1}{3}$ eq.

The net result of the process is a *loss* of $\frac{1}{3}$ equivalent of lithium chloride in the anode compartment and a *gain* of $\frac{1}{3}$ equivalent of the salt in the cathode compartment. If we had not known the transference numbers of the ions, we could calculate them from these changes in concentration at the electrodes.

The Hittorf method of measuring transference numbers was improved by Washburn in 1909. More recently, it has been refined further by Jones and Dole and by MacInnes and Dole. Figure 163 shows the arrangement which the last two investigators used to study chloride solutions. The anode A consists of a silver gauze covered with finely divided silver, and the cathode C is a similar gauze covered with silver chloride. The electrodes are sealed into the glass tube as shown. The two halves of the glass tube are connected at the ground joint B, and the apparatus is filled with a chloride solution and put into a thermostat. The quantity of electricity passed through the solution is measured by the two silver coulometers D, D'. The special stopcocks S, S' are used to prevent constriction in the tube, which causes local heating; while the bends in the apparatus are designed to eliminate convection currents. After the experiment, the stopcocks are closed, separating the anode, middle, and cathode compartments. The portion of the middle solution from S' to N is removed by means of a pipet inserted through P'. Those portions between N and M and between M and S are pipetted out through P. The anode and cathode solutions then are weighed and analyzed. The three middle solutions likewise are weighed and analyzed, and all should show the same concentration.

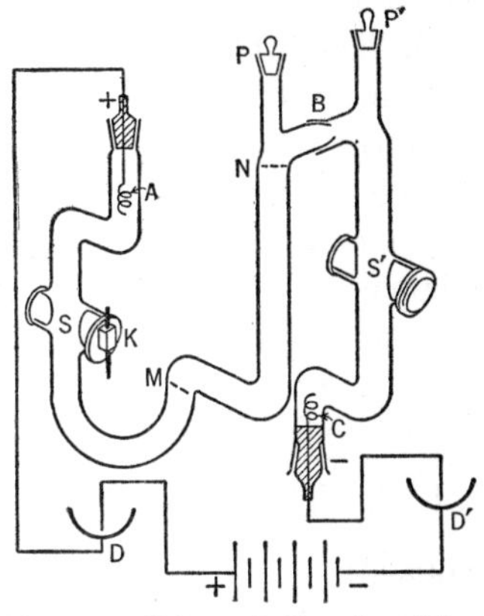

Fig. 163. Schematic Drawing of Apparatus Used by MacInnes and Dole to Determine Hittorf Transference Numbers. The Stopcocks Are Turned by the Removable Brass Key *K*.

The analysis of the cathode solution gives the weight of salt and of water it contains. Assuming that the same weight of water was present in the cathode compartment before the experiment, we can calculate the weight of salt it contained from the analysis of the middle solution. Thus the Hittorf transference number is calculated *on the assumption that the water does not move during the electrolysis.*

A typical experiment carried out by MacInnes and Dole[1] measured the transference number of the cation in 0.5 N potassium chloride at 25°. Using a potential of 10 v., they passed a current of 0.018 amp. through the cell for 26 hours. The two coulometers gained 1.9769 and 1.9767 g. respectively. The average of these indicates the passage of 1.9768 ÷ 107.880 = 0.018324 faraday. The anode portion weighed 119.48 g., and analysis showed that it contained 3.1151 per cent KCl. The anode portion therefore contained 119.48 × 0.031151 = 3.7219 g. KCl and 119.48 × 0.968849 = 115.76 g. of water. The different samples of the middle portion contained 3.6531, 3.6537, and 3.6543 per cent KCl. The average of these, 3.6537 per cent KCl, therefore represents the original concentration of the whole solution. The original anode portion then contained 3.6537 ÷ 96.3463 = 0.037923 g. KCl per g. water. Assuming that the water was unchanged in the process, the anode portion originally contained 115.76 × 0.037923 = 4.3900 g. KCl. The loss at the anode corresponds to $\frac{(4.3900 - 3.7219)}{74.553}$ = 0.008961 eq. KCl. The transference number of the potassium ion as measured by the change at the anode therefore is:

$$n_{K^+} = \frac{0.008961}{0.018324} = 0.4890$$

The cathode portion, weighing 122.93 g., was found to contain 4.1786 per cent KCl after the experiment, yielding a value of

$$n_{K^+} = 0.4903$$

Transference numbers measured by the moving boundary and Hittorf methods are in complete agreement, within the limits of experimental error of about 0.1 per cent.

Change of Transference Numbers with Concentration. The precise study of transference numbers has shown that they change slightly but definitely with concentration. This appears clearly in Figure 164, taken from the data of Longsworth, which are reproduced in more detail in Table 88. The transference numbers of cations like the hydrogen ion in hydrochloric acid, which are *large*

[1] MacInnes and Dole, *J. Am. Chem. Soc.*, **53**, 1357 (1931).

TABLE 88

CATION TRANSFERENCE NUMBERS AT VARIOUS CONCENTRATIONS AT 25° C.

Solute	Normality				
	0.00*	**0.01**	**0.05**	**0.10**	**0.20**
HCl	(0.821)	0.825	0.829	0.831	0.834
$NaC_2H_3O_2$	(.551)	.554	.557	.559	.561
KNO_3	(.507)	.508	.509	.510	.512
KCl	(.491)	.490	.490	.490	.489
$CaCl_2$	(.438)	.426	.414	.406	.395
NaCl	(.396)	.392	.388	.385	.382
LiCl	(.337)	.329	.321	.317	.311

* Values at zero normality were obtained by graphical extrapolation.

in dilute solution also *increase* most rapidly with concentration; the transference numbers of cations like the lithium ion in lithium chloride, which are *smallest* in dilute solution, *decrease* most rapidly with concentration. Only in the case of a salt like potassium chloride, where the transference numbers are very nearly 0.5, do they remain nearly constant with concentration. The bearing of these facts upon the nature of electrolytic solutions is discussed on page 391.

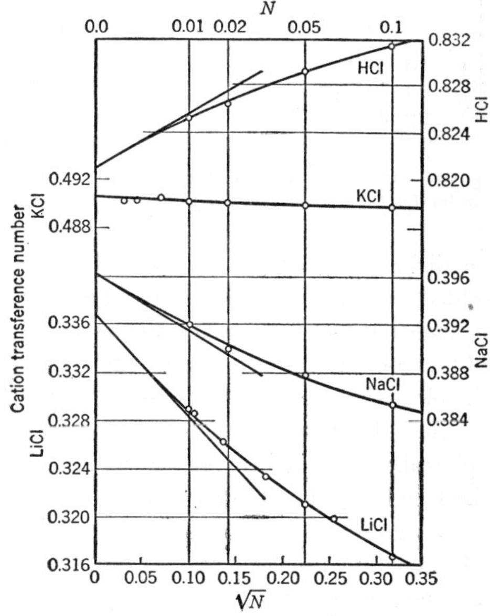

Fig. 164. The Change of Transference Numbers with Concentration.

THE CONDUCTANCE OF SOLUTIONS

The electrical conductance of a substance is a measure of its ability to conduct the electric current. *The* ***electrical conductance*** *of a substance, C, measured in* ***reciprocal ohms,*** *or* ***mhos,*** *is the reciprocal of its resistance, measured in* ***ohms:***

$$C = \frac{1}{R}$$

Thus if a coil of wire has a resistance of 10 ohms, its conductance is 0.1 mho or ohm^{-1}.

The Measurement of Conductance. The most suitable method of measuring the resistance, and hence the conductance, of an electrolytic solution employs an alternating-current Wheatstone bridge, illustrated in Figure 165. The measuring cell C is filled with solution through the long tubes I, I', which are then covered with ground glass caps. The cell is mounted in an oil-filled thermostat, adjusted to the desired temperature. For the most accurate work, the thermostat must be constant within $\pm 0.001°$ C., since larger changes will cause an appreciable difference in the conductance. The cell contains two electrodes P, P'. These are disks of heavy sheet platinum, to the centers of which are welded stout pieces of platinum wire. The wires are sealed through the ends of glass tubes which act as mercury cups, making electrical contact between the cell and the copper wires from the bridge. The electrodes are covered with *platinum black* — a layer of spongy platinum deposited by the electrolysis of chloroplatinic acid. Such a platinized electrode exposes a very large surface to the electrolyte, which reduces the amount of chemical reaction due to the passage of the current.

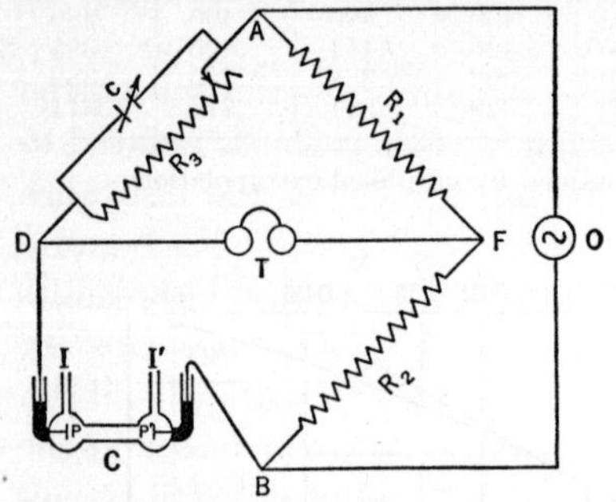

Fig. 165. Alternating-Current Wheatstone Bridge for Conductance Measurements.

In general, direct current cannot be used in measuring the conductance of solutions of electrolytes, because the passage of the current brings about chemical changes at the electrodes. These effects are not caused by alternating current of fairly high audible frequency, since the small changes which are initiated during one half-cycle are reversed in the next half-cycle. The bridge current is supplied by an audio-frequency oscillator O, tuned to a frequency of 1000 to 2500 cycles per second. A simple vacuum tube circuit makes an inexpensive and satisfactory oscillator.

The oscillator is connected to the bridge at the points A and B. Part of the current flows through the right arm of the bridge, comprising the resistances R_1 and R_2, and part through the left arm made up of the resistance R_3, shunted by the small variable condenser c, and the conductance cell C. The telephone receiver T is connected across the points D and F and serves to indicate the balance point of the bridge. As long as there is a difference in potential between D and F, a hum can be heard in the receiver. This note will become fainter as the difference in potential is decreased and will disappear completely when the difference in potential has been reduced to zero.

To determine the conductance of a solution in the cell C, the resistance R_3 is varied until the sound in the receiver is reduced to a minimum. Usually, however, no adjustment of the resistance alone is adequate to cause silence in the receiver. This is because the conductance cell not only has a certain resistance between its electrodes but also has a definite amount of electrostatic capacity as well. It acts like a resistance and condenser in parallel and can only be balanced by the parallel resistance and condenser in the measuring arm. The condenser c must be adjusted until it balances the capacity in the conductance cell, and then R_3 is changed until the sound in the receiver disappears. The bridge is now balanced, and the resistance of the solution is determined exactly as though we were dealing with a direct-current bridge. The simple method of calculation may be deduced very easily.

By applying Ohm's law to the different arms of the bridge we find:

$$E_1 = I_1R_1 = \text{potential drop from } A \text{ to } F$$
$$E_2 = I_2R_2 = \text{potential drop from } F \text{ to } B$$
$$E_3 = I_3R_3 = \text{potential drop from } A \text{ to } D$$
$$E_4 = I_4R_4 = \text{potential drop from } D \text{ to } B$$

Since the bridge has been adjusted until there is no sound in the receiver, no current is flowing between F and D; hence these points must be at the same potential. In other words:

$$E_1 = E_3 \qquad \text{or} \qquad I_1R_1 = I_3R_3$$

and

$$E_2 = E_4 \qquad \text{or} \qquad I_2R_2 = I_4R_4$$

Dividing the first of the right-hand equations by the second gives:

$$\frac{I_1R_1}{I_2R_2} = \frac{I_3R_3}{I_4R_4}$$

In addition, the current through R_1 must be the same as that through R_2, since they are connected in series and no current is diverted through the receiver between D and F. Similarly, the current flowing through R_3 must be the same as that flowing through R_4, *i.e.*,

$$I_1 = I_2 \quad \text{and} \quad I_3 = I_4$$

Substituting these values into the equation above and canceling like terms gives as a final result the equation of balance of the Wheatstone bridge:

$$\frac{R_1}{R_2} = \frac{R_3}{R_4}$$

Usually in electrolytic conductance bridges the resistances R_1 and R_2 are made equal, so that, when the bridge is balanced, $R_3 = R_4$. The resistance of the cell is then read directly from that of the bridge arm R_3.

In one experiment, the resistance R_3 at balance was 4670 ohms, hence the resistance of the solution also was 4670 ohms, and its conductance was:

$$C = \frac{1}{4670} = 0.0002141 \text{ mho or ohm}^{-1}$$

A simple apparatus for measuring conductance to about one per cent, suitable for use in a student laboratory, is shown in plate IX, facing page 388. The letters on this plate correspond as closely as possible to those of Figure 165. In this arrangement the resistance arms R_1 and R_2 are variable by means of the slider S, so that the resistance of the solution at balance is given by the expression:

$$R_4 = R_3 \times \frac{R_2}{R_1}$$

The Specific Resistance and Conductance. The resistance or conductance of any solution in a particular *conductance cell* depends not only upon the solution but also upon the size of the electrodes and the distance between them in the cell. In order to obtain a useful figure, characteristic of the solution, we must refer to the resistance, or conductance, in a cell of standard dimensions. *The* ***specific resistance*** *is the resistance of the material between similar parallel plates 1 square centimeter in area and 1 cm. apart, i.e., it is the resistance of a 1 cm. cube. The* ***specific conductance*** *is the conductance of the material under the same conditions.* The specific resistance usually is designated by the Greek letter rho, ρ, and the specific conductance by the Greek latter kappa, κ. Figure 166 illustrates the measurement of specific resistance or conductance between the opposite faces of a centimeter cube. The specific resistance or conductance of a solution is a characteristic property of the solution. We can determine the specific conductance of a solution in any standardized conductance cell. The specific conductance κ always is proportional to the observed conductance C:

$$\kappa = KC$$

where the proportionality factor K is called the cell constant. *The* ***cell constant***, *K, is the number by which the measured conductance, C, must be multiplied to obtain the specific conductance, κ.*

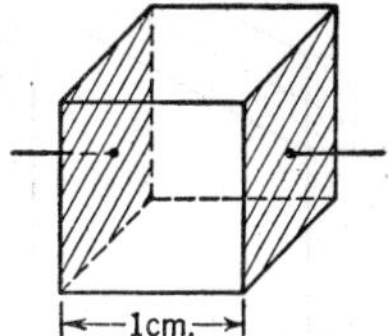

Fig. 166. Specific Resistance or Conductance.

The cell constant is determined by measuring the conductance of any solution of known specific conductance. Solutions of potassium chloride usually serve as standards, since this salt is easily purified and dehydrated by fusion in a dry atmosphere. There are two methods of measuring the specific conductance of the standard solutions. The first method, employed by Kohlrausch, Holborn, and Diesselhorst [1] requires a special cell, the constant of which can be determined from its dimensions. Most conductance data are based upon their standard solutions. A second method has been employed recently by Jones and Bradshaw,[2] who give a detailed description of the procedure. They used a very long capillary cell in which the conductance of a solution could be compared directly with that of mercury. They studied a number of solutions and found for a solution containing 7.41913 g. of potassium chloride in 1000 g. of water specific conductances of 0.0071379, 0.0111667, and 0.0128560 mho at 0°, 18°, and 25° C., respectively.

The Equivalent Conductance. A quantity more useful than the specific conductance in the case of solutions is the ***equivalent conductance,*** *which is defined as the conductance, between plane parallel plates 1 cm. apart, of a solution containing 1 gram equivalent weight of the solute.* It is symbolized by the Greek capital letter lambda, Λ. The relationship between the specific and equivalent conductances is derived as follows: If the concentration of the solution

[1] *Wiedemann's Annalen der Physik und Chemie, Neue Folge*, **64,** 417 (1898).
[2] Jones and Bradshaw, *J. Am. Chem. Soc.*, **55,** 1780 (1933).

is c equivalents per 1000 cc., the volume containing 1 equivalent of the solute will be $\frac{1000}{c}$ cc. The solution therefore will cover $\frac{1000}{c}$ square cm. of each of the plates, and its conductance will be $\frac{1000}{c}$ times that of each centimeter cube, or:

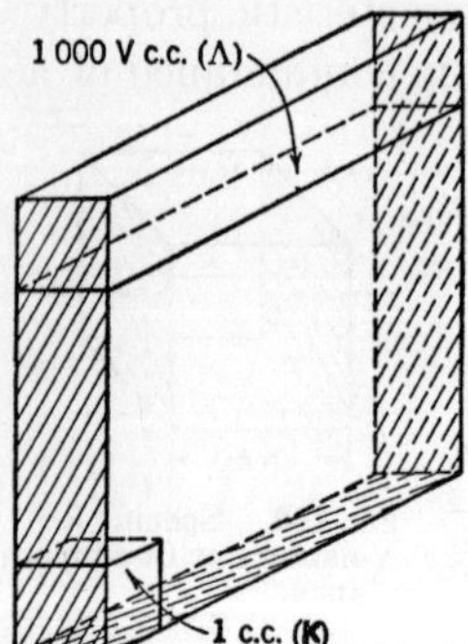

Fig. 167. Comparison of Specific and Equivalent Conductances.

$$\Lambda_c = \frac{1000\,\kappa}{c}$$

Here Λ_c is the *equivalent conductance at the concentration c.* The specific and equivalent conductances are compared in Figure 167.

The conductance-concentration curves are quite different for specific and equivalent conductances. At zero concentration, the specific conductance is that of the pure solvent, which is practically zero. As the concentration increases, the specific conductance likewise increases at first. If the electrolyte is soluble enough, however, the specific conductance may go through a maximum value and then decrease, as shown in Figure 168. The first addition of electrolyte greatly increases the number of ions, but further addition is less effective. This is because, according to the modern view, the equivalent conductance decreases. At the point of maximum conductance, the opposing forces balance each other.

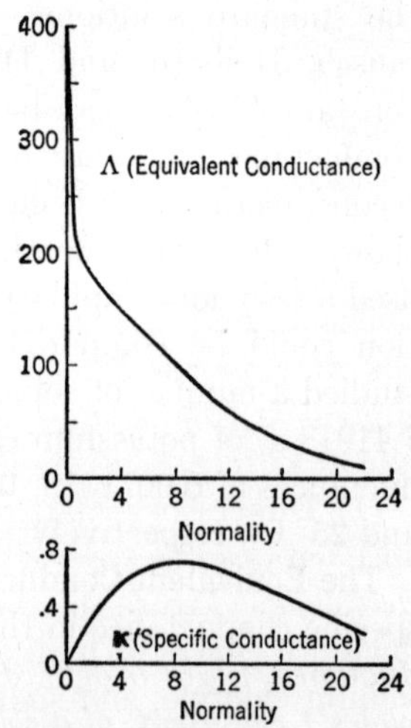

Fig. 168. Comparison of Specific and Equivalent Conductances of Sulfuric Acid at 25° C.

With equivalent conductances, we are always dealing with the same quantity of electrolyte. As the concentration approaches zero, the volume approaches infinity, and the conductance is that of one equivalent of each of the free ions. As the concentration increases, the equivalent conductance always decreases more or less regularly. The equivalent conductance for sulfuric acid is compared with the specific conductance in Figure 168. The initial steep drop in the equivalent conductance is due to the formation of the bisulfate ion, a fairly weak electrolyte for which K_a'' is 2×10^{-2}.

TABLE 89

EQUIVALENT CONDUCTANCES OF CERTAIN ELECTROLYTES AT 0.01 N CONCENTRATION AND 25° C.

SOLUTE	$\Lambda_{0.01}$ (MHOS)	SOLUTE	$\Lambda_{0.01}$ (MHOS)
Hydrochloric acid	412.0	Lead nitrate	121.1
Nitric acid	407.3	Sodium chloride	118.6
Barium hydroxide	235.0	Sodium sulfate	112.4
Sodium hydroxide	234.0	Lead acetate	52.1
Ammonium chloride	141.4	Acetic acid	16.3
Potassium permanganate	127.4	Ammonium hydroxide	11.5

Chiefly from *I. C. T.*, **VI,** 229 *et seq.*

In Table 89, the equivalent conductances of a number of typical electrolytes are given at the same concentration. Strong acids have the highest equivalent conductances, followed by strong bases and typical salts. Weak salts, like lead acetate, and weak acids and bases have low equivalent conductances and evidently are incompletely ionized.

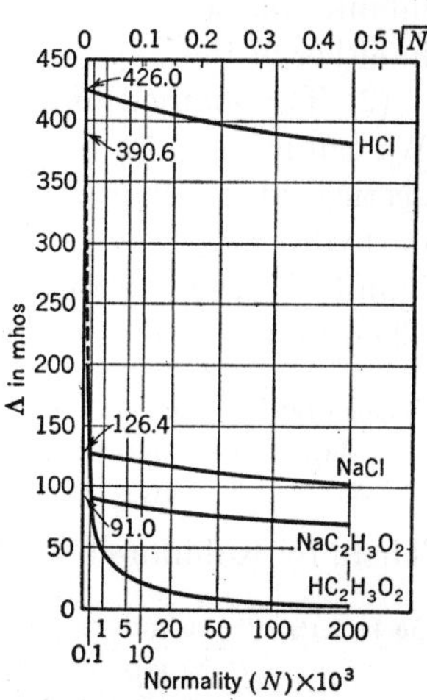

Fig. 169. Equivalent Conductance Curves for Strong and Weak Electrolytes.

Equivalent Conductances at Zero Concentration. Three different methods may be used to determine the equivalent conductance of an electrolyte at zero concentration.

(1) **Direct extrapolation** of conductance data can be applied to any *strong electrolyte*. Figure 169 shows the conductance curves of hydrochloric acid, sodium chloride, and sodium acetate, all of which are typical strong electrolytes. These curves all increase regularly and gradually as the concentration decreases, and approach the concentration axis nearly at right angles. If we plot the equivalent conductance against the

square root of the normality, the curve becomes nearly linear at low concentrations. Measurements can be made to a concentration as low as 0.0001 N, and the short extrapolation to zero concentration can be made with considerable accuracy.

This method is not applicable to *weak electrolytes*, because their equivalent conductance curves, like that of acetic acid in Figure 169, bend sharply at low concentrations and approach the zero axis at an oblique angle. A small error in the angle at which this line is extrapolated makes a large error in the value at zero concentration. In this case, however, there are two other methods which may be applied. Both are based upon the law of the independent conductance of the ions in a dilute solution, discovered by Kohlrausch in 1875. *As the concentration of an electrolyte approaches zero, its conductance may be expressed as the sum of the conductances of the anion* λ_a *and the cation* λ_c, thus:

$$\Lambda_0 = \lambda_{0,a} + \lambda_{0,c}$$

Kohlrausch's law has been verified for all strong electrolytes, where the Λ_0 values may be obtained by extrapolation. Since the ionization of even the weakest electrolyte must be complete at infinite dilution, we can apply the law safely to these substances in either of the ways decribed below.

(2) The **method of differences** involves *only conductance data.* We can illustrate it by determining the equivalent conductance of acetic acid at infinite dilution. First, the equivalent conductances of hydrochloric acid, sodium chloride, and sodium acetate at infinite dilution are obtained by the method of direct extrapolation. Then we can write the following equations:

$$\Lambda_{0,\,NaC_2H_3O_2} = \lambda_{0,\,Na^+} + \lambda_{0,\,C_2H_3O_2^-} = 91.0 \text{ mhos}$$
$$\Lambda_{0,\,HCl} = \lambda_{0,\,H_3O^+} + \lambda_{0,\,Cl^-} = 426.0 \text{ mhos}$$
$$\Lambda_{0,\,NaCl} = \lambda_{0,\,Na^+} + \lambda_{0,\,Cl^-} = 126.4 \text{ mhos}$$

Then, by Kohlrausch's law:

$$\begin{aligned}\Lambda_{0,\,H\cdot C_2H_3O_2} &= \lambda_{0,\,H_3O^+} + \lambda_{0,\,C_2H_3O_2}\\ &= \lambda_{0,\,H_3O^+} + \lambda_{0,\,Cl^-} + \lambda_{0,\,Na^+} + \lambda_{0,\,C_2H_3O_2^-} - (\lambda_{0,\,Na^+} + \lambda_{0,\,Cl^-})\\ &= \Lambda_{0,\,HCl} + \Lambda_{0,\,NaC_2H_3O_2} - \Lambda_{0,\,NaCl}\\ &= 426.0 + 91.0 - 126.4\\ &= 390.6 \text{ mhos}\end{aligned}$$

This is the value to which the curve in Figure 169 has been extrapolated, but direct extrapolation might have yielded any value

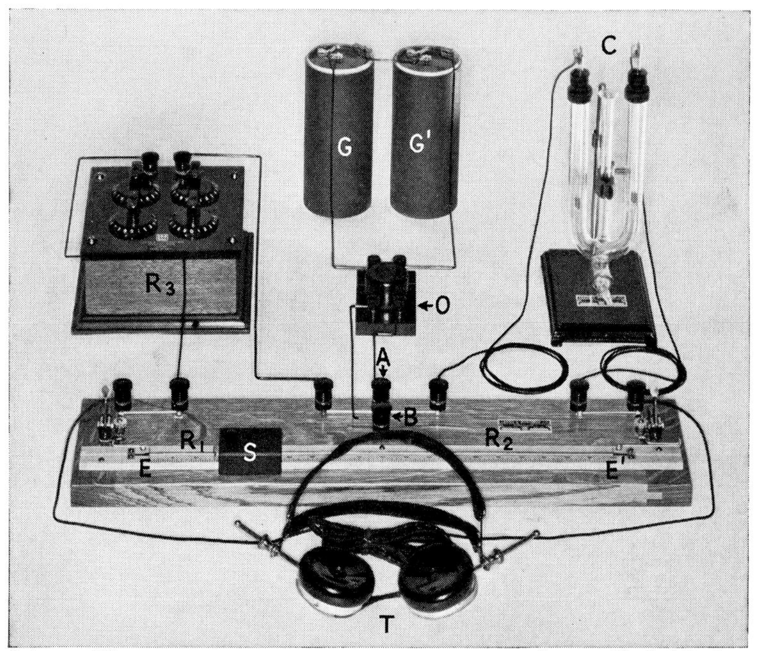

facing page 388

Courtesy of Leeds & Northrup

Plate IX. STUDENT EQUIPMENT FOR MEASURING ELECTROLYTIC CONDUCTANCE

Dry cells, G, G′; 1000-cycle buzzer, O; conductance cell, C; 4-decade variable resister, R_3; resistance wire, E, E′; slide, S, making contact between the connection, B, from the buzzer and the resistance wire, which it divides into the two resistance arms, R_1, R_2; and telephone headset, T.

between 350 and 450. The method of differences allows us to calculate the *sum* of the ionic conductances for any electrolyte but not their *individual* values.

(3) The individual **ionic conductances** can be determined *by combining transference numbers with conductance data.* For any electrolyte, the fraction of the current carried by each ion is simply the conductance of that ion divided by the total conductance of the electrolyte:

$$n_{0,c} = \lambda_{0,c}/\Lambda_0$$

Rearranging this equation, we find:

$$\lambda_{0,c} = n_{0,c}\,\Lambda_0$$

An analogous equation holds for the anion. Thus the limiting equivalent conductance of either ion is the product of its limiting transference number and the limiting equivalent conductance of the electrolyte.

MacInnes, Shedlovsky, and Longsworth[1] have studied a number of electrolytes. Their values for hydrochloric acid at 25° are:

$$\Lambda_{0,\,HCl} = 426.04 \text{ mhos}$$

$$n_{0,\,H_3O^+} = 0.8210; \quad n_{0,\,Cl^-} = 0.1790$$

therefore $\lambda_{0,\,H_3O^+} = 0.8210 \times 426.04 = 349.78$ mhos

and $\lambda_{0,\,Cl^-} = 0.1790 \times 426.04 = 76.26$ mhos

They also have calculated the limiting ionic conductances of the ions in solutions of lithium chloride, sodium chloride, and potassium chloride. The *mean* value of the limiting equivalent conductance of the chloride ion is:

$$\lambda_{0,\,Cl^-} = 76.32 \text{ mhos}$$

Taking this value as standard, the limiting equivalent conductances of the other ions can be determined by difference, from the corresponding values for the salts. In this way most of the values in Table 90 were calculated.[2]

The limiting equivalent conductance of an electrolyte is found by adding the values for the ions. Thus for acetic acid:

$$\Lambda_{0,\,H\cdot C_2H_3O_2} = \lambda_{0,\,H_3O^+} + \lambda_{0,\,C_2H_3O_2^-} = 349.72 + 40.87 = 390.59 \text{ mhos}$$

[1] "The Limiting Equivalent Conductances of Several Univalent Ions in Water at 25°," by MacInnes, Shedlovsky, and Longsworth, *J. Am. Chem. Soc.*, **54**, 2758 (1932): Shedlovsky and Brown, *ibid.*, **56**, 1070 (1934): Longsworth, *ibid.*, **57**, 1190 (1935).

[2] The value for OH^- is from Jeffrey and Vogel, *Phil. Mag.* (7), **15**, 395 (1933); **17**, 582 (1934).

TABLE 90

LIMITING EQUIVALENT IONIC CONDUCTANCES AT 25° C.

Ion	Λ_0 (Mhos)	Ion	Λ_0 (Mhos)
H_3O^+	349.72	OH^-	210.78
Li^+	38.68	Cl^-	76.32
Na^+	50.10	Br^-	78.45
K^+	73.50	I^-	76.90
NH_4^+	73.59	NO_3^-	71.42
Ag^+	61.90	$C_2H_3O_2^-$	40.87
Mg^{++}	53.08	$CH_3CH_2COO^-$	35.81
Ca^{++}	59.52	$CH_3(CH_2)_2COO^-$	32.59
Sr^{++}	59.48	SO_4^{--}	79.73
Ba^{++}	63.66		

The ionic conductances in Table 90 allow us to calculate the equivalent conductances of all the acids, bases, and salts which can be formed by combination. They also allow us to calculate the transference numbers of each ion in any of these electrolytes. For instance, in sodium nitrate:

$$\Lambda_0 = 50.10 + 71.42 = 121.52 \text{ mhos}$$

$$n_{0,\,\mathrm{Na^+}} = \frac{50.10}{121.52} = 0.4123$$

$$n_{0,\,\mathrm{NO_3^-}} = \frac{71.42}{121.52} = 0.5877$$

The Conductance Ratio. *The conductance ratio is defined as the ratio of the equivalent conductance Λ_c of an electrolyte at any concentration to Λ_0, that at zero concentration.* Since Arrhenius considered that the conductance ratio represented the degree of dissociation of the electrolyte, we shall designate it by the Greek letter alpha, with the subscript $_\Lambda$, thus α_Λ, to distinguish it from the van't Hoff coefficient, α_v. Thus we shall write:

$$\alpha_\Lambda = \frac{\Lambda_c}{\Lambda_0}$$

As we have seen (page 388), Kohlrausch proved experimentally that the ions of a salt carry the current independently in very dilute solution. Kohlrausch also *assumed* that the ionic conductances were independent of concentration, and Arrhenius made the same assumption in order to explain the decrease of equivalent conductance with concentration and to calculate the degree of dissociation at any concentration. Since the equivalent conductance at any concentration must be the product of the ionic conductance and the number of ions, we can write:

$$\alpha_\Lambda = \frac{\Lambda_c}{\Lambda_0} = \frac{(\text{number of ions at concentration } c) \times (\text{ionic conductance})}{(\text{number of ions at concentration } 0) \times (\text{ionic conductance})}$$

If the ionic conductance is the same at all concentrations, then the conductance ratio represents the relative numbers of ions at the two concentrations.

If the ionic conductance changes with concentration, Arrhenius' interpretation no longer is justified, and the conductance ratio does not represent the degree of dissociation. It is impossible to measure ionic conductances directly at finite concentrations, in order to test the validity of the Kohlrausch-Arrhenius postulate, but it is possible to measure the transference numbers, which are proportional to the ionic conductances. If the transference numbers change with concentration, the ionic conductances also must change. Jahn, in 1900, first seriously criticized the Kohlrausch-Arrhenius assumption of constant ionic conductance. In 1912, G. N. Lewis studied the available data and concluded that, in general, transference numbers change with concentration. The more recent studies of transference numbers, carried out with greater accuracy, have fully confirmed this conclusion. We have seen (page 380) that the transference numbers of the two ions of a salt become more different the higher the concentration; hence the conductance ratio cannot give us the true degree of dissociation of an electrolyte.

Another line of evidence, available many years before precise transference numbers had been obtained, indicates that the conductance ratio does not represent the true degree of dissociation. If the ionization constant is determined from the conductance ratio, by means of the equation of Ostwald's dilution law:

$$K_i = \frac{\alpha^2 c}{1 - \alpha} \qquad \text{(for a 1-1 electrolyte)}$$

the "constant" holds reasonably well for *weak* electrolytes, but not at all for *strong* electrolytes. Solutions of strong electrolytes contain high ionic concentrations, and the *interionic attraction forces* cause large deviations from the behavior of perfect solutes.

One interesting application of the interionic-attraction theory of Debye and Hückel was their explanation of the decrease of the equivalent conductance of a salt with increasing concentration. They showed that the mobility of an ion was cut down by the presence of other ions surrounding it in solution. Onsager worked out the theory in greater detail. There are two effects which retard the motion of ions in a concentrated solution. First, *there is the electrostatic effect of the surrounding ions.* Before a current is passed through the solution, the *ionic atmosphere* is distributed in a regular way about each ion. When the current is turned on, the ions move in opposite directions, and the ionic atmosphere is distorted in such a way as to oppose the motion. In the second place, *as the ions move, they tend to drag along molecules of water,* and the motion of the ions is retarded by the stream of water carried by the ions of opposite charge. Both of these retarding effects increase with increasing concentration of the ions. The theory predicts that, in very dilute solutions, the equivalent conductance will be a linear function of the *square root of the concentration,* as Kohlrausch found empirically in 1900:

$$\Lambda = \Lambda_0 - A\sqrt{N}$$

The constant A is not the same for all electrolytes, but can be calculated for any particular salt from the valence and mobility of the ions, the dielectric constant and viscosity of the solvent, and certain natural constants. The excellent data of Shedlovsky,[1] plotted in Figure 170, agree quite well with this equation. They show that, at extremely low concentration, the equivalent conductance curves do become tangent to straight lines when they are plotted against the square root of the concentration, and that these tangents have the slope A predicted by the theory.

The interionic-attraction theory also explains the change of transference number with concentration. As the concentration of the solution increases, both ions are slowed down, but the slower is affected more than the faster. As a result, the transference number of the slower ion, which is less than 0.5 at infinite dilution, decreases at higher concentration, while that of the faster ion increases.

Although the conductance ratio is no measure of the degree of dissociation of a strong electrolyte and is only an approximate measure of that of a weak electrolyte like acetic acid, conductance data can be used to determine accurately the degree of dissociation

[1] Shedlovsky, *J. Am. Chem. Soc.*, **54**, 1411 (1932).

of a weak electrolyte in a dilute solution. The method was used by Sherrill and Noyes, and by MacInnes, in 1926. The equivalent conductance in pure water, Λ_0, is corrected for the influence of the ions present in the solution to obtain the value of Λ_ϵ, which is *the*

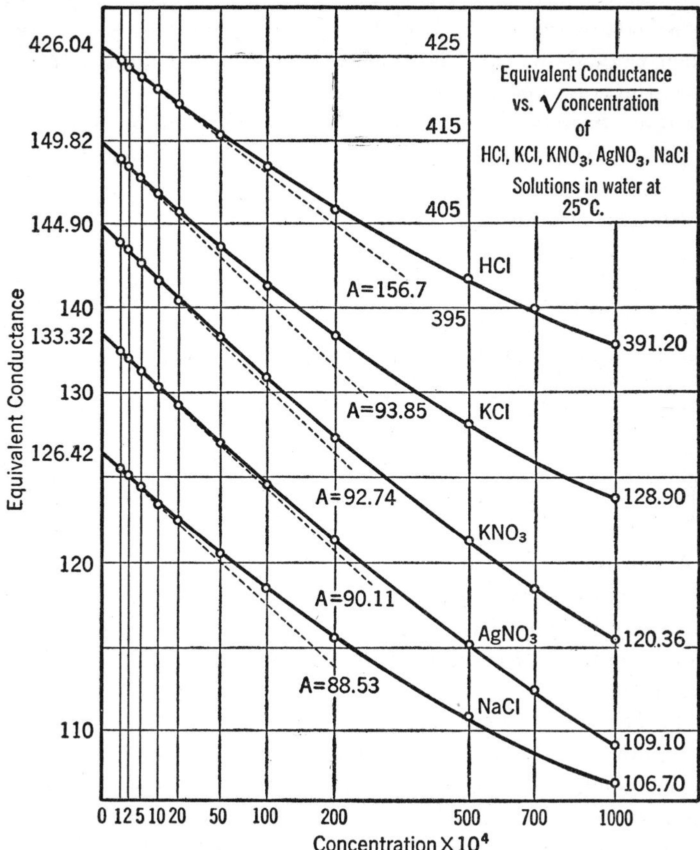

Fig. 170. Equivalent Conductance Curves of Five Strong Electrolytes at Low Concentration, Plotted against the Square Root of the Normality. (*J. Am. Chem. Soc.*, 54, 1427 (1932).)

equivalent conductance of completely dissociated ions in a dilute solution as calculated by the theory of interionic attraction. The ratio of the observed conductance to this corrected conductance gives the "true" degree of dissociation:

$$\alpha = \frac{\Lambda}{\Lambda_\epsilon}$$

The work of MacInnes and Shedlovsky[1] gives an idea of the size of the correction. According to them, the equivalent conductance of completely dissociated acetic acid would change from 390.59 in pure water to 384.15 in a 0.23 N solution of acetic acid. Although the ionic concentration in this solution is only 0.0020 N, the uncorrected conductance ratio is 1.7 per cent less than the corrected ratio. Their work shows that the classical ionization constant, calculated from the corrected conductance ratio, changes only 6 per cent in the range from 0.23 N to 0.00003 N. The value obtained by extrapolation to 0 concentration, $K_a = 1.753 \times 10^{-5}$, corresponds to the *activity ionization constant.* Some of the results of MacInnes and Shedlovsky are given in Table 91.

TABLE 91

Classical Ionization Constant of Acetic Acid at 25°

Normality	0.00	0.00003	0.0001	0.001	0.006	0.01	0.10	0.23
Λ_c	(390.59)	210.32	127.71	48.133	20.956	16.367	5.200	3.391
Λ_ϵ	(390.59)	390.02	389.68	388.94	387.99	387.61	385.29	384.15
$10^5 K_a$	(1.753)	1.768	1.778	1.797	1.823	1.832	1.846	1.814

The values of K_a listed above were calculated by MacInnes and Shedlovsky from the equation of Ostwald's dilution law, taking, for the degree of dissociation, values of the conductance ratio corrected for the interionic attraction effects. The values at 0 concentration were obtained by extrapolation.

Applications of Conductance Measurements. Conductance measurements may be applied to a number of problems in physical and analytical chemistry. They may be used to determine the ion product of water, the solubility of insoluble salts, and the endpoints of titrations.

(1) The ion product for water, K_w. The conductance of tap water obviously depends upon the locality from which it is drawn, but its specific conductance might be given a value of about 2×10^{-5} mho. Ordinary distillation will reduce this to about 4×10^{-6} mho. In 1894, Kohlrausch and Heidweiler prepared water with a specific conductance of only 4.3×10^{-8} mho at 18°. Even this water, however, had some electrolytic impurities, the amount of which they estimated from the temperature coefficient of the resistance. They concluded that the specific conductance of pure water at 18° would be $3.7_7 \times 10^{-8}$ mho. The resistance of a layer of this water, 1 cm. long, would equal that of a copper wire of the same cross section, 34,000,000 miles in length! The observed specific conductance of

[1] MacInnes and Shedlovsky, *J. Am. Chem. Soc.*, **54**, 1429 (1932).

the purest water studied by Kohlrausch and Heidweiler is given in Table 92.

TABLE 92

SPECIFIC CONDUCTANCE OF PUREST WATER MEASURED AT VARIOUS TEMPERATURES

Temperature, ° C.	**0**	**18**	**25**	**34**	**50**
$\kappa \times 10^7$ mho	0.14	0.43	0.55	0.84	1.70

The calculation of the ion product from the conductance may be illustrated by use of the value at 18°. The conductance of 1 liter of water, between electrodes 1 cm. apart, would be:

$$0.37_7 \times 10^{-7} \times 1000 = 3.7_7 \times 10^{-5} \text{ mho}$$

At the same temperature, the conductances of the two ions concerned are 315.2 for the hydrogen and 173.8 for the hydroxyl. If the liter of water contained 1 mole of *ionized* water, its conductance between electrodes 1 cm. apart would be:

$$\Lambda_{0,\,H_2O} = 315.2 + 173.8 = 489.0 \text{ mhos}$$

Assuming that *the ionic concentration is proportional to the conductance,* which must be very nearly true for such a dilute ionic solution, and knowing that each pair of water molecules yields one hydrogen and one hydroxyl ion, we can write:

$$[H_3O^+] = [OH^-] = \frac{3.7_7 \times 10^{-5}}{489} = 7.7 \times 10^{-8}$$

The ion product constant is then:

$$K_w = [H_3O^+][OH^-] = 5.9 \times 10^{-15} \text{ (at 18°)}$$

This result agrees excellently with that obtained from the electromotive force of cells, as described on page 451.

(2) **The solubility of slightly soluble salts.** The solubilities of those salts classified as "insoluble" are so low that they cannot be determined accurately by such a direct method as the evaporation of the solution and weighing of the residue. Not only is the weight of residue very small, but the formation of a colloidal suspension may lead to entirely erroneous results. The conductance method is free from these objections and is applicable to all salts which are soluble enough so that their specific conductance is larger than that

of the conductivity water in which they are dissolved. It is only necessary to make a saturated solution of the salt in water, determine its specific conductance, subtract that of the water, and calculate the ionic concentrations as in the case of the water described above. The determination of the solubility of calcium sulfate will serve as an illustration of the method.

Calcium sulfate, formed by the reaction of a soluble calcium salt and a soluble sulfate, is filtered, washed free of other ions, and shaken with distilled water. The saturated solution, with excess of the solid, is put into a conductance cell at 25° and the conductance is measured at intervals until it becomes constant, indicating that equilibrium has been reached. The specific conductance of the saturated solution is found to be 0.0042 mho. This is about one thousand times the conductance of the solvent water, for which no correction need be made. The conductance of 1 liter of this solution, between electrodes 1 cm. apart, would be:

$$0.0042 \times 1000 = 4.2 \text{ mhos}$$

The equivalent conductance of calcium sulfate, at infinite dilution, would be the sum of the ionic conductances, or 139 mhos. Assuming again that *the conductance is proportional to the ionic concentration,* the concentration of the ions will be:

$$[Ca^{++}] = [SO_4^{--}] = \frac{4.2}{139} = 0.030\ N = 0.015\ M$$

In such a dilute solution of a strong electrolyte, this figure also represents the solubility of the salt, which will be:

$$0.015 \times 136 = 2.0 \text{ g./l.}$$

(3) **Conductometric titrations.** Another interesting application of conductance measurements is the determination of the endpoints in titrations. If the titration is carried out in a conductance cell, the conductance will change with the course of the reaction and the endpoint may be determined by plotting the conductance against the volume of solution added. This method may be applied to dark-colored acids or bases, or to oxidizing or reducing ones where ordinary indicators would be useless. It may also be applied to reactions in which precipitates are formed.

There are many different types of conductometric titration vessel. That illustrated in Figure 171 is the classical model developed by Dutoit. The glass conductance cell *C* contains the two electrodes *E*, *E*, welded to the ends of stout platinum wires, which are sealed through the walls of the cell and rigidly supported by two glass pillars near the electrodes. The ends of these wires are bent down into mercury cups in the paraffined wooden block *W* which supports the cell. The temperature of the solution is determined by means of the sensitive thermometer *T*, fitted through a stopper in the neck of the cell. The titrating solution is run out of the buret *B*, the tip of which passes through the side neck in the cell.

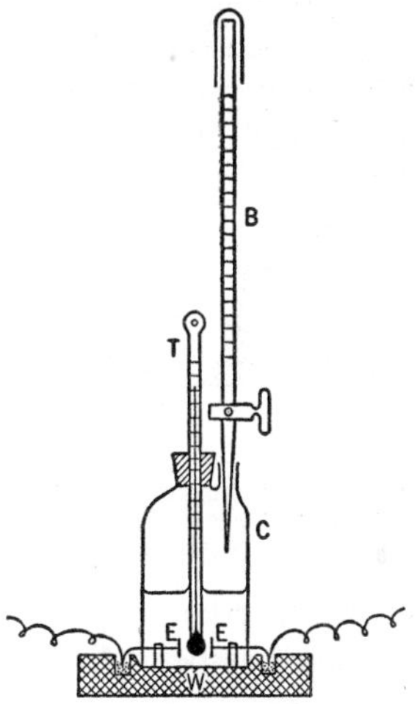

Fig. 171. Dutoit's Conductometric Titration Vessel.

In carrying out an acid-base titration, one of the solutions, *e.g.*, the acid, is measured into the cell, which is adjusted to the desired temperature, and connected to a resistance bridge. In order to avoid the complicating effect of the dilution of the solution, the base is from 10 to 100 times as concentrated as the acid, and is measured from a microburet, graduated in hundredths of a ml. After each addition of base, the cell is cooled to the starting temperature, to avoid the complicating increase in conductance of about 2 per cent per degree, and the conductance of the solution is measured. A considerable excess of base is added in measured portions, and the endpoint is determined graphically.

When a strong acid and a strong base are titrated, a curve like that shown in Figure 172 is obtained. At first the specific conductance decreases linearly, because the hydrogen ion is used up to form water, and the sodium ion, with a lower equivalent conductance, is substituted for it, as shown in the figure. Beyond the endpoint, the conductance increases linearly, because of the increased concentration of sodium hydroxide, with its high specific conductance. The endpoint is determined graphically, by drawing two straight lines through the experimental points and finding the point of their intersection.

When either the acid or the base is weak and slightly ionized, its specific conductance will be low, and the addition of the strong

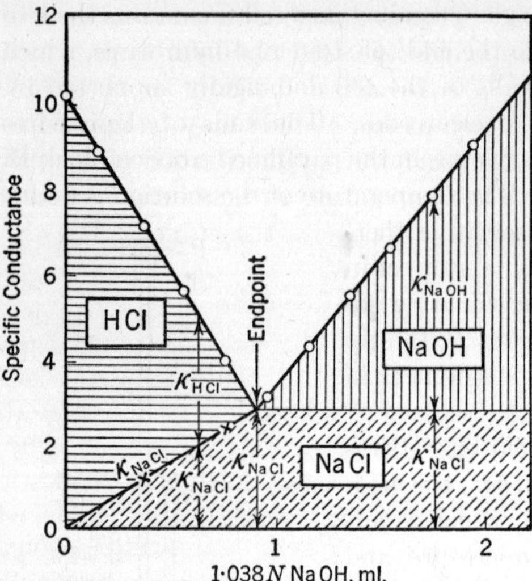

Fig. 172. Conductometric Titration Curve of Strong Acid and Base. Titration of 100 ml. of 0.0099 *N* HCl with 1.038 *N* NaOH.

base or acid will form a salt which is a better conductor. In this case, the titration curve will increase, as shown in Figure 173. Beyond the endpoint, the increase will be steeper still, because the additional base is a better conductor than the salt. The graph will therefore consist of two straight lines, intersecting at an oblique angle. Near the endpoint, the lines will be joined by a curved portion, due to hydrolysis. However, the endpoint is determined as before by projecting the straight lines and finding the

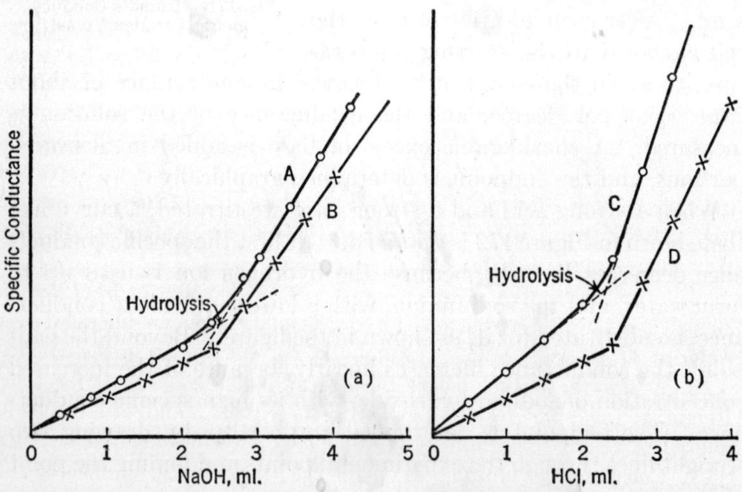

Fig. 173. Conductometric Titration Curves of (*a*) Very Weak Acid and (*b*) Very Weak Base, Showing Effect of Hydrolysis. Titration of 25 ml. of (*A*) 0.01 *N* Boric Acid and (*B*) 0.1 *N* Boric Acid with 1.035 *N* NaOH; (*C*) 0.0096 *M* Urotropine with 0.10 *N* HCl; (*D*) 0.096 *M* Urotropine with 1.0 *N* HCl.

point of their intersection. Thus the conductometric method of determining the endpoint avoids the effect of hydrolysis, which masks the endpoint when a colorimetric indicator or the e.m.f. method is used. The conductometric method may be applied to extremely weak acids or bases and even to the titration of as weak an acid as acetic acid with as weak a base as ammonia. In such cases the use of a color indicator is never satisfactory.

PROBLEMS AND EXERCISES

1. (*a*) How much current will flow through a resistance of 125 ohms, connected to a battery which delivers 5.78 volts? (*b*) If the current flows for 10 min. 37 sec., how much heat will be generated in the resistance (i) in joules? (ii) in calories?

2. An electric current was passed through a solution of Na_2SO_4 in which were a mercury cathode and a platinum anode. After 11.2 ml. of oxygen (measured dry at S.T.P.) were evolved at the anode, the sodium amalgam formed at the cathode was removed and allowed to react with water. How much 0.1 *N* HCl was required to neutralize the resulting NaOH?

3. A uniform current is passed through a solution of sodium acetate for 4 hours, yielding ethane and CO_2 at the platinum anode and depositing sodium in the mercury cathode. All of the sodium amalgam is allowed to react completely with water. The resulting hydrogen gas occupies a volume of 156.8 ml., measured dry at S.T.P. (*a*) What current was flowing through the circuit? (*b*) What volume of ethane (dry, S.T.P.) was formed? (*c*) What volume of 0.5 *N* NaOH is required to form $NaHCO_3$ with the CO_2 resulting from the electrolysis?

4. A solution containing copper and silver is electrolyzed between platinum electrodes under such conditions that both metals are deposited together at the cathode. During the experiment 1.12 liters of oxygen (dry at S.T.P.) are evolved at the anode, and the cathode gains 10.16 g. How many grams of each metal are deposited?

5. A uniform current passes through a gas coulometer for 1 hr. 25 min. 30 sec., and 47.52 ml. of the mixed hydrogen and oxygen are liberated over water at 20° C. and 1 atm. Calculate the current flowing in the circuit.

6. A uniform current passes through an iodine coulometer for 1 hr. 10 min. 17 sec. The resulting iodine reacts with 41.35 ml. of a 0.1034 *N* solution of sodium thiosulfate. Calculate the current flowing in the circuit.

7. Calculate the limiting values of the transference number of the *cation* in (*a*) HNO_3; (*b*) KOH; (*c*) $BaBr_2$; (*d*) K_2SO_4.

8. If the equivalent conductances of the ions Ag^+ and NO_3^- are 62 and 71 mhos respectively, explain in detail what happens when 1 faraday is passed through a solution of $AgNO_3$ contained in a Hittorf transference apparatus with Ag electrodes. What are the transference numbers of the two ions of this salt?

9. A solution of HCl was electrolyzed in a transference apparatus with platinum electrodes. At the anode, 0.0825 g. of chlorine was liberated. The cathode compartment contained 0.1770 g. of chloride ion before the experiment and 0.1630 g. afterwards. (*a*) Draw a diagram of the apparatus. (*b*) Calculate the transference numbers of the chloride and of the hydrogen ions.

10. A dilute solution of $AgNO_3$ is electrolyzed between silver electrodes at 25° C. After 3.0000 g. of Ag have deposited on the cathode, the cathode solution has lost 2.5311 g. of $AgNO_3$. Calculate the transference number of each ion. Calculate also the equivalent conductance of each ion, if that of the salt is 133.32 mhos.

11. At 25°, the resistance of a 0.01 N solution of $KMnO_4$ is 981.2 ohms, in a cell the constant of which is $K = 1.250$. Calculate (*a*) the specific conductance, and (*b*) the equivalent conductance of this solution.

12. Calculate the cell constant in a cell in which a 0.01 N solution of NaCl has a resistance of 1027 ohms. The equivalent conductance of this solution is given in Table 89 on page 387.

13. The limiting equivalent conductances at 25° are: for NaCl, 126.42 mhos; for NaOH, 260.88; for NH_4Cl, 149.91. From these values calculate the limiting equivalent conductance of NH_4OH.

14. From the data of Table 88 on page 381 and Table 89 on page 387, calculate the conductance of the sodium ions in NaCl and the hydrogen ion in HCl at 0.01 N concentration.

READING LIST

M. de K. Thompson, *Theoretical and Applied Electrochemistry*, 3d ed. The Macmillan Company, New York, 1939.

M. Dole, *Principles of Experimental and Theoretical Electrochemistry*. McGraw-Hill Book Company, New York, 1935. Pp. 40–64; 129–159.

A. S. Fedorow, "A Rule to Demonstrate the Migration of Ions." *J. Chem. Ed.*, **12,** 93 (1935).

D. A. MacInnes and L. G. Longsworth, "Transference Numbers by the Method of Moving Boundaries." *Chem. Rev.*, **11,** 171 (1932).

I. M. Kolthoff, "Conductometric Titrations," Analytical Ed., *J. Ind. Eng. Chem.*, **2,** 225 (1930). Contains a discussion of experimental arrangements and the scope of the method.

Hubert T. S. Britton, *Conductometric Analysis*. D. Van Nostrand Company, New York, 1934. A complete treatment of the subject.

Cecil W. Davies, *The Conductivity of Solutions and the Modern Dissociation Theory*. John Wiley & Sons, New York, 1930.

CHAPTER 15

ELECTROMOTIVE FORCE

Galvanic Cells. In the action of galvanic cells, we see the transformation of chemical into electrical energy, which is the reverse of the transformation brought about during electrolysis in an electrolytic cell. The electromotive force of the cell is a quantitative measure of the intensity of the chemical reaction taking place in it and allows us to determine the **free energy change** or *driving force* of the reaction. The measurement of the electromotive force of a cell at different temperatures enables us also to calculate the thermal effects of the process.

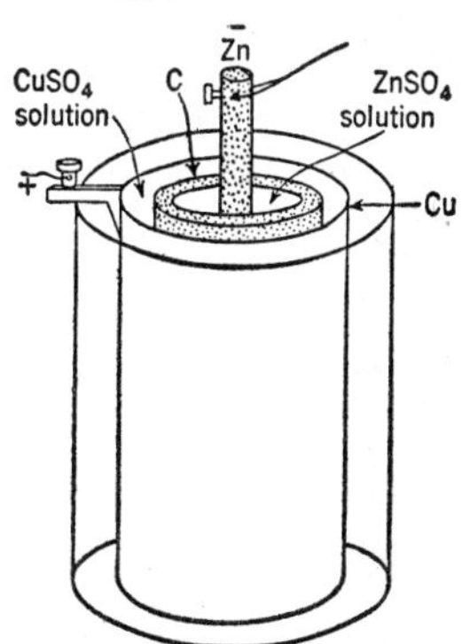

Fig. 174. The Daniell Cell.

One of the most familiar galvanic cells was devised by Daniell in 1836. The **Daniell cell** is illustrated in Figure 174. It consists of a bar of zinc, dipping into a dilute solution of zinc sulfate, contained in the porous earthenware cup *C*. Outside of this cup is a concentrated solution of cupric sulfate in which an electrode of sheet copper is immersed. The zinc is the negative, and the copper the positive pole of this cell, which develops a potential of about 1.1 volts. Another form of the same cell, the **gravity cell,** is shown in Figure 175. Here the lighter zinc sulfate solution simply floats upon the top of the denser cupric sulfate solution, which usually contains crystals of the solid, to insure its saturation. A small current must be drawn from the cell all the time, in order to prevent interdiffusion of the two solutions. This arrangement is often called the **crowfoot cell,** from the shape of the zinc electrode.

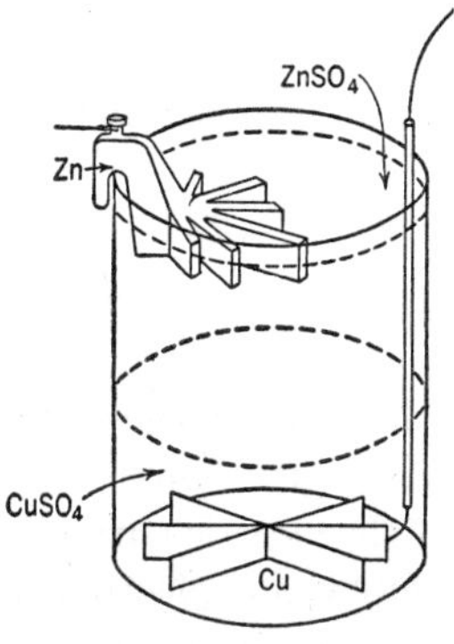

Fig. 175. The Gravity Cell.

In either case, the cell consists of a zinc electrode, dipping into a solution of zinc sulfate, in contact with a solution of cupric sulfate containing a copper electrode. The cell, illustrated in Figure 176, may be represented by the following conventional abbreviation:

$$(-)\ \ Zn \mid Zn^{++} \mid Cu^{++} \mid Cu\ \ (+)$$

The negative pole is written on the left and the positive pole on the right; the metals and ions are designated by their usual chemical symbols, while a single vertical line, |, represents a **phase boundary,** *i.e.*, a solid-liquid junction between electrode and solution or a liquid-liquid junction between two solutions.

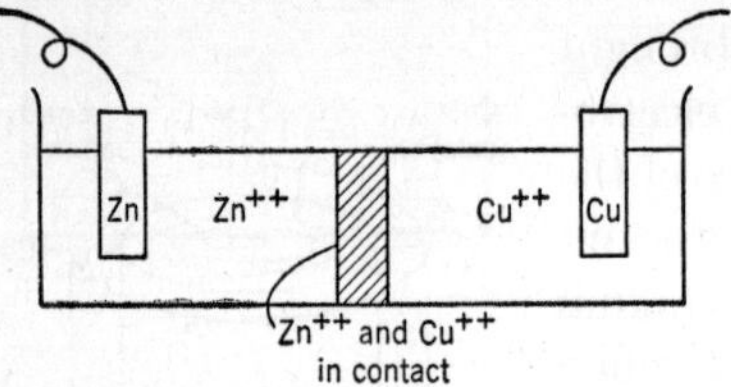

Fig. 176. Schematic Daniell Cell.

Many other electrodes and electrolytes may be used in galvanic cells. A few of the possible combinations and the approximate potential developed by each when the ionic concentrations are 1 *m* are given below:

Zn	Zn^{++}	Cu^{++}	Cu	$E = 1.1$ volts
Zn	Zn^{++}	Ag^{+}	Ag	$E = 1.6$ volts
Cu	Cu^{++}	Ag^{+}	Ag	$E = 0.5$ volt
Mg	Mg^{++}	Cu^{++}	Cu	$E = 2.7$ volts

A comparison of the voltages of the first three of these cells shows that the Cu : Ag cell is the difference between the Zn : Cu and the Zn : Ag cells. The same holds in all cases. Thus we could calculate the electromotive force of the Mg : Zn cell as the difference between that of the Mg : Cu and the Zn : Cu cells, *i.e.:*

$$E = 2.7 - 1.1 = 1.6 \text{ volts}$$

The electrodes of the cell need not be metals or solid elements but can also be gases, provided the electrode is an inert material, which will adsorb the gas and will also conduct the electric current. Platinized platinum electrodes are very satisfactory, and electrodes of porous gas carbon, like those used in dry cells, are convenient for purposes of demonstration. The electrodes may be saturated with the desired gas by bubbling a stream of it over the surface, or a temporary electrode may be set up by electrolysis, as shown in

Figure 177. If a solution of hydrochloric acid is electrolyzed between suitable electrodes, they become saturated with the hydrogen and the chlorine. When the electrolyzing current is turned off, the gases tend to go back into solution as ions and will set up an electromotive force which is measured with the voltmeter *V*. The voltage gradually falls off until it reaches zero when all the gases have been used up. The electrodes themselves are inert, exerting no electromotive force, but merely serving to carry the gases which react. Hydrochloric and hydrobromic acids yield the $H_2 : Cl_2$ and $H_2 : Br_2$ cells respectively. Sulfuric acid, sodium sulfate, and other acids or salts yielding no *primary* products of electrolysis, will give the $H_2 : O_2$ cell:

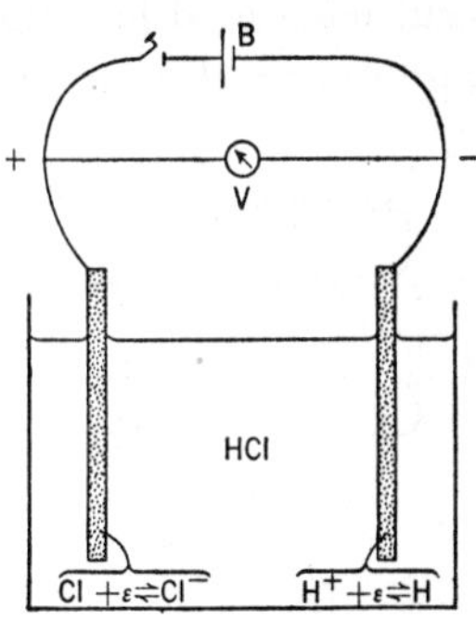

Fig. 177. A Demonstration Gas Cell.

$$\mathbf{C}, H_2 \mid H_3O^+, OH^- \mid O_2, \mathbf{C}$$

Here the **bold-face C** represents the solid inert electrode. The same convention is used throughout the book.

In all of these cells, whether the electrodes are metals or gases, *the electromotive forces are additive,* the total e.m.f. being the sum of the potentials of the half cells, *i.e.*, the **electrode potentials**. All that is required in order to determine electrode potentials is *an accurate method of measuring the electromotive forces of cells,* and a convenient *standard reference electrode.* These will now be considered.

The Potentiometer. Rough measurements of the e.m.f. of a cell can be made with a voltmeter, the resistance of which is made high to minimize the current. However, there are two reasons why the voltmeter does not measure the true e.m.f. of the cell: (1) The small current uses up a corresponding part of the e.m.f. as *IR* drop in the cell, making the potential drop through the voltmeter less than the e.m.f. of the cell, and (2) the current may cause changes at the electrodes which change the e.m.f. of the cell. For accurate measurements, a potentiometer must be used with a galvanometer which draws no appreciable current from the cell. Even in 1881, Helmholtz said: "With the newest galvanometers you can very well observe currents which would require to last a century before decomposing one milligram of water."

The potentiometer is shown diagrammatically in Figure 178. The *working circuit* consists of the *working cell*, *B* (usually a storage cell) connected in series with a rheostat *F* and a *slide wire AC* of uniform resistance. The *measuring circuit AGD* is connected at *A* to one end of the slide wire, and at *D* to the movable contact. It contains the galvanometer *G* and either a standard cell *S* or the unknown cell *X*, depending upon the direction in which the switch *E* is turned.

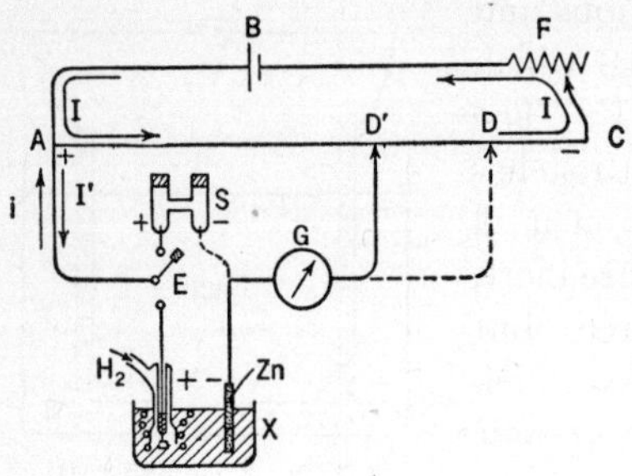

Fig. 178. Potentiometer (Schematic).

The working cell forces a steady current *I* through the working circuit, in the direction shown by the arrows. It also tends to force the current *I'* through the measuring circuit from *A* to *D*. The cell in the measuring circuit is so connected that it opposes the flow of this current, with a current *i* flowing in the opposite direction. By moving the slider *D* along the wire *AC*, a point is reached at which the opposing currents *I'* and *i* exactly balance each other and *no current* flows through the galvanometer *G*. At this point, the potential difference on the slide wire, between *A* and *D*, exactly balances the e.m.f. of the cell in the measuring circuit.

If the resistance of the slide wire is uniform throughout its length, the fall of potential along the wire will also be uniform, and proportional to the distance between *A* and *D*. By Ohm's law, the difference in potential between *A* and *D* will be:

$$E_{AD} = IR_{AD} = Irl = el$$

In this equation, *I* is the current flowing along the wire, *r* is the resistance per unit length of slide wire, *l* is the distance between *A* and *D*, and $e = Ir$ is the potential drop per unit length of the wire. By properly choosing the value of *r*, and correctly adjusting the current *I* by means of the rheostat *F*, *e* is made an even decimal fraction of a volt (*e.g.*, 0.01 volt) and the scale reads directly in volts and decimal fractions of a volt.

When a potentiometer is in use, the working cell slowly runs down, and the current *I* gradually decreases. In order to compensate this change, the resistance of the rheostat *F* must be decreased

facing page 404

Courtesy of Leeds & Northrup

Plate X. APPARATUS FOR THE DETERMINATION OF *p*H WITH THE HYDROGEN ELECTRODE

Cylinder, A, of compressed hydrogen; furnace, B, containing copper to remove traces of oxygen; bubbler, C; cell, D, with hydrogen electrode at left and calomel electrode at right; thermometer, E; potentiometer, F; standard cell, G; working cells, H; galvanometer, I; transformer, J, furnishing 6 volts for galvanometer light.

from time to time. The correct adjustment is made by comparison with a *standard cell* of definite voltage. If the standard cell is a Weston cell, described in the next section, its e.m.f. will be 1.018300 volts at 20° C. To standardize the potentiometer, the switch E is thrown to the upper position, so as to connect the standard cell into the measuring circuit. The slider D is then set at 1.0183 on the scale, and the rheostat F is adjusted until no current flows through the galvanometer G. The scale now reads correctly at 1.0183 volts, and gives the correct value of the voltage at every other point, if the slide wire is uniform.

Once the potentiometer is standardized, the e.m.f. of an unknown cell X is measured by connecting it as shown, throwing the switch E down so as to put it into the measuring circuit, moving the slider to some other point, *e.g.*, D', at which no current flows through the galvanometer, and reading the scale. In the case illustrated in Figure 178, if the hydrogen and zinc ions are each 1 m, the e.m.f. of the cell will be 0.76 volt. As we shall see later, the e.m.f. changes with the concentration of the ions, and the concentrations must be specified in order to give significant and reproducible measurements of e.m.f.

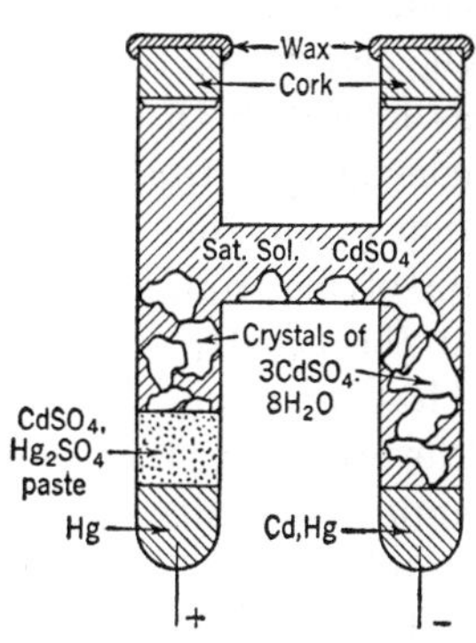

Fig. 179. Weston Standard Cell.

Standard Cells. Although many cell combinations will give definite electromotive forces, only a few of them have the characteristics necessary in a standard cell. Such a cell must give a reproducible potential, must be compact and portable, and must not deteriorate in normal use over a period of years. The two standard cells which are used commonly are the **Weston or cadmium cell** and the **Clark or zinc cell.** Figure 179 shows the construction of the Weston cell, which is very much the same as that of the Clark cell.[1] The H-shaped glass container, designed by Lord Rayleigh, has a platinum wire sealed through the bottom of each leg, to make contact with the electrodes. The positive electrode is a pool of specially purified mercury, above which is a layer of specially purified mercurous sulfate,

[1] A good discussion of the development of these two cells, the detailed specifications of construction and the merits of each, is contained in F. A. Laws, *Electrical Measurements*. McGraw-Hill Book Company, New York, 1917, pp. 294 *et seq.*

ground up into a paste with mercury and a saturated solution of cadmium sulfate. The electrolyte of the whole cell is the same saturated solution of cadmium sulfate, which is maintained by contact with clear crystals of the hydrated salt having the formula $3\,CdSO_4 \cdot 8\,H_2O$. The negative electrode is an amalgam containing 12.5 per cent of cadmium. The cell is sealed to prevent evaporation of the water and maintains its voltage constant over a long period of years. The cell may be written:

(−) Hg, Cd (12.5% Cd amalgam)	$CdSO_4$ (satd. soln. of $3\,CdSO_4 \cdot 8\,H_2O$),	Hg_2SO_4 (satd. soln. in satd. soln. of $3\,CdSO_4 \cdot 8\,H_2O$)	Hg (+)

The corresponding chemical reaction in the cell is:

$$Cd + Hg_2^{++} \rightleftharpoons Cd^{++} + 2\,Hg$$

If a current is drawn from the cell, cadmium goes into solution at the negative electrode, displacing an equivalent amount of mercury, which is deposited at the positive electrode. Since the amalgam contains two phases — a solid phase of mercury in cadmium and a liquid phase of cadmium dissolved in mercury — the activity of the cadmium at the negative electrode is constant as long as both phases are present. This arrangement ensures a constant electrode potential. At the other electrode, the deposition of any mercurous ion is compensated by mercurous sulfate dissolving from the paste, while an excess of cadmium ion formed at the negative electrode deposits as hydrated cadmium sulfate. These reactions tend to maintain a constant e.m.f. in the cell. Nevertheless, the compensation is not instantaneous, and no appreciable current should be drawn from a cell which is used as a standard.

The e.m.f. of the saturated Weston cell described above is used as the practical standard of electromotive force, and is taken as 1.018300 international volts at 20° C. *This serves as a definition of the **international volt**.* The e.m.f. of this cell diminishes only slightly, 0.0000406 volt per degree, with rising temperature.

Another type of Weston cell, made with a solution of cadmium sulfate saturated at 4° C., and hence unsaturated at room temperature, has an even smaller temperature coefficient. This advantage is somewhat offset by the fact that the e.m.f., of the **unsaturated Weston cell,** which is about 1.0187 international volts, differs slightly from one cell to another. Each cell must be calibrated against a standard saturated cell, but it remains constant over long periods of time. This type of cell is used extensively as a secondary standard.

The cell invented by Latimer Clark, in 1874, was used as a standard cell until it was displaced by the Weston cell. It contains a zinc amalgam instead of a cadmium amalgam, and a zinc salt. The temperature coefficient of this cell is thirty times as great as that of the Weston cell, and it has the added disadvantage of cracking around the wire sealed through the arm of the vessel containing the negative electrode. The cell may be written:

(−) Hg, Zn (10% Zn amalgam)	$ZnSO_4$ (satd. soln. of $ZnSO_4 \cdot 7\ H_2O$),	Hg_2SO_4 (satd. soln. in satd. soln. of $ZnSO_4 \cdot 7\ H_2O$)	Hg (+)

The potential of this cell is 1.4328 volts at 15° C., and it decreases by 0.00119 volt per degree with rising temperature.

Reference Electrodes. In order to determine the electrode potentials of half cells, some standard of reference must be chosen. The **hydrogen electrode** is the primary standard. The construction

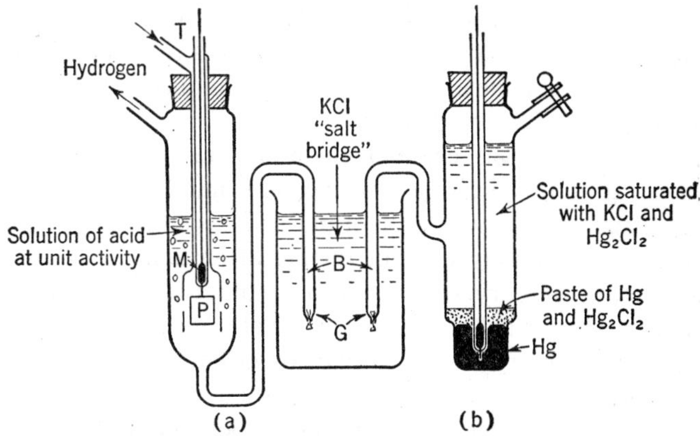

Fig. 180. (a) **Hydrogen Half Cell.** (b) **Calomel Half Cell.**

of one form of this electrode is shown in Figure 180 (*a*). The electrode itself consists of a sheet of platinum *P*, to which is welded a platinum wire, sealed through the end of a glass tube. A drop of mercury *M* makes contact with the outside circuit through a copper wire. The surface of the electrode is covered with a layer of platinum black to adsorb the gas. Hydrogen gas, specially purified to remove the last traces of oxygen, is admitted through the side tube T and bubbles over the surface of the electrode. The excess gas escapes in a steady stream of small bubbles from the holes HH in the side of the bell surrounding the electrode. In this way the platinum black is kept saturated with hydrogen gas at atmospheric pressure. When the electrode is used as the standard for electrode potentials, it is immersed in a solution in which the acid is at *unit activity* ($a = 1$). Electrical connection with the other electrode of the cell is made through a salt bridge B, the end of which usually is packed with a plug of cotton, filter paper, or glass wool, G, to hinder diffusion of the solutions. The standard hydrogen electrode may be written thus:

$$\mathbf{Pt},\ H_2\ (1\ \text{atm.})\ |\ H_3O^+\ (a = 1)\ |\ \text{salt bridge}$$

Usually this is abbreviated by using a pair of vertical lines, ||, to symbolize the salt bridge, thus:

$$\mathbf{Pt},\ H_2\ (1\ \text{atm.})\ |\ H_3O^+\ (a = 1)\ \|$$

The purpose of the salt bridge is to minimize the e.m.f. arising at the liquid-liquid junction, known as the **liquid junction potential**, which is discussed further on pages 411 and 441. In general, we shall assume that a suitable salt bridge reduces the liquid junction potential to a negligible amount, although this question is discussed further on pages 429 and 441.

For general use, the **calomel electrode**, one form of which is shown in Figure 180 (*b*), is more convenient than the hydrogen electrode. This requires no stream of purified gas and, once made up, can be used indefinitely without further attention. It consists of an electrode of mercury, connected to the outer circuit by means of a platinum wire sealed through the end of a glass tube as shown. On top of the mercury is a paste made by grinding together calomel and mercury with a solution of potassium chloride. The electrolyte above the electrode is a solution of potassium chloride, connected to the other electrode through a salt bridge, as in the case of the hydrogen electrode. The potential of this half cell depends upon the concentration of the potassium chloride solution, which affects the solubility of the calomel. Two calomel electrodes are in common use — the *saturated* and the *decinormal*, named according to the concentration of the potassium chloride. The saturated calomel electrode may be written thus:

$$|\ \text{KCl (satd.)}\ |\ Hg_2Cl_2\ \text{(satd. KCl)}\ |\ \text{Hg}$$

The saturated solution of KCl serves as a salt bridge by which the calomel electrode is connected to a second electrode.

The difference in potential between the hydrogen and the saturated calomel electrode is determined by measuring the e.m.f. of the cell shown in Figure 180, which may be represented thus:

Pt, H_2 (1 atm.) | H_3O^+ (a = 1) | KCl (satd.) | Hg_2Cl_2 (satd. KCl) | Hg

The e.m.f. of this cell is found to be 0.2458 volt. Since the calomel electrode is the positive pole, at which electrons are removed from the external circuit when the circuit is closed, the potential of the calomel electrode is 0.2458 volt more positive than that of the hydrogen electrode.

A similar measurement with the decinormal calomel electrode, also connected through a saturated potassium chloride salt bridge, shows that it is 0.3358 volt more positive than the standard hydrogen electrode.

A third reference electrode, similar in principle to the calomel electrode, is the **silver chloride electrode.** It may be made very small, and used in some cases where it is more convenient than the calomel electrode. As shown in Figure 181, the silver chloride electrode consists of a spiral of platinum wire, sealed through the end of a glass tube to provide electrical contact in the usual way. This spiral is immersed in a cyanide bath and coated heavily with silver. The silver-plated spiral then is washed thoroughly free of cyanide and heavily coated with purified silver oxide, which is reduced to spongy silver by heating to 325° C. Finally, this spongy silver is coated with silver chloride by making it the anode in a solution of 0.1 N sodium chloride and electrolyzing for several hours with a low current of about 0.001 ampere. The reaction is:

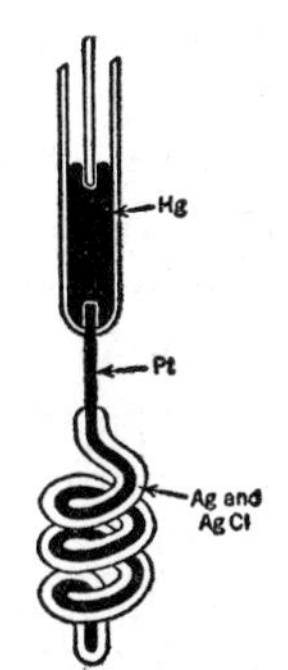

Fig. 181. The Silver Chloride Electrode.

$$\underline{Ag} + Cl^- = \underline{AgCl} + \epsilon$$

Electrodes made up in this way will give the same potential within a few hundredths of a millivolt. The solubility of the silver chloride will depend upon the concentration of chloride ion in the solution, and for this reason a solution of definite chloride ion concentration must be used.

As we shall show on page 428, Scatchard's results for the e.m.f. of the cell,

$$\textbf{Pt}, H_2 \text{ (1 atm.)} \mid HCl(0.1\ N), AgCl \text{ (satd. soln. in 0.1 } N \text{ HCl)} \mid Ag$$

at 25° C. yield the value 0.3524 volt. This cell finds important use in connection with the glass electrode (page 450).

Other reference electrodes designed for special purposes have been used, and some of these will be described in the following chapter, "Hydrogen Ion Concentration and *p*H."

Standard Electrode Potentials. Although the electrode potentials are additive in any cell, it is impossible to tell how much of the e.m.f. of the whole cell is contributed by each electrode. We can measure the e.m.f. of the cell, but we cannot measure that of either half cell separately. If we take any one half cell as an *arbitrary standard*, we can compare all the other electrodes with it, and list the potentials of these, relative to the chosen standard. This is exactly analogous to the determination of the altitude of any point on the surface of the earth, by measuring its height relative to that of the *mean sea level*, which is arbitrarily chosen as the datum line. In the case of electrode potentials, different standards have been used in the past, but the one which now is in general use is the hydrogen electrode at unit activity. Potentials measured on the hydrogen scale are compared with this standard hydrogen electrode in exactly the same way in which the calomel electrode was compared in the preceding section. Thus, if we want to determine approximately the standard electrode potential of zinc, neglecting the small liquid-junction potential, we would set up a cell in which a standard hydrogen half cell was connected by means of a salt bridge to a solution of a zinc salt at unit activity, into which dipped a stick of zinc. The cell would be:

$$\textbf{Pt}, H_2 \text{ (1 atm.)} \mid H_3O^+ (a = 1) \parallel Zn^{++} (a = 1) \mid Zn$$

Measurement with the potentiometer shows that this cell has an e.m.f. of 0.7620 volt at 25° C. The zinc is the *negative* pole; hence the standard electrode potential of zinc, on the hydrogen scale, is − 0.7620 volt. The standard electrode potential on the hydrogen scale is designated $E°$, and for the half cell, writing first the *oxidized* and then the *reduced* state of the metal, we would set down:

$$Zn^{++} (a = 1) \mid Zn \qquad E° = -0.7620 \text{ volt}$$

If we wish to determine the standard electrode potential of silver, we would set up the cell:

$$(-) \quad \mathbf{Pt}, H_2 \text{ (1 atm.)} \mid H_3O^+ (a = 1) \parallel Ag^+ (a = 1) \mid \mathbf{Ag} \quad (+)$$

In this case, the standard electrode potential of silver is + 0.7995 volt.

In general, *we may define the* **standard electrode potential** *of an element as the potential, compared to that of the standard hydrogen half cell, of a half cell consisting of the element in contact with a solution of its ion at unit activity.* The sign of the potential is taken as that of the electrode.[1] In the case of other gaseous elements, as for hydrogen, the potential is measured at a *fugacity* (the pressure, corrected for deviations from the gas laws as discussed on page 642) of 1 atmosphere.

Cells with liquid junctions, of the type illustrated above, are not suitable for exact determination of standard electrode potentials, because small potential differences are developed at the liquid junctions themselves. These liquid junction potentials are hard to evaluate exactly, but they can be avoided by the use of cells without liquid junctions. A discussion of these cells is given in the section devoted to activities and activity coefficients (page 425).

Table 93 contains a representative list of standard electrode potentials on the hydrogen scale. In order to find the corresponding values on the saturated calomel scale, subtract 0.2458 volt, which is the difference in potential of the two reference electrodes.

The arrangement of the elements in Table 93 is the same as that variously known as the *electromotive series, reactivity series,* or *displacement series.* The elements which are the strongest *reducing agents* are found at the *top,* and those which are the strongest *oxidizing agents* at the *bottom.* The reactivity of the metals decreases from top to bottom, while that of the nonmetals increases in the same direction. Since all of the electrode reactions, as they are written, involve the addition of one or more electrons, the table is also a list of the **electron affinities** of the elements or ions

[1] This is the convention adopted by the American Electrochemical Society, the Bunsen Gesellschaft, most English and Continental chemists, and the majority of writers on electrochemistry in the United States. Some writers use the opposite sign — the "sign of the solution." The reader should be aware of this fact, but it need not cause undue concern. If there is a clear statement of the convention used, the sign causes no confusion.

A discussion of this sign convention, which has changed several times in the past, is contained in an article by W. D. Bancroft, *Trans. Am. Electrochem. Soc.*, **33,** 79 (1918).

which comprise the reduced state in each case. The auric ion has the greatest and the lithium ion the least electron affinity of those listed. Similarly, of the four halogens, fluorine has the greatest electron affinity and iodine the least.

TABLE 93

STANDARD ELECTRODE POTENTIALS (25° C.)

ELECTRODE REACTION	ELECTRODE	S.E.P. ($E°$)
$Li^+ + \epsilon \rightleftharpoons Li$	$Li^+ \mid Li$	− 3.02 v.
$K^+ + \epsilon \rightleftharpoons K$	$K^+ \mid K$	− 2.922
$Na^+ + \epsilon \rightleftharpoons Na$	$Na^+ \mid Na$	− 2.712
$Mg^{++} + 2\,\epsilon \rightleftharpoons Mg$	$Mg^{++} \mid Mg$	− 2.34
$Al^{+++} + 3\,\epsilon \rightleftharpoons Al$	$Al^{+++} \mid Al$	− 1.67
$Zn^{++} + 2\,\epsilon \rightleftharpoons Zn$	$Zn^{++} \mid Zn$	− 0.7620
$S + 2\,\epsilon \rightleftharpoons S^{--}$	$S \mid S^{--}$	− .508
$Fe^{++} + 2\,\epsilon \rightleftharpoons Fe$	$Fe^{++} \mid Fe$	− .440
$Cd^{++} + 2\,\epsilon \rightleftharpoons Cd$	$Cd^{++} \mid Cd$	− .4020
$Co^{++} + 2\,\epsilon \rightleftharpoons Co$	$Co^{++} \mid Co$	− .277
$Ni^{++} + 2\,\epsilon \rightleftharpoons Ni$	$Ni^{++} \mid Ni$	− .250
$Sn^{++} + 2\,\epsilon \rightleftharpoons Sn$	$Sn^{++} \mid Sn$	− .136
$Pb^{++} + 2\,\epsilon \rightleftharpoons Pb$	$Pb^{++} \mid Pb$	− .126
$\mathbf{2\,H_3O^+ + 2\,\epsilon \rightleftharpoons H_2 + 2\,H_2O}$	$\mathbf{H_3O^+ \mid H_2}$	**± .0000**
Saturated Calomel Electrode		.2458
Decinormal Calomel Electrode		.3358
$Cu^{++} + 2\,\epsilon \rightleftharpoons Cu$	$Cu^{++} \mid Cu$	.3448
$I_2 + 2\,\epsilon \rightleftharpoons 2\,I^-$	$I_2 \mid I^-$	.5345
$Ag^+ + \epsilon \rightleftharpoons Ag$	$Ag^+ \mid Ag$	.7995
$O_2 + 4\,H_3O^+(10^{-7}m) + 4\,\epsilon \rightleftharpoons 6\,H_2O$	$O_2, H_3O^+ \mid H_2O$	.815
$Br_2\ (l) + 2\,\epsilon \rightleftharpoons 2\,Br^-$	$Br_2 \mid Br^-$	1.0652
$Cl_2 + 2\,\epsilon \rightleftharpoons 2\,Cl^-$	$Cl_2 \mid Cl^-$	1.3583
$Au^{+++} + 3\,\epsilon \rightleftharpoons Au$	$Au^{+++} \mid Au$	1.42
$F_2 + 2\,\epsilon \rightleftharpoons 2\,F^-$	$F_2 \mid F^-$	2.85

Most of the values in this table are taken from Latimer, *The Oxidation States of the Elements and Their Potentials in Aqueous Solutions*. The reader is referred to this authoritative book for many other standard potentials, references to the original literature, and a discussion of the uses of these data.

Calculation of the E.M.F. of Cells at Unit Activity. From the standard electrode potentials listed in Table 93, we can calculate the e.m.f. of cells made from any combination of electrodes, when the corresponding salts are at unit activity. *By convention, we write the negative electrode to the left, and the positive to the right.* The e.m.f. of the cell is then the value listed in the table for the positive electrode, minus that of the negative electrode. In the case of the Zn : Cu cell, we write:

$$(-)\quad Zn \mid Zn^{++}\ (a = 1) \parallel Cu^{++}\ (a = 1) \mid Cu \quad (+)$$

This cell can be considered as equal to the combination of the two cells:

$$(-)\quad Zn \mid Zn^{++}\ (a = 1) \parallel H_3O^+\ (a = 1) \mid H_2\ (1\ \text{atm.}),\ \mathbf{Pt} \quad (+)$$
$$(-)\quad \mathbf{Pt},\ H_2\ (1\ \text{atm.}) \mid H_3O^+\ (a = 1) \parallel Cu^{++}\ (a = 1) \mid Cu \quad (+)$$

connected in series through the hydrogen electrodes thus:

$$(-)\quad Zn \mid Zn^{++} \parallel H_3O^+ \mid H_2\ \mathbf{Pt} - \mathbf{Pt},\ H_2 \mid H_3O^+ \parallel Cu^{++} \mid Cu \quad (+)$$

The hydrogen electrode has the same potential in each cell. Since it is the *positive* pole of one cell and the *negative* pole of the other, the two exactly cancel each other and the net effect is zero. The standard electrode potential of copper is + 0.3448 volt, while that of zinc is − 0.7620 volt, hence the e.m.f. of the cell is:

$$E^\circ = E^\circ_{Cu} - E^\circ_{Zn} = 0.3448 - (-0.7620) = 1.1068 \text{ volts}$$

This is shown graphically in Figure 182 (*a*). Other cell combinations, in which both half cells are negative or both positive, are shown in Figures 182 (*b*) and 182 (*c*), which are self-explanatory.

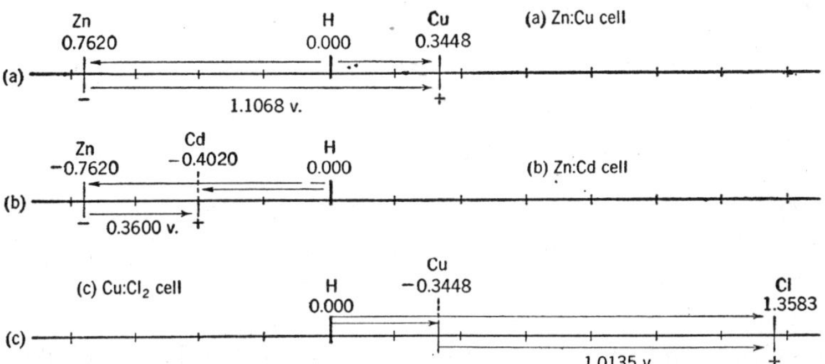

Fig. 182. Graphical Representation of E. M. F. of Cells Composed of Various Electrode Combinations.

Chemical Reactions in Galvanic Cells. The table of standard electrode potentials allows us to determine immediately the course of all the chemical reactions involving these half cells, and later the extent of the reactions. Whenever a galvanic cell is set up and allowed to furnish current, the material at the negative pole, which furnishes electrons, is *oxidized* in the process, while the material at the positive pole, which takes on these electrons, is *reduced.* By writing down the galvanic cell involving the two substances, and determining the positive and negative poles, we can find out the electrode reactions and hence the over-all reaction involved. For example:

(1) In the Daniell cell, the zinc is the *negative* and the copper the *positive* pole: hence zinc must be oxidized to zinc ion, and cupric ion reduced to copper. The reactions at the electrodes are:

$$\underline{\mathrm{Zn}} \longrightarrow \mathrm{Zn^{++}} + 2\,\epsilon \quad (-) \quad \text{(Zinc oxidized)}$$
$$\mathrm{Cu^{++}} + 2\,\epsilon \longrightarrow \underline{\mathrm{Cu}} \quad (+) \quad \text{(Cupric ion reduced)}$$

The complete cell reaction is:

$$\underline{\mathrm{Zn}} + \mathrm{Cu^{++}} \longrightarrow \mathrm{Zn^{++}} + \underline{\mathrm{Cu}}$$

Zinc is oxidized to zinc ion, while it reduces cupric ion to copper.

(2) In the zinc-hydrogen cell:

$$(-) \quad \mathrm{Zn} \mid \mathrm{Zn^{++}}\ (a = 1) \parallel \mathrm{H_3O^+}\ (a = 1) \mid \mathrm{H_2}\ (1\ \text{atm.}),\ \mathbf{Pt} \quad (+)$$

zinc is oxidized and hydrogen ion is reduced. The complete cell reaction is:

$$\underline{\mathrm{Zn}} + 2\,\mathrm{H_3O^+} \longrightarrow 2\,\mathrm{H_2O} + \mathrm{H_2}\uparrow + \mathrm{Zn^{++}}$$

(3) In the copper-chlorine cell:

$$(-) \quad \mathrm{Cu} \mid \mathrm{Cu^{++}}\ (a = 1) \parallel \mathrm{Cl^-}\ (a = 1) \mid \mathrm{Cl_2}\ (1\ \text{atm.}),\ \mathbf{Pt} \quad (+)$$

copper is oxidized and chlorine is reduced, according to the equation:

$$\underline{\mathrm{Cu}} + \mathrm{Cl_2} \longrightarrow \mathrm{Cu^{++}} + 2\,\mathrm{Cl^-}$$

Oxidation-Reduction Potentials. Reversible electrodes are not limited to the type which we have considered above, in which an uncharged substance and an ion comprise the two states of oxidation. Many substances form ions of two different states of oxidation, and these may form a reversible half cell if a suitable inert electrode is furnished to conduct the current. For instance, a mixture of ferrous and ferric salts in solution will impart a potential to a platinum wire dipped into the solution, and this half cell may be connected to any other by means of a salt bridge to form a galvanic cell. To determine the **standard oxidation-reduction potential** of such a half cell, we connect it to the standard hydrogen half cell thus:

$$(-)\ \mathbf{Pt},\ \mathrm{H_2}\ (1\ \text{atm.}) \mid \mathrm{H_3O^+}\ (a = 1) \parallel \mathrm{Fe^{+++}}\ (a = 1),\ \mathrm{Fe^{++}}\ (a = 1) \mid \mathbf{Pt}\ (+)$$

The e.m.f. of this cell is 0.771 volt, which therefore is the standard oxidation-reduction potential of the ferric-ferrous electrode, written thus:

$$Fe^{+++}\ (a = 1),\ Fe^{++}\ (a = 1)\ |\ \mathbf{Pt} \qquad E^\circ = 0.771 \text{ volt}$$

Under standard conditions, the reaction would be:

$$H_2 + 2\ H_2O + 2\ Fe^{+++} \longrightarrow 2\ H_3O^+ + 2\ Fe^{++}$$

Therefore ferric ion *oxidizes* hydrogen to form hydrogen ion.

Table 94 contains a number of standard oxidation-reduction potentials involving only ions. They may be used to calculate the direction of chemical reactions involving the ions, in exactly the same way as the standard electrode potentials given in Table 93.

TABLE 94

STANDARD OXIDATION-REDUCTION POTENTIALS (25° C.)

ELECTRODE REACTION	E° (HYDROGEN SCALE)
$Eu^{+++} + \epsilon \rightleftharpoons Eu^{++}$	− 0.43 v.
$Cr^{+++} + \epsilon \rightleftharpoons Cr^{++}$	− .41
$V^{+++} + \epsilon \rightleftharpoons V^{++}$	− .20
$Sn^{++++} + 2\,\epsilon \rightleftharpoons Sn^{++}$	+ .15
$Fe(CN)_6^{---} + \epsilon \rightleftharpoons Fe(CN)_6^{----}$	.36
$Ti^{+++} + \epsilon \rightleftharpoons Ti^{++}$	.37
$H_3AsO_4 + 2\ H_3O^+ + 2\,\epsilon \rightleftharpoons HAsO_2 + 4\ H_2O$	.559
$MnO_4^- + \epsilon \rightleftharpoons MnO_4^{--}$	.54
$Fe^{+++} + \epsilon \rightleftharpoons Fe^{++}$	.771
$MnO_4^- + 8\ H_3O^+ + 5\,\epsilon \rightleftharpoons Mn^{++} + 12\ H_2O$	1.52
$Ce^{++++} + \epsilon \rightleftharpoons Ce^{+++}$	1.61
$MnO_4^- + 4\ H_3O^+ + 3\,\epsilon \rightleftharpoons MnO_2 + 6\ H_2O$	1.67
$Co^{+++} + \epsilon \rightleftharpoons Co^{++}$	1.84
$Ag^{++} + \epsilon \rightleftharpoons Ag^+$	1.98
$S_2O_8^{--} + 2\,\epsilon \rightleftharpoons 2\ SO_4^{--}$	2.05

Values from Latimer, *The Oxidation States of the Elements and Their Potentials in Aqueous Solutions.*

Electrode Potentials and Free Energy Change. All of the standard electrode and oxidation-reduction potentials are measured under *balanced conditions*, when the e.m.f. of the cell is exactly matched by the fall in potential along the slide-wire of the potentiometer. If the potentiometer setting is slightly lower, the cell will send a small current through the galvanometer; if it is slightly higher, the working cell will force a current through the galvanometer and cell, reversing the reaction in the latter. Such a reversible system enables us to determine the *free energy* of the chemical reaction in the cell, *i.e.*, the natural tendency of the reaction to proceed. The e.m.f. of the cell measures the *intensity factor* of the energy. The *capacity factor* is the quantity of electricity which would have to be transferred in accordance with the chemical equation. In general, the decrease in free energy in the course of the reaction, when it proceeds in solutions of the constant concentrations indicated, is given by the equation:

$$-\Delta F = n\boldsymbol{F}\boldsymbol{E}$$

where $\boldsymbol{E}$ is the e.m.f. of the cell, $\boldsymbol{F}$ is the faraday, and n the number of faradays transferred during the reaction, which is equal to the number of electrons appearing in the chemical equation for the reaction. If $\boldsymbol{E}$ is expressed in volts and $\boldsymbol{F}$ in coulombs, the change in free energy will be given in joules, and must be divided by 4.1833 to yield calories.

If standard potentials are used, the change in free energy is called the **standard free energy change** of the reaction, $\Delta F°$, since the factors and products all are in their standard states. To take a numerical example of the calculation of the standard free energy change, in the reaction:

$$\underline{Cu} + Cl_2 \longrightarrow Cu^{++}Cl^{-}Cl^{-}\ (a = 1)$$

each atom of copper loses two electrons, and each molecule of chlorine gains two; hence $n = 2$. The decrease in free energy accompanying the formation of one mole of cupric chloride, in a solution of unit activity, therefore is:

$$-\Delta F° = n\boldsymbol{F}\boldsymbol{E}° = 2 \times 96{,}494 \text{ coulombs} \times 1.0135 \text{ volts} = 195{,}593 \text{ joules}$$

$$\text{or, } -\Delta F° = \frac{195{,}593}{4.1833} = 46{,}756 \text{ cal.}$$

This free energy decrease is a quantitative measure of the vigor with which copper and chlorine react. A great deal of the available information about the free energy changes in chemical reactions comes from studies of the potentials of reversible cells, as well as from the study of gaseous equilibria.

As an illustration of the use of free energy equations involving ionic reactions, let us calculate the standard electrode potential of the ferric ion-iron electrode. This would be hard to determine experimentally in aqueous solution, but it can be calculated from the standard ferric-ferrous reduction potential and the standard ferrous ion-iron electrode potential. We cannot simply add these potentials algebraically, for different numbers of electrons are involved in the different steps. The corresponding free energy equations, however, are additive, and may be used to calculate the desired electrode potential. From the chemical equations, we can write down the cells and compute the free energy decrease in the reaction. The calculations are outlined as follows:

$$\text{(1)} \quad Fe^{++} + H_2 + 2\,H_2O = Fe + 2\,H_3O^+ \quad n = 2 \quad E^\circ = -\,0.440 \text{ v.}$$
$$-\,\Delta F^\circ_1 = 2 \times (-\,0.440)\boldsymbol{F} = -\,0.880\,\boldsymbol{F}$$
$$\text{(2)} \quad Fe^{+++} + \tfrac{1}{2}\,H_2 + H_2O = Fe^{++} + H_3O^+ \quad n = 1 \quad E^\circ = 0.771 \text{ v.}$$
$$-\,\Delta F^\circ_2 = 0.771\,\boldsymbol{F}$$
$$\text{(3)} \quad Fe^{+++} + \tfrac{3}{2}\,H_2 + 3\,H_2O = Fe + 3\,H_3O^+ \quad n = 3 \quad E^\circ = ?$$
$$\begin{aligned} -\,\Delta F^\circ_3 &= -\,\Delta F^\circ_1 - \Delta F^\circ_2 \\ &= -\,0.880\,\boldsymbol{F} + 0.771\,\boldsymbol{F} \\ &= -\,0.109\,\boldsymbol{F} \end{aligned}$$
$$-\,\Delta F^\circ_3 = 3\,\boldsymbol{F}E^\circ \quad \text{or} \quad -\,0.109\,\boldsymbol{F} = 3\,\boldsymbol{F}E^\circ$$

Hence,

$$E^\circ = -\,\frac{0.109}{3} = -\,0.036 \text{ volt}$$

This is the desired standard ferric ion-iron electrode potential. A comparison with the values of Table 93 shows that iron, in going to ferric ion, is a weaker reducing agent than lead. This is in line with the well-known fact that elements are less strongly metallic in their higher states of valence than in their lower.

Electromotive Force and Concentration. A galvanic cell connected to a potentiometer comprises a system at equilibrium, in which the driving force of the chemical reaction, measured by its e.m.f., is balanced by the potential drop from the working cell. If we consider the cell:

$$(-) \quad Zn \mid Zn^{++}\,(a = 1) \parallel H_3O^+\,(a = 1) \mid H_2\,(1 \text{ atm.}),\, \mathbf{Pt} \quad (+)$$

a difference of potential of 0.7620 volt is required to balance the e.m.f., and thus to prevent the zinc from going into solution and displacing hydrogen. We can represent the equilibrium at the zinc electrode as:

$$\underline{Zn} \rightleftharpoons Zn^{++}\,(a = 1) + 2\,\epsilon$$

If the activity of the zinc ion is decreased, by diluting the solution, the principle of Le Chatelier predicts that the zinc would tend to ionize further, leaving more electrons on the electrode, thus making it more negative and *increasing* the e.m.f. of the cell. Conversely, an *increase* in the activity of the zinc ion will *decrease* the e.m.f. of the cell.

In the case of the Daniell cell, with ions at unit activity,

$$(-)\quad Zn \mid Zn^{++}\,(a = 1) \parallel Cu^{++}\,(a = 1) \mid Cu \quad (+)$$

the e.m.f. is 1.1068 volts. If the concentration of the zinc ion is *decreased* and that of the cupric ion is *increased*, the potential of the zinc electrode should become more negative and that of the copper electrode more positive, so that the e.m.f. of the cell should *increase*. This expectation is verified by experiment, and the practical Daniell cell is made with a saturated solution of cupric sulfate around the copper electrode, and dilute sulfuric acid, initially containing no zinc sulfate, around the zinc pole.

Concentration Cells and the Nernst Equation. Since the potential at an electrode is changed by changing the concentration of the ions with which it is in contact, a cell can be constructed with two identical electrodes, dipping into solutions of different concentrations. This is one form of **concentration cell.** The driving force in such a cell is the tendency of the concentrated solution to diffuse into the dilute, as long as there is any difference in concentration. A concentration cell with two zinc electrodes and two solutions of a zinc salt, *e.g.*, zinc sulfate, at different concentrations, could be represented thus:

$$Zn \mid Zn^{++}\,(a) \parallel Zn^{++}\,(a') \mid Zn$$

Here a' and a represent the activities of zinc ions in the two different solutions. The cell process would be:

$$Zn^{++}\,(a') \longrightarrow Zn^{++}\,(a) \qquad (a' > a)$$

corresponding to the dilution of the more concentrated solution. It can be shown by thermodynamics that the free energy change in this process is:

$$\Delta F = RT \ln \frac{a}{a'}$$

Since the free energy change also is given by the equation,

$$\Delta F = -\,nFE_{cell}$$

it can be eliminated between these two equations. Solving for the e.m.f. of the cell, we find:

$$E_{cell} = -\frac{RT}{nF} \ln \frac{a}{a'}$$

If $a' = 1$, the second electrode will be at standard conditions, and its potential will be $E°$. Hence, $E_{cell} = E° - E$, and E, the potential of the other electrode on the hydrogen scale then will be:

$$E = E° + \frac{RT}{nF} \ln a_{Zn^{++}}$$

This equation for the change of a single electrode potential with the activity of the ion is known as **the Nernst equation.** If the deviations of the ions from the behavior of perfect solutes is ignored, which may be done safely in dilute solutions, the concentration may be used in the equation, instead of the activity of the ion. Thus the preceding equation would become:

$$E = E° + \frac{RT}{nF} \ln [Zn^{++}]$$

It was in this form that Walther Nernst[1] derived the equation in 1889.

A similar line of argument, applied to an oxidation-reduction system, yields the more general equation:

$$E = E° + \frac{RT}{nF} \ln \frac{a_{ox.}}{a_{red.}}$$

From this we see that, in dealing with a single ion, the logarithmic term will be *added* if the ion is positively charged (the oxidized form) and *subtracted* if the ion is negatively charged (the reduced form). In other words, for any single ion:

$$E = E° \pm \frac{RT}{nF} \ln a$$

where the plus sign is taken for positive ions, and the minus for negative ions.

[1] Walther Nernst was born at Briesen, Prussia, in 1864. He received his doctorate in physics at Wurzburg in 1887, but during the following two years he developed a keen interest in physical chemistry while an assistant to Ostwald at Leipzig. After fifteen years at Göttingen he became professor of physical chemistry at the University of Berlin. He is best known for his work in the field of thermodynamics and his development of the *third law of thermodynamics*, but his contributions to the study of electrolytes and electrochemistry were also fundamentally important. He received the Nobel prize in chemistry in 1920. He died in 1941. For a portrait of Nernst, see Plate XI, facing page 420.

In using the Nernst equation at 25° C., we can substitute numerical values for the constants $\boldsymbol{F}$, R and T, and change from natural to common logarithms to obtain the useful equation:

$$\boldsymbol{E} = \boldsymbol{E}^\circ \pm \frac{0.05915}{n} \log a$$

To illustrate the use of the Nernst equation, we can calculate the potentials of several electrodes, on the hydrogen scale.

(1) The potential of a zinc electrode, dipping into a solution in which the zinc ion activity is 0.001 m, would be:

$$\boldsymbol{E} = -\,0.7620 + \frac{0.05915}{2} \log 10^{-3} = -\,0.7620 + \frac{0.05915}{2} \times (-\,3)$$
$$= -\,0.7620 - 0.0887 = -\,0.8507 \text{ volt}$$

(2) The potential of a chlorine electrode, in a solution in which the chloride ion activity is 0.01 m would be:

$$\boldsymbol{E} = 1.3583 - \frac{0.05915}{1} \log 10^{-2} = 1.4766 \text{ volts}$$

(3) The potential of a ferric-ferrous electrode, in which the activities of the respective ions are 2.4×10^{-5} and 4.7×10^{-3} would be:

$$\begin{aligned} \boldsymbol{E} &= 0.771 + 0.05915 \log \frac{2.4 \times 10^{-5}}{4.7 \times 10^{-3}} \\ &= 0.771 + 0.05915\,[(0.38 - 5) - (0.67 - 3)] \\ &= 0.771 + 0.05915 \times (-\,4.62 + 2.33) \\ &= 0.771 - 0.135 = 0.636 \text{ volt} \end{aligned}$$

Notice that in this case it is the *ratio* of the two activities which determines the potential. The potential of the half cell will equal the standard oxidation-reduction potential in any solution in which the activities of the two ions are equal, for the logarithm of unity is always zero. Notice also that the *homogeneous* logarithms − 4.62 and − 2.33 are required in this equation, and not the usual heterogeneous logarithms, in which the mantissa is always positive.

The potential of a concentration cell consisting of two copper electrodes, one dipping into a solution in which the cupric ion activity is 10^{-6}, and the other into a solution in which the cupric ion activity is 0.1, is given by the equation:

$$\boldsymbol{E} = \frac{0.05915}{2} \log \frac{10^{-1}}{10^{-6}} = 0.0296 \times 5 = 0.148 \text{ volt}$$

facing page 420

Plate XI. WALTHER NERNST

(For biographical note see page 419.)

Here the standard electrode potential has no effect upon the e.m.f. of the cell, which is determined entirely by the *ratio* of the activities of the ion in the two cases.

Applications of the Nernst Equation. A few of the many ways in which the Nernst equation may be applied are given in this section and the succeeding one.

(1) To determine the approximate ionic activity in a solution. A cell suitable for such measurements is made easily. An electrode reversible to the ion under consideration is put into the solution. This half cell is connected by means of a salt bridge to a suitable reference electrode, and the e.m.f. of the resulting cell is measured. By means of the Nernst equation, the activity of the ion is calculated. In the case of dilute solutions, this is substantially the same as the concentration of the ion. This method is often employed to determine the solubility of an "insoluble" salt. For example, if we want to determine the solubility of silver iodide, we can prepare some of the pure salt, wash it thoroughly to remove any of the excess of either ion, and shake it with pure water in order to form a saturated solution. Setting up the following cell:

$$(-) \quad Hg \mid Hg_2Cl_2 \text{ (satd. KCl)} \parallel AgI \text{ (satd. soln.)} \mid Ag \quad (+)$$

we find that its e.m.f. is 0.0872 volt. Knowing the standard electrode potential of silver and the potential of the saturated calomel electrode, the e.m.f. of the cell is given by the equation:

$$E = 0.7995 + 0.05915 \log a_{Ag^+} - 0.2458 = 0.0872$$

Hence:

$$\log a_{Ag^+} = \frac{-\ 0.5537 + .0872}{0.05915} = -\ 7.887 = -\ 8 + 0.113$$

and

$$a_{Ag^+} = 1.3 \times 10^{-8}\ m$$

In this dilute solution, the activity of the silver ion may be considered the same as its concentration and as the concentration of the salt in the water; hence the solubility of silver iodide is $1.3 \times 10^{-8}\ m$.

This method is applicable to salts which cannot be studied by the conductrometric method. The latter method fails in very dilute salt solutions, because the conductance of the ions of the salt is inappreciable in comparison with that of the ions of water, but this does not interfere with e.m.f. measurements. In addition to its application to insoluble salts, the Nernst equation is used in determining hydrogen ion activity, but a discussion of this important field is reserved for the next chapter.

(2) To find the valence of an ion. If a concentration cell is set up, containing the ion of unknown valence at two known concentrations, a determination of the e.m.f. of the cell allows a calculation of the valence of the ion.

In 1898, Ogg[1] used this method to determine the valence of mercurous ion, which had been in dispute for a long time. He set up a cell containing two different concentrations of mercurous nitrate, with a large excess of nitric acid of the same concentration in each half cell, to prevent the hydrolysis of the salt. The cell was:

$$\text{Hg} \left| \begin{matrix} 0.001\,N \text{ mercurous nitrate} \\ 0.1\,N \text{ nitric acid} \end{matrix} \right\| \begin{matrix} 0.01\,N \text{ mercurous nitrate} \\ 0.1\,N \text{ nitric acid} \end{matrix} \right| \text{Hg}$$

and its observed e.m.f. at 18° C. was 0.029 volt. Substituting this value and that for the other terms in the equation $E = \frac{RT}{nF} \ln \frac{a}{a'}$ for the e.m.f. of a concentration cell in which the activity ratio is considered equal to the ratio of the concentrations, we find:

$$0.029 = \frac{0.058}{n} \log 10$$

from which $n = 2$. The valence of mercurous mercury therefore is *2 per ion* and, since it is known to be *1 per atom*, the formula of the ion must be Hg_2^{++}.

(3) To calculate the completeness of displacement reactions. Analytical procedures involve many displacements of one substance by another, the completeness of which we can calculate by means of the principles which we have just developed. If a piece of tin is immersed in a solution of a cupric salt, the copper will plate out upon the tin, leaving the solution colorless. As well as the eye can judge, the copper is removed *completely*, but is this actually the case? Does some small trace of copper remain in the solution, so that this reaction might not be suitable for a separation in quantitative analysis? The reaction might be written:

$$\underline{\text{Sn}} + \text{Cu}^{++} \rightleftharpoons \underline{\text{Cu}} + \text{Sn}^{++}$$

If all the ions were at unit activity, we could calculate the driving force of the reaction from the e.m.f. of the cell:

$$(-)\quad \text{Sn} \mid \text{Sn}^{++}\,(a = 1) \parallel \text{Cu}^{++}\,(a = 1) \mid \text{Cu} \quad (+)$$

[1] Ogg, *Zeit. physik. Chem.*, **27**, 285 (1898).

which is:

$$E^\circ = E^\circ_{Cu} - E^\circ_{Sn} = 0.345 - (-0.136) = 0.481 \text{ volt}$$

This corresponds to a free energy decrease of:

$$-\Delta F^\circ = \frac{2 \times 96494}{4.1833} \times 0.481 = 22{,}200 \text{ calories}$$

Under these standard conditions, therefore, tin has a strong tendency to displace copper. In order to duplicate the conditions when the tin is in contact with a solution of cupric salt, however, we would have to allow current to flow in the cell, so that tin would go into solution at the negative electrode, and copper plate out at the positive pole. As these changes occur, the potential of the tin electrode will *increase* gradually (*i.e.*, become *less* negative), while that of the copper will *decrease* correspondingly. The quantitative changes will be given by the Nernst equation, as follows:

$$E_{Cu} = 0.345 + \frac{0.0592}{2} \log a_{Cu^{++}}$$

$$E_{Sn} = -0.136 + \frac{0.0592}{2} \log a_{Sn^{++}}$$

The e.m.f. of the cell is therefore given by the difference between these two, as usual, and will be:

$$E = E_{Cu} - E_{Sn} = 0.481 + 0.0296 (\log a_{Cu^{++}} - \log a_{Sn^{++}})$$

$$= 0.481 - 0.0296 \log \frac{a_{Sn^{++}}}{a_{Cu^{++}}}$$

As the concentration of stannous ion increases and that of the cupric ion decreases, the numerical value of the logarithmic term continually increases, and the e.m.f. of the cell gradually decreases to zero. When this occurs, the free energy decrease will also vanish, and the system will be in equilibrium, with nothing to drive it further. The value of the equilibrium constant for the equation is calculated easily by setting the e.m.f. of the cell equal to zero, and solving the resulting equation:

$$E = 0.481 - 0.0296 \log \frac{a_{Sn^{++}}}{a_{Cu^{++}}} = 0$$

$$\log K = \log \frac{a_{Sn^{++}}}{a_{Cu^{++}}} = \frac{0.481}{0.0296} = 16.3$$

$$K = \frac{a_{Sn^{++}}}{a_{Cu^{++}}} = 2 \times 10^{16}$$

Under these conditions, even if the stannous salt activity were 10, the concentration of cupric ion would be only 5×10^{-16}, and this reaction could be considered "complete" for any analytical purpose. If we had wanted to displace lead, however, instead of copper, a similar calculation would show that tin is not a sufficiently active metal to employ, since the displacement would only proceed a short distance before equilibrium is reached. A more active metal, such as iron or zinc, would be required in this case.

Another reaction which does not normally go to completion is the reduction of ferric ion with metallic silver:

$$\underline{Ag} + Fe^{+++} \rightleftharpoons Ag^+ + Fe^{++}$$

The corresponding cell would be:

$$(-) \quad Pt \mid Fe^{+++}, Fe^{++} \parallel Ag^+ \mid Ag \quad (+)$$

Under standard conditions, the e.m.f. of this cell is found to be:

$$E^\circ = 0.800 - 0.771 = 0.029 \text{ volt}$$

Since under these conditions the ferric-ferrous is the negative and the silver the positive electrode, silver ion oxidizes ferrous to ferric. However, the e.m.f. is so small that a slight change in ionic concentrations will change the course of the reaction. If the silver ionic concentration is decreased, or the ferric-ferrous ratio increased by a factor of 10, the reaction will be reversed and silver will reduce ferric ion. An experiment shown by A. A. Noyes illustrates this fact in a striking way. In one test tube, a 1 *m* solution of ferrous nitrate is mixed with a 1 *m* solution of silver nitrate, forming a gray precipitate of finely divided silver and darkening also with the formation of colloidal ferric hydroxide:

$$Fe^{++} + Ag^+ = \underline{Ag}\downarrow + Fe^{+++}$$

followed by:

$$Fe^{+++} + 6\,H_2O = \underline{Fe(OH)_3}\downarrow + 3\,H_3O^+$$

In a second test tube, powdered silver is added to a ferrithiocyanate solution, which is gradually decolorized as the ferric iron is reduced to ferrous. In this case, the silver ion formed in the reaction immediately precipitates as the insoluble silver thiocyanate. The silver ion concentration is thus kept down to 8.4×10^{-7} *m* or less by the reaction:

$$Fe(SCN)_6^{---} + \underline{Ag} = Fe^{++} + 5\,SCN^- + \underline{AgSCN}$$

In many cases, substances with high standard electrode potentials are not affected even by very powerful oxidizing agents, unless the resulting compound is insoluble or un-ionized, so that the concentration of the oxidized ion is kept vanishingly small. For instance, the standard reduction potential of the cobaltic-cobaltous couple is 1.84 volts, which is far above even such a strong oxidizing agent as chlorine, with a standard reduction potential of 1.36 volts. Ordinarily, chlorine will not oxidize cobaltous ion, but it is strong enough to form the insoluble cobaltic hydroxide, or the stable cobaltinitrite complex ion. In both of these cases, the concentration of cobaltic ion is kept vanishingly small.

Activities and Activity Coefficients. Since the Nernst equation relates the change in potential at an electrode with the change in activity of the ion in question, it can be used to determine the change in activity if the change in potential is measured. This is one of the most important methods of determining activities and activity coefficients of the ions. Since *the* ***activity coefficient*** *of an ion is defined as the ratio of the activity of the ion to its molal concentration*, we may write:

$$a = \gamma m$$

The equation for a concentration cell at 25° C. then becomes:

$$E = \frac{0.059}{n} \log \frac{\gamma m}{\gamma' m'}$$

The simplest way to investigate the activity coefficients in solutions of hydrochloric acid would be to set up cells of the type:

(−) **Pt,** H_2 (1 atm.) | HCl (m) || HCl (m') | H_2 (1 atm.), **Pt** (+)

Unfortunately, such a cell does not allow us to calculate the activity coefficient of the hydrogen ion, because it involves a liquid junction, the potential of which cannot be determined or calculated exactly. Such cells are not suitable for exact determinations.

A cell can be made without liquid junctions, by connecting together two suitable cells, each containing a pair of reversible electrodes, *e.g.*:

Pt, H_2 (1 atm.) | HCl (m) | AgCl | Ag—Ag | AgCl | HCl (m') | H_2 (1 atm.), **Pt**

Here the two silver chloride electrodes take the place of the liquid junction. With this arrangement, however, the e.m.f. of the cell is not determined by the activities of the hydrogen ions alone.

The silver chloride electrodes are reversible to chloride ions, and their activities affect the e.m.f. of the cell as much as those of the hydrogen ions. Let us assume that the activity of the HCl is 1 in the solution of molality m'. Then the change in free energy when 1 mole of HCl is transferred from the solution at unit activity to the other solution is:

$$\Delta F = RT \ln \gamma_{H_3O^+} m_{H_3O^+} + RT \ln \gamma_{Cl^-} m_{Cl^-}$$

In this case the molalities of the two ions are the same, and the geometrical mean of the activity coefficients is defined as the **mean activity coefficient:**

$$\gamma_{\pm} = \sqrt{\gamma_{H_3O^+} \gamma_{Cl^-}}$$

The change in free energy therefore is, in terms of the mean activity coefficient and the molality m of the salt:

$$\Delta F = 2\,RT \ln \gamma_{\pm} m$$

Also, if the e.m.f. of the cell containing HCl at unit activity is $\boldsymbol{E}^{\circ}$, while that of the other cell is $\boldsymbol{E}$, the change in free energy when 1 mole of HCl is transferred is:

$$\Delta F = F(\boldsymbol{E}^{\circ} - \boldsymbol{E})$$

Eliminating ΔF between these two equations gives:

$$\frac{2\,RT}{F} \ln \gamma_{\pm}\, m = \boldsymbol{E}^{\circ} - \boldsymbol{E}$$

Changing to common logarithms and inserting the numerical values of the constants at 25° C. gives:

$$0.1183 \log \gamma_{\pm} = \boldsymbol{E}^{\circ} - (\boldsymbol{E} + 0.1183 \log m)$$

The right-hand term in parentheses is designated $\boldsymbol{E}^{\circ\prime}$. If we measure the e.m.f. of a series of cells of the type:

Pt, H_2 (1 atm.) | HCl (m) | AgCl | Ag

in which the molality of acid m is varied, calculate $\boldsymbol{E}^{\circ\prime}$ in each case, and plot the values against $m^{\frac{1}{2}}$, we find that they lie along a smooth curve. If this is extrapolated to infinite dilution, the mean activity coefficient $\gamma_{\pm} = 1$, its logarithm $= 0$, and the extrapolated value of $\boldsymbol{E}^{\circ\prime}$ must equal $\boldsymbol{E}^{\circ}$. The value of the mean activity coefficient at any concentration then is given by the equation:

$$\log \gamma_{\pm} = \frac{\boldsymbol{E}^{\circ} - \boldsymbol{E}^{\circ\prime}}{0.1183} = 8.453\,(\boldsymbol{E}^{\circ} - \boldsymbol{E}^{\circ\prime})$$

TABLE 95

E.M.F. OF CELL PT, H_2 (1 ATM.) | HCL(m) | AGCL | AG AT 25° C., AND CALCULATIONS INVOLVED IN DETERMINING THE MEAN ACTIVITY COEFFICIENTS OF HCL

m MOLALITY	$m^{\frac{1}{2}}$	E MEASURED	$E^{\circ\prime} =$ ($E + 0.1183$ LOG m)	$-$ LOG $\gamma_\pm$	$\gamma_\pm$
0.0	0.0		(0.2226)	0.0	1.000
.000136	.0117	0.6805 v.	.2231	.004	.991
.000242	.0156	.6514	.2236	.008	.982
.000483	.0220	.6161	.2238	.010	.977
.001000	.0316	.5791	.2242	.014	.968
.004826	.0695	.5002	.2262	.030	.933
.00965	.0982	.4658	.2274	.041	.910
.04836	.2199	.3874	.2317	.077	.838
.09642	.3105	.35393	.23376	.095	.804
.2030	.4506	.31774	.23582	.112	.773
.3981	.6310	.28407	.23675	.120	.759
.6367	.7979	.25902	.23583	.112	.773
1.0008	1.0004	.23290	.23294	.087	.818
1.5346	1.2388	.20534	.22734	.040	.912

G. Scatchard, *J. Am. Chem. Soc.*, **47**, 641 (1925). The data up to and including 0.04836 m are quoted from Linhart, *ibid.*, **39**, 2001 (1917).

This method of calculation was devised by Lewis and Randall.[1] We shall illustrate its use by means of the measurements of Linhart, supplemented by those of Scatchard, given in Table 95. The first column gives the molality, the second its square root, the third the observed e.m.f., the fourth the calculated value of $E^{\circ\prime}$. In Figure 183 we have given a plot of the values of $E^{\circ\prime}$ against $m^{\frac{1}{2}}$. The dotted line is the limiting slope predicted by the Debye-Hückel theory, which the experimental points fit within experimental error. The limiting value for $E^{\circ\prime}$ obtained by Scatchard was 0.2226, which therefore corresponds to E° for this cell. Using this value we determined the values of $-\log \gamma_\pm$ given in the fifth column, and obtained the corresponding values of $\gamma_\pm$ given in the last column.

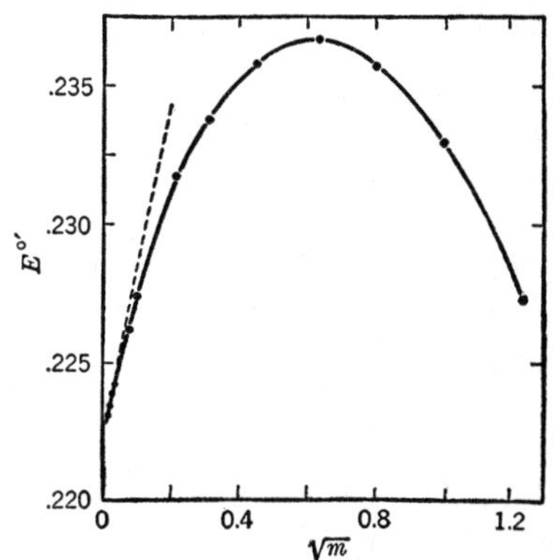

Fig. 183. Plot to Determine Activity Coefficients of HCl.

[1] G. N. Lewis and Merle Randall, *Thermodynamics and the Free Energy of Chemical Substances.* McGraw-Hill Book Co., New York, 1925, p. 332 *et seq.*

These results also may be used to obtain the e.m.f. of the cell often used in connection with the glass electrode:

Pt, H_2 (1 atm.) | HCl(0.1 *N*), AgCl (satd. soln. in 0.1 *N* HCl) | Ag

Since $E^{\circ\prime}$ is defined as $E + 0.1183 \log m$, the e.m.f. of the cell at any molality is given by:

$$E = E^{\circ\prime} - 0.1183 \log m$$

Calculating the molality of a 0.1 *N* solution of HCl, and reading from the graph the value of $E^{\circ\prime}$, we can calculate E. The value which MacInnes and Dole obtained was 0.3524 volt.

By setting up a series of cells involving the silver chloride electrode and another electrode, *e.g.*, a zinc electrode, at a series of concentrations, we can determine the value of E° for this cell and, combining this value with the E° value for the hydrogen-silver chloride cell, we can calculate the E° value of the zinc electrode on the hydrogen scale, without the uncertainty of liquid junction potentials. Such measurements form the basis for standard electrode potentials on the hydrogen scale.

The Source of the E.M.F. in a Galvanic Cell. As the English chemist Eric Rideal, professor of physical chemistry at the University of Liverpool, has said, "One of the oldest unsolved problems in physical chemistry is the source of the e.m.f. in the simple galvanic cell and the mechanism of its production." In the preceding sections we have shown that the ultimate source of the electromotive force in any galvanic cell is the chemical reaction which would take place if we allowed the current to flow. Standard electrode potentials and reduction potentials can be defined and used without any knowledge of the *mechanism* by which the e.m.f. is produced. Despite the utility of this thermodynamic approach, it is interesting to speculate upon the mechanism by which the e.m.f. is produced. Even though no single theory has won universal acceptance, the different suggestions indicate how many factors are involved.

Any galvanic cell, like the Daniell cell shown in Figure 184, contains a number of different junctions between unlike materials making up the circuit. There is a junction between the copper and zinc electrodes, which in this illustration is at *A*, where the copper lead wire from the copper electrode and voltmeter *V* is connected to the zinc electrode. There is a junction at each of the electrodes, between it and the solution around it, and a junction between the two solutions at *B*. The e.m.f. of the cell, here measured by the voltmeter *V*, is the sum of differences in potential which may arise at all of these points.

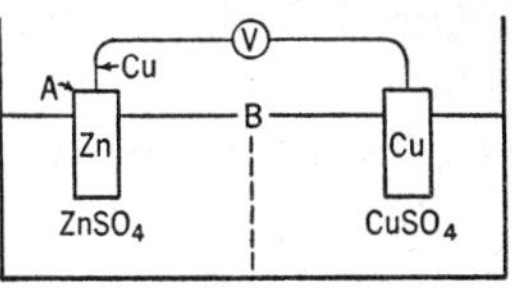

Fig. 184. Possible Sources of E.M.F. in a Cell.

The *liquid junction potential,* set up by the unequal diffusion of the ions at the junction of the two liquids, may be made negligibly small by separating the solutions by means of a salt bridge, usually consisting of a saturated solution of potassium chloride. It cannot be considered the chief source of the e.m.f., except in the case of a concentration cell.

There has been a historic dispute as to whether the metal-metal junction or the junctions between electrodes and solutions are the most important source of the e.m.f. Volta thought he had demonstrated the existence of differences in potential when different metals were brought into contact with each other, and for a long time most physicists championed the **Volta potential difference theory.** Chemists usually have favored the second explanation, which Walther Nernst developed in detail in 1889. It now appears that there is some truth in both theories.[1]

Nernst's idea was that any metal or other element which could form ions would have a definite tendency to dissolve in the ionic condition as soon as it was put in contact with water. Since the formation of ions leaves an opposite charge upon the electrode, the attraction between ions and electrode soon stops further ionization, and an equilibrium condition is reached at the electrode. If the electrode is put into a solution which already contains a concentration of the ions, these will reduce the tendency for further ionization by the usual mass-action effect. *The tendency of an element to pass into solution in the form of ions, in a solution already molal in the ion, is called the* **solution tension** *of the element.* Active metals, like zinc, which have a large tendency to ionize, would be considered to exert a high solution tension, while inactive metals, like copper, would exert a low solution tension. The e.m.f. of a cell involving a displacement reaction would be the resultant of the

[1] A good historical résumé of the controversy between these two different points of view is contained in an article by Irving Langmuir, "The Relation between Contact Potentials and Electrochemical Action," *Trans. Amer. Electrochem. Soc.*, **29,** 125 (1916).

two opposing solution tensions, and the chemical reaction would go in the direction of the greater solution tension.

The type of equilibrium which Nernst postulated is shown in Figure 185, illustrating the equilibrium at a zinc electrode. The solution tension of the metal causes it to dissolve, while this tendency is opposed by the osmotic pressure of the ions in solution and the electrostatic attraction of the electrode. He calculated the conditions for equilibrium at such an electrode, and on this basis derived the Nernst equation which we have derived on a different basis on pages 418 and 419.

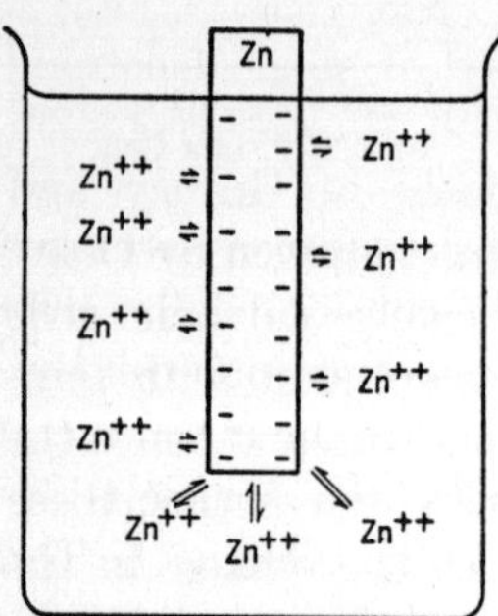

Fig. 185. Electrode Equilibrium (after Nernst).

The solution tension of an element according to the Nernst theory might be *positive*, indicating a tendency for the element to go into solution as ions, or *negative*, indicating a tendency for the ions to lose their charge and deposit upon the electrode. Nernst thought that he could determine the absolute potentials of the ions, and hence their solution tensions, by comparing the half cells to a dropping mercury reference electrode, but this idea proved incorrect, and the results of different investigators were contradictory and inconclusive. It is now generally agreed that there is no way of measuring single electrode potentials and hence determining the numerical values of the solution tensions.

A more serious difficulty with the theory of Nernst is the assumption that all of the e.m.f. of the cell arises at the electrode-solution junction. The reality of the Volta potential difference between dry metals, questioned for some time, recently has been demonstrated by many workers. *We now know that the valence electrons, which carry the current in metals, move freely within the metal, but cannot be removed either thermally or photoelectrically without the application of a definite potential which varies from one metal to another.* The energy, measured in electron volts, required to remove an electron from a metal is least for active metals like sodium and greatest for inactive metals like silver. Gurney and Fowler and other theoretical physicists now believe that, when two different metals are brought into contact, the electrons will tend to flow from the more active to the less active metal. The positive charge on the electrode of the more active metal will allow the ions of this metal to leave the electrode, while the negative charge on the electrode of the less active metal will cause its ions to deposit. This would explain the difference in the standard electrode potentials, but the change of electrode potentials with concentration must be due to a displacement of the equilibrium at the electrode, as Nernst postulated.

A quantitative verification of any theory of single electrode potentials seems impossible, without a method of measuring such potentials. A general discussion of the ideas of Gurney and Fowler, with references to the original literature, is given by Dole.[1]

Electromotive Force and Temperature. Since galvanic cells involve chemical equilibria, and most equilibria shift with temperature, we should expect the equilibrium constant, and hence the e.m.f. to change with temperature. Experience shows that these changes usually are not large. For instance, the change in the e.m.f. of the Daniell cell is only 0.04 volt for a change of 80° C., which is the same order of magnitude as the changes in the other cells listed in Table 96. Because of these changes in the e.m.f. of cells with temperature, which must be due to a corresponding change in the standard electrode potentials, the temperature as well as the ionic activity must be specified in order to fix the standard potentials definitely. The standard temperature is usually taken as 25° C., as shown in Tables 93 and 94.

As in the case of all other chemical equilibria, there must be a thermodynamic relationship between the change in the equilibrium constant of a reaction in a galvanic cell, and the decrease in heat content in the same reaction. This is expressed by the van't Hoff equation:

$$\frac{d \ln K}{dT} = \frac{\Delta H^\circ}{RT^2}$$

where the activity equilibrium constant takes the place of the pressure constant previously discussed (page 302). Since the standard free energy decrease in a galvanic cell can be equated to two expressions:

$$-\Delta F^\circ = RT \ln K = n\boldsymbol{F}E^\circ$$

we find that:

$$\ln K = \frac{n\boldsymbol{F}E^\circ}{RT}$$

[1] M. Dole, *Experimental and Theoretical Electrochemistry*, McGraw-Hill Book Co., New York, 1935, Chapter XXIX, "Quantum Mechanics and Electrochemistry."

Differentiating this equation with respect to T and rearranging terms gives the **Gibbs-Helmholtz equation:**

$$T\left(\frac{dE^\circ}{dT}\right) = E^\circ + \frac{\Delta H^\circ}{nF}$$

which relates the e.m.f. in a galvanic cell, its temperature coefficient, and the change in heat content. Although the preceding discussion, based entirely upon the equilibrium constant, deals only with the standard e.m.f. and change in heat content, the same equation holds for the e.m.f. of any cell and the change in heat content in the same process. This point is discussed in more detail on page 641. Some comparisons between changes of heat content determined calorimetrically and those calculated from potentiometric measurements by means of the Gibbs-Helmholtz equation, are given in Table 96.

TABLE 96

COMPARISON OF ΔH CALCULATED FROM THE GIBBS-HELMHOLTZ EQUATION WITH CALORIMETRIC VALUES, 25° C.

REACTION	E (V.)	$-\frac{dE}{dT}$ (V./DEG.)	$-\Delta H$ (KCAL.)	
			Calc.	Calorimeter
$Pb + 2\,AgI = PbI_2 + 2\,Ag$ *	0.21069	0.000138	11.61	11.65
$Cd + 2\,AgCl + 2.5\,H_2O = CdCl_2 \cdot 2.5\,H_2O + 2\,Ag$ **	.67531	.00065	40.03	39.53
$Cd + PbCl_2 + 2.5\,H_2O = CdCl_2 \cdot 2.5\,H_2O + Pb$ **	.18801	.00048	15.25	14.65

* Taylor, *J. Am. Chem. Soc.*, **38**, 2303 (1916).
** Taylor and Perrott, *ibid.*, **43**, 489 (1921).

Standard Electrode Potentials and Heats of Formation. The heat absorbed when one gram molecule of a substance is formed from its elements is the *heat of formation* of that compound (page 212). In the case of an electrovalent compound like solid sodium chloride we may write the thermal equation thus:

$$Na + \tfrac{1}{2}\,Cl_2 \longrightarrow NaCl - 98.36 \text{ kcal.}$$

We may consider this reaction as made up of two steps: (1) the loss of an electron by the sodium atom:

$$Na \longrightarrow Na^+ + \epsilon$$

and (2) the gain of the electron by the chlorine atom:

$$Cl + \epsilon \longrightarrow Cl^-$$

the result being what we usually represent by the formula NaCl. Presumably, each of these steps is accompanied by a heat change, so that we may rewrite the above to represent these two effects:

$$Na \longrightarrow Na^+ + \epsilon - a \text{ kcal.}$$
$$Cl + \epsilon \longrightarrow Cl^- - b \text{ kcal.}$$

Now if we consider the similar changes involved in the formation of the chlorides of the various metals, we notice that one step in the formation, and hence one of the two heat effects, is common to all, viz.:

$$Cl + \epsilon \longrightarrow Cl^- - b \text{ kcal.}$$

and the differences in the heats of formation of one gram equivalent of each of the various chlorides are presumably due to the other term in the thermal equation, that involving the *loss of an electron by the metal*, which we may denote by x in the general equation:

$$M \longrightarrow M^+ + \epsilon - x \text{ kcal.}$$

In a series of chlorides the differences in the heats of formation will be due to the different reactivities of the metals. We have already seen that the reactivities of the metals are measured quantitatively by their reduction potentials, hence the heats of formation should vary linearly with the standard electrode potentials. The same should be true for any series of salts with a common anion. In Table 97 we include the heats of formation of a series of chlorides and a series of sulfates and the corresponding values of the standard electrode potentials. The heats of formation are not those of the solid salts, but of the salts in a solution approximately 1 molal, so that they are more directly comparable with the standard electrode potentials.

If we take a series of salts with a common cation, the heats of formation vary nearly linearly with the reactivities of the nonmetals. This is also shown by the values given in the second part of Table 97. The results are plotted in Figure 186, where the linear relationship for the sulfates and chlorides of all the metals and for the potassium salts is at once apparent. The values for the sodium salts are omitted from the graph because they nearly coincide with those of the potassium salts.

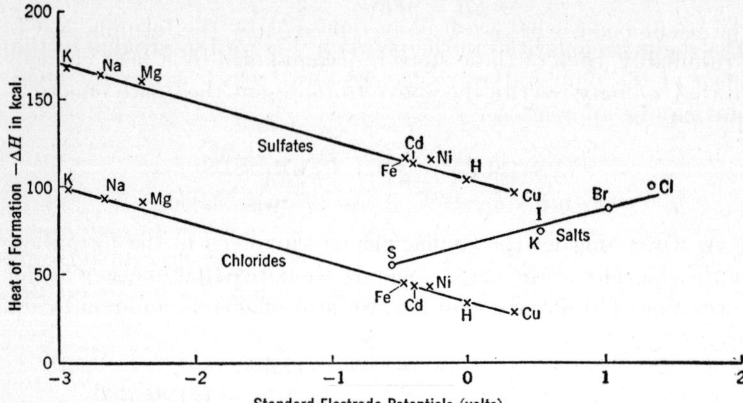

Fig. 186. Heats of Formation and Standard Electrode Potentials.

TABLE 97

A COMPARISON OF STANDARD ELECTRODE POTENTIALS AND HEATS OF FORMATION PER GRAM EQUIVALENT IN SOLUTION $MX \cdot 50\ H_2O$

ELEMENT	STANDARD ELECTRODE POTENTIAL	HEAT OF FORMATION (18° C.) $-\Delta H$ IN KCAL.	
(*Metal*)	(*Volts*)	(*Chlorides*)	(*Sulfates*)
K	− 2.92	100.1	166.7
Na	− 2.72	97.3	164.1
½ Mg	− 2.40	94.3	160.6
½ Fe	− 0.44	49.9 *	116.0
½ Cd	− 0.40	47.8	114.0
½ Ni	− 0.23	46.7	113.5 *
H	0.00	39.2	103.6
½ Cu	+ 0.34	30.4	97.2
(*Nonmetal*)		(*Potassium Salts*)	(*Sodium Salts*)
½ S	− 0.51	55.5	52.7
I	+ 0.54	73.7	70.9 **
Br	+ 1.06	89.0	86.5
Cl	+ 1.36	100.1	97.3

Data from *I.C.T.* V, pp. 176 *et seq.* * $MX \cdot 400\ H_2O$. ** $MX \cdot 200\ H_2O$.

That the standard electrode potential and the heat of formation are so related might be predicted from the **Gibbs-Helmholtz equation** (page 432), which may be rearranged to:

$$-\Delta H = nFE - nFT\left(\frac{dE}{dT}\right)$$

The variation would be exactly linear if the temperature coefficient of the electromotive force were zero. Then the last term in the above equation would vanish and:

$$-\Delta H = nFE$$

The slight irregularities in the points in Figure 186 are due to the effect of the temperature coefficient term, which is usually small but may be appreciable.

PROBLEMS AND EXERCISES

(Temperature 25° C. unless otherwise stated.)

1. Define and explain the following terms:

(*a*) calomel electrode
(*b*) concentration cell
(*c*) Clark cell
(*d*) Daniell cell
(*e*) free energy change
(*f*) gravity cell
(*g*) hydrogen electrode
(*h*) Nernst equation
(*i*) potentiometer
(*j*) solution tension
(*k*) standard electrode potential
(*l*) Weston cell

2. Describe the way in which you would determine the standard electrode potential of (*a*) the copper electrode; (*b*) the chlorine electrode; (*c*) the ceric-cerous electrode.

3. (*a*) Starting with the general Nernst equation:

$$E = E^\circ \pm \frac{RT}{nF} \ln a$$

substitute the numerical values of the constants and show that, at 25° C., it becomes:

$$E = E^\circ \pm \frac{0.05915}{n} \log a$$

(*b*) Calculate the corresponding values of the constant at 0 and at 40° C.

4. Calculate the e.m.f. in each of the following cells, indicating the + and − poles, the direction of the current in the external circuit, the chemical reaction which furnishes the energy for the cell, and the direction in which the reaction proceeds:

(*a*) $Zn \mid Zn^{++}\ (a = 0.1) \parallel Cu^{++}\ (a = 0.001) \mid Cu$
(*b*) $Cd \mid Cd^{++}\ (a = 0.01) \parallel Cl^{-}\ (a = 1) \mid Cl_2$ (1 atm.), **Pt**
(*c*) $Ag \mid Ag^{+}\ (a = 0.1) \parallel Fe^{+++}\ (a = 0.01),\ Fe^{++}\ (a = 0.1) \mid$ **Pt**
(*d*) $Sn \mid Sn^{++}\ (a = 0.1) \parallel Pb^{++}\ (a = 0.001) \mid Pb$
(*e*) **Pt,** Cl_2 (1 atm.) $\mid Cl^{-}\ (a = 1) \parallel Br^{-}\ (a = 10^{-4}) \mid Br_2$ (l), **Pt**
(*f*) **Pt** $\mid Sn^{++++}\ (a = 10^{-5}),\ Sn^{++}\ (a = 0.1) \parallel Cl^{-}\ (a = 0.01) \mid Cl_2$ (0.01 atm.), **Pt**

5. The following cell is set up:

$$Ag \mid Ag^{+}\ (a = 1) \parallel Cu^{++}\ (a = 1) \mid Cu$$

(*a*) Which is the positive and which the negative pole, and how should the cell be represented? (*b*) What is the e.m.f. of the cell? (*c*) What is the chemical reaction in the cell, and in which direction does it tend to proceed? (*d*) What is the standard free energy change in this reaction? (*e*) If a bar of copper is put into a solution of $AgNO_3$, what will be the final concentration of silver ion, if the final concentration of cupric ion is 0.01 *m*?

* **6.** (*a*) Write down the balanced equation for the oxidation of arsenite ion by iodine. (*b*) Write the corresponding electrode reactions and the Nernst equation for each. (*c*) Draw a diagram showing the relative values of the two potentials (1) when all the reactants are at unit activity; (2) when the $pH = 8$; (3) when the hydrogen ion activity is 4. (*d*) Explain the conditions necessary for the arsenite titration in terms of the diagram in (*c*).

* **7.** Calculate the potential of a permanganate mixture which is 0.05 *M* in Mn^{++}, has a *p*H of 0, and contains 0.1 ml. of 0.1 *M* MnO_4^- in a total volume of 20 ml. In this case, assume that the activity is equal to the molarity.

8. A cell consists of an iron electrode in contact with a solution in which the ferrous ion activity is 0.1, connected through a salt bridge with a cadmium electrode in contact with a solution in which the activity of cadmium ion is 0.001. (*a*) Represent the cell in the usual way, with the negative electrode to the left. (*b*) Calculate the e.m.f. of the cell. (*c*) What chemical reaction is represented by this cell, and in which direction would it proceed? (*d*) What is the standard free energy decrease in this reaction?

9. The potential of a cell made up of a standard saturated calomel half cell and an electrode of silver immersed in a saturated solution of silver bromide, is measured and found to be 0.1853 v. Calculate the solubility of silver bromide from these data.

10. An iron nail is put into a solution of a nickel salt. Calculate the ratio of the activities of nickelous and ferrous ions when the reaction has ceased.

11. A piece of tin is immersed in a 1 *m* solution of a lead salt. Calculate the ratio of the activities of plumbous and stannous ions at the end of the reaction and also the concentration of plumbous ion, assuming that the activity coefficients are unity.

12. For the cell:

$$Zn \mid ZnCl_2\ (d = 1.391),\ Hg_2Cl_2\ (\text{satd. soln.}) \mid Hg$$

the e.m.f. is 1.00000 volt at 15° C. and 1.00094 volts at 25° C. (*a*) Write down the equation for the chemical reaction in this cell.

(*b*) Calculate the free energy change in the reaction at 20° C. (*c*) Calculate the heat of the reaction at the same temperature.

13. For the cell:

$$\text{Cd} \mid \text{CdSO}_4 \text{ (soln.)} \mid \text{Hg, Cd (10\% amalgam)}$$

the e.m.f. at any centigrade temperature t is given by the equation:

$$E = 0.05160 - 0.000242\,(t - 20)$$

(*a*) Write the equation for the chemical reaction in this cell. (*b*) Calculate the e.m.f. of the cell at 25° C. (*c*) Calculate the free energy change at the same temperature. (*d*) Calculate the value of ΔH at 20° C.

14. From the data given on page 406, calculate the value of ΔF and ΔH in the saturated Weston cell at 20° C. Write the chemical equation for the reaction in this cell.

15. Write down the chemical equation for the reaction which occurs in the Clark standard cell. From the data on page 407, calculate the potential of this cell at 20° C., and the corresponding values of ΔF and ΔH at the same temperature.

16. From the data of Tables 93 and 94, calculate the standard electrode potentials of (*a*) the $Sn^{++++} \mid Sn$ electrode, (*b*) the $Co^{+++} \mid Co$ electrode, (*c*) the $Ag^{++} \mid Ag$ electrode.

READING LIST

M. Dole, *Experimental and Theoretical Electrochemistry.* McGraw-Hill Book Company, New York, 1935. Pp. 211–226; 242–268; 307–321. The pages cited in this book deal at greater length with the subject matter covered in this chapter.

W. M. Latimer, *The Oxidation States of the Elements and Their Potentials in Aqueous Solutions.* Prentice-Hall, Inc., New York, 1938. This book is very useful for study and reference in connection with e.m.f. It includes a brief discussion of methods of determining oxidation-reduction potentials, their relation to electron affinities, lattice energies, etc., and a systematic evaluation of these potentials for the elements, arranged according to the periodic table. Tables of oxidation-reduction potentials, free energies of formation, equilibrium constants, and activity coefficients are particularly useful for reference.

H. J. M. Creighton, *Electrochemistry*, 3d ed. John Wiley & Son, New York, 1935. This is Vol. 1 of Creighton and Koehler's *Electrochemistry* and deals with the principles of electrochemistry. Pp. 176–249 include a discussion of galvanic cells and electrode potentials. The second volume, by W. A. Koehler, covers the applications.

CHAPTER 16

HYDROGEN ION CONCENTRATION AND *p*H

Hydrogen ion concentration has been the subject of very extensive study, since it is a controlling factor in many commercial processes and in most biological systems. In order to avoid the use of negative exponents and to provide a more convenient way of expressing the acidity or alkalinity of such solutions, Sørensen introduced the logarithmic or *p*H scale, described on page 351. This scale now has come into wide use in all branches of science.

***p*H, *p*OH, and *pK*$_w$.** We have seen before that *the **p**H of a solution is the negative exponent of the hydrogen ion concentration*, and *the **p**OH is the negative exponent of the hydroxyl ion concentration.* Since in any dilute aqueous solution the activity of the water is constant, and the activities and concentrations may be considered equal, we have shown on page 349 that the product of the concentrations of the hydrogen and hydroxyl ions is a constant at any temperature:

$$[H_3O^+][OH^-] = K_w$$

On taking the logarithms of both sides of this equation and changing signs, we find:

$$-\log [H_3O^+] - \log [OH^-] = -\log K_w$$

The first two terms we have defined already as *p*H and *p*OH. The last term, $-\log K_w$, *is called the* ***ionization exponent of water, pK$_w$***, hence we may write:

$$pH + pOH = pK_w$$

At 25° C., the ion product for water is 10^{-14}, hence $pK_w = 14$, and at this temperature the sum of the hydrogen and hydroxyl exponents has the constant value of 14:

$$pH + pOH = 14$$

Thus, if the value of *p*H is 7.542, that of *p*OH is $14 - 7.542 = 6.458$. At other temperatures, the sum of the hydrogen and hydroxyl exponents has a different constant value, which can be calculated from the values of K_w given in Table 84.

TABLE 98

HYDROGEN AND HYDROXYL ION CONCENTRATIONS AND CORRESPONDING VALUES OF pH AND pOH IN WATER SOLUTION AT ROOM TEMPERATURE

	ACID; $[H_3O^+] > 10^{-7}$ $[OH^-] < 10^{-7}$			NEUTRAL	BASIC; $[H_3O^+] < 10^{-7}$ $[OH^-] > 10^{-7}$		
$[H_3O^+]$	10	1	10^{-4}	10^{-7}	10^{-10}	10^{-14}	10^{-15}
$[OH^-]$	10^{-15}	10^{-14}	10^{-10}	10^{-7}	10^{-4}	1	10
pH	− 1	0	4	7	10	14	15
pOH	15	14	10	7	4	0	− 1

The pH and pOH scales afford a convenient way to express the acidity or alkalinity of a solution. The pH increases as the acidity decreases. At 25° C., any solution in which the pH is greater than 7 is basic; any in which the pH is 7 is neutral; any in which the pH is less than 7 is acid. When the hydrogen ion concentration is 1, the pH is 0, since the logarithm of unity is zero. Negative values of pH indicate solutions in which the hydrogen ion concentration is greater than 1. Such solutions are rarely met in biological systems, hence in practice the pH usually is positive. The same considerations apply equally to alkalinity and pOH. An increasing pOH corresponds to decreasing alkalinity. These relationships are shown in Table 98.

Although pH and pOH are defined strictly in terms of the *concentrations* of the hydrogen and hydroxyl ions, all of the potentiometric methods of determination yield the corresponding *activities*. As we shall see on page 442, the *experimental definition based on e.m.f. measurements is more nearly in terms of the negative logarithm of the hydrogen ion activity.* Since the activities enter all exact thermodynamic equations relating to solutions, they are more significant and useful than the concentrations. In dilute solutions, where the activity coefficients are nearly unity, the concentrations may be considered equal to the activities.

POTENTIOMETRIC METHODS OF MEASURING pH

Many methods of measuring pH have been devised and applied in biological and commercial processes. Potentiometric methods will be described in this chapter, and colorimetric methods, employing indicators, in the next.

The Hydrogen Electrode. The fundamental potentiometric method involves the hydrogen electrode described on page 407.

In principle, it consists in setting up a concentration cell of the type:

$$\textbf{Pt}, H_2 \text{ (1 atm.)} \mid H_3O^+ \, (a) \parallel H_3O^+ \, (a = 1) \mid H_2 \text{ (1 atm.)}, \textbf{Pt}$$

from which the activity a of the hydrogen ion in the first half cell can be calculated by means of the equation for a concentration cell. In practice, the concentration usually is so low that it can safely be set equal to the activity, without appreciable error. In order to use such a cell with confidence, there are two points which should be considered.

(1) The e.m.f. of any cell involving a gaseous electrode is dependent upon the partial pressure of the gas. In the case of the hydrogen-hydrogen ion couple, the equilibrium is:

$$2\,H_2O + H_2 \rightleftharpoons 2\,H_3O^+ + 2\,\epsilon$$

Since the hydrogen ion is the *oxidized* and the hydrogen gas the *reduced* state of the couple, the electrode potential at 25° C. is given by the usual equation for an oxidation-reduction system:

$$\boldsymbol{E} = \boldsymbol{E}^\circ + \frac{0.05915}{2} \log \frac{a^2_{H_3O^+}}{a_{H_2}}$$

In this case, $\boldsymbol{E}^\circ = 0$ by convention. For small changes in pressure, deviations from the gas laws are inappreciable, and the activity of the gaseous hydrogen can be set equal to its partial pressure above the electrode. For a cell consisting of two hydrogen electrodes, with hydrogen gas at different pressures, dipping into the same solution containing hydrogen ions at any definite concentration:

$$(-) \quad \textbf{Pt}, H_2 \, (p_1) \mid H_3O^+ \mid H_2 \, (p_2), \textbf{Pt} \quad (+) \quad (p_1 > p_2)$$

the equation for the e.m.f. becomes:

$$\boldsymbol{E} = \frac{0.05915}{2} \log \frac{p_1}{p_2}$$

This is a second type of concentration cell, where the difference is in the activity of the gas over the two electrodes, and there is no difference in the electrolytic solution.

This equation shows that there is a change of 59 millivolts for a ten-fold change in the gaseous pressure. The change is correspondingly less for small changes in the pressure. For exact measurements, carried down to tenths of a millivolt, there is an appreciable difference between the potential of a hydrogen electrode saturated with hydrogen at a partial pressure of 1 atmosphere, and one saturated with hydrogen over a solution, where the *total* pressure is one atmosphere. If the aqueous tension from the solution at 25° C. is the same as that from pure water at the same temperature, *i.e.*, 23.8 mm., the partial pressure of the hydrogen would be 736.2/760 atmosphere. Such an electrode would have a potential higher, *i.e.*, more positive, than that of the standard hydrogen electrode by the amount:

$$\boldsymbol{E} = \frac{0.0592}{2} \times \log \frac{760}{736.2} = 0.0296 \times 0.0138 = 0.00041 \text{ v.}$$

Obviously the barometric pressure must be corrected for the vapor pressure of water in order to obtain accurate results with the hydrogen electrode.

(2) The e.m.f. of any cell containing a liquid junction will involve the liquid junction potential. Nernst, in 1889, suggested that the cause of the liquid junction potential was the unequal rates at which the ions diffused across the junction. This idea has been accepted generally ever since, but it does not lead to exact numerical results even in the simplest cases. We can see, however, that the smallest liquid junction potentials should result in those solutions in which the ionic diffusions are most nearly equal. For ions of the same valence the ionic conductance should be proportional to the diffusion rate; hence salts with equal ionic conductances should be best for liquid junctions. As we can see from Table 90, the potassium and chloride ions have nearly the same limiting ionic conductance, and this equality holds in more concentrated solutions, because the transference numbers change very little with concentration (Table 88). Potassium chloride is generally employed in salt bridges. One reason why it is preferred to potassium or ammonium nitrate is that the calomel electrode is commonly used as reference electrode. The other salts often are employed with solutions which would precipitate with chlorides.

Experimental and theoretical evidence both point to the conclusion that a saturated solution of potassium chloride is most satisfactory in reducing liquid junction potentials. Unless the solutions are very acid or very alkaline, with high concentrations of the mobile hydrogen or hydroxyl ion, the current is carried almost entirely by the potassium and chloride ions, which diffuse at nearly equal rates. This arrangement is thought to reduce the liquid junction potential to a few millivolts at most. It has the advantage of a uniform procedure, which gives comparable results in the hands of different investigators.

The uncertainty with regard to the liquid junction potential makes it impossible to determine the hydrogen ion activities exactly, and this restriction should be kept clearly in mind at all times. However, within this unavoidable uncertainty, we can employ the hydrogen electrode to determine hydrogen ion activities. The whole problem of determining *exact* ionic activities is summed up admirably by H. S. Harned.[1] "We are thus confronted with the interesting perplexity that it is not possible to compute liquid junction potentials without a knowledge of individual ion activities, and it is not possible to determine individual ion activities without an exact knowledge of liquid junction potentials." A whole chapter of W. Mansfield Clark's authoritative treatise, *The Determination of Hydrogen Ions* [2] is devoted to a discussion of liquid junctions, and the reader is referred to this for greater detail.

***p*H Defined on the Basis of E.M.F. Measurements.** Formally, we can define *p*H on the basis of measurement of the e.m.f. of the cell:

$$\textbf{Pt}, H_2 \text{ (1 atm.)} \mid H_3O^+ (a) \parallel H_3O^+ (a = 1) \mid H_2 \text{ (1 atm.)}, \textbf{Pt}$$

Neglecting the liquid junction potential, the e.m.f. of this cell at 25° C. is given by the familiar expression:

$$E = 0.0592 \log \frac{1}{a_{H_3O^+}} = 0.0592 \log \frac{1}{\gamma m_{H_3O^+}}$$

If the value of the activity coefficient γ is unity, this becomes:

$$E = 0.0592\ p\text{H} \quad \text{or} \quad p\text{H} = \frac{E}{0.0592} = 16.9\ E$$

In practice, it is inconvenient to use two hydrogen electrodes, and a secondary standard is substituted for the standard hydrogen electrode. The most satisfactory standard is the decinormal calomel half cell, connected through a saturated potassium chloride salt

[1] H. S. Harned, *A Treatise on Physical Chemistry*, 2d ed., D. Van Nostrand Company, Inc., New York, 1931, p. 813.

[2] W. Mansfield Clark, *The Determination of Hydrogen Ions*, 3d ed., The Williams and Wilkins Company, Baltimore, 1928, Chapter XIII.

bridge to the solution of unknown *p*H, containing the hydrogen electrode. The cell therefore is:

$$\text{Pt}, H_2\,(1\text{ atm.}) \mid H_3O^+\,(a) \mid \underset{J}{KCl\,(\text{satd.})} \mid Hg_2Cl_2\,(\text{satd. soln. in } 0.1\,N\,KCl) \mid Hg$$

Neglecting the possible change of the liquid junction potential at J, as we immerse the hydrogen electrode in different solutions, gives the working definition of *p*H which is most widely used, namely:

$$p\text{H} = \frac{E - E^\circ_{\text{cal.}}}{0.00019839\,T}$$

where the numerical factor in the denominator is $2.3026\,\frac{R}{F}$, E is the measured e.m.f. of the cell, and $E^\circ_{\text{cal.}}$ is the standard potential of the decinormal calomel electrode connected through the saturated potassium chloride salt bridge. Values of $E^\circ_{\text{cal.}}$ at different temperatures are given in Table 99. These values, which probably

TABLE 99

THE STANDARD POTENTIAL, AT DIFFERENT CENTIGRADE TEMPERATURES, OF THE HALF-CELL SYSTEM: | KCL (SATD.) | Hg_2Cl_2 (SATD. SOL. IN 0.1 N KCL | HG

Temp.	12°	15°	20°	25°	30°	35°	38°
$E^\circ_{\text{cal.}}$	0.3364	0.3363	0.3360	0.3358	0.3355	0.3353	0.3352

MacInnes, Belcher and Shedlovsky, *J. Am. Chem. Soc.*, **60,** 1094 (1938).

are accurate within 0.5 mv. when measuring the *p*H of a buffered salt solution (see page 462), should be increased by 1 mv. for measurements carried out in solutions of hydrochloric acid.

On the basis of the procedure outlined above, the value of the *p*H of a solution at 25° C. is given by the equation:

$$p\text{H} = \frac{E - 0.3358}{0.05915}$$

For a detailed discussion of the problem of standardizing the *p*H scale as measured potentiometrically, the reader is referred to M. Dole, *The Glass Electrode*, Chapter XVI, "Significance and Standardization of the *p*H Scale."

Clark's *p*H Cell with Rocking Hydrogen Electrode. Many types of hydrogen half cell have been devised, and many methods have been employed to combine these two systems for the measurement of *p*H. One of the most widely used is the system shown in Figure 187, which was devised by W. Mansfield Clark, professor of physiological chemistry at the Johns Hopkins University. This makes use of the **rocking electrode** for maintaining equilibrium

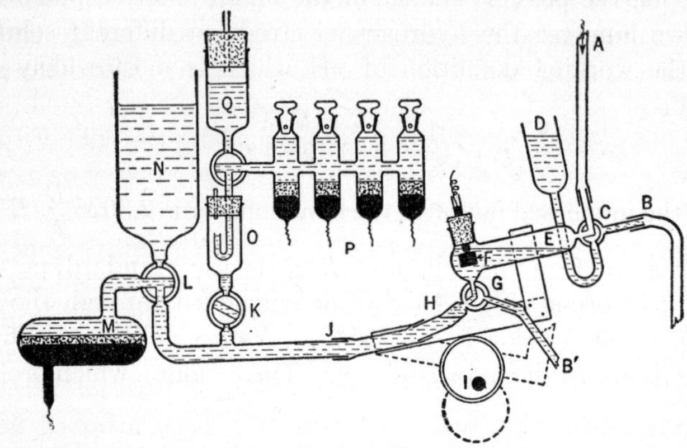

Fig. 187. Clark's System Employing the Rocking Electrode for Measuring *p*H.

between the hydrogen gas and the hydrogen ions, instead of a stream of hydrogen bubbled over the electrode. This arrangement does not require large quantities of scrupulously pure hydrogen, since any trace of oxygen is soon removed at the electrode itself. It also avoids the changes in pressure as the individual bubbles pass over the electrode, and thus insures a more definite pressure of the gas. The rocking electrode is connected to the rest of the system by a piece of rubber tubing between *H* and *J*, and is rocked by means of the eccentric circular cam *I*, so that the electrode *F* is alternately covered with the solution under investigation (as shown) or with hydrogen, when the cam is in the lower (dotted) position.

In making a measurement, the vessel *E* is first flushed out with purified hydrogen. This is done by filling the vessel with pure water, and then allowing it to drain out through *B′*, while hydrogen displaces it through the tube *A* and the stopcock *C*. Excess of water is drained out of the reservoir *D* through the outlet *B*. *D* is then rinsed and filled with the solution under investigation. The vessel is rocked so that *C* is at its lowest point, and the solution is allowed to flow through it until *E* is half filled, while excess hydrogen escapes through *G* and *B′*. Finally, *G* is closed and *C* is turned so as to connect *E* to the known pressure of hydrogen flowing from the generator through *A*. The motor is then started and the solution rocked at a speed which mixes the solution without churning it. After equilibrium has been reached at the electrode, the rocking is stopped to take a measurement. The reference electrode *M* is a saturated calomel electrode, which may be connected directly to the saturated potassium chloride salt bridge through the stopcock *L*, turned in the direction shown. When the stopcock *G* is properly turned, a small amount of the saturated potassium chloride is squeezed out of *B′* by pinching the rubber tubing between *J* and *H*. *G* is then turned in the position shown, when the release of the tubing sucks some of the solution out of *E* and forms a broad mixed junction at *H*. After the measurement of the e.m.f. of the cell, the stopcocks *G* and *L* are turned and the old junction is flushed out through *B′* by means of saturated potassium chloride flowing from the reservoir *N*. The measurements are repeated until additional rocking causes no change in the e.m.f., indicating that equilibrium has been attained at the hydrogen electrode.

The saturated calomel electrode *M* is a secondary standard, which may be calibrated against any of the carefully made decinormal calomel electrodes *P*. Connection is made by allowing decinormal potassium chloride solution to flow from the reservoir *Q* until the level in *O* has risen above the end of the siphon tube, then opening *K*. Before a measurement with the hydrogen electrode, the connection at *O* is broken by draining out the saturated potassium chloride solution through *B′* until the level stands as shown.

Clark's *p*H cell is widely used, particularly in biological work. It does not require a great deal of solution, since the vessel *E* holds about 10 ml. and is only half full. Other cells, some designed for use with small amounts of material as in the study of blood, are described by Clark.[1]

The Quinhydrone Electrode. Quinhydrone consists of a molecule of quinone, $C_6H_4O_2$, combined with one of hydroquinone, $C_6H_4(OH)_2$. In water it is only slightly soluble, and dissociates into its constituent quinone, Q, and hydroquinone, H_2Q. The latter further ionizes as a weak dibasic acid:

$$H_2Q + 2\,H_2O \rightleftharpoons 2\,H_3O^+ + Q^{--}$$

[1] Clark, *loc. cit.*, Chapter XIV, "Hydrogen Half Cells."

the anion of which can be oxidized to quinone by taking away 2 electrons. The over-all reaction therefore can be written:

$$2\,H_2O + H_2Q \rightleftharpoons 2\,H_3O^+ + Q + 2\,\epsilon$$

Since this is an oxidation-reduction reaction, an inert electrode, *e.g.*, a platinum wire, dipped into a solution saturated with quinhydrone, will acquire a definite potential, the value of which will be given by the equation:

$$E = E^\circ + \frac{0.05915}{2} \log \frac{a_Q a^2_{H_3O^+}}{a_{H_2Q}}$$
$$= E^\circ + \frac{0.05915}{2} \log \frac{a_Q}{a_{H_2Q}} + 0.05915 \log a_{H_3O^+}$$

If the solution has a *p*H of 8 or less, the ionization of the hydroquinone will be so slight that the concentrations of quinone and hydroquinone, from the dissociation of the original quinhydrone, will be practically equal. If we assume that the activity coefficients of these neutral substances are equal, then:

$$a_Q = a_{H_2Q}$$

and the second term in the equation will vanish, leaving the electrode potential as a function of the hydrogen ion activity alone, thus:

$$E = E^\circ + 0.05915 \log a_{H_3O^+}$$

Experiments have shown that the quinhydrone electrode does act as a hydrogen electrode up to a *p*H of 8, and it has found extensive application for this purpose. The value of E° is given by a determination of the e.m.f. of the cell:

$$\text{Pt., } H_2 \text{ (1 atm.)} \mid H_3O^+\text{, quinhydrone} \mid \textbf{Pt}$$

According to Harned and Wright,[1] the most probable value of E° for the quinhydrone electrode at 25° C. is 0.6997 volt, while its value at any temperature between 18 and 40° C. is given within 0.2 mv. by the equation:

$$E^\circ = 0.7181 - 0.00074\,t$$

If the quinhydrone electrode is used with the reference system recommended on page 443 for the determination of *p*H, the cell would be:

$$Hg \mid Hg_2Cl_2 \text{ (satd. soln. in 0.1 } N \text{ KCl)} \mid \text{KCl (satd.)} \mid H_3O^+ (a)\text{, QH} \mid \textbf{Pt}$$

[1] Harned and Wright, *J. Am. Chem. Soc.*, **55**, 4849 (1933).

The e.m.f. of this cell at 25° C. is given by the equation:

$$E = (0.6997 - 0.05915\,pH) - 0.3358$$

whence

$$pH = \frac{0.3639 - E}{0.05915}$$

Notice that with this measuring system the e.m.f. of the cell decreases to zero at a *p*H of 6.152, beyond which the quinhydrone becomes the negative electrode.

The quinhydrone electrode is much simpler than the hydrogen electrode, since there is no gas phase to control. The electrode is a piece of gold or platinum wire which requires no platinizing. It is put into the solution under investigation, in contact with a small amount of quinhydrone to saturate the solution. The half cell then is connected to the saturated calomel or other reference electrode, by means of a saturated potassium chloride salt bridge. Quinhydrone is well adapted to microelectrodes, for studying minute amounts of physiological fluids. One such half cell, designed by Ettisch in 1925, is shown in Figure 188. The drop of solution S is put into the cup, through the side of which is sealed the platinum electrode P. The end of this fits into an indentation in the bottom of the cup, containing a few crystals of quinhydrone QH. Connection is made by means of a capillary salt bridge B containing agar, as shown.

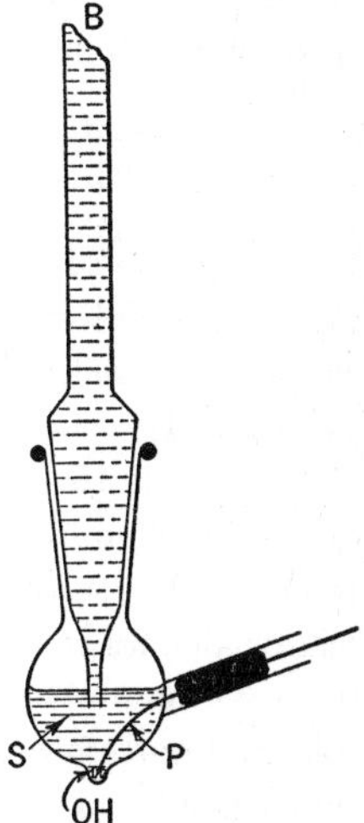

Fig. 188. Quinhydrone Microelectrode of Ettisch (1925).

Quinhydrone electrodes may be used to study the hydrogen ion concentration in dilute solutions of nitric acid, unsaturated organic acids, and other solutions which would be attacked by hydrogen in the presence of the strongly catalytic platinum black on the hydrogen electrode. With the quinhydrone electrode, equilibrium is reached very rapidly — in the course of a few minutes at most. It can be used satisfactorily with any oxidizing or reducing agents except those which are strong enough to react appreciably with the quinhydrone in the course of a few minutes. A very strong oxidizing or reducing agent would destroy enough hydroquinone or quinone to prevent the system from functioning as a hydrogen electrode.

The Glass Electrode. If a solution containing hydrogen ion is separated from a reference solution by a thin glass membrane, the system will show an e.m.f., which is a function of the hydrogen ion concentration. This fact was discovered by Cremer, a biologist, in 1906, and first studied by Haber and Klemensiewicz in 1909. Subsequent workers have investigated the glass electrode thoroughly and have used it in a number of applications, since it will measure hydrogen ion concentrations of systems which cannot be studied by the hydrogen or quinhydrone electrodes.

The general arrangement for measuring *p*H with the glass electrode is the following:

Reference electrode	Solution of unknown *p*H	Glass	Solution of known *p*H	Reference electrode

Under proper conditions, the glass allows the passage of hydrogen ions only, and therefore acts as a true hydrogen electrode. The range of reliability for the best modern glass electrodes is from 0 to 12 or 13 *p*H. Dole has shown that the errors in strongly acid solutions are due to a change in the activity of the water, one molecule of which accompanies the proton through the glass presumably as H_3O^+. The same type of error occurs if a large amount of salt or alcohol is added to the solution. The glass electrode cannot be used in nonaqueous solutions, in which the hydrogen ion is solvated and no longer is the H_3O^+ with which equilibrium can be established in the glass. If a glass could be found in which the hydrogen ion migrated as the proton, H^+, this restriction could be overcome, but no such glass is known.

In strongly alkaline solutions the glass electrode no longer serves as a hydrogen electrode, probably because the other cations, which so far outnumber the hydrogen ions, migrate through the glass membrane and carry increasing amounts of the current. In a 0.01 *N* solution of sodium hydroxide, for instance, the hydrogen ion concentration is 10^{-12}, while the sodium ion concentration is 10^{10} times as great. Under these conditions, if a sodium-glass electrode is used, it will function as a sodium electrode. Other glasses will function as electrodes of other metals in solutions of the corresponding salts.

In measuring the e.m.f. of cells containing the glass electrode, the usual galvanometer cannot be used with a potentiometer, because the resistance of the glass membrane is too high to allow an appreciable current to flow. The fragile quadrant electrometer, which early workers substituted for the galvanometer, now has been largely superseded by electron-tube amplifying circuits.

Various forms of the glass electrode have been designed. MacInnes and Dole,[1] in the course of a detailed study of the glass electrode, designed a type with a very thin glass membrane, shown in Figure 189. The membrane *D* is made from a special glass having the composition 72 per cent SiO_2, 6 per cent CaO, and 22 per cent Na_2O. This is the lowest-melting mixture which can be made from these three components. It has the lowest electrical resistance and functions as a hydrogen electrode over the widest range of *p*H. The glass is blown into a very thin bubble, only a few microns thick, which shows red and green diffraction colors. A tube *B* of ordinary soft glass is then heated to dull redness at the bottom, and pushed against the bubble, to which it fuses. The rest of the bubble is broken away, leaving the electrode tube as shown. An electrode of the size shown has a resistance of 10 megohms (10^7 ohms) if made from the special glass, and 100 megohms if made from ordinary soft glass. Other workers have reduced the resistance of their electrodes by making them of long capillary tubes, with a much larger surface. Many commercial *p*H meters use glass electrodes made of a bulb blown on the end of a tube, which has the advantage of mechanical strength. A form of glass electrode designed by Kerridge for the study of small amounts of biological solutions is shown in Figure 190. The glass electrode is formed by sucking in a cup on the end of a glass bulb. The unknown solution is put into the cup and connected to a calomel electrode through a tube *T* covered with a ground cap *C*. Such a ground joint, if ungreased, hinders the diffusion of solutions, yet does not greatly increase the resistance of the salt bridge.

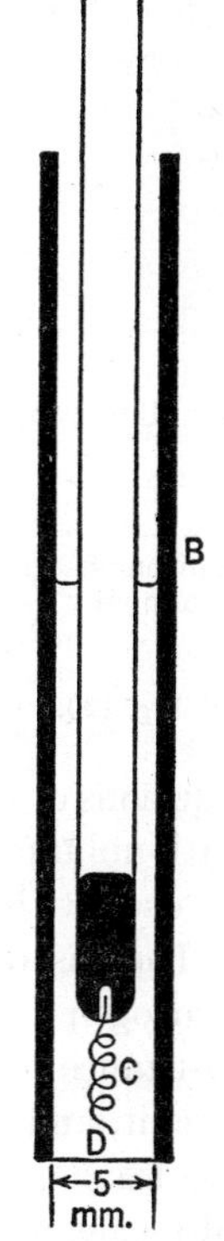

Fig. 189. Glass Electrode of MacInnes and Dole.

[1] MacInnes and Dole, *Ind. Eng. Chem., Anal. Ed.*, **1**, 57 (1929).

Connection between the solution of known *p*H and its reference electrode is made through the tube T' covered with the ground cap C'.

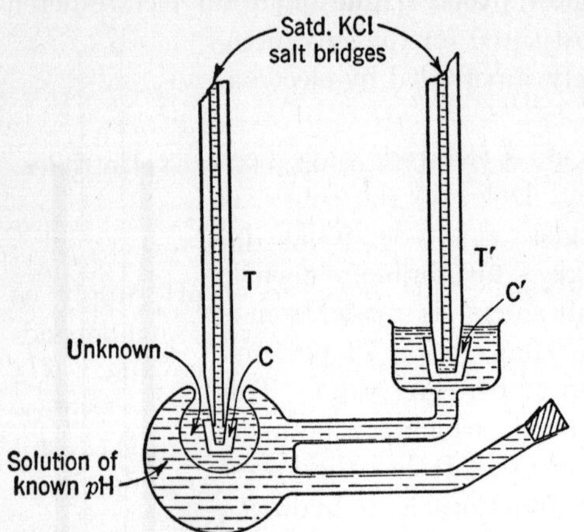

Fig. 190. Glass Microelectrode of Kerridge.

Dole [1] lists the advantages of the glass electrode as follows:

(1) The glass electrode comes to equilibrium immediately and can be read rapidly. (2) It requires no additional material, such as the pure hydrogen or hydroquinone used with those other electrodes. (3) It can be used in colored or turbid solutions and in solutions of any oxidizing or reducing strength. (4) It can be used with unbuffered solutions and near the neutral point. (5) It can be used with very small quantities of solution.

The disadvantage of the glass electrode, as compared to the hydrogen or quinhydrone electrode, is that its high electrical resistance requires special precautions in insulating all parts of the circuit, and a special potentiometer. Some types of the electrode are fragile, most are accurate only over a range of 0 to 9 on the *p*H scale, and all are limited to aqueous solutions.

In measuring *p*H with the glass electrode, the relation between *p*H and the observed e.m.f. will depend upon the reference electrodes and the reference solution of known *p*H which is used. MacInnes and Dole employed a silver chloride electrode in 0.1 *N* hydrochloric acid with their glass electrode. Their system was:

Ag	AgCl (satd. soln. in 0.1 *N* HCl)	Glass	Solution of unknown *p*H	KCl (satd.)	Hg_2Cl_2 (satd. soln. in satd. KCl)	Hg

Since the standard potential of the first reference electrode is 0.3524 volt at 25° C. (page 410) and that of the system to the right of

[1] Dole, *Experimental and Theoretical Electrochemistry.* Chapter XXV, "The Glass Electrode" contains an admirable discussion by an authority on the subject.

the glass membrane is (0.2458 + 0.05915 pH), the e.m.f. of the total cell will be given by the equation:

$$E = -0.1066 + 0.05915\, p\text{H}$$

whence:

$$p\text{H} = \frac{E + 0.1066}{0.05915}$$

Suitable equations are easily derived for other reference electrodes.

Applications of pH Measurement

The Ion Product of Water. Measurements of pH supply us with a method of determining the value of K_w which is an independent check upon the results of conductance measurements. If a hydrogen electrode is immersed in a solution of a base, a determination of the e.m.f. of a suitable cell will give the pH in this solution. Knowing the activity coefficients in the basic solution, we can determine the activity of the hydroxyl ion and hence the corresponding value of pOH. The sum of these two values is $pK_w = -\log K_w$, from which K_w is calculated. The results of e.m.f. measurement agree with those of conductance measurements in giving for the ion product of water the values collected in Table 84 on page 350. During the last decade Harned and his collaborators at Yale University have published in the *Journal of the American Chemical Society* extensive studies of the dissociation of water in salt solutions of different concentrations, from which they determined the value of K_w by extrapolation to zero concentration of salt, where the activity coefficients become unity.

Ionization Constants of Weak Acids and Bases. There are two ways in which pH measurements may be used to determine the ionization constants of acids or bases. The first of these, involving a study of the hydrolysis of salts, is discussed here, and the second, based upon neutralization curves, on page 457.

We have already (page 355) derived equations for the hydrogen ion concentration in a solution of a salt which has been hydrolyzed. Thus the salt of a weak base and a strong acid which is slightly hydrolyzed will give, at a concentration c, a solution in which:

$$p\text{H} = \tfrac{1}{2}\, pK_w - \tfrac{1}{2}\, pK_b - \tfrac{1}{2} \log c$$

If we make up a solution of a known concentration of a salt at a temperature for which pK_w is known, and measure its pH, we can determine the ionization exponent of the weak base by rearranging the foregoing equation. For example, in a 0.001 N solution of ammonium chloride at 25° C., the pH is found to be 6.13, hence for ammonia:

$$\begin{aligned} pK_b &= pK_w - 2\,p\text{H} - \log c \\ &= 14 - 2 \times 6.13 - \log 10^{-3} \\ &= 14 - 12.26 + 3 \\ pK_b &= 4.74, \text{ hence } K_b = 1.8 \times 10^{-5} \end{aligned}$$

In the same way, if a salt of a weak acid and a strong base is dissolved in water, the ionization exponent of the acid is related to the pH, ionization exponent of water, and concentration by the equation:

$$pK_a = 2\,p\text{H} - pK_w - \log c$$

Obviously, this equation may be used to determine the ionization constant of a weak acid, from a measurement of the pH in a solution of a salt of the acid with a strong base.

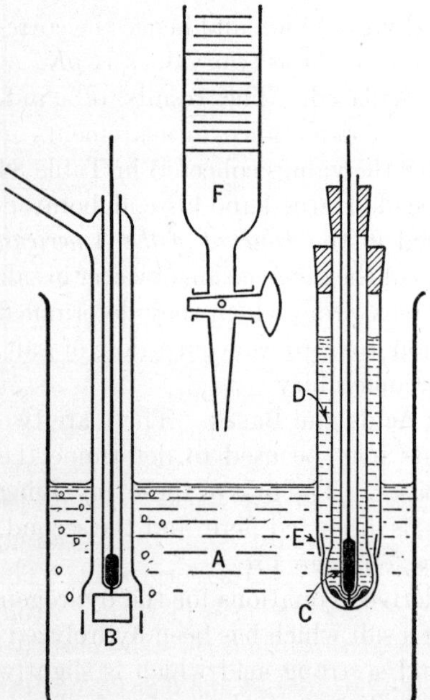

If the base or acid in the discussion above is so weak that the salt is appreciably hydrolyzed, the simple equations are not applicable, and the hydrogen ion concentration must be set equal to the quadratic expression derived on page 357.

Fig. 191. Apparatus for Electrometric Neutralization Titration.

Neutralization Titration Curves. An important use of pH measurements is in following the course of a neutralization titration and determining the endpoint of the titration without employing an indicator. The apparatus shown in Figure 191 is suitable for such work. A compact type of calomel reference electrode is very convenient in such titrations. The central tube of this half cell carries a platinum wire sealed through the bottom end to make contact with the mercury electrode in the usual way. The mercury and calomel are contained in a small bulb *C*, blown in the bottom of the middle tube as shown. Several small holes above the bulb connect the saturated potassium chloride solution *D* which covers the electrode with the same solution which fills the outer tube and moistens the broad, ungreased ground joint *E*, thus forming a liquid junction with the solution *A*. This solution, which in the case under consideration is a measured amount of base, is run into the beaker, and the cell is completed by the hydrogen electrode *B*. Connection is made from the lead wires to the potentiometer on which the e.m.f. is measured. The second solution, in this case the acid, is run out from the buret *F*. After each addition of acid, the solution is stirred thoroughly and the e.m.f. of the cell is measured. From this the *p*H is calculated in the usual way.

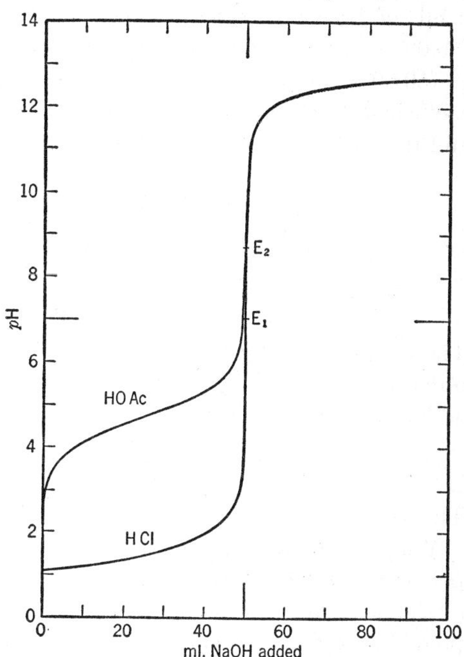

Fig. 192. Titration Curves for 50 ml. of 0.1 *N* Solutions.

Titration Curves of Strong Acids and Strong Bases. Figure 192 shows a plot of the *p*H against the quantity of 0.1 *N* sodium hydroxide added to 50.00 ml. of 0.1 *N* hydrochloric acid. This curve is typical of the titration of any strong acid with a strong base. The *p*H changes gradually at first, then rises steeply when the neutralization is complete, and flattens out again as excess base is added. These changes in *p*H can be calculated with sufficient accuracy for our purposes in the following simple way: In the original solution of 0.1 *N* hydrochloric acid, the activity coefficient is 0.796, according to Table 80, page 334. In this solution the hydrogen ion activity therefore is 0.0796 or 7.96×10^{-2}, and the *p*H is 2 − log 7.96 = 1.10. David I. Hitchcock and Alice C. Taylor, of the Yale University School of Medicine, measured the *p*H of this solution and found it to be 1.085, which agrees satisfactorily with the calculated value. The addition of the sodium hydroxide acts in two ways: *First*, it neutralizes an equivalent quantity of hydrogen ion; and *second*, it increases the volume of the solution. When x ml. of base are added, they neutralize x ml. of acid, leaving $(50.00 - x)$ ml. unneutralized. The total volume of solution then is $(50.00 + x)$ ml. In the more dilute solutions, the activity coefficients can be considered unity without any appreciable error, and the hydrogen ion activity equal to its concentration:

$$[H_3O^+] = 0.1 \times \frac{(50.00 - x)}{(50.00 + x)}$$

or

$$pH = 1 + \log \frac{(50.00 + x)}{(50.00 - x)}$$

These equations show that a great deal of base must be added in order to change the *p*H by one unit. When 40 ml. have been added, the result will be:

$$pH = 1 + \log \tfrac{90}{10} = 1 + \log 9 = 1.95$$

This corresponds to a change of only 0.85 *p*H unit.

When 49.99 ml. of base have been added, and the acid is 99.98 per cent neutralized, the *p*H has only changed to 5. The addition of the next 0.01 ml. of base brings the solution to the equivalence point E_1, which is the neutral point of *p*H 7, and the same amount of excess base will increase the *p*H to 9. Beyond the neutral point, the hydrogen ion concentration no longer is given by the equation above, since the excess hydroxyl ion is simply diluted but not neutralized. In this range, the equation for the *hydroxyl ion concentration* is:

$$[OH^-] = 0.1 \times \frac{(x - 50.00)}{(x + 50.00)}$$

The equation for the hydrogen ion concentration therefore is:

$$[H_3O^+] = \frac{10^{-14}}{[OH^-]} = \frac{10^{-14}}{0.1} \times \frac{(x + 50.00)}{(x - 50.00)}$$

or

$$pH = 13 + \log \frac{(x - 50.00)}{(x + 50.00)}$$

The student should verify these equations. In the neutralization of a 0.1 *N* solution of any strong acid and base, the addition of 0.02 ml. of either solution will change the *p*H at the neutral point by 4 units. From an experimental determination of *p*H during such a neutralization, the endpoint is easily found by making the *p*H plot and determining the volume of base corresponding to the vertical portion of the curve. Such experiments require no back titration as in the case of colored indicators. In practice, only a few readings need be made until near the endpoint, and the curve need not be continued far on the alkaline side.

Titration Curves of Weak Acids and Strong Bases. The situation is somewhat different in the titration of a weak acid, as shown in Figure 192, which includes the curve for the titration of 50.00 ml. of 0.1 *N* acetic acid with 0.1 *N* sodium hydroxide. It starts at a much higher *p*H, increases more rapidly at first, then flattens out before it becomes vertical. The vertical part of the curve is only about half as long as in the case of the hydrochloric acid, and it lies above the neutral point of *p*H 7. This curve also is analyzed easily in terms of the ionization theory. With such a weak acid, there is no appreciable difference between the activity and the concentration of the hydrogen ion. At the beginning, the 0.1 *N* acetic acid is only 1.34 per cent ionized, so that the *p*H is 2.87. The addition of the first portions of base cause a rapid increase in *p*H because the base not only neutralizes an equivalent amount of acid, as in the case of the strong acid, but also forms an equivalent amount of ionized sodium acetate. The acetate ions repress the ionization of the weak acetic acid. This second effect is not operative in the case of the strong acid. The hydrogen ion concentration and *p*H at any point of the curve until the immediate neighborhood of the equivalence point, is determined by rearranging the equation for the ionization constant of the acid into the form:

$$[H_3O^+] = K_a \frac{[HOAc]}{[OAc^-]}$$

or

$$pH = pK_a + \log \frac{[OAc^-]}{[HOAc]}$$

For any mixture of a weak acid with its salt of a strong base, the same general equation holds:

$$pH = pK_a + \log \frac{[salt]}{[acid]}$$

This is known as the **Henderson-Hasselbalch equation.** Since the concentration of salt is equal to that of the neutralized acid, and that of the acid is the concentration unneutralized, the Henderson-Hasselbalch equation in the case of a titration may be written:

$$pH = pK_a + \log \frac{x}{(a - x)}$$

where a is the original volume of weak acid and x is the volume of base of the same concentration, which has been added.

When 5 ml. of base has been added, it neutralizes 10 per cent of the acid, and the pH becomes:

$$pH = -\log (1.81 \times 10^{-5}) + \log \left(\frac{5}{45}\right)$$

$$= 4.74 - \log 9 = 4.74 - 0.95$$

$$pH = 3.79$$

The addition of 5 ml. of base therefore causes an increase of 0.95 pH, compared to 0.85 pH for the change caused by the addition of 40 ml. of base to a strong acid. The change is nearly nine times as rapid for the weak as for the strong acid, over the first 5 ml. of base added. There is a decrease in the rate of change of pH until the point at which the acid is half neutralized; when $x = (a - x)$, the logarithmic term involving the quotient vanishes and:

$$pH = pK_a$$

After this point, the curve increases more rapidly, in much the same way as that for a strong acid. The vertical portion of the curve falls *above* pH 7 and is nearly equally spaced above and below the equivalence point. In the immediate vicinity of this point, the Henderson-Hasselbalch equation no longer is applicable, since the ions of water enter into the equilibrium. At the equivalence point E_2, the pH is simply that of the resulting salt of a weak acid and a strong base, namely:

$$pH = \tfrac{1}{2}\, pK_a + \tfrac{1}{2}\, pK_w + \tfrac{1}{2} \log c$$

For 0.05 N NaOAc the pH is 8.72.

As in the case of a strong acid, the endpoint of the titration is determined from the vertical portion of the curve. With a weak acid, however, this portion is much less pronounced and the endpoint is less easily fixed with precision. For very weak acids, the vertical portion becomes merely a point of inflection which practically disappears. If the acid exponent is as large as $pK_a = 10$, the potentiometric method will not give a satisfactory determination of the end-point.

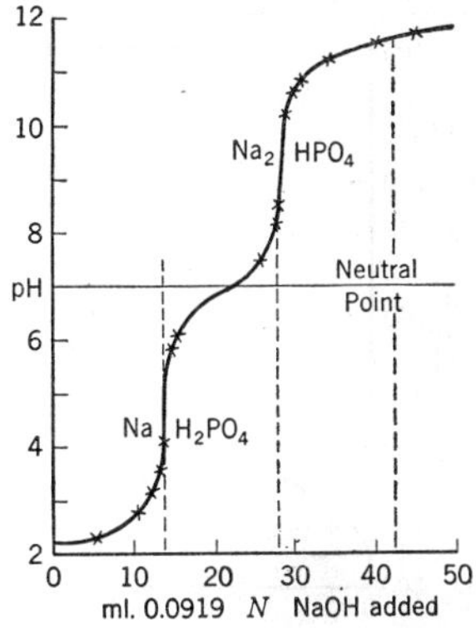

An application of the Henderson-Hasselbalch equation gives us another method of determining the ionization exponent of a weak acid. When the acid is half neutralized, as we showed above:

$$pH = pK_a$$

It is only necessary to plot the titration curve of the acid with a strong base, determine the equivalence point, and then read the ordinate at a point on the axis of abscissas half way between the origin and the equivalence point.

Fig. 193. Titration of 0.01227 *M* H_3PO_4 with NaOH.

Titration Curves of Mixed or Polybasic Acids. When a mixture of acids of different strength is titrated electrometrically, the resulting curve will have successive vertical points of inflection, provided that the successive ionization exponents differ by 4. If the difference is smaller than this, the corresponding breaks in the curve will merge into one slope. The same is true of the titration curves of polybasic acids. An experimental titration curve for phosphoric acid is shown in Figure 193. Here there are two distinct breaks, corresponding to the neutralization of the first and second hydrogen ions, the

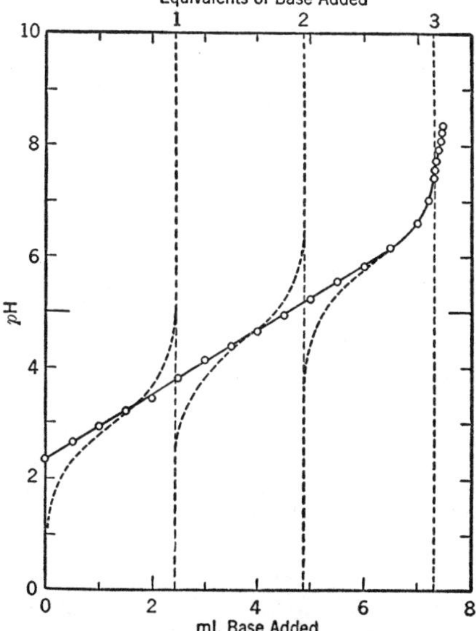

Fig. 194. Titration of "Tribasic" Citric Acid.

ionization exponents of which differ by 5. Such a titration does not, however, distinguish the neutralization of the third hydrogen ion, the exponent of which, 12.5, is too near that of water. Citric acid, which is also tribasic, behaves very differently, as Figure 194 shows. The titration curve proceeds smoothly and almost in a straight line from pH 3.3 to 5.5, because the successive ionization exponents differ by only about 1. The dotted curves show the behavior of single acids with ionization exponents of 3.00, 4.45, and 5.85 respectively, corresponding to those of the successive stages in the ionization of citric acid. The observed curve is the resultant of these.

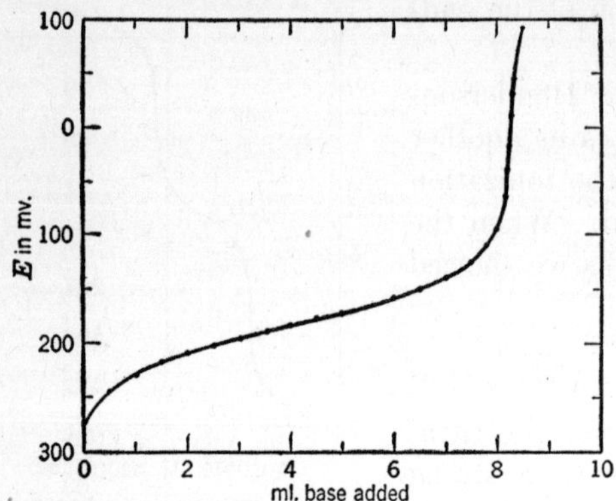

Fig. 195. The Titration of 10 ml. of 0.1025 *N* HOAc with 0.1244 *N* NaOH.

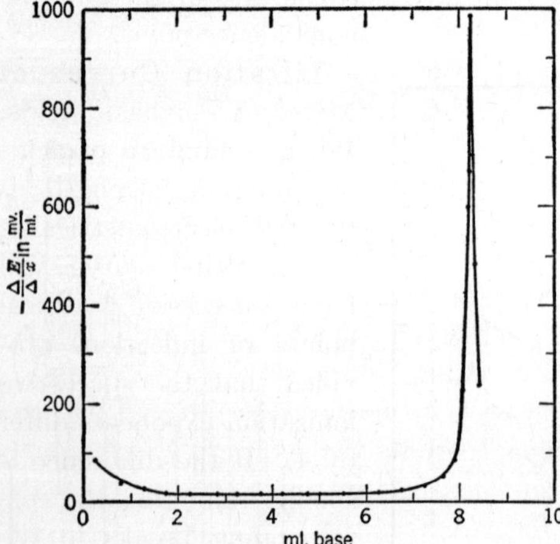

Fig. 196. Differential Titration Curve for 10 ml. of 0.1025 *N* HOAc Titrated with 0.1244 *N* NaOH.

Differential Titration Curves. In all of the titration curves which we have described, the change in e.m.f. and hence in pH is rather small for the addition of any definite increment of base until near the neutralization point. At this point the change becomes much larger. This is shown very clearly for the titration curve of 0.1025 *N* acetic acid with 0.1244 *N* sodium hydroxide given in Figure 195, taken from the data of Table 100. Another method of plotting observations brings out this change more clearly and helps to locate the endpoint more exactly. Instead of plotting

TABLE 100

THE TITRATION OF 10 ML. OF 0.1025 N ACETIC ACID WITH 0.1244 N SODIUM HYDROXIDE AT 20° C.

x (ML. BASE)	E (MV.)	$-\frac{\Delta E}{\Delta x}$	x (ML. BASE)	E (MV.)	$-\frac{\Delta E}{\Delta x}$
0.00	288.8		6.50	150.0	
		85			20
0.51	245.1		7.00	139.8	
		32			30
1.02	229.0		7.50	124.9	
		24			51
1.52	217.4		7.80	109.5	
		17			74
2.00	209.1		8.00	94.8	
		14			227
2.53	201.6		8.14	63.0	
		13			598
3.01	195.6		8.18	39.1	
		12			672
3.54	189.1		8.21	16.9	
		12			985
4.00	183.6		8.24	− 10.6	
		13			703
4.50	177.3		8.27	− 31.7	
		11			481
5.00	171.8		8.30	− 46.1	
		14			236
6.01	157.9		8.50	− 93.3	
		16			

Data from Auerbach and Smolczyk, *Zeit. phys. Chem.*, **110,** 65 (1924).

the pH or e.m.f. directly, we can plot the *change* in e.m.f. for each small addition of base, against the *average* value of x, the total base added. Such a plot is equivalent to the *tangent* of the neutralization curve, which becomes very large at the endpoint. Figure 196 shows the corresponding differential plot for the neutralization of acetic acid. The very large change permits the endpoint to be fixed accurately at 8.24 ml.

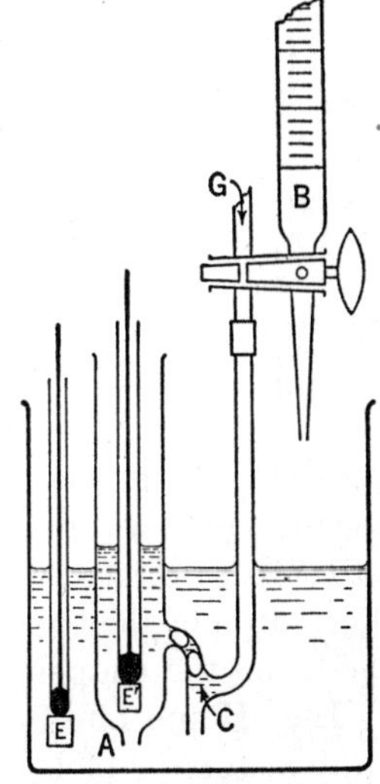

Fig. 197. Differential Potentiometric Titration Cell of MacInnes *et al.*

Instead of measuring the e.m.f. of the solution against a reference electrode, the *change* in e.m.f. can be measured directly at any point of the titration. This differential method, first used by Cox in 1925, has been developed by MacInnes and his collaborators into a compact and convenient apparatus giving results of the highest precision. Their differential cell, shown in Figure 197, employs two identical electrodes E and E', which may be pieces of platinum wire or foil immersed in the solution. As long as the solution is uniform, there is no e.m.f. between these electrodes. When the titrating solution is added from the buret B, the pH in the outer portion of the beaker, in contact with E, is changed correspondingly, while that in contact with the "sheltered" electrode E' remains the same. The resulting difference in potential between the two electrodes is read. Then the special stopcock of the buret is turned to the position shown, when bubbles of air passing through the bore G and down the side arm of the titration cell lift solution through the tube C, whence it circulates over the electrode E', emerging at A. As soon as the solution has become uniform, the stopcock is turned, stopping the air and allowing another portion of the solution in B to flow into the beaker. With this arrangement, no salt bridge or reference electrode is required, yet the endpoint can be determined very accurately.

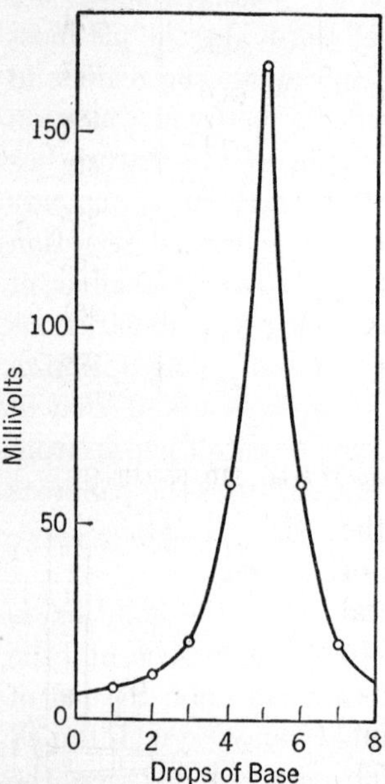

Fig. 198. Differential Titration of 0.27138 m HCl with 0.03395 m NaOH.

To illustrate the use of this differential apparatus, in Figure 198 we have reproduced a plot used to determine the endpoint in the standardization, against a 0.27138 m solution of HCl, of a solution of NaOH found to be 0.33947 m. Using weight burets, a sample of the acid was measured out and nearly neutralized with the basic solution. The final measurement was made by adding dropwise from a buret a solution of the base diluted to $\frac{1}{10}$ its original concentration, or 0.03395 m. Each drop of the base corresponded to 0.01 per cent of the original acid, and the endpoint was determined to a fraction of a drop.

The pH and Life Processes. The pH is one of the most important factors in biological processes, influencing, for example, the growth of microorganisms and plants, the reactivity of enzymes, the rate of ciliary movement, and the permeability of cell membranes.

Growth of bacteria. The spores of fungi germinate best in an acid environment, at a *p*H of 3 or 4, but do not germinate if the *p*H is lower than about 1.5. Nitrifying bacterial action in soils will occur over a range from 3.5 to 11.9 on the *p*H scale but is most rapid between 6.5 and 7.5. Different nitrifying bacteria show specific ranges of action and optimum conditions. The common intestinal *B. coli* thrives best at a *p*H of 6.5, and will not grow in a medium more acid than 4.4 or more basic than 7.8.

Enzyme activity. In the digestive tract, different foods are attacked by different enzymes, and the body provides the *p*H most suitable for each. Much useful information about the regions in which different enzymes function, differences between digestion in infancy and adult life, and other problems of this nature has been obtained by *p*H measurements, while these measurements are also used clinically in the diagnosis of the abnormal secretion of hydrochloric acid in the stomach. The study of the effect of *p*H upon enzymes is very comprehensive, but a few illustrations will show the differences which have been found. The optimum *p*H for the activity of amylase (diastase) from saliva is 6; that of lipase from the gastric juice is 4.0 to 5.0; while that of pepsin from the stomach is 1.2 to 1.6. Trypsin and erepsin from the pancreas function best over the range from 7.5 to 9.5 *p*H, depending somewhat upon the material upon which they are acting.

Ciliary movement decreases when the *p*H of the solution is changed from 7.2 to 6.0. Amoeboid motion, phagocytosis, and the activity of spermatozoa also are found to depend upon the *p*H of the medium. Considerable differences in *p*H may be maintained between different parts of a biological system. For instance, the normal cytoplasmic *p*H of starfish eggs is 6.7, but that of the nucleus is 7.5.

Plant growth. The growth and the crop yield of plants are influenced most profoundly by the *p*H of the soil in which they grow. Sometimes this affects the plant's welfare directly, sometimes indirectly, by its effect upon the bacteria which help to supply the nutrition to the plant and upon parasites which destroy it. Each type of plant thrives best at some particular *p*H, and this fact largely determines the flora of a particular locality. Thus wild flowers which flourish in the woods, where decaying leaves make the soil distinctly acid, may wither and die in the more alkaline soil of a garden. The yield of food crops may be affected profoundly by the soil *p*H. O. Arrhenius, the well-known soil chemist and son of Svante Arrhenius, reported in 1926 that sugar beets grown in a soil of *p*H between 7.0 and 7.5 gave the highest yield and had the highest sugar content. The *p*H of the soil is regulated by the addition of slaked lime to reduce the acidity or of free sulfur, which is oxidized to sulfuric acid, to increase it. The use of sulfur dusts in combating various insect pests depends upon the same principle.

The *p*H of the Blood. In a person in normal health, the *p*H of the blood is very nearly 7.4. According to D. D. van Slyke of the Rockefeller Institute for Medical Research (1921), the normal limits of variation, due to exercise or other causes, are only $\pm$ 0.1 unit. Even in unusual conditions caused by disease, variations of more than $\pm$ 0.4 unit are fatal. Such fine control of the acidity of the blood, exceeding the control of bodily temperature, is achieved by means of the *buffering* action of the constituents of the blood plasma as will be explained on page 467.

Buffer Solutions. It is possible to make a solution of any desired *p*H by the addition of a larger or smaller amount of a strong acid or base. However, if the *p*H of such a solution is near the neutral point, it is unstable and easily changed. Thus a dilute solution of hydrochloric acid, if stored in a bottle made of soft glass, soon will be neutralized more or less completely by soda or potash leached from the glass. Similarly, a dilute solution of an alkali soon will pick up enough carbon dioxide from the air to become nearly neutralized. Neither of these solutions has any reserve power to absorb hydrogen or hydroxyl ions without changing *p*H. On the other hand, we have seen that the blood and other biological systems are maintained constant at a *p*H near the neutral point. Such systems are said to be *buffered* or to show *buffering action. A* ***buffer solution*** *is one which maintains a nearly constant* pH *despite the addition of considerable quantities of acid or base.*

A consideration of the neutralization curve of a weak acid and strong base shows that most of this curve lies within a comparitively narrow range of *p*H, which is higher the weaker the acid. When the acid is partially neutralized, it will not increase in *p*H rapidly when more base is added, nor will the system decrease in *p*H if acid is added. Such a system, therefore, has considerable buffering action and resists the addition of either acid or base. Application of the Henderson-Hasselbalch equation allows us to treat this problem quantitatively. In terms of x, the volume of base added to a ml. of acid of equal concentration, we derived the equation:

$$pH = pK_a + \log \frac{x}{(a - x)}$$

When the acid is half neutralized, $x = (a - x)$, and the pH is equal to the ionization exponent of the acid. An inspection of Figure 192 on page 453 shows that the slope of the curve is least at this point. The middle of the curve therefore corresponds to the smallest change in pH for the addition of a fixed amount of acid or base, *i.e.*, the greatest buffer action of the system.

The same relationship is shown even more directly as follows: The preceding equation is rearranged by dividing the numerator and denominator of the last term by a to give:

$$pH = pK_a + \log \frac{\alpha}{(1 - \alpha)}$$

where $\alpha = x/a$. Here α represents the *fraction of acid neutralized*, or the concentration of the anion of the acid, divided by the total concentration of undissociated acid plus acid anion. It should not be confused with the degree of dissociation of the acid, which it equals only in the absence of the salt. The *slope* s of the curve given by the equation above is:[1]

$$s = \frac{dpH}{d\alpha} = \frac{0.4343}{\alpha(1 - \alpha)}$$

Plotting s against α as in Figure 199, we see that it falls from an infinitely large value when α is zero, passes through a flat minimum at 0.5, then increases to infinity when α is unity. The central portion of the curve is nearly horizontal, changing only 15 per cent for a change of 20 per cent in α on either side of the middle point. Thus any system, containing nearly equivalent quantities of a weak acid and its salt, will act as a buffer. The same will be true of a weak base and its salt.

[1] The equation for the slope is obtained by the usual method of the calculus, which consists in taking the derivative of pH with respect to α. It is easy to determine analytically the value of α for which the slope is a minimum. By a well-known theorem of the calculus, s will be a minimum when *its* slope is zero. Taking the derivative of s with respect to α and equating this to zero gives $\alpha = \frac{1}{2}$.

A quantitative measure of the buffering action of a solution was introduced by van Slyke in 1922.[1] This is the *buffer value* or *buffer index*. *The buffer value (index) of a solution is the fraction of an equivalent of strong acid or base required to change the* pH *of the solution by one unit.* In such a definition, an addition of acid is considered as a *decrease* in base. Since this causes a *decrease* in pH, the buffering value is always positive, whether acid or base is added.

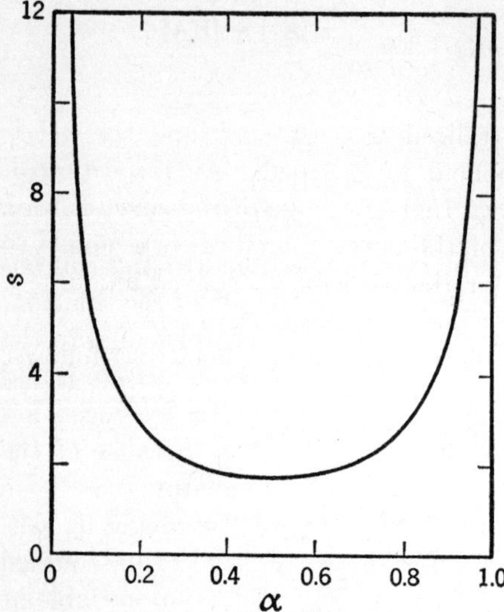

Fig. 199. The slope *s* of the *p*H-α Curve Plotted Against α.

In calculating the numerical value of the buffer index, we can start from our equation for the slope of the *p*H-α curve. In this case we are interested in the reciprocal of this slope, or the change of α with *p*H:

$$\frac{1}{s} = \frac{d\alpha}{dp\text{H}} = 2.303\ \alpha(1 - \alpha)$$

Now

$$\alpha = \frac{[\text{B}]}{[\text{A}]} = \frac{\text{Concentration of base added}}{\text{Concentration of original acid}}$$

Hence,

$$d\alpha = \frac{d[\text{B}]}{[\text{A}]}$$

The buffer value, β, is defined as the change of [B] with *p*H:

$$\beta = \frac{d[\text{B}]}{dp\text{H}} = 2.303\ \alpha(1 - \alpha)[\text{A}]$$

For actual calculations, it is more convenient to be able to determine the buffering index at any specified *p*H rather than

[1] Van Slyke, "On the measurement of buffer values and on the relationship of buffer value to the dissociation constant of the buffer and the concentration and reaction of the buffer solution." *J. Biol. Chem.*, **42,** 525 (1922).

at a specified fraction of acid neutralized. By combining the equations:

$$\frac{[A^-][H_3O^+]}{[HA]} = K_a \qquad \text{and} \qquad \alpha = \frac{[A^-]}{[A^-] + [HA]}$$

we find

$$\alpha = \frac{K_a}{K_a + [H_3O^+]}$$

whence

$$\beta = \frac{d[\mathbf{B}]}{dp\text{H}} = 2.303\,[\mathbf{A}]\,\frac{K_a[H_3O^+]}{(K_a + [H_3O^+])^2}$$

The buffer index therefore is directly proportional to the concentration of the buffer acid and changes with the pH of the solution. It is greatest when the hydrogen ion concentration is equal to the ionization constant of the acid, when the last term reduces to $\frac{1}{4}$, and $\beta = 0.576\,[\mathbf{A}]$. At higher and lower values of the hydrogen ion concentration, it decreases fairly rapidly to zero, because of the predominance of the squared term in the denominator.

In addition to the buffering action of the weak acid and its salt, treated in the preceding paragraph, the strong acid or base added to the solution exhibits a buffering action which is appreciable at values of the pH lower than 4 and higher than 10. This is simply because the pH scale is logarithmic, and increases less rapidly than the change in the concentration of acid or base. More acid or base must be added to a concentrated than to a dilute solution to bring about the same change in pH. Quantitatively, the effect is calculated by assuming complete dissociation of the acid and base, whence $d\,[\mathbf{B}] = d\,[OH^-]$ and:

$$\beta_{\text{s.b.}} = \frac{d[\mathbf{B}]}{dp\text{H}} = \frac{d[OH^-]}{d\log[OH^-]} = 2.303\,[OH^-]$$

Thus the buffering effect in the strongly basic solution is proportional to the hydroxyl ion concentration. A similar line of reasoning shows that the buffering action of the strong acid is proportional to the hydrogen ion concentration:

$$\beta_{\text{s.a.}} = \frac{d[\mathbf{B}]}{dp\text{H}} = 2.303\,[H_3O^+]$$

The sum of these two factors is the buffering effect due to the addition of either a strong acid or a strong base to water, *i.e.*:

$$\beta = \frac{d[\mathbf{B}]}{dp\text{H}} = 2.303\,([H_3O^+] + [OH^-])$$

These effects only become appreciable some distance away from the neutral point, when either hydrogen or hydroxyl ion concentration has risen to an appreciable quantity.

Figure 200 shows a plot of the buffer values in solutions of acetic acid of two different concentrations, mixed with strong acid or base. As the figure shows, the most effective buffering of this system is over the range from about 4.1 to 5.2 pH. At a pH of about 3.5, the buffering action of the strong acid becomes important, and the buffer index of the system is the sum of the index of

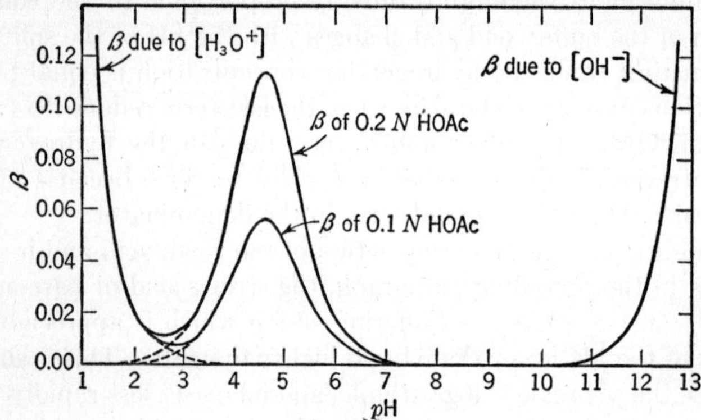

Fig. 200. The Buffer Values for Acetic Acid Mixtures with Strong Base or Acid. (After Van Slyke.)

the two components, shown by dotted lines. Above pH 10 the buffering effect of the base predominates. Many such systems would be required to provide uniform buffering over a wide band of pH. In practice, it is more convenient to use a mixture of several buffering agents added in varying proportions to cover a wide range of pH. *In such systems, the buffer values of the individual components may be added to give that of the whole system.* This is one of the advantages of the formulation of buffer values. Many such standard buffer solutions have been studied and tabulated.[1]

One of the simplest systems of mixed buffers is that devised by McIlvaine and given in Table 101. It is made by mixing solutions of secondary sodium phosphate and citric acid in the proportions indicated in the table. Although there are only two stock solutions required to cover the range of pH from 2.2 to 8.0, there are

[1] See, for example, Clark, *The Determination of Hydrogen Ions*, Chapter IX, "Standard Buffer Solutions for Colorimetric Comparison."

TABLE 101

McIlvaine's Standard Buffer Solutions

*p*H	0.2 *M* Na_2HPO_4	0.1 *M* Citric Acid	*p*H	0.2 *M* Na_2HPO_4	0.1 *M* Citric Acid
2.2	0.40	19.60	5.2	10.72	9.28
2.4	1.24	18.76	5.4	11.15	8.85
2.6	2.18	17.82	5.6	11.60	8.40
2.8	3.17	16.83	5.8	12.09	7.91
3.0	4.11	15.89	6.0	12.63	7.37
3.2	4.94	15.06	6.2	13.22	6.78
3.4	5.70	14.30	6.4	13.85	6.15
3.6	6.44	13.56	6.6	14.55	5.45
3.8	7.10	12.90	6.8	15.45	4.55
4.0	7.71	12.29	7.0	16.47	3.53
4.2	8.28	11.72	7.2	17.39	2.61
4.4	8.82	11.18	7.4	18.17	1.83
4.6	9.35	10.65	7.6	18.73	1.27
4.8	9.86	10.14	7.8	19.15	.85
5.0	10.30	9.70	8.0	19.45	.55

McIlvaine, *J. Biol. Chem.*, **49,** 183 (1921).

really five buffering agents. The first of these is phosphoric acid-monophosphate; the second, third, and fourth are citric acid-monocitrate, monocitrate-dicitrate, and dicitrate-tricitrate, respectively; and the fifth is the monophosphate-diphosphate system. The corresponding ionization exponents are 2.1, 3.1, 4.4, 5.5, and 7.2, which cover the range of *p*H tabulated, giving values which are fixed to 0.1 *p*H. Other systems, usually covering much smaller ranges, have been evaluated to 0.01 *p*H and are more suitable for exact comparisons.

Buffer Action in the Blood. The high buffering effect in the blood, according to Alexander Findlay, professor of chemistry at the University of Aberdeen, "is shown by the fact that 40–70 times as much NaOH must be added to blood serum as to water, in order to give a normal red coloration with phenolphthalein; and more than 300 times as much HCl must be added to serum as to water, in order to give a normal coloration with methyl orange."

The *p*H of the blood is controlled by a number of different buffering systems, one of the most important of which is the carbonic acid-bicarbonate system. The following equilibria are involved:

$$HCO_3^- + H_3O^+ \rightleftharpoons H_2CO_3 + H_2O \rightleftharpoons CO_2 + 2\,H_2O$$

The secondary ionization of carbonic acid is inappreciable at the normal *p*H of 7.4 and need not be considered here. This system helps to neutralize the lactic, phosphoric, and carbonic acids, which are normal products of cell metabolism, and even the excess acids produced in such diseases as diabetes. Even a *large* amount of acid causes only a *slight* decrease in *p*H, because the whole equilibrium is displaced toward the right, and the only result is to increase the carbon dioxide in the blood. However, this change also is compensated automatically. The respiratory rate, which determines the rate of elimination of carbon dioxide in the lungs, appears to be controlled by the *p*H of the blood. When the *p*H falls, breathing is stimulated, the blood is aerated more rapidly in the capillaries of the lungs and the excess carbon dioxide is removed. When the *p*H rises to its normal value, the respiratory rate decreases once more. Because of its stimulation of the respiratory nerves, a small amount of carbon dioxide always is administered along with the oxygen in a respirator used for resuscitation.

Although the carbonic acid-bicarbonate system is important, it does not exert so powerful a buffering action as the various protein systems present in the blood. The chief among these is the hemoglobin-oxyhemoglobin system, which functions in two distinct ways. The first is the ordinary buffering action. The second is a shift in the carbon dioxide equilibrium, because oxyhemoglobin behaves as though it were a stronger acid than hemoglobin. Thus when hemoglobin is oxidized in the lungs, the resulting oxyhemoglobin tends to decrease the *p*H of the blood, and this changes additional bicarbonate to carbon dioxide, which is eliminated. In the tissues, the reverse change takes place. As the oxyhemoglobin is used up, the *p*H tends to increase, and this change is balanced by the absorption of additional carbon dioxide to form bicarbonate. This equilibrium therefore increases the capacity of the blood to carry away carbon dioxide, and the blood pigment is the most important carrier for carbon dioxide as well as for oxygen.

The function of the kidneys is closely connected with the regulation of the *p*H of the blood. They serve to eliminate the non-volatile products of metabolism, among which are the "fixed" acids resulting from incomplete combustion in the tissues, which are important factors in the *p*H equilibrium in the blood. The determination of the *p*H of urine by the colorimetric methods described in the next chapter is a simple procedure which often supplements other data in giving a complete picture of bodily function.

PROBLEMS AND EXERCISES

1. Define and explain the following terms:

(*a*) buffer index
(*b*) buffer solution
(*c*) rocking hydrogen electrode
(*d*) differential titration curve
(*e*) glass electrode
(*f*) Henderson-Hasselbalch equation
(*g*) pH in terms of e.m.f.
(*h*) pK_w
(*i*) quinhydrone electrode
(*j*) titration curve

2. (*a*) From the data of Table 84, page 350, calculate the value of the ionization exponent of water, pK_w at each of the temperatures listed. (*b*) Plot pK_w against temperature and interpolate the values at 20° C. and 38° C. (*c*) Calculate the pH of a solution at each of these temperatures if the hydroxyl ion concentration is 1.32×10^{-5} moles per liter in each case.

3. Assuming that the hydrogen behaves like an ideal gas, calculate the e.m.f. of the following cell:

$$\text{Pt, } H_2 \text{ (15 atm.)} \mid H_3O^+ \ (a = 0.027) \parallel Cu^{++} \ (a = 0.15) \mid Cu$$

4. If tin is added to a solution of hydrochloric acid in a sealed bomb, calculate the pressure of hydrogen which will be built up before the system comes to equilibrium, assuming that the activities of hydrogen and stannous ions are equal.

5. Making use of the data in Table 99, on page 443, calculate the equation for pH in terms of e.m.f. measured with the hydrogen and decinormal calomel electrodes at 12° C. and at 38° C.

6. Calculate the pH corresponding to a measured e.m.f. of 0.3000 v. at 12° C., 25° C., and 38° C.

7. Calculate the pH of a solution in which the e.m.f. measured with the hydrogen and decinormal calomel electrodes at 38° C. is (*a*) 0.3176 v.; (*b*) 417.2 mv.; (*c*) 367.0 mv.

8. Using the equation of Harned and Wright, given on page 446, calculate the standard potential of the quinhydrone electrode at 12° C. and at 38° C. and hence, referring to Table 99, write down the equations for determining pH with this electrode and the decinormal calomel half-cell system at these temperatures.

9. Calculate the pH in solutions in which the e.m.f., as measured with the quinhydrone system described in the preceding problem, has the values: (*a*) 0 v. at 12° C.; (*b*) 0.0876 v. at 12° C.; (*c*) − 0.0812 v. at 25° C.; (*d*) 42.5 mv. at 38° C.; (*e*) − 135.4 mv. at 38° C.

10. If a glass electrode system is set up at 25° C., employing a silver chloride electrode in 0.1 *N* HCl and a saturated calomel electrode, calculate the pH when the measured e.m.f. is (*a*) 320.6 mv.; (*b*) 0.0 mv.; (*c*) − 20.6 mv.

11. Calculate the equation for the *p*H of a solution measured with a glass electrode system like that in the preceding problem, except that a decinormal calomel electrode is substituted for the saturated calomel electrode. Using this system, what will be the values of *p*H corresponding to the measured differences in potential given in the preceding problem?

12. A solution of sodium lactate, $Na(CH_3CHOHCOO)$, is made by dissolving 0.1432 g. of the salt in 20.27 ml. of solution. The *p*H of this solution at 20° C. is measured with a quinhydrone electrode and found to be 8.42. Calculate the value of the ionization exponent and of the ionization constant for this acid, using the value of pK_w determined in problem 1.

13. (*a*) In the titration of 50.00 ml. of 1 *N* HCl with 1 *N* NaOH, calculate the *p*H after the addition of the following quantities of base: 0.00, 25.00, 40.00, 49.00, 49.99, 50.01, 51.00, 60.00, 75.00, and 100.00 ml. Plot the values of *p*H against ml. of base added, and draw the titration curve. (*b*) Repeat the calculations and draw the curve for the titration of 0.1 *N* HCl with 0.1 *N* NaOH. (*c*) Calculate and draw the curve for the titration of 0.01 *N* HCl with 0.01 *N* NaOH.

***14.** In the titration of 10.00 ml. of 0.1277 *N* lactic acid with 0.1244 *N* NaOH at 20° C., the following results were obtained with a quinhydrone electrode system:

ml. base	0.00	2.00	4.00	5.00	6.00	8.00	9.99	10.26
*p*H	2.72	3.33	3.69	3.85	4.04	4.43	5.88	8.00

If the ionization constant of lactic acid at this temperature is 1.33×10^{-4}, calculate the *p*H corresponding to each of the additions of base listed above and compare with the experimental values. Plot the calculated values in the form of a titration curve and show the experimental results as points for comparison.

15. In titrating 50 ml. of 0.02114 *N* benzoic acid with 0.1244 *N* NaOH at 20° C., the following results were obtained:

ml. base	0.00	1.07	2.46	4.77	6.73	7.48	7.82
*p*H	2.91	3.38	3.78	4.29	4.77	5.04	5.25
ml. base	8.33	8.42	8.63	8.67	8.71	9.82	11.86
*p*H	6.00	6.43	8.04	8.21	8.28	9.41	9.95

(*a*) Plot the values of *p*H against the ml. of base, calculate the endpoint from this plot, and compare it with the value calculated from the concentrations of acid and base. (*b*) Calculate the differences in *p*H and in x (ml. base added) between successive readings, calculate the ratio $\frac{\Delta pH}{\Delta x}$, and plot these chords as ordinates against the *average* value of x in each case, to obtain a *differential* titration curve, from which the endpoint of the titration can be determined more accurately than from the curve in (*a*).

(*c*) Estimate the value of pK_a for benzoic acid from the point of inflection in the titration curve and the minimum in the differential curve. (*d*) Calculate pK_a from the pH of the pure acid. (*e*) Calculate pK_a by reading from the titration curve the value of the pH when the acid is half neutralized: *i.e.*, when a volume of base has been added which is half that required to reach the endpoint of the titration.

16. The ionization constants of ammonia and acetic acid at high temperatures are found to be:

Temperature, ° C.	50	100	218
K_b for NH_3	1.81×10^{-5}	1.35×10^{-5}	1.80×10^{-6}
K_a for $HC_2H_3O_2$	1.8×10^{-5}	1.1×10^{-5}	1.7×10^{-6}

(*a*) Calculate the degree of hydrolysis, the pH, and the pOH in a 0.1 *N* solution of NH_4Cl at each of these temperatures, making use of the values of pK_w calculated in problem 2 whenever necessary. (*b*) Carry out the same calculations for a 0.01 *N* solution of $KC_2H_3O_2$ at the same temperatures. (*c*) Calculate the degree of hydrolysis of a 0.04 *N* solution of $NH_4C_2H_3O_4$ at each of these temperatures. (*d*) What do these calculations indicate about the effect of increased temperature upon hydrolysis?

17. (*a*) Calculate the buffer index of each of the buffering agents in McIlvaine's standard buffer solution at pH values of 2, 4, 6, and 8, and plot these values against pH on the same graph. Which buffering agent is most important at each pH? (*b*) Add the individual buffer indices to find the total buffer index of the solution at each pH and plot this curve on the same graph. Does this system show a uniform buffering action over the whole range of pH, or is it appreciably better at one or more points?

READING LIST

W. Mansfield Clark, *The Determination of Hydrogen Ions*, 3d ed. The Williams & Wilkins Company, Baltimore, 1928. This is the most valuable single book dealing with the topic of this chapter, although many of the numerical results quoted by the author have been modified by more recent experiments. It is written in a readable manner, and discusses completely the material to which the reader is introduced in the present chapter. References to particular sections have been made in the text.

H. T. S. Britton, *Hydrogen Ions, Their Determination and Importance in Pure and Industrial Chemistry*, 2d ed. D. Van Nostrand Company, New York, 1932. The first 250 pages of this book deal with the general theory and practice of determining pH. The last 250 pages deal with the influence of pH in such widely different fields as the precipitation of basic salts and hydroxides, the electrodeposition of metals, the tanning of leather, the manufacture of sugar and of pulp and paper, brewing, baking, water purification, soil fertility, dyeing, and ore flotation.

M. Dole, *Experimental and Theoretical Electrochemistry.* McGraw-Hill Book Company, New York, 1935. Chapter XXIV, "Potentiometric Methods of Analysis," and Chapter XXV, "The Glass Electrode," contain good descriptions of this material by a writer who has done much to develop the theory and practice of this subject.

M. Dole, *The Glass Electrode.* John Wiley & Sons, New York, 1941. This authoritative treatise on the subject deals with the experimental methods of measurement as well as the applications of the glass electrode in many fields.

S. Glasstone, *The Electrochemistry of Solutions*, 2d ed. Methuen and Co., London, 1937. Chapter X, "Neutralization and Buffer Action," deals with many of the topics of this chapter as well as additional material.

I. M. Kolthoff and H. A. Laitinen, *p*H *and Electro Titrations*, 2d ed. John Wiley & Sons, New York, 1941.

Auerbach and Smolczyk, "On the Theory and Practice of the Electrometric Titration of Acids," *Zeit. physik. Chem.*, **110,** 65–141 (1924). This article gives an exhaustive treatment of the theory of all types of electrometric titrations, and presents experimental data on a large number of acids, including determinations of ionization constants from the data.

CHAPTER 17

INDICATORS

Any substance which shows a characteristic change in a physical property, usually color, at some reproducible point in a chemical reaction, may be used as an *indicator* in the study of that particular reaction. In this chapter we shall consider the behavior of two classes of indicators — those used in neutralization reactions and those used in oxidation-reduction reactions. Both have wide use in volumetric analysis and in the study of properties of biological systems.

Neutralization Indicators

The simplest way to find out whether a solution is basic or acid is to test it with a drop of one of the familiar color indicators. Nature has provided a wide variety of substances which show change of color corresponding to certain changes in *p*H, and the chemist has synthesized an enormous number of pure organic compounds which possess the same property, and which often are superior to the natural products. Among the natural products which may be used as indicators, blueberry juice and grape juice are familiar examples, showing a characteristic color change when they are acidified with as weak an acid as citric acid, the chief acid constituent of lemon juice, or made alkaline with washing soda or soap. An extract of the common red cabbage, which changes from a red color in acid solution to a green in basic, was one of the indicators first to be used in neutralization titrations. The familiar litmus is obtained from lichens, usually of the genera *Roccella* and *Lecanora,* by the oxidation of the orcin they contain, in the presence of ammonia. It contains a group of indicating compounds, the most important of which is *azolitmin.* Although litmus paper is very convenient for test purposes, the extract is not suitable for precise titrations. At least one dye, formerly used as an indicator, *cochineal,* is of animal origin, extracted from the dried females of a small insect, *Coccus cacti* Linn.

Although neutralization indicators change color with changing *p*H, a systematic study shows that individual indicators change at different values of pH. Furthermore, the change is not abrupt, but takes place gradually over a pH range of several units. Some indicators change in the acid range, some in neutral solution, and some in the basic range. All of these facts are explained satisfactorily by the theory which Wilhelm Ostwald advanced in 1891 and which has been elaborated but modified only slightly as a result of subsequent work.

Ostwald's Theory of Neutralization Indicators. Ostwald[1] assumed that a ***neutralization indicator*** *is a weak acid (or base) with a color different from that of the anion (or cation) derived from it.* In some cases, only one form of the indicator is colored, and it is known as a **one-color indicator.** Phenolphthalein and other phthalein indicators are examples of this class. **Two-color indicators,** in which both forms are colored, are more common. The same theory applies to both types. In either case, the ionization of the indicator, like that of any other weak acid or base, depends upon the pH of the solution. Since the color depends upon the relative amounts of the indicator in the two forms, it also will depend upon the pH of the solution.

The equilibrium in the case of an acid indicator, HIn, would be:

$$\mathrm{HIn} + \mathrm{H_2O} \rightleftharpoons \mathrm{H_3O^+} + \mathrm{In^-}$$

For this reaction the ionization constant, which in this case is called the **indicator constant,** is written:

$$K_{\mathrm{in}} = \frac{[\mathrm{H_3O^+}][\mathrm{In^-}]}{[\mathrm{HIn}]}$$

Rearranging this equation and changing to the pH scale, as on page 455, gives:

$$\log \frac{[\mathrm{In^-}]}{[\mathrm{HIn}]} = p\mathrm{H} - pK_{\mathrm{in}}$$

where pK_{in}, the **indicator exponent,** is simply the ionization exponent of the indicator. When enough base has been added to

[1] Wilhelm Ostwald (1853–1932) was born in Riga. He became professor of chemistry in the Polytechnic Institute in that city in 1881 and attracted the attention of chemists by his work on the affinity constants of organic acids. In 1887 he was appointed professor of physical chemistry at the University of Leipzig. Here he established the first laboratory for instruction in physical chemistry and trained students from all over the world. Wm. Ramsay, T. W. Richards, and A. A. Noyes were among those who worked under this inspiring teacher. His studies of the ionization of electrolytes and the oxidation of ammonia to nitric acid were of fundamental importance. He founded the *Zeitschrift für physikalische Chemie* and was its first editor. He received the Nobel prize in chemistry in 1909.

neutralize 9 per cent of the indicator, the ratio of indicator ion to indicator acid is:

$$\frac{[\mathrm{In}^-]}{[\mathrm{HIn}]} = 0.1$$

or

$$p\mathrm{H} = pK_{\mathrm{in}} - 1$$

Similarly, when the indicator is 91 per cent neutralized:

$$\frac{[\mathrm{In}^-]}{[\mathrm{HIn}]} = 10$$

or

$$p\mathrm{H} = pK_{\mathrm{in}} + 1$$

In general, the eye does not distinguish a change in the color of the solution until about 10 per cent of the indicator has been neutralized, and cannot observe a further change after about 90 per cent has been neutralized. For this reason, the ***color range*** *of the indicator, that is, the range of* pH *over which its color change is apparent,* is about 2 *p*H units. The theory indicates, moreover, that the change in color over this range should not be abrupt, but should be a gradual transition from the full acid color to the full basic color. This is exactly what is observed. Quantitative studies of the absorption spectra of indicator solutions show that

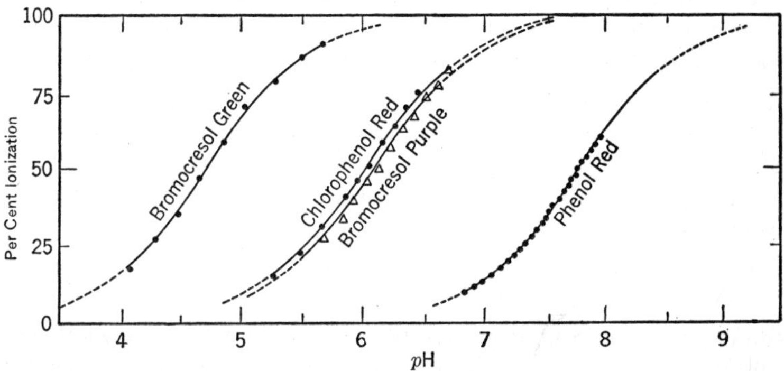

Fig. 201. Calculated Curves and Observed Dissociation for Indicators Used in Determining the *p*H of Urine. (After Hastings, Sendroy, and Robson (1925).)

both colored forms of the indicator exist beyond the range where the visible color change occurs and that their relative amounts are those predicted by the theory. The agreement between the simple Ostwald theory of indicators and their actual behavior is shown by the curves of Figure 201, where the values of the per cent ionization of the indicator are plotted against the pH. The theory predicts that the relationship between α (the fraction of the indicator acid which is neutralized) and the pH will be given by the same equation derived for any weak acid on page 463:

$$pH = pK_{in} + \log \frac{\alpha}{(1 - \alpha)}$$

The per cent ionization is simply 100 α. The experimental points in general agree with the curves which represent the theoretical equations and show that the behavior of indicators can be described adequately by the Ostwald theory.

When an indicator is *half neutralized,* the concentration of the ionic (*salt*) and un-ionized (*acid*) forms of the indicator are equal, and

$$\frac{[In^-]}{[HIn]} = 1$$

whence

$$pH = pK_{in}$$

The color of the solution under this condition is called the ***middle tint*** *of the indicator.* If the colors of the two forms of the indicator are of equal intensity, the middle tint will coincide with the color of the solution at the ***endpoint,*** *which is the pH where the greatest visible color change occurs.* Usually neutralization titrations are carried to the endpoint of the indicator. In the case of one-color indicators, the greatest visible color change occurs long before half of the indicator has been changed to the colored form. Thus according to Clark "in the case of the one-color indicator phenolphthalein, the useful zone lies between about 8.4 and 9.8 instead of being centered at 9.7 which corresponds to the point of half-transformation." In the case of two-color indicators, the shift of the indicator range is in the same direction, although somewhat less pronounced. The endpoint always occurs before the concentration of the form of dominant color has reached that of the paler color. Thus neutral red, which has an indicator exponent of 6.9 is much more highly colored in the red acid form than in the yellow basic form. For this reason, the useful range of the indicator is from 6.8 to 8.0, and the endpoint is about in the middle of this. Different experimenters may differ by about 0.1 pH unit in estimating the endpoint of the same indicator. The useful ranges of a number of representative indicators are shown graphically in Figure 202. The indicator exponents of the pure compounds are shown by the horizontal lines. These and other data are collected later in Table 102, page 480.

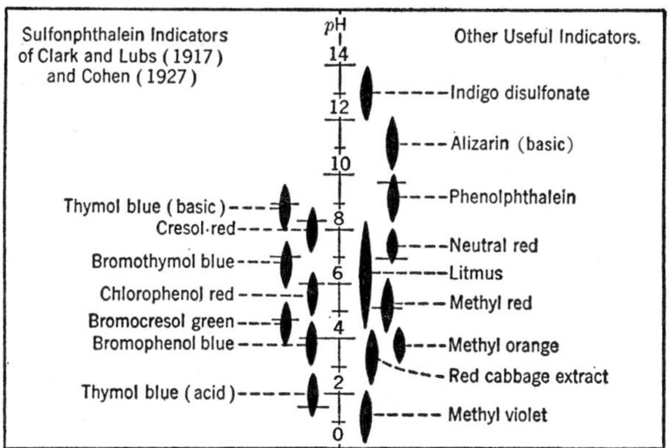

Fig. 202. The Useful Ranges of Some Common Indicators. Known Values of pK_{in} Are Shown as Horizontal Lines.

The simple theory of indicators which we have treated requires some amplification and revision in the light of the work of Hantzch and his collaborators, although Ostwald's equations are not materially altered. The color change cannot now be explained on the basis of ionization alone, but appears to be due to a tautomeric change of the undissociated acid into a *pseudo acid* which has a color different from that of the true acid and the salt. For instance, in the case of phenolphthalein, which is typical of all the phthalein indicators, the substance in the solid state and in acid solution is chiefly in the form of the colorless *lactone,* formulated in Figure 203. The heterocyclic ring set off by the dashed circle in the figure is characteristic of the lactone structure. This pseudo acid is in equilibrium with a very small amount of the tautomeric *quinone* form, characterized by the group set off by the dashed ellipse in Figure 203. The tautomeric shift involves the migration of the hydrogen from the phenolic hydroxyl group to the oxygen in the lactone ring, as indicated. The lactone form is not an acid, but the quinone form is a fairly strong acid. Its carboxyl group reacts with water to give the hydrogen ion, H_3O^+, and the negative radical, In^-, according to the schematic equation at the bottom of the figure. The formulation of this system requires two equilibrium constants:

$$\frac{[\mathrm{HIn'}]}{[\mathrm{HIn}]} = K_1$$

$$\frac{[\mathrm{H_3O^+}][\mathrm{In^-}]}{[\mathrm{HIn'}]} = K_2$$

Multiplying these equations together we obtain:

$$\frac{[\mathrm{H_3O^+}][\mathrm{In^-}]}{[\mathrm{HIn}]} = K_1K_2 = K_{\mathrm{in}}$$

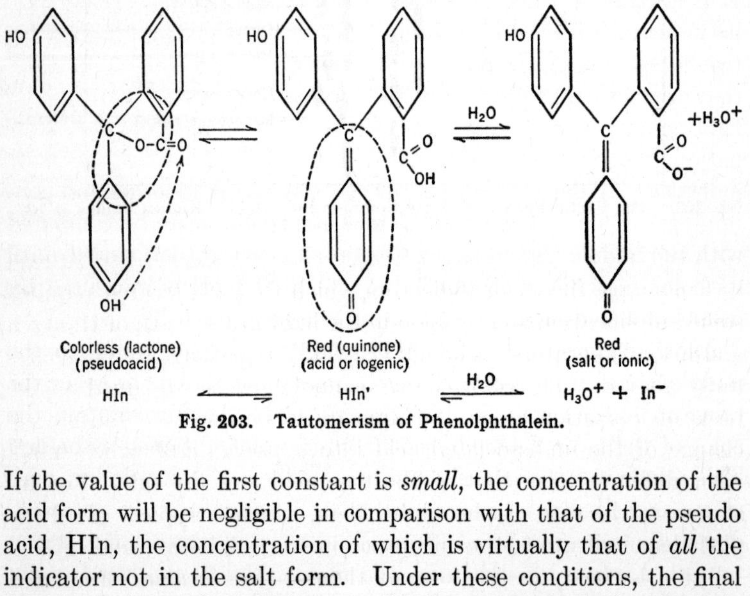

Colorless (lactone) (pseudoacid) — Red (quinone) (acid or iogenic) — Red (salt or ionic)

$$\mathrm{HIn} \rightleftharpoons \mathrm{HIn'} \overset{H_2O}{\rightleftharpoons} \mathrm{H_3O^+ + In^-}$$

Fig. 203. Tautomerism of Phenolphthalein.

If the value of the first constant is *small*, the concentration of the acid form will be negligible in comparison with that of the pseudo acid, HIn, the concentration of which is virtually that of *all* the indicator not in the salt form. Under these conditions, the final equation obtained according to the formulation of the chromophoric theory above is the same as that obtained by Ostwald. The value of K_{in}, however, is not interpreted as that of the ionization constant of the indicator, but as the product of the true ionization constant of the acid, K_2, and the equilibrium constant for the transformation from the pseudo acid to the acid, K_1. The constant K_{in} represents the *apparent ionization constant* of the indicator. Values of K_{in} are much smaller than the ionization constants of other organic acids similar in structure to the quinone form, apparently because of the very small factor K_1 by which K_2 is multiplied.

Determination of pK_{in}. The apparent indicator exponent is determined most easily by adjusting the pH of the solution until the indicator shows its middle tint, when the value of pK_{in} is equal numerically to the pH. The arrangement shown in Figure 204 affords a simple method of obtaining the middle tint of the indicator and matching it. The two tubes on the left contain equal quantities of the indicator in equal volumes. Tube I is made acid enough to convert all of the indicator into the acid form, and tube II is alkaline enough to convert all of its indicator into the basic form. The two tubes are superimposed, and when they are viewed from above by diffused light coming from beneath, the combination will show the middle tint of the indicator. Tube III, equal in length to I and II together and containing as much indicator as the two other tubes, can be compared with the middle tint from the others. Its pH is then varied until its color matches the middle tint, when the pH is measured by means of a hydrogen or other suitable electrode.

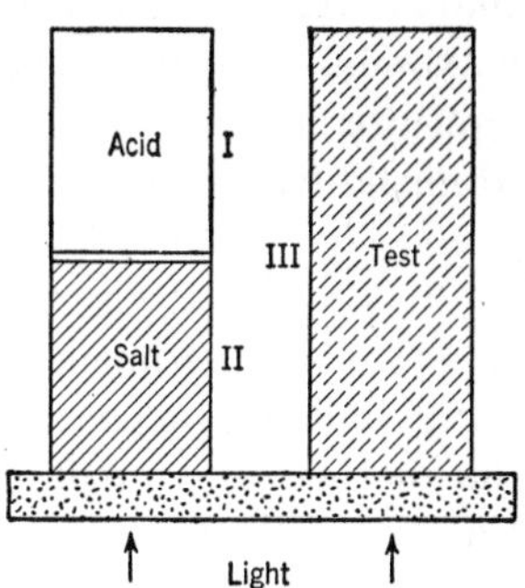

Fig. 204. Colorimetric Determination of pK_{in}.

Another method of determining the pH corresponding to the middle tint is to prepare a series of buffered solutions to cover the range in small steps, and determine in which buffer solution the color of the indicator matches the middle tint obtained as before. This eliminates the use of a hydrogen or other electrode but may give a slightly different result if the buffer solution is concentrated, due to the *salt effect* which we shall take up on pages 486 to 489.

With a one-color indicator, the middle tint is produced easily by taking a *single* tube on the left-hand side, and putting in it half the quantity of indicator in the test tube, with enough base or acid to convert it completely into the colored form. The test solution is then adjusted to the same intensity of color as the standard.

Another method, involving more complicated apparatus but capable of greater precision, is especially suited to one-color indicators. A series of solutions containing equal quantities of the indicator are adjusted to different values of pH over the range of the indicator. The color intensity is then measured by means of a colorimeter. Assuming that the intensity of the color is proportional to the concentration of the indicator, the ratio of the intensity at any known pH to that at a pH where the full color of the indicator has been developed will be the fraction of indicator in the colored form. For an indicator like phenolphthalein, with a colored salt form and a colorless acid form, the fraction of the maximum color intensity will give immediately α, the fraction of indicator ionized, from which the indicator exponent may be determined from the equation:

$$pK_{\text{in}} = p\text{H} - \log \frac{\alpha}{(1 - \alpha)}$$

A series of experiments carried out in this way will give values of the indicator exponent which serve as independent checks upon the method and upon the applicability of the simple indicator equation. Studies of phenolphthalein show that it does not conform exactly to the behavior of a simple indicator because the usual ionization of the carboxyl group is followed at higher pH by the acid ionization of the phenolic OH group.

TABLE 102

USEFUL DATA FOR CERTAIN INDICATORS

TYPE	INDICATOR	pK_{in}	PRACTICAL pH RANGE	COLOR		pH FOR "FULL"	
				Acid Solution	Basic Solution	Acid Color	Basic Color
Acid	Methyl violet	—	0.2–3.2	yellow	violet		
	Thymol blue (acid)	1.5	1.2–2.8	red	yellow	−1	6
	Red cabbage extract	—	2.4–4.5	red	green		
	Methyl orange	3.7	3.1–4.4	red	yellow		
	Bromophenol blue	3.98	3.0–4.6	yellow	blue	0	7
	Bromocresol green	4.67	3.8–5.4	yellow	blue	1	8
	Methyl red	(5.1)	4.2–6.3	red	yellow		
	Chlorophenol red	5.98	4.8–6.4	yellow	red	2	9
	Alizarin (neutral)	—	5.5–6.8	yellow	red		
Neutral	Neutral red	6.85	6.8–8.0	red	yellow		
	Bromothymol blue	7.0	6.0–7.6	yellow	blue	4	10
	Litmus	—	4.5–8.3	red	blue		
Basic	Cresol red	8.3	7.2–8.8	yellow	red	5	11
	Thymol blue (basic)	8.9	8.0–9.6	yellow	blue	6	12
	Phenolphthalein	9.7	8.3–10.0	colorless	red		
	Thymolphthalein	—	9.3–10.5	colorless	blue (color fades)		
	Alizarin (basic)	—	10.1–12.1	violet	purple		
	Indigo disulfonate	—	11.6–14.0	blue	yellow		

Selected from the comprehensive collection of 185 indicators in Clark, *The Determination of Hydrogen Ions*, Chapter IV, "Choice of Indicators."

Table 102 contains a list of useful indicators covering the pH range, selected from the collection of 185 listed by Clark. In addition to the familiar indicators and others which could be used for titrations, there are six which Clark and Lubs or Barnett Cohen studied thoroughly and found satisfactory for accurate *p*H determinations. For these, the *p*H required to develop the "full" acid and basic colors is included. This series covers the most important part of the *p*H scale, from 1.2 to 9.6. Clark lists a number of other indicators which duplicate parts of the scale covered by those given in Table 102.

Colorimetric Determination of *p*H. Knowing the indicator exponent of the different indicators, we can determine *p*H colorimetrically by the same methods. Unless we already know approximately the *p*H of the solution, it must be determined before we can pick out an indicator having the proper range for the measurement. The approximate *p*H of the solution usually is determined by means of a ***universal indicator*** — *a mixture of several different indicators which changes through a succession of colors as the* pH *is varied.* One such universal indicator, developed by Bogen and called a **rainbow indicator,** is made by dissolving in 500 ml. of absolute alcohol 0.1 g. of phenolphthalein, 0.2 g. methyl red, 0.3 g. dimethylaminoazobenzene, 0.4 g. bromothymol blue and 0.5 g. thymol blue. Sodium hydroxide solution is added dropwise until the color changes to the yellow corresponding to the neutral region. The colors over the whole *p*H scale are given in Table 103.

TABLE 103

BOGEN'S RAINBOW INDICATOR

pH . . .	**2**	**4**	**6**	**8**	**10**
Color . . .	red	orange	yellow	green	blue

After the approximate hydrogen exponent of the solution has been found, a more exact value is determined by means of an indicator which includes this *p*H in its useful range. For instance, if the rainbow indicator gives an orange color, indicating a *p*H of about 4, bromophenol blue would be chosen to make the careful comparison, since its range centers at *p*H = 3.98. Bromocresol green, the range of which also includes *p*H = 4, would be less suitable because the center of the range, where measurements may be made with the greatest accuracy, is about 4.6.

Wedge colorimeter. There are a number of methods of matching colors in order to find the exact *p***H**. One of the first of these is the **wedge method** used by Bjerrum in 1914 and modified by several later investigators. The apparatus consists of a glass trough, 30 cm. long, 2 cm. wide, and 10 cm. high, divided into two wedge-shaped halves by a diagonal plate of glass, as shown in plan in Figure 205. One of the wedges contains a definite

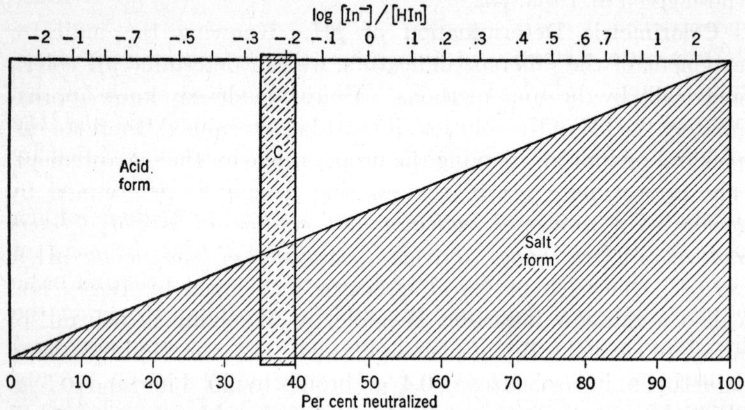

Fig. 205. Bjerrum Wedge Colorimeter.

concentration of the indicator in the acid form, while the other contains an equal concentration of the same indicator in the salt form. The unknown solution is contained in a narrow comparison cell *C*, the ends of which are closed with plane glass windows. The length of this cell is the same as the width of the double wedge, and it contains the same concentration of indicator. The cell is mounted on top of the wedge. Both are illuminated by diffused light from the back. The cell is moved along the top of the wedge until its color matches that of the wedge underneath. When the colors are matched, the ratio of salt to acid form of the indicator must be the same in the unknown solution as in the wedge, where it is simply the ratio of the thickness of the two wedges, and the *p*H is determined from the fundamental equation:

$$pH = pK_{in} + \log \frac{[In^-]}{[HIn]}$$

The Bjerrum wedge colorimeter usually is fitted with a logarithmic scale which furnishes the last term directly. This scale, as shown on the top of Figure 205, is most open at the center, where the units are widely spaced. On either side the scale becomes more and more condensed. The limit of accurate measurement is about $\pm$ 0.7, and the extreme limit is about $\pm$ 1.0. The change from 1 to 2 is less than that from 0 to 0.1. Near the center of the scale a small change in pH causes a large change in color, while near the ends the same change in pH causes no visible color change. This is why the center of the indicator range must be used for accurate measurement.

Drop-ratio method. In 1920 Gillespie [1] introduced the **drop-ratio method,** which is a simplified arrangement of the wedge principle. A double row of test tubes is employed, and the intensity of the acid and basic color of the indicator is varied by using different concentrations in the different tubes, instead of different thicknesses of solution, as in the wedge method. Each *pair* of tubes contains 10 drops of indicator, and the color of the pair depends upon the number of drops in the acid and basic forms. Thus the first pair contains 1 drop of indicator in the first tube, with enough acid to bring out the full *acid color,* and 9 drops of indicator in the second tube, with enough base to bring out the full *basic color.* The necessary pH in each case is listed in Table 102 with the indicators suitable for these measurements. Acids or alkalies of too great concentration cannot be used to bring out the colors of the indicators, since they sometimes cause undesired color changes. Thus phenolphthalein becomes colorless in very alkaline solutions, and all of the sulfonphthalein indicators, for which complete data are given in Table 102, are changed to a red color in strongly acid solutions.

The Gillespie drop-ratio method is illustrated in Figure 206. Looking through any *pair* of tubes we see a tint which corresponds to the same ratio of acid and salt form of the indicator as that of the drops of indicator in the two forms. The hydrogen exponent corresponding to this color is given by the formula:

$$p\text{H} = pK_{\text{in}} + \log \frac{\text{drops in basic form}}{\text{drops in acid form}}$$

Gillespie called the ratio in the last term as the **drop ratio,** and writes the equation as:

$$p\text{H} = pK_{\text{in}} + \log \textit{drop ratio}$$

[1] Gillespie, *J. Am. Chem. Soc.*, **42**, 742 (1920).

In the Gillespie method, the colors are spaced evenly on the scale of *per cent neutralization*, but unevenly on the pH scale, as shown in Figure 206. As compared with the wedge method, it is

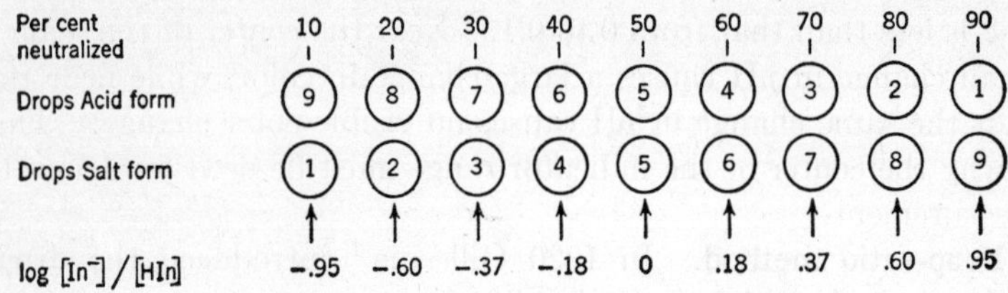

Fig. 206. Gillespie's "Drop-Ratio" Method.

simpler but lacks the continuous gradation in color. This can be remedied, however, by subdividing the interval between any two successive integral drop ratios. The indicator solution is diluted, *e.g.*, 1 to 10, and a total of 100 drops used in the pair of tubes.

Block comparator. The simplest way to test the pH of an unknown solution is to take the same volume used in the standard tubes, add 10 drops of indicator, and match it to the nearest pair of standard tubes. If its color is intermediate between that of two pairs, the value can be interpolated roughly. A better method is to back the unknown solution with a test tube containing water, which helps to compensate some of the optical effects of the pair of standard solutions. A still more satisfactory method, introduced by Walpole in 1910, is to use a simple **block comparator,** such as that shown in Figure 207(*a*). This is made from a block of wood in which holes for the test tubes are bored as close together as possible. *Small* holes are bored through the centers of the other pairs of holes. When the solutions are viewed through these smaller holes, much of the distortion of viewing the open tubes is eliminated. All the holes are painted inside with a flat optical black which eliminates reflection. If the unknown solution is colorless before the indicator is added, it may be backed with a tube of water and compared with successive pairs of standards. If

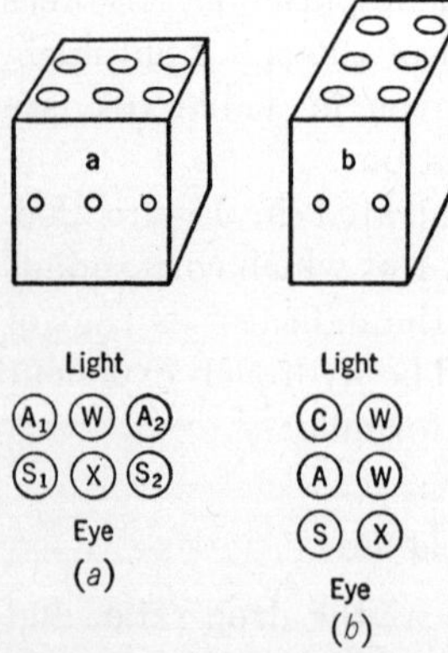

Fig. 207. Block Comparators.

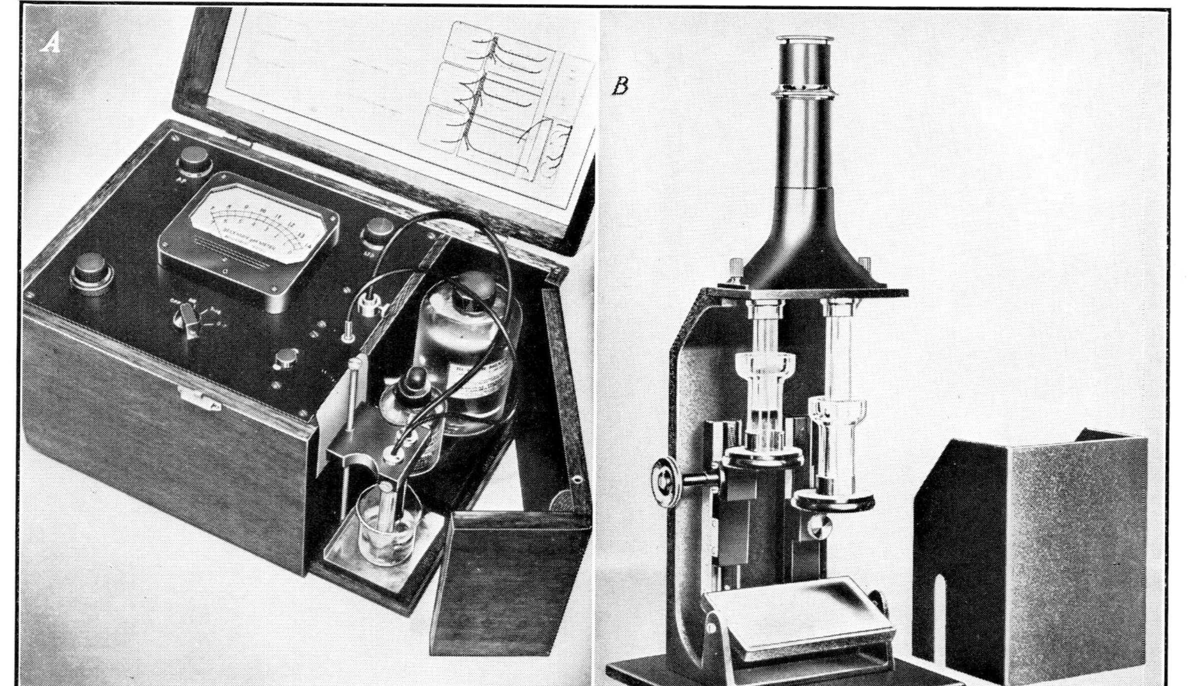

facing page 484

Courtesy of Arnold O. Beckman

Courtesy of Bausch & Lomb

Plate XII. (A) A *p*H METER (B) A MODERN BIOLOGICAL COLORIMETER

the unknown solution is colored, like many physiological fluids, an arrangement like that in Figure 207 (*b*) is necessary. Behind the alkali tube *S* and the acid tube *A*, a control tube *C* of the unknown solution is inserted, and comparison is made with the unknown solution *X* to which indicator has been added, backed by two tubes *W*, *W* containing water.

Precise colorimeter. More accurate colorimetric comparison requires some form of colorimeter, in which the two beams of light, reflected through the standard and unknown solutions respectively, converge through an optical system and are seen side by side in the eyepiece. One valuable type of colorimeter was developed by Gillespie in 1921. It is illustrated in Figure 208. The vessels *A*, *B*, *C*, *D*, *E* are made of colorless glass, with optically plane, parallel bottom plates. The unknown solution, with a suitable amount of indicator, is contained in *E*. If it is colored, an equal depth of the same solution is put into *A* as a control, and *D* is filled with water as in the Walpole system of compensation. The measuring system on the left consists of the two fixed tubes *A* and *C* and the movable tube *B*. *C* contains a solution of the alkaline form of the indicator and *B* a solution of the acid form. Both of these solutions have the same concentration of indicator as the unknown. *B* is connected to a graduated scale and may be raised from the 0 mark at the bottom, when it is in contact with *C*, to the 100 mark at the top, when it is in contact with *A*. At any intermediate point on the scale, the light passes through two layers of solution, the depth of the alkaline form of the indicator corresponding to the scale reading x and the depth of the acid form corresponding to $100 - x$. The *p*H of the unknown solution is found by matching colors and using the same equation as that of the wedge method.

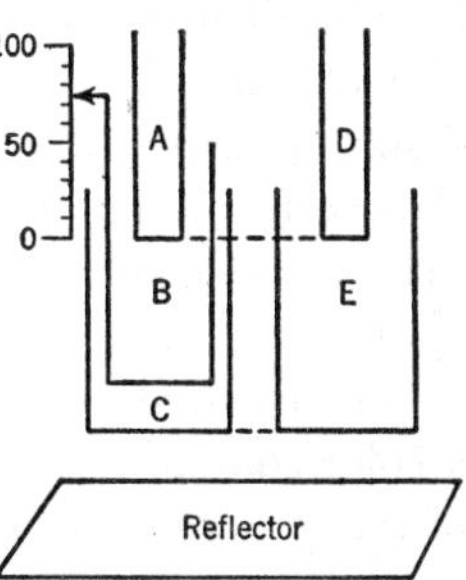

Fig. 208. Diagrammatic Section of Gillespie's Colorimeter.

A modern colorimeter is shown on Plate XII, facing page 484.

Dichromatism. All of the methods discussed above are based upon the assumption that the color intensity of a solution containing one form of an indicator is proportional to the *length of the column* and the *concentration of the indicator*. Experiment shows that this is not strictly true for most indicators and is far from true with some. *Substances in solution which change color when the concentration or depth of the solution is changed are said to be* **dichromatic** *or* **dichroic.** An excellent example of a dichromatic substance is bromocresol purple, one of the sulfonphthalein indicators, which changes from yellow in strong acid to purple in neutral solution, over a *p*H range of from 5.2 to 6.8, with an indicator exponent of 6.3. The purple color is a mixture of red and blue-green. As the concentration is increased, the relative intensity of the red light increases, and the indicator appears to change to a red color. This is clearly seen when a long tube of the indicator in the salt form is viewed lengthwise and then sidewise. Bromophenol blue is another indicator which exhibits troublesome dichromatism. It is difficult to distinguish the dichromatic color change from that caused by changing *p*H and to determine the *p*H of the solution accurately by any of the methods outlined above.

One method of avoiding error from dichromatism is to use a color comparator block or colorimeter, and to compare the color of the indicator in the unknown solution with that of the indicator at the same concentration in a similar tube containing the same quantity of a buffered solution of known *p*H. By making up a series of buffered solutions, the colors can be matched to any desired degree of accuracy, and hence the corresponding *p*H can be determined. Here again, however, the definite limitations of the colorimetric method must be taken into account.

Spectrophotometer. Another method of determining *p*H colorimetrically without the errors of dichromatism is to use a ***spectrophotometer,*** *which consists of a monochromator to supply light of a single narrow band of wave lengths, and a suitable arrangement for measuring the absorption of light in the solution.* Photoelectric cells with suitable vacuum-tube amplifying systems allow the measurement of changes of color intensity to 0.01 per cent. This method can be employed with suitable indicators to measure *p*H to $\pm$ 0.0002 unit within 1 unit of the indicator exponent, and to $\pm$ 0.01 unit within 2 units of the indicator exponent. It is much more sensitive than direct visual measurements and applicable over a far wider range.

Salt and protein errors. The color of indicators in solution is found to change when salts, proteins, or other substances are added to the solution, even though there is no change in *p*H. Thus if two solutions are made up with the same pH, as measured by the hydrogen electrode, and one of them contains a foreign substance, the two may give distinctly different colors with the same concentration of the same indicator and so may be assigned different pH values. *This difference due to salts is called the* ***salt effect*** *or* ***salt error****, and that due to proteins is called the* ***protein effect*** *or* ***protein error.*** The effect depends on the individual indicator, and on the concentration and valence type of the salt or the concentration and nature of the protein or other material. The effect varies from a few hundredths of a pH unit in the case of suitable indicators in solutions of salts like sodium chloride at 0.1 N concentration to nearly 1 pH unit for the protein error in a 1 per cent gelatin solution. Before making colorimetric measurements in systems involving salts or proteins or both, the only safe procedure is to determine the error for the particular indicator, over the range of concentration to be studied. The results of such a study of the salt error of *cresol red* in sea water of various salinities, carried out by Ramage and Miller, are shown graphically in Figure 209. The pH determined by the indicator is high by an amount varying from 0.11 to 0.27 pH, when the total salinity changes from 5 to 35 parts per thousand.

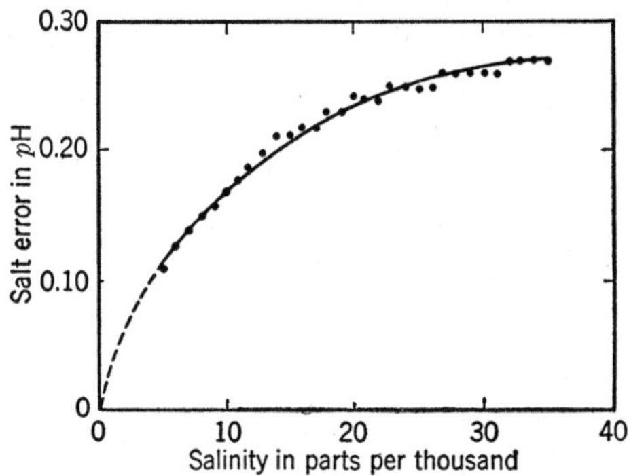

Fig. 209. Salt Error of Cresol Red in Sea Water of Varying Salinity.

The protein error of *bromophenol blue* and *thymol blue* in solutions of 0.4 and 1.0 per cent gelatin, as determined by St. Johnston and Peard in 1926, is shown in Figure 210. The error changes markedly with pH. It is least at the isoelectric point (see page 361) of the gelatin, $p\text{H} = 4.7$, and increases to a maximum at about $p\text{H} = 2.5$ for *bromophenol blue,* for which the error seems to be independent of the concentration of gelatin. In the case of *thymol blue,* the error decreases, and is decidedly less for the more dilute solution of gelatin.

In order to understand the cause of the salt and protein effects, we must reconsider the equation for the pH as determined colorimetrically:

$$pH = pK_{in} + \log \frac{[In^-]}{[HIn]}$$

This was derived on the basis of *concentrations*, but is completely valid only on the basis of *activities*. Since we have defined pH on the basis of hydrogen ion activity, the difference we are considering

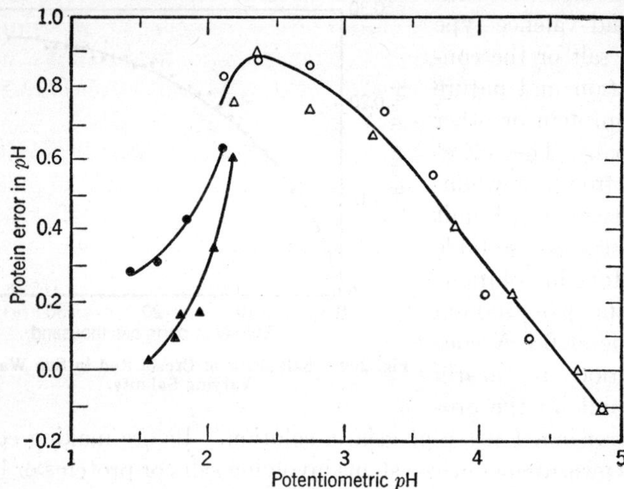

Fig. 210. Variation with pH of the Protein Error of Two Indicators in Gelatin Solution of Two Different Concentrations.

▲ and △ = thymol blue and bromophenol blue in 0.4 per cent gelatin.
● and ○ = same in 1 per cent gelatin.

here does not involve the hydrogen ion. However, if the addition of a foreign substance changes the activity coefficient of the indicator ion or the indicator acid or both, the ratio of the activities of these two forms will not be the same as that of the concentrations. The correct equation is:

$$pH = pK_{in} + \log \frac{a_{In^-}}{a_{HIn}} = pK_{in} + \log \frac{[In^-]}{[HIn]} + \log \frac{\gamma_{In^-}}{\gamma_{HIn}}$$

If the activity coefficient ratio is *less than unity*, the last term will be *negative*. The true pH will be *less* than that calculated by means of the simple equation; in other words, the salt correction will be *negative*. If the activity coefficient ratio is *greater than unity*, the last term, representing the salt correction, will be *posi-*

tive. As we have seen on pages 334 and 335, the usual effect of increasing the ionic concentration in moderately dilute solutions is to decrease the mean activity coefficient of the salt. With such solutions therefore, if the change is wholly in the activity of the indicator ion, we would expect the salt effect correction should be negative. In dilute solutions, the salt error can be explained satisfactorily on the basis of the interionic-attraction effect of the salt upon the indicator ions, as calculated by the Debye-Hückel equations and their extensions (see page 338). In addition, however, there often are specific effects of individual ions, which account for the positive salt corrections at higher concentrations. Positive corrections in the case of some proteins might be due to a relative increase of the activity coefficient of the ion or a relative decrease of that of the undissociated acid. Care must be taken to distinguish between the salt or protein *error* and the *correction,* which has the opposite sign.

These errors sometimes are expressed in a different way — as the change with salt or protein concentration of the classical indicator exponent or constant, defined in terms of *concentrations* as:

$$K_{\text{in}} = \frac{[H_3O^+][In^-]}{[HIn]}$$

This treatment seems to us less logical than that based on the effect of changing activity coefficients.

Use of Indicators in Neutralization Reactions. Acid-base titrations are fundamental to all analytical work, and a thorough knowledge of the use of indicators is of prime importance. The strengths of the acid and the base determine the indicator which must be used, the accuracy with which the endpoint can be found, and even the possibility of determining it at all. The object of such a titration is to find the *equivalent* quantities of the two solutions. *The* ***endpoint*** *of the titration is the point at which an equivalent quantity of base has been added.* The pH at the endpoint is that of a solution of the resulting salt. It may be greater or less than the neutral point of $p\text{H} = 7$, depending upon the extent of hydrolysis of the salt. Thus, in the titration of a strong acid with a strong base, the endpoint will be almost exactly at a pH of 7, at room temperature; in the titration of a weak acid with a strong base it will be greater than 7, and in the titration of a strong acid with a weak base, less than 7.

In choosing an indicator for any particular titration, *the indicator should change color at the* pH *of the solution of the resulting salt.* A neutral indicator like *bromothymol blue* would be suitable for the titration of a strong acid with a strong base. An acid indicator like *methyl orange* or *methyl red* would be used in the titration of ammonia with hydrochloric acid, while a basic indicator like *phenolphthalein* would be required in the titration of acetic acid with sodium hydroxide. The exact tint to which the titration should be carried can be determined by the use of a comparison buffer solution of the desired pH or one of the other colorimetric methods discussed in the preceding sections. In most cases, such exact comparison is not necessary.

In the titration of polybasic acids, different indicators can be used to distinguish the neutralization of primary, secondary, and tertiary hydrogen ions. Here a careful choice is imperative. In the case of carbonic acid, the following equilibria are involved:

$$CO_2 + 3\,H_2O \rightleftharpoons H_2CO_3 + 2\,H_2O \rightleftharpoons H_3O^+ + HCO_3^- + H_2O$$
$$\rightleftharpoons 2\,H_3O^+ + CO_3^{--}$$

Carbon dioxide, the anhydride, is soluble to the extent of about 0.03 M, under a partial pressure of 1 atmosphere, at room temperature. In this case, the primary ionization alone is appreciable, and:

$$[H_3O^+] = \sqrt{K'_a[H_2CO_3]} = \sqrt{4.5 \times 10^{-7} \times 0.03} = 1.16 \times 10^{-4}$$

or pH = 3.94. Although this is in the range of methyl orange, it is slightly too high to develop an appreciable acid color. This solution is *basic* to methyl orange. It would react *neutral* to bromophenol blue, but *acid* to neutral red, phenolphthalein, or any other neutral or basic indicator. These facts are clearly evident on referring to Figure 202, on page 477.

Water which is in equilibrium with the small amount of carbon dioxide in the air is only 1.5×10^{-5} M at room temperature. In this case, a similar calculation shows that the pH is 5.59. This solution would be basic to bromophenol blue and bromocresol green, as well as to methyl orange, but would be acid to the other more basic indicators.

When the first hydrogen ion of carbonic acid is neutralized, forming the bicarbonate ion, the hydrogen ion concentration is reduced to 5.0×10^{-9} M, as we have calculated on page 346. The pH of this solution is 8.30, which is on the range of phenolphthalein. A solution of a bicarbonate thus gives a weakly basic reaction to phenolphthalein.

When the second hydrogen ion is neutralized and the carbonate ion is formed from the bicarbonate, the solution becomes distinctly basic. If the resulting solution is 0.1 *M* Na_2CO_3, we have calculated on page 359 that the *p*H is 11.63. Although this is within the range of *alizarin yellow R* and also of *indigo disulfonate*, it would not be practical to titrate carbonic acid to the completion of this second stage.

Although the titration of carbonic acid is not often carried out, the reverse process is important in analytical work. Sodium carbonate can be neutralized quantitatively with an acid and actually serves as one of our most important acidimetric standards. The process warrants more detailed consideration. If the sodium carbonate is diluted with water to a 0.1 *M* solution, the *p*H will be 11.63. The addition of acid causes a decrease in *p*H which is gradual, due to the buffering of the carbonate-bicarbonate system, until the salt is nearly *half acidified*, as shown in Figure 211. The first break occurs at the *p*H of 8.30, corresponding to the bicarbonate solution. Since this is on the range of phenolphthalein, a titration can be carried to this point, using phenolphthalein as an indicator. The acid is added until the color is barely visible. A comparison solution of pure bicarbonate, containing the same concentration of the indicator, is a useful reference in fixing this endpoint. The addition of more acid makes the solution distinctly acid to phenolphthalein, the color of which disappears. The *p*H falls gradually, because of the buffering action of the bicarbonate-carbonic acid system, until nearly all the bicarbonate is converted into carbonic acid. Then the *p*H falls more rapidly to the second endpoint, corresponding to a solution of carbonic acid at a *p*H of 3.94. This is within the range of methyl orange, which may serve as indicator. The *p*H exactly at the second endpoint is slightly too low to give the middle tint of the indicator, but a fraction of a drop of the 0.1 *N* strong acid used

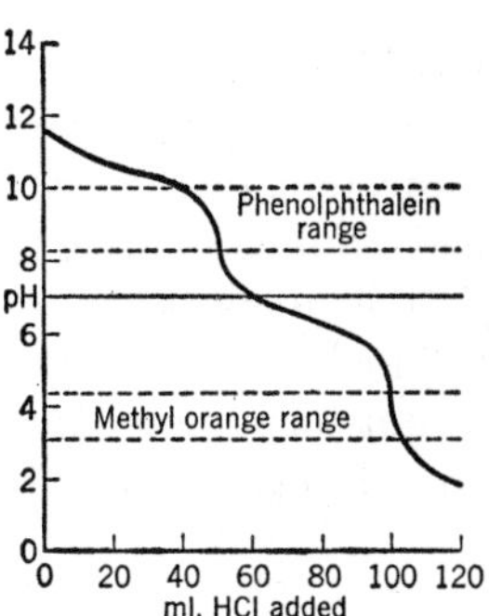

Fig. 211. Titration Curve for 50 ml. of 0.1 *M* Na_2CO_3 with 0.1 *N* HCl.

in the titration will change the color. The titration to the second endpoint therefore is exactly like the titration of any weak base with a strong acid.

Since the second endpoint is less than sharp that obtained with a strong acid and base, due to the buffering action of the carbonate-carbonic acid system, an alternate procedure is to use bromocresol green instead of methyl orange as the second indicator, carry the titration to the intermediate green color, then boil the solution for a minute or two to remove the excess carbon dioxide. During this procedure the pH increases and the color changes to blue and finally to a purple, caused by the mixture of the color of the bromocresol green and phenolphthalein. When the solution is cooled to room temperature, the titration is continued until the green color is reached.

The titration outlined above can be applied to a mixture of a carbonate and a bicarbonate or of a carbonate and a hydroxide, and allows the determination of both constituents of these mixtures. In either case a known quantity of the mixture is titrated successively. In the carbonate-bicarbonate titration, the volume of acid required to bring the solution to the phenolphthalein endpoint, V_1, is equivalent to ($\approx$) *one half the carbonate.* The additional acid required to bring the solution to the methyl orange endpoint, V_2, is equivalent to *the bicarbonate* originally present plus that formed from the carbonate. The difference, $V_2 - V_1$, therefore represents

TABLE 104

Titrations of Carbonate-Bicarbonate and Carbonate-Hydroxide Mixtures

Carbonate-Bicarbonate Mixture	Carbonate-Hydroxide Mixture
$V_2 \approx \frac{1}{2}$ carbonate + bicarbonate $V_1 \approx \frac{1}{2}$ carbonate	$V_1 \approx \frac{1}{2}$ carbonate + hydroxide $V_2 \approx \frac{1}{2}$ carbonate
$V_2 - V_1 \approx$ bicarbonate	$V_1 - V_2 \approx$ hydroxide

the volume of acid equivalent to the original bicarbonate. In the carbonate-hydroxide titration the volume of acid required to bring the solution to the phenolphthalein endpoint is equivalent to *one half the carbonate plus the hydroxide,* while the additional acid required to reach the methyl orange endpoint is equivalent to *one half the carbonate.* In this case the difference $V_1 - V_2$ represents the volume of acid equivalent to the hydroxide. These relationships are shown in Table 104. In practice these titrations are less accurate and convenient than titrations of single substances, because of the difficulty in determining the bicarbonate endpoint accurately, and because back titration is not practicable at the two endpoints.

Titration Errors. In the titration of a moderately concentrated solution of a strong acid with a strong base of the same normality, a fraction of a drop of either solution will change the pH by several units at the endpoint, because the titration curve is nearly vertical for some distance on both sides of the endpoint. When 50 ml. of 0.1 N acid is titrated with a base of the same concentration, the volume at the endpoint will be 100 ml. An excess of 0.01 ml. of either acid or base, representing 10^{-6} gram equivalent of hydrogen or hydroxyl ion respectively, will change the pH by 2 units. Since this quantity corresponds to an error of 0.02 per cent, which is less than that involved in reading the burets, any indicator with an endpoint between 5 and 9 on the pH scale would be satisfactory for this titration. If bromophenol blue were used as indicator, however, its endpoint color would be reached at a pH of about 3.8, before enough base had been added to neutralize all of the acid. This is a hydrogen ion concentration of 1.6×10^{-4} mole per liter, corresponding to an excess of 0.16 ml. of the original acid and an error of 0.32 per cent. Since this is 8 times the error in reading the buret, bromophenol blue is not suitable for this titration, unless the proper correction is applied.

If more concentrated solutions are titrated, the error will be correspondingly reduced; and if more dilute solutions are compared, the error will be larger. This is because the height of the vertical portion of the titration curve of a strong acid and base depends upon the concentration of the solution, as shown in Figure 212. In general, the error at the endpoint is inversely proportional to the strength of the solutions. Of course, if the final volume of the solution is increased by the addition of water, the error will also be directly proportional to the final volume. The error in the titration of 50 ml. of 0.1 N acid and base in a final volume of 1 liter, instead of 100 ml., will be 3.2 per cent if bromophenol blue is used as indicator. This is the same as the error in the titration of 0.01 N solutions of the same substances, if no water is added.

When weak acids are titrated with strong bases or vice versa, the break in the neutralization curve is much less than in the case of strong acids and bases of the same concentration. The change in *p*H is much less for the same addition of either reagent, due to the buffering action of the solution; hence the colorimetric endpoint, like the electrometric one, is much less sharp in the titration of weak acids or bases. In such cases it is imperative to use an indicator with the correct range and to match the tint *exactly* against a standard. To take a specific illustration from the titration which we discussed in the previous section, Kolthoff and Furman [1] show that when 0.1 *N* sodium carbonate is titrated with a strong acid of the same concentration an error of 2.5 per cent is made at the bicarbonate endpoint if the *p*H is in error by 0.3. Even when all precautions are used in this titration, an accuracy of better than 1 per cent usually is impossible. The reader is referred to Kolthoff and Furman's book for a detailed consideration of these more complicated cases, which are beyond the scope of the present volume.

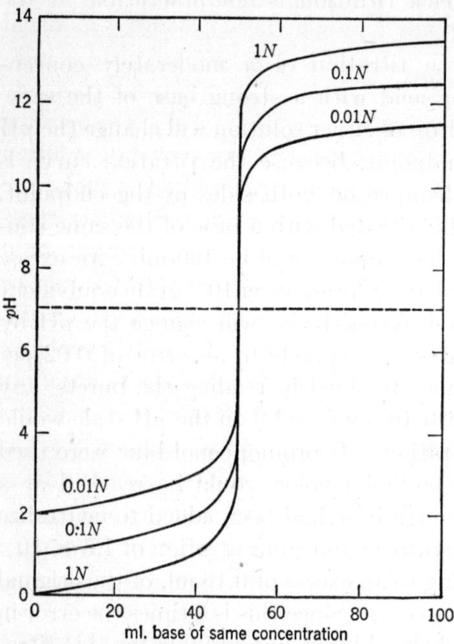

Fig. 212. Titrations of 50 ml. of a Strong Acid at Different Concentrations.

With extremely weak acids or bases the change of *p*H is so gradual at the endpoint that satisfactory titrations cannot be carried out with indicators any more than with a hydrogen electrode. If both acid and base are weak, the solution will be buffered on both sides of the endpoint, which will be much less distinct than if only one of the substances is weak. Hence a weak acid never

[1] *Volumetric Analysis*, Vol. 1, page 126 *et seq.*

is titrated against a weak base but always against a strong base. Similarly a weak base always is titrated with a strong acid.

Another possible source of error in acid-base titrations is the volume of reagent required to neutralize the indicator acid or base. The molecular weight of most indicators is about 300 or more, and usually they are employed in 1 per cent solution. Two drops (0.1 ml.) of an indicator which is a monobasic acid (or a monacid base) therefore will contain about 3×10^{-6} gram equivalent of indicator, which will require 0.03 ml. of 0.1 N solution for complete neutralization. If the solution is brought to the pH corresponding to the indicator exponent, only half of this quantity of solution will be used up. Since the resulting error is about the same as the uncertainty in reading the burets, it is not appreciable for these solutions. However, if 0.01 N solutions are being titrated, or if the quantity of indicator is increased to 1 ml., the error would be ten times as great and would have to be considered in careful work. Excessive quantities of indicator not only introduce the possibility of error as outlined above but also color the solution so intensely that the color change at the endpoint is less distinct.

Oxidation-Reduction Indicators

Oxidation-Reduction Curves. The potential of an oxidation-reduction system changes with the ratio of the two forms according to the equation:

$$E = E^\circ + \frac{RT}{nF} \ln \frac{a_{\text{oxidized}}}{a_{\text{reduced}}}$$

as we have seen on page 419. At 25° C., this becomes:

$$E = E^\circ + \frac{0.059}{n} \log \frac{a_{\text{oxidized}}}{a_{\text{reduced}}}$$

If we call x the fraction of the material in the oxidized state, then $1 - x$ will be the fraction in the reduced state. If the system is in a solution dilute enough so that the activities can be put equal to the concentrations, the equation then can be written:

$$E = E^\circ + \frac{0.059}{n} \log \frac{x}{1 - x}$$

This is exactly the same type of equation as that connecting the pH and α, the fraction of an acid in the salt form, which we have applied to an indicator acid on page 476, namely:

$$pH = pK_{in} + \log \frac{\alpha}{1 - \alpha}$$

The curve of the oxidation-reduction potential against the fraction of material in the oxidized state therefore is like that of pH against fraction of acid in the ionic form. This fact is clearly seen in Figure 213, which contains a plot of E against x for several common oxidation-reduction systems. The curves are all of the same type. They are displaced up or down the electrode potential axis, depending upon the value of the standard oxidation-reduction potential, which is the potential when the substance is half oxidized and the final term of the equation vanishes. They also differ in slope, depending upon the value of n, the number of electrons transferred in the equation for the reaction.

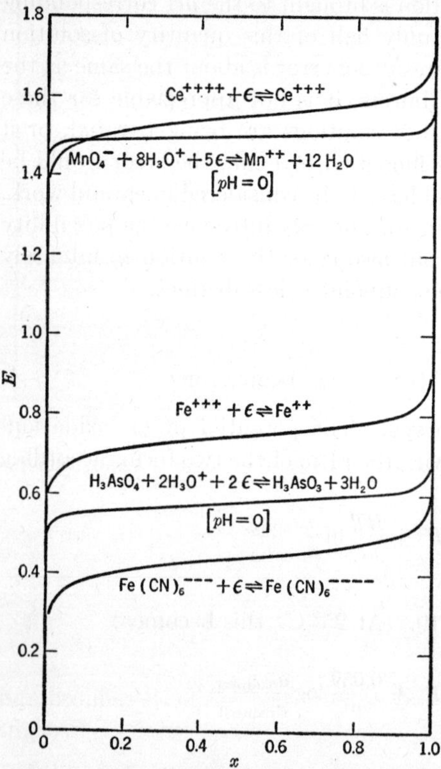

Fig. 213. Change of Oxidation-Reduction Potential with Fraction in Oxidized Form.

When an oxidation-reduction titration is carried out, two oxidation-reduction systems are involved. At every stage of the reaction, however, the relative amounts of the different ions adjust themselves so as to equalize the potentials of the two half cells into which the system could be divided. Hence an inert electrode inserted in the system and connected to a suitable reference electrode will give an e.m.f. which is that of the whole system which is being titrated. Such an oxidation-reduction titration can be carried out like a potentiometric acid-base titration, and the plot of the e.m.f. of the cell against the volume of oxidant added is similar to the plot obtained for the neutralization of an acid with a base.

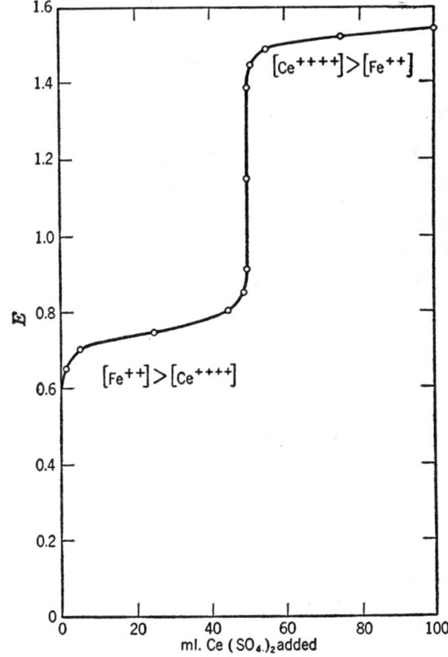

Fig. 214. **Titration of 50 ml. of $FeSO_4$ with the Same Concentration of $Ce(SO_4)_2$.**

Figure 214 shows a plot of an electrometric titration of 50 ml. of 0.1 *N* ferrous sulfate with ceric sulfate of the same concentration, using a standard hydrogen electrode as a reference electrode. The course of the curve is calculated as follows:

The chemical equation is:

$$Fe^{++} + Ce^{++++} \rightleftharpoons Ce^{+++} + Fe^{+++}$$

for which the equilibrium constant is:

$$K = \frac{a_{Ce^{+++}} \times a_{Fe^{+++}}}{a_{Ce^{++++}} \times a_{Fe^{++}}}$$

Upon each addition of the ceric sulfate, the cerium is reduced and the iron oxidized until the potential of the two electrodes is brought to the same value:

$$E_{Fe} = E_{Ce}$$

The potential of each electrode is given by the Nernst equation, taking the values of the standard oxidation-reduction potentials from Table 94, page 415. Equating the two gives:

$$0.77 + 0.059 \log \frac{a_{Fe^{+++}}}{a_{Fe^{++}}} = 1.61 + 0.059 \log \frac{a_{Ce^{++++}}}{a_{Ce^{+++}}}$$

Solving this equation for log K we find:

$$\log K = \log \frac{a_{Fe^{+++}}}{a_{Fe^{++}}} \times \frac{a_{Ce^{+++}}}{a_{Ce^{++++}}} = \frac{0.84}{0.059} = 14.2$$

or

$$K = \frac{a_{Fe^{+++}}}{a_{Fe^{++}}} \times \frac{a_{Ce^{+++}}}{a_{Ce^{++++}}} = 2 \times 10^{14}$$

This number is so large that each drop of ceric sulfate will be reduced practically *completely* to cerous and will oxidize an equivalent quantity of ferrous to ferric ion. Hence, until the equivalence point is reached, the fraction of iron oxidized is simply equal to the ratio of the volume of ceric sulfate solution, divided by the original ferrous sulfate solution. In other words, the potential of the system will follow the ferric-ferrous curve of Figure 213. The same is true for any titration where the oxidant is sufficiently powerful, *i.e.*, where its standard oxidation-reduction potential is considerably greater than that of the reductant.

Near the equivalence point, the potential of the system starts to rise rapidly. At the equivalence point, the chemical equation for the reaction shows that:

$$[Fe^{+++}] = [Ce^{+++}] \qquad \text{and} \qquad [Fe^{++}] = [Ce^{++++}]$$

hence

$$\frac{[Fe^{+++}]}{[Fe^{++}]} \times \frac{[Ce^{++++}]}{[Ce^{+++}]} = 1$$

Assuming as before that the concentrations are the same as the activities, we may *add* the Nernst equations for the potentials of the two electrodes to give:

$$2\,E = E^\circ_{Fe} + E^\circ_{Ce} + 0.059 \log \frac{[Fe^{+++}]}{[Fe^{++}]} \times \frac{[Ce^{++++}]}{[Ce^{+++}]}$$

Since at the equivalence point the last term is zero, the potential of the system is simply the mean of the two standard oxidation-reduction potentials:

$$E = \frac{E^\circ_{Fe} + E^\circ_{Ce}}{2} = \frac{0.77 + 1.61}{2} = 1.19 \text{ v.}$$

Beyond the equivalence point, the potential of the system depends upon the ceric-cerous ratio alone. The ceric ion concentration is proportional to the *excess* of ceric sulfate beyond the equivalent volume, and the cerous ion concentration to the quantity of ceric sulfate required to reach the equivalence point.

The values of the potentials at different points on the titration curve, and the method of calculating each, are given in Table 105 and plotted in Figure 214.

TABLE 105

THE POTENTIAL, ON THE HYDROGEN SCALE, DURING THE TITRATION OF 50 ML. OF FERROUS SULFATE SOLUTION WITH A CERIC SULFATE SOLUTION OF THE SAME CONCENTRATION, ASSUMING ACTIVITIES ARE EQUAL TO CONCENTRATIONS

ML. CERIC SOLUTION ADDED	$\frac{[Fe^{+++}]}{[Fe^{++}]}$	$\frac{[Ce^{++++}]}{[Ce^{+++}]}$	E (HYDROGEN SCALE)
1	0.022		$0.77 - 0.10 = 0.67$ v.
5	0.11		$0.77 - 0.05 = 0.72$
25	1.0	$[Fe^{++}]$	$0.77 \pm 0.00 = 0.77$
45	9	>	$0.77 + 0.05 = 0.82$
49	49	$[Ce^{++++}]$	$0.77 + 0.10 = 0.87$
49.9	499		$0.77 + 0.16 = 0.93$
50	$[Fe^{++}] = [Ce^{++++}]$		$\frac{0.77 + 1.61}{2} = 1.19$
50.1		0.002	$1.61 - 0.16 = 1.45$
51		0.02	$1.61 - 0.10 = 1.51$
55	$[Ce^{++++}]$	0.10	$1.61 - 0.06 = 1.55$
75	>	0.50	$1.61 - 0.04 = 1.57$
100	$[Fe^{++}]$	1.0	$1.61 \pm 0.00 = 1.61$

The considerations which we have outlined above account for the general shape of oxidation-reduction titration curves. However, they do not exactly reproduce the curves obtained with solutions of the concentrations normally employed in analysis. The activity coefficients in such solutions usually are appreciably different from unity. Since the activity coefficients of oxidizing and reducing ions cannot be studied by the ordinary methods, little is known of their numerical values, and they can only be inferred from those of similar ions which have been determined. In practice this is no handicap, since potentiometric titrations are carried to the equivalence point, which is marked by the vertical portion of the curve. Differential titrations also can be carried out with oxidation-reduction systems, and the curves are like those for the differential titrations of acids and bases, shown in Figures 196 and 198 on pages 458 and 460, respectively.

Whenever oxidation-reduction systems involve the gain or loss of oxygen, they also involve the reaction with hydrogen ions to form water or the reverse reaction. In such cases the potential of the electrode depends upon the pH of the solution. Thus oxidation with permanganate is carried out in acid solution if manganous ion is to be produced quantitatively according to the equation:

$$MnO_4^- + 8\,H_3O^+ + 5\,\epsilon \longrightarrow Mn^{++} + 12\,H_2O$$

The electrode potential will depend upon the activities of all the ions involved, assuming that of the water remains constant. The equation would be:

$$\boldsymbol{E} = \boldsymbol{E}^\circ + \frac{0.059}{5} \log \frac{a^8_{H_3O^+} \times a_{MnO_4^-}}{a_{Mn^{++}}}$$

This equation does not hold exactly, because the mechanism of the reaction is less simple than that which we have written, and involves ions intermediate in valence between the two upon which we have focused our whole attention. Since the reaction as written is not strictly reversible, the equation does not give exactly the effect of changing *p*H upon the oxidation-reduction potential, but it does show why this potential increases greatly with increase in hydrogen ion concentration. For all such reactions the *p*H of the solution must be known to allow an estimation of the potential.

Oxidation-Reduction Indicators. Many oxidizing agents change color when they are reduced, and thus indicate the endpoint of the reaction. The color changes with permanganate and iodine are familiar. Ceric salts, which are coming into general use as oxidizing reagents, change from yellow to colorless when they are reduced. In other cases the color change is not sharp; *e.g.*, with dichromate, the green of the chromic ion masks the orange of the dichromate. In such cases, it is convenient to add an ***oxidation-reduction indicator*** — *a substance which changes color at a characteristic and definite potential.* The oxidation-reduction change of the indicator should be reversible, and may be symbolized by the equilibrium:

$$I_{ox.} + n\epsilon \rightleftharpoons I_{red.}$$

For such an indicator the oxidation-reduction potential $\boldsymbol{E}$ is related to the standard oxidation-reduction potential $\boldsymbol{E}^\circ$, and the ratio of the activities of the two oxidation states of the indicator. Substituting concentrations for activities, we obtain the approximate equation:

$$\boldsymbol{E} = \boldsymbol{E}^\circ + \frac{0.059}{n} \log \frac{[I_{ox.}]}{[I_{red.}]}$$

facing page 500

Courtesy of Frederick G. Keyes

Plate XIII. ARTHUR AMOS NOYES

(*For biographical note see page 335.*)

Most oxidation-reduction indicators lose hydrogen when they are oxidized, so that the potential at which the color changes depends upon the *p*H of the solution.

One of the first oxidation-reduction indicators was **diphenylbenzidine,** which is formed easily by the oxidation of diphenylamine. Both are nearly insoluble in water but dissolve in concentrated sulfuric acid to form the sulfates. The indicator consists of a solution of diphenylamine in sulfuric acid. The oxidizing agent first changes this irreversibly to diphenylbenzidine, which it then oxidizes reversibly to diphenylbenzidine violet. The reactions are:

$$\underset{\text{diphenylamine}}{2\,C_6H_5{\cdot}NH{\cdot}C_6H_5} + O \longrightarrow \underset{\text{diphenylbenzidine}}{C_6H_5{\cdot}NH{\cdot}C_6H_4{\cdot}C_6H_4{\cdot}NH{\cdot}C_6H_5} + H_2O$$

$$2\,H_2O + \underset{\text{diphenylbenzidine}}{C_6H_5{\cdot}NH{\cdot}C_6H_4{\cdot}C_6H_4{\cdot}NH{\cdot}C_6H_5} \underset{0.76\text{ v.}}{\rightleftharpoons}$$

$$\underset{\text{diphenylbenzidine violet}}{C_6H_5{\cdot}N{:}C_6H_4{:}C_6H_4{:}N{\cdot}C_6H_5} + 2\,H_3O^+ + 2\,\epsilon$$

In this reversible oxidation-reduction reaction, the colorless diphenylbenzidine changes to diphenylbenzidine violet at a potential of + 0.76 v.

The closely related diphenylbenzidine sulfonic acid, which has the advantage of forming sodium and barium salts which are soluble in water, changes color at a slightly higher potential.

Another oxidation-reduction indicator, which is useful in titrations with ceric salts, is the complex *o*-phenanthroline-ferrous ion, which is oxidized to the ferric complex according to the equation:

$$\underset{\textit{red}}{Fe(C_{12}H_8N_2)_3^{++}} \underset{1.14\text{ v.}}{\rightleftharpoons} \underset{\textit{blue}}{Fe(C_{12}H_8N_2)_3^{+++}} + \epsilon$$

The blue color is so faint in the dilute solution of the indicator that it is practically a one-color indicator.

Oxidation-Reduction Indicators for Analytical Work. Table 106 includes some of the oxidation-reduction indicators most useful in analytical work, together with their standard oxidation-reduction potentials. These $E°$ values correspond to the *middle tints* of the indicators, when they are half in the reduced and half in the oxidized form. The visible *range* of color change covers a range of potential from 0.06 v. *less* than the standard potential, when the concentration of the oxidized form of the indicator is 0.1 that of the

TABLE 106

Some Oxidation-Reduction Indicators Useful in Analytical Work

Indicator	E°	Color	
		Reduced Form	Oxidized Form
Methylene blue	0.53 v.	colorless	blue
2,4-Diaminodiphenylamine	0.70	colorless	red
Diphenylbenzidine	0.76	colorless	violet
Diphenylbenzidine sulfonic acid	0.87	colorless	violet
Erioglaucine	1.00	green-yellow	rose
p-Nitrodiphenylamine	1.06	colorless	red-violet
o-Phenanthroline-iron complex	1.14	pink	faint blue
Nitro-*o*-phenanthroline-iron complex	1.25	pink	faint blue

reduced, to 0.06 v. *more* than the standard potential, when the concentration of the oxidized form is 10 times that of the reduced. If one form of the indicator is more intensely colored than the other, the *endpoint* may differ from the E° potential.

The choice of an indicator for a particular reaction depends upon the same considerations which we discussed in detail in the case of acid-base indicators. The endpoint of the indicator should be as near as possible to the potential of the system at the equivalence point, and small quantities of indicator must be used to avoid an appreciable error from the amount of reagent required to react with the indicator.

Potential Mediators. Reactions in many oxidation-reduction systems are sluggish and do not reach equilibrium rapidly in the presence of an inert electrode. In such cases it would be very difficult to determine the standard oxidation-reduction potential directly. However, the addition of a minute quantity of a more active oxidation-reduction system often will afford a mechanism by which the sluggish system may reach equilibrium rapidly and impress its true equilibrium potential upon the electrode. Thus in the measurement of the potential of the arsenate-arsenite system in acid solution, the addition of a small quantity of potassium iodide will speed up the attainment of equilibrium, which otherwise would be reached too slowly. In this case the reaction is:

$$H_3AsO_4 + 2\,H_3O^+ + 2\,I^- \rightleftharpoons H_3AsO_3 + 3\,H_2O + I_2$$

If only a trace of the iodide is added, it will not affect the original equilibrium appreciably, and the potential of the system will be that of the arsenate-arsenite couple, which then can be measured.

An oxidation-reduction system which speeds the attainment of equilibrium in a sluggish system is called a ***potential mediator.*** Ceric carbonate added to the arsenate-arsenite system furnishes the ceric-cerous couple, which also acts as a potential mediator in this case. Many of the oxidation-reduction indicators act thus as potential mediators.

Oxidation-Reduction Indicators in Biological Systems. Indicators are used extensively in biological systems to determine the oxidation-reduction potential, which frequently is as important as the *p*H. These systems usually are in the neighborhood of zero on the scale, so that they require indicators different from those used in analytical work. A series of such indicators is given in Table 107. Since most of these indicators are sensitive to changes in *p*H and some, like *neutral red*, are used as acid-base indicators, we have listed their oxidation-reduction potential in a neutral

TABLE 107

SOME OXIDATION-REDUCTION INDICATORS USEFUL IN BIOLOGICAL WORK

INDICATOR	$E^{\circ\prime}$ (*p*H = 7)	INDICATOR	$E^{\circ\prime}$ (*p*H = 7)
Methyl viologen	− 0.445 v.	Ethyl Capri blue	− 0.072
Sulfonated rosindone	− 0.380	Methylene blue	+ 0.011
Neutral red	− 0.325	Cresyl blue	+ 0.047
Rosinduline scarlet	− 0.296	Lauth's violet (thionine)	+ 0.063
Phenosaphranine	− 0.252	Toluylene blue	+ 0.115
Cresyl violet	− 0.173	2,6-Dichlorophenol indophenol	+ 0.217
Indigo disulfonate	− 0.125	Phenol blue	+ 0.224

solution, $E^{\circ\prime}$. This is more nearly applicable to biological systems, although for exact work the standard potential must be determined in a solution of the same *p*H as that under investigation. Its value also is affected by the presence of neutral salts, which change the activity coefficients of the ions involved in the equilibria.

In general, the oxidation of materials during cell metabolism does not take place by the direct addition of oxygen but by the removal of hydrogen or the addition of oxygen through a series of intermediate compounds which are called **respiratory enzymes.** These have definite oxidation-reduction potentials which differ progressively throughout a particular chain of enzymes. The potentials of these and other biological substances can be tested by adding small quantities of a series of different oxidation-reduction indicators and observing which of these indicators changes color.

Succinic and fumaric acids apparently form a reversible oxidation-reduction system, in the presence of **succinic dehydrogenase,** an enzyme found in muscle tissue. The equilibrium is:

$$\begin{array}{l}CH \cdot COOH\\ \|\\ CH \cdot COOH\\ \text{fumaric acid}\end{array} + 2\,H_3O^+ + 2\,\epsilon \rightleftharpoons \begin{array}{l}CH_2 \cdot COOH\\ |\\ CH_2 \cdot COOH\\ \text{succinic acid}\end{array} + 2\,H_2O$$

Using methylene blue as a potential mediator, the value of $E^{\circ\prime} = +\ 0.005$ v. is obtained for the potential of this system at a *p*H of 7.

Similarly, in the presence of another enzyme, lactic and pyruvic acids form a reversible couple, for which at a *p*H of 7 the value of $E^{\circ\prime}$ is $-\ 0.18$ v. The equilibrium is:

$$\underset{\text{pyruvic acid}}{CH_3{\cdot}CO{\cdot}COOH} + 2\,H_3O^+ + 2\,\epsilon \rightleftharpoons \underset{\text{lactic acid}}{CH_3{\cdot}CH(OH)COOH} + 2\,H_2O$$

These potentials indicate that lactic acid should reduce fumaric acid at a *p*H of 7, according to the equation:

$$HOOC{\cdot}HC{:}CH{\cdot}COOH + CH_3{\cdot}CH(OH)COOH = HOOC{\cdot}H_2C{\cdot}CH_2{\cdot}COOH + CH_3{\cdot}CO{\cdot}COOH$$

However, experiment shows that if the two systems are mixed the reaction is barely appreciable, unless a suitable mediator, such as ethyl Capri blue, is added. Here the ethyl Capri blue acts as a *hydrogen carrier,* which is reduced in removing hydrogen from the lactic acid, then subsequently oxidized again when it passes the hydrogen along to the fumaric acid. In this case, the potential of the mediator is about midway between those of the two interacting systems. Such an arrangement is found to be most effective, although the reason is not clear. *Processes of this type have been called* ***coupled reactions*** *or* ***carrier-linked reactions.*** Apparently the respiratory enzymes act as a series of such hydrogen carriers, forming a "bucket brigade" to bring about the stepwise oxidation involved in metabolism in the cells.

Studies of biological systems have shown that they are influenced by the oxidation-reduction potential of the environment and that they often tend to change this potential and to act as oxidizing or reducing agents. Thus the eggs of the sea urchin only develop if they are in a medium with a potential between + 0.15 and + 0.65 v., and tetanus spores will not germinate if the potential is higher than a certain threshold value. Anaerobic bacteria will not grow if the potential of the medium is higher than − 0.2 v.; hence the oxygen of the air, by keeping the potential above this value, prevents their development. The aerobic bacteria thrive in more positive (oxidizing) media.

Gillespie, in 1920, demonstrated that the growth of bacteria caused characteristic changes in the potential of their environment, as measured with a suitable inert electrode. Later workers have shown that strongly negative potentials (reducing conditions) result from the metabolic products of the bacteria. The values of these potentials depend upon conditions such as the amount of aeration and the presence of enzymes, and their continued study should clarify the way bacterial organisms operate.

A practical application of these studies has been the methylene blue test for milk. Studies by Clark and B. Cohen, in 1925, showed that in fresh milk at a *p*H of 6.5, the potential registered on a small gold electrode was about + 0.25 v. In milk bottled in the usual way and kept at 30° C., the potential remained nearly constant for a number of hours and then fell more or less rapidly to − 0.2 v. If the milk was obtained under sterile conditions, the fall was slower, while in milk inoculated with *Bacillus coli* the fall was very rapid. At a *p*H of 6.5 the potential of methylene blue is about + 0.05 v., so that when it is used in the test, it indicates that the change of potential is about half completed. The decolorization of methylene blue by milk is an indication that bacteria have developed to a considerable extent.

Methylene blue also can be used to distinguish between fresh and pasteurized milk, as Schardinger showed in 1902. Raw milk contains an enzyme which brings about the reduction of methylene blue in the presence of formaldehyde within 1 or 2 hours. Heat destroys this enzyme so that the methylene blue is not decolorized in the presence of formaldehyde.

Methylene blue can be used as an indicator in the titration of reducing sugars with Fehling's solution. The endpoint in the earlier procedure was taken as the disappearance of the last blue color of the cupric compound. With methylene blue a much sharper change occurs, as the first excess of reducing sugar bleaches the dark blue color immediately.

PROBLEMS AND EXERCISES

1. Define and explain the following terms used in connection with indicators:

(*a*) Bjerrum wedge colorimeter
(*b*) dichromatism
(*c*) endpoint
(*d*) Gillespie drop-ratio method
(*e*) indicator exponent
(*f*) indicator range
(*g*) middle tint
(*h*) oxidation-reduction curve
(*i*) potential mediator
(*j*) protein effect
(*k*) rainbow indicator
(*l*) salt effect

2. Formulate, according to the theory of Ostwald, the ionic equilibrium in a solution of an indicator which is a weak base, InOH. Show the relationship between pOH and pK_{In} in terms of the ratio of salt and basic form of the indicator, and derive an expression for the pH of the solution.

3. To what volume must 10 ml. of 0.2 *M* HNO_3 be diluted so that the resulting solution will give the middle tint with methyl orange?

4. How much must 0.15 *N* NH_4OH be diluted in order to give a solution in which thymol blue will show its middle tint in the basic range?

5. At what concentration will acetic acid develop the middle tint (*a*) with methyl orange? (*b*) with bromocresol green?

6. The middle tint of an indicator is obtained in a buffer solution, the pH of which is measured with a hydrogen electrode at 25° C., using a decinormal calomel electrode for reference. The e.m.f. of the cell is found to be 0.5714 volt, the hydrogen electrode being the negative pole. Calculate the indicator exponent of the indicator.

7. In a buffer solution at a pH of 9.1 a certain indicator is found to be $\frac{2}{3}$ in the salt form. Calculate the indicator exponent and indicator constant.

8. Calculate the ratio of salt to acid form at a pH of 6.35 for (*a*) chlorophenol red; (*b*) bromothymol blue; (*c*) cresol red.

9. Using bromocresol green as indicator in a Bjerrum wedge colorimeter, calculate the pH in solutions which matched at points on the wedge corresponding to (*a*) 13 per cent salt form; (*b*) 37 per cent salt form; (*c*) 42 per cent acid form.

10. A student tested a buffer solution with Bogen's rainbow indicator and found it gave a yellow color. He then tested it with a drop-ratio outfit, using chlorophenol red, and found a drop ratio between $\frac{7}{3}$ and $\frac{8}{2}$. A similar experiment with neutral red gave a drop ratio of $\frac{3}{7}$. (*a*) Were these results consistent? (*b*) What was the pH of the buffer?

11. Using a color comparator, a buffer solution is found to impart to phenolphthalein a color 9.6 per cent as intense as the full basic color. Calculate the pH of the buffer.

12. What indicators might be used instead of phenolphthalein in titrating sodium carbonate to the bicarbonate endpoint? In making up a color standard for matching the endpoint tint, what *drop ratio* would be suitable in each case?

13. In titrating sodium carbonate with a strong acid to the second equivalence point, what indicators might be substituted for methyl orange? What *drop ratio* in each case would be suitable in making a color standard for matching the endpoint?

14. Calculate the error in titrating 50.00 ml. of a 0.01 *N* solution of HCl with 0.01 *N* KOH, using as indicator (*a*) thymol blue; (*b*) bromothymol blue; (*c*) cresol red; (*d*) phenolphthalein.

15. Calculate the error in titrating 50.00 ml. of 0.1 *N* NH_4OH with 0.1 *N* HCl, using cresol red as indicator. Draw the titration curve and explain the situation with the aid of this curve.

16. Calculate the error due to the use of 10 drops (0.5 ml.) of a 1 per cent solution of a monobasic indicator of molecular weight 300, in the titration of 50.00 ml. of 0.08 *N* HCl with 0.08 *N* NaOH.

17. A 25.00 ml. sample of a solution containing a mixture of potassium carbonate and bicarbonate is analyzed by titration with 0.1025 *N* HCl. The volume of acid required to reach the phenolphthalein endpoint is 20.14 ml., and the *total* volume required to reach the methyl orange endpoint is 47.62 ml. Calculate (*a*) the total normality of the basic material; (*b*) the molarity of the bicarbonate; (*c*) the total weight of potassium salt in the original sample of solution.

18. A sample of sodium hydroxide stood for some time in the open, exposed to carbon dioxide of the air. When a 20.00 ml. sample of the solution is titrated with 0.1050 *N* HCl, a volume of 30.16 ml. is required to reach the phenolphthalein endpoint and 5.32 ml. more is required to reach the methyl orange endpoint. Calculate (*a*) the normality of the original hydroxide solution; (*b*) the per cent of the hydroxide which was converted into carbonate; (*c*) the weight of solid in 25.00 ml. of the original solution.

19. Calculate the oxidation-reduction potential at representative points during the oxidation of 50.00 ml. of a dilute K_2MnO_4 solution by a dilute $Ce(SO_4)_2$ solution of the same concentration, and plot the titration curve.

20. Calculate and plot the titration curve for the reaction between 50 ml. of a dilute solution of $FeCl_3$ and a solution of $SnCl_2$ of the same concentration.

21. (*a*) Write down the complete equation for the potential of the diphenylbenzidine violet-diphenylbenzidine couple. From this equation calculate the value of $E^{\circ\prime}$, the oxidation-reduction potential for equal activities of the oxidized and reduced forms, in terms of $\boldsymbol{E}^\circ$ and the *p*H of the solution. (*b*) Calculate the value of $\boldsymbol{E}^{\circ\prime}$ at a *p*H of 7, and compare the oxidizing strength of the couple under standard conditions and in a neutral solution.

22. (*a*) Write down the complete equation for the potential of the arsenate-arsenite electrode. (*b*) Calculate the value of this potential in a solution to which enough $NaHCO_3$ has been added to bring the *p*H to that of this salt. Under these conditions, would arsenite reduce iodine completely? (*c*) Calculate the arsenate-arsenite potential in a 4 *m* solution of HCl. Would arsenite reduce iodine under these conditions? How may these calculations apply to analytical work?

23. Calculate the oxidation-reduction potentials at which (*a*) methylene blue is 0.25 oxidized; (*b*) diphenylbenzidine is 0.90 oxidized; (*c*) erioglaucine is 75 per cent oxidized.

24. Assuming that the endpoint in each titration corresponds to the potential at which the indicator is half oxidized, calculate the error in titrating 0.1 *N* $FeSO_4$ with a 0.1 *N* solution of $Ce(NO_3)_4$ in HNO_3, using as indicator: (*a*) diphenylbenzidine; (*b*) erioglaucine; (*c*) *o*-phenanthroline-iron complex; (*d*) nitro-*o*-phenanthroline-iron complex.

25. If a 0.01 *N* solution of $K_4Fe(CN)_6$ is titrated with 0.01 *N* $KMnO_4$ solution, keeping the $pH = 0$, determine which of the indicators in Table 106 is most suitable for the determination of the endpoint, and calculate the value of the error in its use.

26. Calculate the decrease in free energy when lactic acid is oxidized by fumaric acid at a *p*H of 7.

27. Plot the titration curve for the reaction between lactic and fumaric acids in the presence of the appropriate enzymes and ethyl Capri blue, at a *p*H of 7. If the endpoint of this titration is taken at the middle tint of the indicator, how nearly quantitative is the titration?

READING LIST

I. M. Kolthoff, *The Colorimetric and Potentiometric Determination of p*H. John Wiley & Sons, New York, 1931. This book contains a good discussion of the theory of indicators, and of colorimetric and potentiometric measurement of *p*H.

I. M. Kolthoff, *Indicators*, rev. and enl. by N. H. Furman. John Wiley & Sons, New York, 1926. This book gives a clear discussion of neutralization curves and buffers and the theory and practical applications of indicators. It contains many references to the original literature of the subject.

H. T. S. Britton, *Hydrogen Ions*, 2d ed. D. Van Nostrand Company, New York, 1932. Chapter XII, "Colorimetric Methods for the Determination of Hydrogen Ion Concentrations."

F. L. LaMotte, W. R. Kenny, and A. B. Reed, *p*H *and Its Practical Application.* The Williams & Wilkins Company, Baltimore, 1932. An excellent summary.

W. M. Clark, *The Determination of Hydrogen Ions*, 3d ed. The Williams & Wilkins Company, Baltimore, 1928. Chapter VI of this excellent treatise deals with "Approximate Determinations with Indicators."

E. Brennecke, N. H. Furman, H. Stamm, R. Lang, and K. Fajans, *Newer Methods of Volumetric Chemical Analysis.* D. Van Nostrand Company, New York, 1938. This includes a good discussion of the theory and practice of oxidation-reduction indicators.

S. Glasstone, *Oxidation-Reduction Potentials and Their Applications.* The Institute of Chemistry of Great Britain and Ireland, London, 1937. This lecture of 28 pages gives a concise discussion of the theory and a good résumé of biological applications of these measurements.

Kurt G. Stern, "Biological Oxidations and Reductions," *Ann. Rev. Biochem.* **9,** 1 (1940). This article deals with studies of respiratory enzymes, complex systems of respiratory mediators, catalase, the breakdown of pyruvic acid, and other biological reactions.

CHAPTER 18

ADSORPTION

The property known as *adsorption* was described first in 1773 by the Swedish chemist Scheele,[1] who observed that gases were taken up by charcoal. He showed, for example, that a piece of charcoal, heated to drive out the air and then allowed to rise through a mercury column enclosing air in a tube, took up the air so strongly that the mercury rose in the tube. The fact that charcoal removes organic colors from solutions also has been known for a long time. Although this property of *adsorption* is fundamentally involved in many chemical processes, its importance has been fully realized only within recent years. Its role in chemistry is indicated by the applications discussed on pages 525 to 530.

Definition of Adsorption. *Adsorption* is a property of surfaces. A *surface* exists whenever two phases, such as solid and liquid, solid and gas, liquid and liquid, or liquid and gas, are in contact. When water is contained in an open beaker, there is a surface between water and glass and another between water and air. We ordinarily refer to the latter as the surface of the water, but it might equally well be called the surface of the air. *The same layer of matter forms a surface to each of the two phases and is called the* ***interface.*** Adsorption results in either an increase or a decrease of the concentration of some constituent of the environment in this interfacial layer. Hence, *we may define* ***adsorption*** *as an alteration in concentration in an interface.* The adsorption in a given case may be further described as *positive* or *negative*, depending upon whether there is an increase or a decrease in concentration in the interface.

Surface Energy. Adsorption is linked with two other properties of surfaces, *surface tension* and *surface energy.* The properties at a surface are different from those in the interior of a substance. There is, for example, a difference in the distribution of molecular forces. Each molecule in the interior of a substance is completely surrounded by other molecules so that the attractive forces acting

[1] His work is reprinted in Ostwald's *Klassiker der exakten Wissenschaften*, No. 58, 1894.

upon it are equal in all directions. At the surface, however, there is a net attraction *inwards.* Consequently surface molecules behave differently from those in the interior. This difference is evidenced as *surface tension* (see page 131), which tends to diminish the area of the surface and hence causes liquids to assume the shape presenting *minimum surface area.*

The relation between surface tension and surface area may be shown in another way. *The product of the surface tension, in dynes per cm., and the surface area, in sq. cm., is called the* **surface energy,** *which is expressed in ergs* (dynes $\times$ cm.$^{-1}$ $\times$ cm.^{2} = dyne $\times$ cm. = ergs). According to the principles of thermodynamics (see page 629) equilibrium is attained in a system when the free energy is at a minimum. Therefore, the surface of a substance will tend to assume that form which corresponds to minimum surface energy. This accounts for the fact that a freely falling drop tends to become spherical in shape.

Surface Tension and Adsorption. If a substance which is even minutely soluble is added to an adsorbent, the surface tension of the adsorbent is altered. When the added substance lowers the surface tension of the adsorbent, its concentration will be greater in the interface than in the interior, and the adsorption is *positive.* This fulfills the condition that the surface energy tends to a minimum. If no other influence were at work, the added substance would all remain in the interface, but just as soon as a difference in concentration is established between the interface and the interior of the adsorbent, *diffusion* comes into play, and the actual equilibrium concentration in the interface is the resultant of these two tendencies. When the added substance raises the surface tension of the adsorbent, its concentration will be less in the interface than in the adsorbent, and the adsorption is *negative.* Soaps, fatty acids, alcohols, and amines lower the surface tension of water and show positive adsorption in the water-air interface. Glycerol, sucrose, and dextrose raise the surface tension and are negatively adsorbed.

The greater the surface tension of a liquid the higher it will rise in a capillary tube (see page 133). Hence, if a substance increases the surface tension of water, its solutions rise in the capillary higher than the pure water. Such substances are said to be *capillary active;* those which show a very small positive or a negative effect are called *capillary inactive.*

Adsorbent Materials. Although every solid substance doubtless possesses the property of adsorption to a certain degree, some act much more powerfully than others. Since adsorption is a surface phenomenon, a given substance will adsorb more powerfully the greater the surface it presents to the adsorbed substance, the *adsorbate.* Powerful adsorbents are, in general, porous substances. *Charcoal,* because of its easy preparation and its high porosity, long has been useful as an adsorbent. *Silica gel* and *calcined alumina* also are important. *Colloidal suspensions* adsorb powerfully because of their great surface. Various metals adsorb strongly, and *platinum black, palladium sponge,* and *catalytic nickel* probably owe their catalytic activity to this cause.

The adsorbent power of charcoal depends upon the nature of the organic material from which it is prepared and the method of preparation. Impregnation of the organic material with various substances prior to the heating, careful control of the temperature, and heating with superheated steam yield **activated charcoal** with exceptional adsorptive power. Barker [1] has compared the power of different charcoals as adsorbents for carbon tetrachloride from the saturated vapor at 24° C. One gram of ordinary wood charcoal adsorbed 0.011 g. CCl_4; coconut-shell charcoal, 0.018 g.; the residue from heating lignite, 0.030 g.; activated coconut charcoal, 0.630 g.; activated lignite residue, 0.640 g.; best activated wood charcoal, 1.480 g.; and best activated lignite residue, 2.715 g. Thus **activation** may increase the adsorbent capacity about 15,000 per cent.

Silica gel is made by pouring together, with stirring, equal volumes of sodium silicate solution, of about 1.18 specific gravity, and 10 per cent hydrochloric acid, at about 50° C. A silicic acid jelly forms, which is washed nearly free from electrolyte by repeatedly crushing the jelly with water and is dried by heating to about 300° C. The dried gel is highly porous and strongly adsorbent; it finds extensive industrial application.

The Rate of Adsorption. When the adsorption of a substance by a solid has attained a maximum, a true equilibrium exists in the interface between the adsorbent and the environment. In its earlier stages adsorption is rapid. Thus, in one experiment [2] an activated charcoal was placed in an apparatus through which a

[1] *Ind. Eng. Chem.*, **22**, 926 (1930).
[2] Lamb, Wilson, and Chaney, *Ind. Eng. Chem.*, **11**, 420 (1919).

mixture of chloropicrin and air, containing 7 per cent of the chloropicrin, was flowing rapidly. It was found that 99.99 per cent of the chloropicrin was adsorbed in 0.03 second. The final stage in reaching equilibrium usually is very slow. At room temperature about 1 hour is required for the attainment of equilibrium between acetic acid solution and charcoal. As the temperature is raised, the rate of adsorption becomes more rapid although the amount of substance adsorbed by a given quantity of adsorbent usually is decreased.

Adsorption of a Gas by a Solid. The quantity of gas adsorbed by a given weight of solid depends upon several factors, *e.g.*, the nature of the solid, the method of its preparation, and any treatment, either before or after its preparation, which would alter the surface. It depends also upon the temperature, the pressure, and especially upon the nature of the gas.

The dependence of adsorption upon the nature of the gas and upon the temperature is illustrated by the data in Tables 108 and 109. Since the adsorption of a gas may depend upon the ease with which it is liquefied, some have tried to correlate adsorption with the

TABLE 108

ADSORPTION OF VARIOUS GASES BY CHARCOAL

Gas	B.P. ° C.	Crit. Temp. ° C.	Vol. (S.T.P.) Adsorbed by 1 Ml. Charcoal	
			0° C.	− 185° C.
Helium	− 268.9	− 267.9	2	15
Hydrogen	− 252.7	− 239.9	4	135
Nitrogen	− 195.8	− 147.1	15	155
Oxygen	− 183	− 118.8	18	230

TABLE 109

ADSORPTION OF VARIOUS GASES BY 1 GM. OF CHARCOAL AT 15° C.

Gas	B.P. ° C.	Crit. Temp. ° C.	Ml. Gas (S.T.P.) Adsorbed	Gas	B.P. ° C.	Crit. Temp. ° C.	Ml. Gas (S.T.P.) Adsorbed
H_2	− 252.7	− 239.9	5	N_2O	− 89.5	36.5	54
N_2	− 195.8	− 147.1	8	HCl	− 85	51.4	72
O_2	− 183	− 118.8	8	H_2S	− 59.6	100.4	99
CO	− 192	− 139	9	NH_3	− 33.4	132.4	181
CH_4	− 184	− 82.5	16	Cl_2	− 34.6	144.0	235
CO_2	− 78.5 (subl.)	31.1	48	SO_2	− 10.0	157.2	380

boiling point of the gas, and some with the critical temperature. Both of these temperatures are included in Tables 108 and 109.

From these data several important general conclusions can be drawn: (1) Adsorption of gases by solids is a highly selective process. Hydrogen sulfide, for example, is adsorbed by charcoal much more strongly than is hydrogen or carbon dioxide. (2) The lower the temperature the greater the adsorption. (3) In general the higher the boiling point of the substance or the higher its critical temperature the greater the adsorption.

Effect of Pressure on Gas Adsorption. A solid exposed to a gas at a given temperature will adsorb the gas until equilibrium between the interface and the gas phase has been reached. An

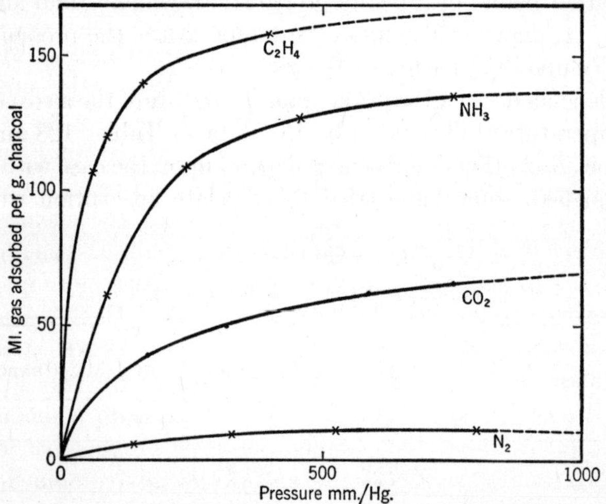

Fig. 215. Adsorption Isotherms for Various Gases at 0° C.

increase in pressure of the gas causes increased adsorption, but the quantity adsorbed is not proportional to the pressure, nor is the increase the same for all gases. The adsorption increases rapidly up to about 400 mm./Hg pressure, then more slowly, and finally approaches a constant value. This is shown by the curves given in Figure 215, in which the quantities of different gases adsorbed per g. of charcoal at 0° C. are plotted against the pressure. Such a curve applying *at constant temperature* is called an **adsorption isotherm.**

Types of Adsorption. The two main types of adsorption are **chemical adsorption,** in which the adsorbed substance is held to the adsorbent by chemical valence bonds, and **physical adsorption,** which is a *condensation* of the adsorbed gas on the surface of the adsorbent and particularly in the capillary pores. The latter is ascribed to the same *van der Waals forces,* which cause attraction between gaseous particles under high pressure. Most cases of adsorption which have been studied in detail have been found to be a combination of these two types.

Theory of Adsorption of Gas on Solid. Of the many attempts to explain the adsorption of a gas on a solid that of Langmuir seems the most adequate.[1] He assumed that the adsorbing surface is made up of uniformly spaced particles, a "checkerboard of atoms" or groups of atoms. This is, in fact, indicated by X-ray studies of crystal structure. These surface atoms have free valences by which they can chemically adsorb atoms or molecules outside the surface. When all of these free valences have been satisfied by the attachment of adsorbed atoms or molecules, the surface is covered with a **monomolecular layer** of adsorbed atoms or molecules. This corresponds to the portion of each curve in Figure 215 which is nearly parallel to the pressure axis.

If the surface is highly irregular, only a few of the surface atoms may project in **active spots** which are able to adsorb gas atoms or molecules. In this case, adsorption may increase more gradually and maximum adsorption corresponds to less than a complete monomolecular layer.

Langmuir has furnished a definite concept of the way in which adsorbed gases attach themselves to carbon or to a metal. He assumes, for example, that oxygen adsorbed on charcoal forms a film which "consists of oxygen atoms chemically combined to the carbon atoms," and that carbon monoxide adsorbed on a tungsten filament is chemically attached to the tungsten. The structures of these adsorbed films are shown in Figure 216 (*a*) and (*b*). When the tungsten filament with its adsorbed layer is heated, "the strength of the union between the oxygen and carbon, and between the tungsten and carbon is so great that the whole group WCO distills off as a single molecule."

A diatomic gas either may be adsorbed as a monomolecular layer

[1] *J. Am. Chem. Soc.*, **38,** 2221 (1916). Irving Langmuir, of the General Electric Co., Schenectady, N. Y., received the Nobel Prize in Chemistry in 1932. He has made many important contributions to chemistry, particularly the chemistry of surfaces and to theories of atomic and molecular structure. Two practical results of his research are the gas filled tungsten lamp and the use of atomic hydrogen in welding.

in the molecular form or it may be dissociated and adsorbed as atoms. Thus, in the adsorption of hydrogen on platinum black there are the two possibilities as illustrated in Figure 216 (*c*) and (*d*).

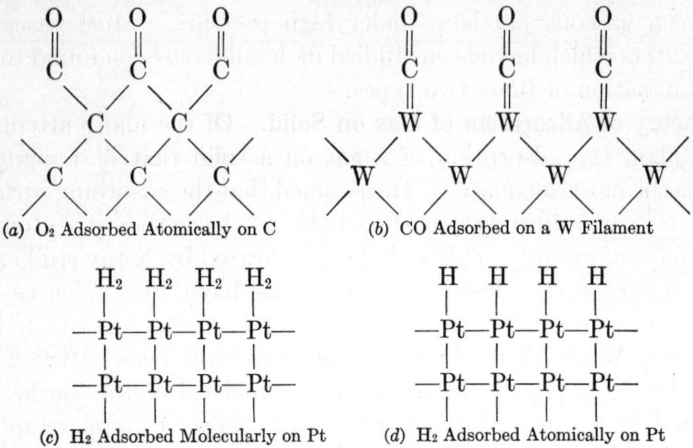

(*a*) O_2 Adsorbed Atomically on C (*b*) CO Adsorbed on a W Filament

(*c*) H_2 Adsorbed Molecularly on Pt (*d*) H_2 Adsorbed Atomically on Pt

Figure 216. Adsorption of Gases on Charcoal or Metals.

The mode in which oxygen is adsorbed on charcoal depends greatly upon conditions. At low temperatures and high pressures, the adsorption seems to be entirely physical, *i.e.*, due to van der Waals forces. At higher temperatures and lower pressures chemical adsorption takes place by one of the following mechanisms:

On *desorption*, both carbon monoxide and carbon dioxide are obtained.

Heat of Adsorption. Adsorption, like condensation, is an *exothermic* process; therefore, according to the principle of Le Chatelier, it should diminish with rising temperature. This is found to be the case, as illustrated by the data in Table 108, page 513. Some heats of adsorption, in kilogram calories per mole of gas adsorbed, are given in Table 110. These compare in magnitude with heats of vigorous exothermic reactions, such as the heat of neutralization, 13.64 kcal. per gram equivalent of acid or base neutralized.

TABLE 110

HEATS OF ADSORPTION OF GASES ON METALS

GAS	METAL	HEAT OF ADSORPTION, $-\Delta H$, KCAL. PER MOLE OF GAS
Hydrogen	Copper	20.0
Ethylene	Copper	16.0
Ethane	Copper	11.0
Carbon monoxide	Copper	10.0
Ammonia	Copper	7.0
Hydrogen	Nickel	20.6
Ammonia	Iron	18.0
Oxygen	Platinum	20.0–80.0

Data from Schwab, Taylor, and Spence, *Catalysis*, D. Van Nostrand Co., New York, 1937, p. 201.

Adsorption from Solution. In general, adsorption from solutions is like adsorption of gases. It is, however, *selective.* Either the solvent or the solute is adsorbed but not both, and if several solutes are present, one will usually be adsorbed more than another.

A solute which *lowers* the surface tension of the solvent will be concentrated in the surface layer and will be adsorbed strongly on any solid adsorbent, *e.g.*, powdered or porous charcoal or silica gel. If the solute *raises* the surface tension, it will be expelled from the surface layer, and the solvent instead of the solute will be adsorbed by the solid.

Data which illustrate the adsorption of a substance from solution are given in Table 111, where the quantities of acetic acid adsorbed by charcoal from solutions of various concentrations are listed.

TABLE 111

ADSORPTION OF ACETIC ACID FROM AQUEOUS SOLUTION BY CHARCOAL, 25° C.

MOLAR CONCENTRATION	MOLES OF ACID ADSORBED PER 1000 G. CHARCOAL	MOLAR CONCENTRATION	MOLES OF ACID ADSORBED PER 1000 G. CHARCOAL
0.018	0.47	0.268	1.55
0.031	0.62	0.471	2.04
0.061	0.80	0.882	2.48
0.126	1.11	2.785	3.76

Organic compounds usually lower the surface tension of water and hence are strongly adsorbed from aqueous solution. Complex compounds often are more strongly adsorbed than simpler ones, *e.g.*, the coloring matter in vinegar or crude sugar solution are adsorbed more strongly than the acetic acid or the sugar, a fact used in decolorizing such solutions. The adsorption depends also upon the solvent as shown by the data in Table 112, which gives the number of moles of benzoic acid adsorbed by 1000 g. of charcoal at 25° C. from 0.01 M solutions in several different solvents.

TABLE 112

ADSORPTION FROM SOLUTIONS IN VARIOUS SOLVENTS

SOLVENT	SOLUTE	ADSORPTION, MOLES SOLUTE PER 1000 G. CHARCOAL
Water	Benzoic acid	3.27
Benzene	Benzoic acid	0.54
Acetone	Benzoic acid	0.30
Diethyl ether	Benzoic acid	0.29

Adsorption Isotherms. Various mathematical equations have been proposed for the *adsorption isotherms.* The two best known are that suggested first by Boedecker, in 1859, and elaborated by Freundlich, and that advanced by Langmuir.

The Freundlich adsorption isotherm. The *Freundlich adsorption isotherm* is a purely empirical equation without theoretical basis. It applies to gases and solutions over a wide range of concentrations, and may be stated:

$$y = kc^n$$

where y is the weight or volume of the substance adsorbed by 1 g. of the adsorbent, k and n are empirical constants, and c is the concentration of the adsorbed substance in the environment when it is in equilibrium with the interface. If the adsorbed substance is a gas, the equilibrium pressure p may be substituted for the concentration c. The equation is usually applied in the logarithmic form, thus:

$$\log y = \log k + n \log c$$

Since y and c are the only variables, the plot of log y against log c should be a straight line. This is realized experimentally as is shown in Figure 217 (*b*) in which the Freundlich equation is applied to the adsorption of acetic acid by blood charcoal from solutions of various concentrations.

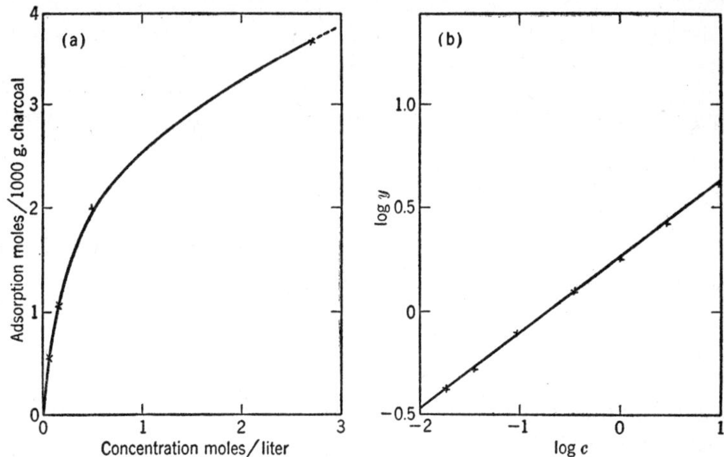

Fig. 217. (a) Adsorption of Acetic Acid by Blood Charcoal at 25° C. (b) Application of the Freundlich Adsorption Isotherm.

Langmuir's adsorption isotherm. This differs from the Freundlich isotherm in having a theoretical basis.

When a gas molecule strikes the surface of a solid, it will either condense upon the surface or be reflected from it. Because of thermal agitation, adsorbed molecules subsequently will escape from the surface whenever their thermal energy is sufficient to overcome the attractive force which holds them. The higher the temperature the greater the thermal agitation and the more rapidly will such evaporation take place. If a dynamic equilibrium exists, the two opposing processes of condensation and evaporation take place simultaneously, and at equilibrium their rates are equal.

If s represents the number of gas molecules striking the surface of 1 g. of adsorbent per second, n the fraction which adhere to the surface, and g the fraction of the total adsorbent area covered by gas molecules, then $(1 - g)$ will be the fraction of unoccupied surface, and the rate of adsorption will be $s(1 - g)$ molecules per second. If r is the number of molecules which would escape per second if the entire surface were covered, the rate of evaporation, or *desorption*, will be gr. At equilibrium,

$$sn(1 - g) = gr \qquad \text{or} \qquad \frac{n}{r} s(1 - g) = g$$

For a given adsorbent and a given adsorbate at constant temperature, $\frac{n}{r}$ is a constant k, hence:

$$g = \frac{ks}{1 + ks}$$

Since s is proportional to p, the pressure of the gas, we may write:

$$g = \frac{pn}{1 + pn}$$

If b is the number of moles of gas that could be adsorbed per sq. cm., the quantity actually adsorbed will be:

$$A = b \times \frac{pn}{1 + pn} \text{ moles per sq. cm.}$$

If y is the quantity of substance adsorbed per g. of adsorbent, *i.e.*, x/m, we have:

$$y = \frac{pbn}{1 + pn}$$

This is one form in which the *Langmuir adsorption isotherm* may be applied. The constants n and b, which hold for a given system, are empirical and must be determined from two or more measurements on the system.

The Langmuir equation may be resolved into the form:

$$\frac{p}{y} = \frac{1}{bn} + \frac{p}{b}$$

Since b and n are constants, this is an equation for a straight line. It applies either to gases, with p as a variable, or to solutions, with c as a variable. In the latter case the expression is:

$$\frac{c}{y} = \frac{1}{bn} + \frac{c}{b}$$

Figure 218 shows a plot of $\frac{c}{y}$ against c for the weights of acetic acid adsorbed by 1 g. of sugar charcoal and the equilibrium concentrations of the acetic acid solution.

Liquid Films. When a little of one liquid A is poured on the surface of another liquid B in which it is insoluble, it will either take the form of a lens-shaped drop or else spread out over the surface of B as a thin film, the extent of which can be observed by powdering talc over the surface. Whether the liquid A will spread as a film or form a drop depends upon the surface tensions of the two liquids and the interfacial tension between them. A high-

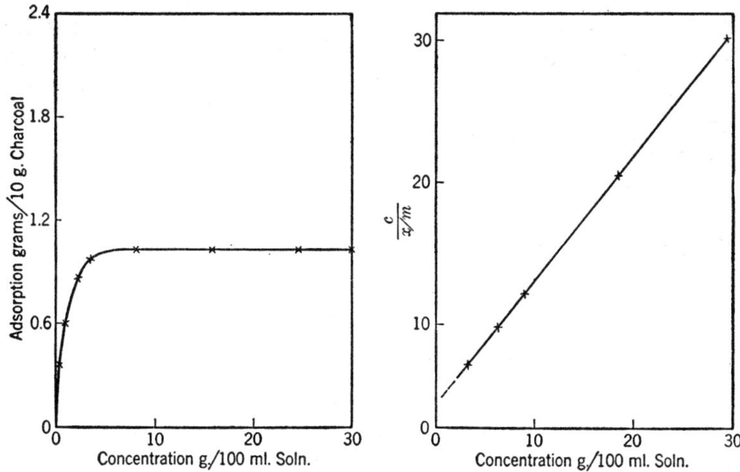

Fig. 218. (a) Adsorption of Acetic Acid on Sugar Charcoal. (b) Application of the Langmuir Adsorption Isotherm.

boiling oil or hydrocarbon on water will form a drop, but most organic liquids, with their low forces of cohesion, will spread to form a film. Even the slightest trace of an impurity in the denser liquid greatly affects the spreading characteristics. For example, most liquids, including water, will spread on clean mercury, but a really *clean* mercury surface is so difficult to secure that we rarely see this spreading in the case of water.

Monomolecular Films. An insoluble liquid drop with low cohesive forces, added to a sufficiently large surface of water, spreads until the resulting film is only one molecule thick, as Langmuir's measurements, to be described, show. This is called a **monomolecular film.** If we know the weight of the added liquid A and its molecular weight, and measure the area of the film produced, then, from Avogadro's number, $N = 6.023 \times 10^{23}$ molecules per mole, we can compute the number of molecules in a known weight of the liquid. The total area of the film divided by the number of molecules will be the area occupied by a single molecule. For most of the higher fatty acids, of the general formula

$C_nH_{2n+1}COOH$, the area occupied by the molecule in the film is found to be about 21 sq. Å. If we consider that the molecule has the form of a square prism, its width is 4.6 Å.

If the density of the liquid spread out as a film is assumed to be the same as that of the liquid in bulk, the thickness of the film may be calculated. For palmitic acid, $C_{15}H_{31}COOH$, it is found to be about 24 Å. Hence we arrive at the interesting conclusion that the molecule of palmitic acid is 24 Å. long and 4.6 Å. wide. We may assume that the thickness of the film is the length of the *carbon chain.* The molecule of palmitic acid, $C_{15}H_{31}COOH$, or other similar saturated acid, is composed of a carboxyl group, —COOH, which is *hydrophilic* (*i.e., water attracting*) and soluble, and a hydrocarbon group, $C_{15}H_{31}$—, which is *hydrophobic* (*i.e., water repelling*) and insoluble. Hence we may picture the molecules in a monomolecular film as shown in Figure 219.

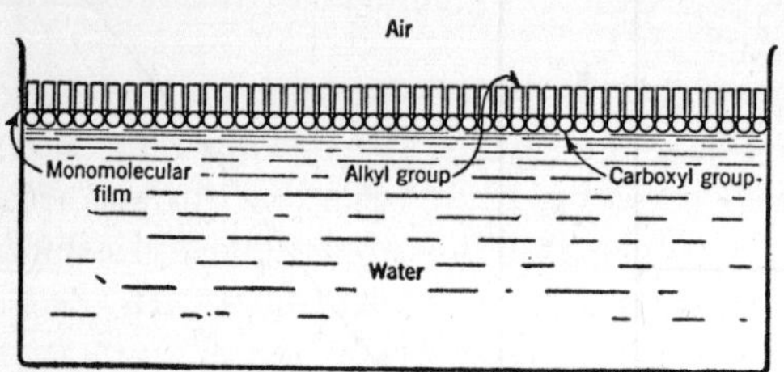

Fig. 219. Monomolecular Film of a Fatty Acid in Water.

Dimensions of the molecules of certain organic acids and other compounds computed from experimental measurements of this kind are given in Table 113. These data indicate that the *normal* saturated compounds, such as palmitic and stearic acids, have molecular surface areas of from 21–25 sq. Å.; but olefinic compounds, such as oleic acid, $CH_3(CH_2)_7CH{:}CH(CH_2)_7COOH$, have molecular surface areas about twice as great.

TABLE 113

MOLECULAR DIMENSIONS OF VARIOUS SUBSTANCES

SUBSTANCE	FORMULA	NUMBER OF CARBONS	THICKNESS OF FILM	MOL. SURFACE AREA	LENGTH PER C ATOM
Myricyl alcohol	$C_{30}H_{61}CH_2OH$	31	41.0 A.	27 sq. A.	1.37 A.
Cetyl palmitate	$C_{15}H_{31}COOC_{16}H_{33}$	32	41.0	23	2.56
Stearic acid . .	$C_{17}H_{35}COOH$	18	25.0	22	1.39
Tristearin . .	$(C_{17}H_{35}COO)_3C_3H_5$	57	25.0	66	1.32
Palmitic acid .	$C_{15}H_{31}COOH$	16	24.0	21	1.50
Triolein . . .	$(C_{17}H_{33}COO)_3C_3H_5$	57	13.0	126	0.69
Oleic acid . .	$(C_8H_{17})CH : CH(C_7H_{14})COOH$	18	11.2	46	0.62

From data of Langmuir.

We may picture these surface films, then, as consisting of elongated molecules, one end of which is a polar group, such as —COOH or —CH_2OH, which is drawn down into the water layer. The hydrocarbon residue, such as —$C_{15}H_{31}$, being nonpolar and insoluble in water, sticks up out of the water layer. Since these chains or rods are essentially parallel to one another, the surface area of the molecule is nearly independent of the number of carbon atoms in the molecule. The number of carbon atoms affects the length, not the width.

In the case of olefinic compounds the molecule is doubled back on itself, thus about doubling the surface area. Thus oleic acid, which is unsaturated, has about twice the molecular surface area of palmitic or stearic acid. The molecule of the glyceryl esters, such as tristearin or glyceryl tristearate, $(C_{17}H_{35}COO)_3C_3H_5$, *i.e.*,

$$\begin{array}{l} C_{17}H_{35}COOCH_2 \\ \qquad\qquad\quad | \\ C_{17}H_{35}COOCH \\ \qquad\qquad\quad | \\ C_{17}H_{35}COOCH_2 \end{array}$$

apparently consists of *three* parallel "rods," held together by the glyceryl group. The surface area of the molecule, 66 sq. Å., is about three times that of palmitic or stearic acid. Glycerol is completely miscible with water, and probably the grouping $(—COO)_3C_3H_5$ penetrates the water surface, leaving the three —$C_{17}H_{35}$ groups pointing away from the surface.

Langmuir devised a method for measuring the forces which must be applied to a film on the surface of another liquid, usually water, in order to contract it to a given area, and the force necessary to cause a monomolecular film to *crumple.* For details the student should consult Langmuir's original paper, to which reference is given on page 525. The apparatus used is illustrated in Figure 220. It consists of a tray *T* containing the water and the film, and a modified balance by means of which a measured force can be applied to the film. The balance mechanism is supported on the plate *F*, attached to a permanent outside support *S*. The beam *K*, provided with a counterpoise *C*, carries an inverted knife-edge which is parallel to the ends of the tray and rests on the plate *F*. Two small glass rods *R*, *R* are attached to the knife-edge and swing one way or the other as the balance arm dips or rises. These rods extend down to the water in the tray, passing through holes in the strip of paper *B*, which is a movable barrier fitting flat against the surface of the water. Thus as the balance arm dips or rises, the barrier *B* moves back or forth on the surface. The barrier *A*, another movable strip of paper, which may be paraffined to prevent softening by the water, also fits flat on the surface from side to side of the tray. One or two drops of a benzene solution of the substance to be investigated, *e.g.*, stearic acid or stearin, are placed on the water. The benzene evaporates and leaves a film of the substance spread over the surface. The paper barrier *A* is moved forward until it begins to exert a force on the paper barrier *B*.

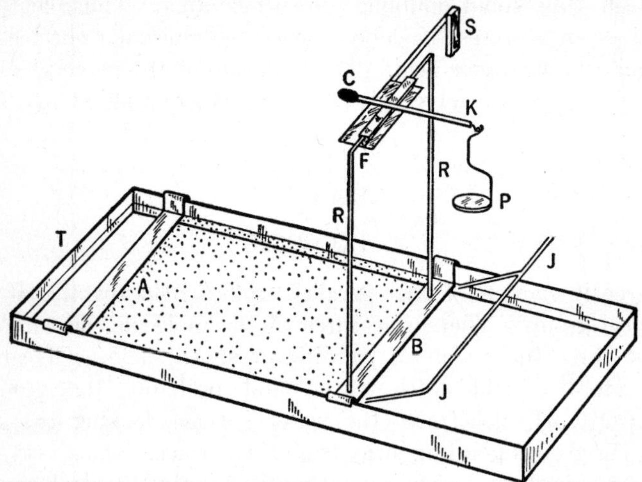

Fig. 220. The Langmuir Apparatus for Studying Monomolecular Films.

By means of carefully regulated jets of air, blown in through the jets *J*, the oily substance is prevented from passing the barrier *B*. By adding weights to the balance pan *P*, the barrier *B* is pushed against the film towards *A*, with a force just sufficient to bring it to its zero point. This gives a measure of the lateral force of compression on the film, which is equivalent to its spreading tendency. This weight is called the *restoring force*, corresponding to the particular film area. The total area of the film is simply that between the sides of the tray and the barriers *A* and *B*, which is measured for each setting of the instrument. From the area of the film, the weight of the substance taken to form it, and Avogadro's number, the surface area occupied by a single molecule of the substance is calculated as on page 521.

From a series of determinations of surface areas corresponding to various restoring forces, we can plot force-area curves like those shown in Figure 221 for palmitic acid. In this figure the ordinate represents the force, in dynes, required to compress the molecule to the surface area plotted as abscissa. With increasing force the

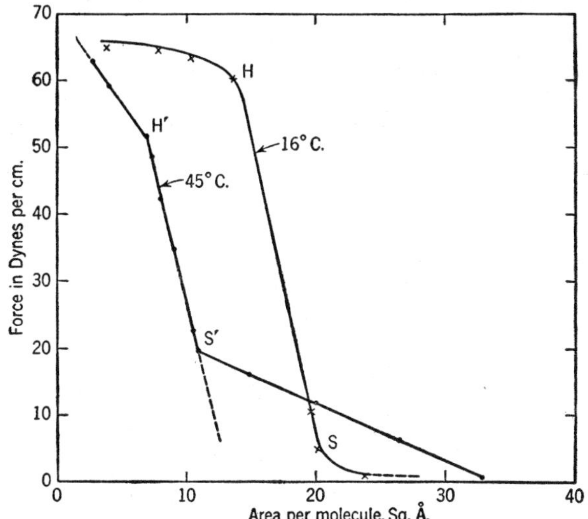

Fig. 221. Force-Area Curves for Palmitic Acid at 16° and 45° C.

molecular surface area, at 16° C., decreases rapidly to S where a monomolecular film is established over the entire surface. From S to H the molecular surface area decreases slightly with rapidly increasing force of compression. Over this interval the molecules are crowding more closely together. At H the film crumples as shown by the abrupt change of area with pressure. At 45° C. the curve $H'S'$ is obtained, the points having the same significance as for the curve HS.[1]

Applications of Adsorption. Among the many ways in which adsorption comes into play in science and industry the following are outstanding.

Catalysis. The catalysis of reactions by solid surfaces depends upon the adsorption of the reactants on the surface of the solid and is of extraordinary importance in industrial chemistry.

[1] The classical experiment of Irving Langmuir, described in the *J. Am. Chem. Soc.*, **39**, pp. 1848–1906 (1917), has been repeated in recent years with greater refinement. For a discussion of the newer techniques see N. K. Adam, *Physics and Chemistry of Surfaces*, Oxford Univ. Press, 1930, pp. 36 ff.

Sugar refining. The juice from the sugar cane or beet is colored with complex organic compounds. The crude sugar, partially purified by one recrystallization, is dissolved in water and the solution is passed through layers of bone charcoal, which adsorbs the colored molecules so that the resulting solution upon evaporation gives *white* sugar.

Adsorption of acids and bases by charcoal. Charcoal does not adsorb bases but adsorbs acids so strongly that neutral salt solutions may become strongly basic because of the adsorption, from the solution, of hydrogen ion and the anion of the salt.[1] The adsorption of acid from dilute solution is so nearly irreversible that the adsorbed acid cannot be removed by washing. When charcoal is prepared from bone or other animal matter, it is usually leached with hydrochloric acid to remove salts; it must then be heated strongly to remove the acid.

Adsorption of dyes. A fairly dilute solution of a dye, like Congo red, methylene blue, or fuchsine, when shaken with charcoal is completely decolorized. In dye plants dyes are recovered from waste solution by adsorbing them with charcoal, dissolving with alcohol, and then distilling off the alcohol.

The process of dyeing also may involve adsorption of the dye on the surface of the fiber or on a mordant, which is itself adsorbed on the fiber.

Adsorption of drugs. Many drugs, such as cocaine, strychnine, and quinine, are strongly adsorbed from solution by *fuller's earth*, a clay used extensively in the chemical industry. The efficacy of drugs is probably dependent upon their adsorption in the cells and tissues. The human body is "largely colloidal," and colloids, because of their great surface, are particularly powerful adsorbents. The adsorption of drugs taken into the human body is an important but difficult subject of study in physiological chemistry. In this connection an observation by Alvarez is of interest. If the $\mathrm{O{=}\underset{|}{C}{-}CH_2{-}}$ grouping in morphine is altered to $\mathrm{HO{-}\underset{|}{C}{=}\underset{|}{C}{-}H}$, the anesthetic power is increased about fivefold and the habit-forming property of morphine is almost completely lost. Gortner[2] states: "In this case we are presumably dealing with adsorption and specific orientation of the original morphine on at least two

[1] E. J. Miller, *J. Am. Chem. Soc.*, **47**, 1270 (1925).
[2] R. A. Gortner, *Topics in Colloid Chemistry*, Cornell University Press, Ithaca, N. Y., 1937, p. 120.

brain centers, one which has to do with habit formation and the other with pain. Apparently a slight change in chemical configuration of the molecule intensifies adsorption and orientation on the pain center and destroys adsorption affinities of the drug on the habit-forming center."

Gas masks. An important application of adsorption was developed during the war of 1914–1918 and subsequently has found extensive peacetime use. Activated charcoal was the gas-mask adsorbent since it adsorbs powerfully most of the "war gases." When the surface of the charcoal has become saturated, the gas mask no longer affords protection.

Production of high vacua. In 1874 Sir James Dewar and Tait first used charcoal cooled with liquid air to aid in the production of a high vacuum. The pressure in a bulb was lowered from 1.7 mm. to 0.00005 mm. Pressures as low as 2×10^{-7} mm. have been obtained in this way. Langmuir has used tungsten filaments to adsorb final traces of hydrogen. This "clean-up" of gases by a metallic filament can be effected even at room temperature.

Adsorption on glass. Glass adsorbs gases, including water vapor. Since the adsorption depends upon the temperature and the partial pressure of the gas, a variation in either between two weighings of a glass vessel may have a very appreciable effect. In gas-density experimentation (page 105) the density bulb is weighed against a counterpoise carefully matched for volume and surface to obviate the error; approximately equal adsorption occurs on both the bulb and the counterpoise.

Adsorption in analytical chemistry. The contamination of precipitates by adsorbed electrolyte is a source of error in quantitative analysis. Thus in the case of barium sulfate certain anions are strongly adsorbed; *chloride* is adsorbed more than *iodide,* and *nitrate* much more than *chloride;* this explains why barium chloride is preferable to barium nitrate as a precipitant for sulfate. Precipitates which are partially colloidal adsorb very strongly.

Chromatographic analysis. The method known as **chromatographic analysis,** depending upon the principles of selective adsorption, makes it possible to separate, concentrate, and quantitatively determine several different solutes present in very low concentration.

The method was first employed by Tswett, the Russian botanist, in 1906, in an attempt to concentrate dissolved constituents in biological fluids.[1] He showed that chlorophyll and other plant pigments were adsorbed from solution in petroleum ether by finely pulverized sulfur, zinc oxide, and alumina. He also found that a more strongly adsorbed substance would displace one which was less strongly adsorbed. Tswett allowed the solution to percolate through a tube containing the pulverized adsorbent. The most strongly adsorbed substance was concentrated in a layer near the top of the tube, and those less strongly adsorbed formed successive layers lower in the tube. The discovery of Tswett did not become generally known and was not applied extensively until after 1930.

In 1931 Kuhn employed the method to separate the isomeric carotenes.[2] Since then its application has extended rapidly.[3] H. N. Holmes and his co-workers at Oberlin College have used a Tswett column containing charcoal as adsorbent, followed by further concentration using magnesia as adsorbent, to obtain a concentrate of vitamin A said to be 40 per cent more potent than any previously prepared. Although colored substances are most easily observed, colorless substances may be detected by means of ultraviolet light, if fluorescent, or after separation they may be identified by chemical means.

To illustrate the application of the method let us suppose that we have three substances, A, B, and C, in solution in petroleum ether, ethanol, or some other solvent. A **Tswett column,** shown diagrammatically by Figure 222 (*a*), is prepared. This consists of finely pulverized alumina, dextrose, or some other suitable adsorbent, compressed uniformly and fairly tightly into the tube and supported by the perforated disk D. The solution is poured into the tube and drawn through by gentle suction. As the solution slowly descends, adsorption takes place. The most strongly adsorbed substance A is adsorbed at the top, together with some of B, less strongly adsorbed, and of C, which is still less. As the upper layers of adsorbent become saturated, the oncoming supply of A displaces B and C, which are carried further down and again adsorbed. Thus when all the solution has passed through the column we would have the result represented in Figure 222 (*b*).

The layers of A, B, and C are fairly close together and somewhat overlapping. The *chromatogram* shown in Figure 222 (*b*) may then

[1] *Ber. deut. botan. Ges.*, **24,** 216 (1906).
[2] *Ber.*, **64,** 1349 (1931).
[3] See Zechmeister and von Cholnoky, *Die chromatographische Adsorptionsmethode*, Julius Springer, Berlin, 2d ed., 1939.

be *developed* by passing more of the solvent through the column. At the adsorbing surface there is a dynamic equilibrium of adsorbed material between the solvent and the adsorbed layer. Each substance dissolves slightly as the solvent passes through the layer

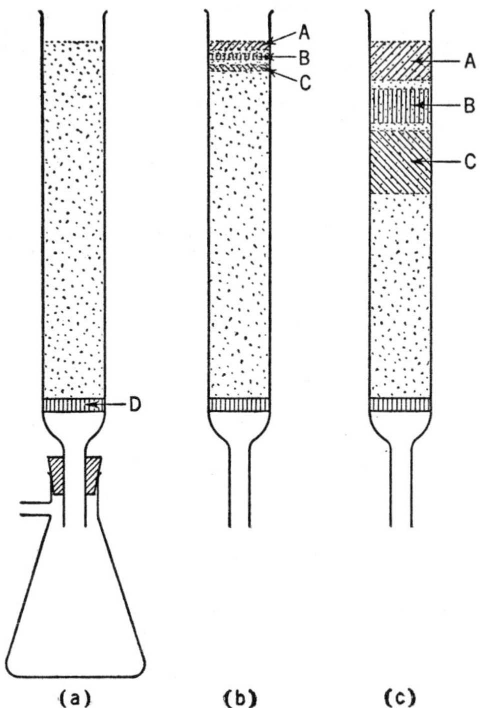

Fig. 222. Tswett Adsorption Column; (*a*) Tube with Adsorbent; (*b*) Column after Adsorption; (*c*) Column after Development.

but is readsorbed lower down. The net effect is to remove the less readily adsorbed material *B* from the upper layer and carry it further down in the column and also to thicken the layer containing *A*. The same change takes place in each layer, and the column finally shows a separate and much wider band for each substance, the thickness of which may indicate the quantity of substance. The *developed* chromatogram is shown in Figure 222 (*c*).

The Tswett column can be so constructed that the adsorbent can be pressed out of the containing tube intact. The various layers may then be separated by slicing with a knife and the adsorbed substances extracted by suitable solvents. *Micro methods* are applied for the quantitative determination of the adsorbed substance. The adsorption depends upon the surface tension of the solvent and is also affected by salts and other solutes present in the solution.

READING LIST

N. K. Adam, *The Physics and Chemistry of Surfaces*, 2d ed. Oxford University Press, 1938.

S. Glasstone, *Textbook of Physical Chemistry*. D. Van Nostrand Company, New York, 1940. Pp. 1172–1194.

R. J. Hartman, *Colloid Chemistry*. Houghton Mifflin Company, New York, 1939. Pp. 17–113.

H. B. Weiser, *Colloid Chemistry*. John Wiley & Sons, New York, 1939. Pp. 15–113. This, like the preceding reference, gives a brief but excellent summary of adsorption.

H. G. Cassidy, in *J. Chem. Ed.*, **16,** 88 (1939), gives an interesting account of the use of the chromatographic method.

Irving Langmuir, "Fundamental Properties of Solids and Liquids. II." *J. Am. Chem. Soc.*, **39,** 1848 (1917).

CHAPTER 19

COLLOIDS

Although colloidal materials like the alchemical *aurum potabile* (potable gold) and *purple of Cassius* have been known for a long time, and others, like the colloidal clay used in making chinaware, have been used in certain industries, it was not until 1861 that a colloidal material was recognized as having distinctive properties. In that year Thomas Graham, at the University of Edinburgh, after long studies on the diffusion of substances in solution, divided solutes into two classes: those which diffuse with *normal* rapidity, such as acids, bases, salts, and simple organic compounds, and those which diffuse *very slowly*, such as starch, glue, and gelatin. Graham termed the former group **crystalloids,** and the latter **colloids.**[1] He also showed that crystalloids and colloids could be separated by permitting the *crystalloid* to diffuse through a suitable membrane, a process which he termed **dialysis.**

Graham's classification of substances as *crystalloids* and *colloids* implied a difference in the *nature* of the substance. However, it is possible to prepare in the colloidal condition almost *any* substance — even such typically crystalline substances as barium sulfate, silver, and iodine; thus the difference between crystalloid and colloid is no longer regarded as a difference in the *nature* of the substances but merely a difference in state. Another suggested distinction is that a crystalloid, *i.e.*, a substance in true solution, is dispersed as *molecules* or *ions*, while a substance in colloidal solution is dispersed as *agglomerates of molecules.* However, although colloidal solutions of simple substances consist of agglomerates of molecules, the complex proteins, with molecular weights as high as 3,000,000, may be dispersed molecularly, probably with the addition of adsorbed solvent, and yet are colloidal.

The basis for the definition of a colloid now used most successfully is *particle size.* This was the result of a classification of dispersions suggested by Wolfgang Ostwald in 1907. The limiting sizes of the particles composing each class were selected arbitrarily and have been somewhat altered by Ostwald and others in the light

[1] *Gluelike,* from κόλλα, *glue. Trans. Roy. Soc.,* **151,** 183 (1861).

of later study. The classification at present accepted is as follows: (1) **Coarse dispersions:** The particles have diameters larger than 5×10^{-5} cm., *i.e.*, 0.5 μ; they are visible under the microscope, do not diffuse, and do not pass through a filter paper or a dialyzing membrane. (2) **Colloidal dispersions:** The particles have diameters from 1×10^{-7} cm. to 5×10^{-5} cm., *i.e.*, from 1 $m\mu$ to 0.5 μ; they are visible with the ultramicroscope but not with the microscope; they diffuse extremely slowly and pass through an ordinary filter paper but not through an ultrafilter or a dialyzing membrane. (3) **Molecular dispersions:** The particles have diameters less than 1×10^{-7} cm., *i.e.*, 1 $m\mu$; they are not visible with the ultramicroscope; they diffuse and pass through an ultrafilter and a dialyzing membrane.

Classification of Colloids. *A colloidal solution is a heterogeneous mixture, one component of which, the* ***dispersed phase****, is scattered among the molecules of the other component, which is called the* ***continuous phase****, or* ***dispersion medium.*** Every colloidal system must include these two essential components.

Colloidal systems of all types are known, except a colloidal *gas-gas* system. A classification of colloids based upon the possible combinations of solid, liquid, or gas as dispersed phase and dispersion medium, offered by Ostwald, is shown in Table 114 together with the term commonly applied to each type of colloidal solution and a few familiar examples.

TABLE 114

Classification of Colloidal Systems

Dispersed Phase	Dispersion Medium	Name of Colloid	Examples
Solid	Liquid	Sol	As_2S_3 in water; gold in water
Solid	Gas	Solid aerosol	Smoke; NH_4Cl fumes
Solid	Solid	Solid sol	Gold in ruby glass
Liquid	Liquid	Emulsion	Milk; cod-liver oil in water
Liquid	Gas	Liquid aerosol	Mist; fog
Liquid	Solid	Solid emulsion	Opal; milky quartz
Gas	Liquid	Foam	Whipped egg white; soap foam
Gas	Solid	Solid foam	Pumice

In this elementary treatment of the subject we shall limit our discussion to those types most important in physical and physiological chemistry; namely, the **sol,** or *dispersion of a solid in a liquid,* and the **emulsion,** or *dispersion of a liquid in a liquid.*

Sols. A *sol* may be classified according to the liquid acting as dispersion medium. Thus a *hydrosol* is a solid dispersed in water, an *alcosol* a solid dispersed in alcohol, and so on. Hydrosols may be divided into *hydrophilic sols* which attract water and form a gelatinous agglomerate, and *hydrophobic sols* which do not attract water and hence do not tend to become gelatinous.[1] The hydrophilic sols include the hydrous oxides, such as ferric oxide and stannic oxide, and sols of starch, protein, or other insoluble organic substances, and the hydrophobic sols include metal sols, sulfide sols, and such sols as silver chloride and barium sulfate. The more general terms are ***lyophilic*** *i.e., solvent-attracting*, and ***lyophobic***, *i.e., solvent-repelling.*

Preparation of Sols. Sols are prepared, first, by *dispersion methods,* by which larger aggregates of matter are disintegrated into particles of colloidal dimensions, and, second, by *condensation methods,* by which ions or molecules coalesce into colloidal particles.

(1) Dispersion methods. (*a*) *Mechanical disintegration.* Material may be reduced to colloidal particles by pulverizing in an agate mortar, but the process is a very tedious one. A practical device for reducing material to particles of colloidal size is the **colloid mill,** which consists of two hard steel disks, placed very close together, which rotate in opposite directions and thus exert a large shearing force on any material placed between them. In addition to its use in the chemical laboratory, the colloid mill finds important commercial application in the grinding of relatively soft materials, such as zinc oxide and lithopone for paint, mica for lubricant, and the solid materials for the manufacture of inks.

(*b*) *Electrolytic disintegration.* When sodium hydroxide solution is electrolyzed, at high current density, with a cathode of lead, tin, antimony, or bismuth, the solution darkens because of the formation of the corresponding metal sol.

(*c*) *Peptization by the dispersion medium.* Reasoning from the analogy of the action of pepsin on proteins in the digestive process, Graham termed the disintegration of a substance into the colloidal form "peptonization," a term which has been altered to *peptization.* We may define ***peptization*** *as the conversion of a material into the colloidal state by any process involving direct subdivision of*

[1] The term *hydrophilic* comes from ὕδωρ, *water,* + φίλος, *loving,* thus *water-attracting; hydrophobic* comes from ὕδωρ, *water* + φόβος, *fear, aversion,* thus *water-hating* or *water-repelling.*

the material. All of the disintegration methods of preparing sols are, in fact, peptizations, although the term is more often applied to disintegrations under the influence of solvents or solutions. *A substance which aids in the conversion of a solid into the colloidal state is called a* ***peptizing agent.*** The rate of peptization usually is much increased by raising the temperature.

In general, peptization depends upon the adsorption of the *dispersion medium* by the substance dispersed, which occurs most strongly with substances that form lyophilic sols. Starch, dextrin, agar, gelatin, soap, and some other organic substances which do not dissolve in water swell and become gelatinous when allowed to stand in contact with water. All of these substances are *hydrophilic* and hence adsorb water strongly. Cellulose nitrate is lyophilic towards a number of organic solvents and is peptized by acetone, amyl alcohol, or a mixture of ethanol and ether. The *peptizing agent* in all these cases is the *dispersion medium* itself.

A recent accomplishment of great interest and importance is the preparation of dried blood *serum*, or *plasma*, in such a form that it can be peptized by adding the requisite quantity of water.[1] To prepare the plasma, the fresh whole blood is allowed to clot and the corpuscles are removed; then it is treated with sodium citrate and centrifuged. The resulting clear, amber-colored solution is frozen and dried *in vacuo* in the frozen state. The dried material may be kept indefinitely, need not be typed, occupies small bulk, and when peptized with water is ready for transfusion. Extensive application already has been made in treating shock in World War II.

(*d*) *Peptization by dissolved electrolyte.* Many salts and oxides are peptized by ions which they adsorb. Silver chloride, for example, is peptized by low concentrations of either silver or chloride ion. Stannic oxide is readily peptized by low concentrations of hydroxyl ion and ferric oxide by salts, the positive ions being adsorbed. Arsenious, antimonous, and other sulfides are peptized by hydrogen sulfide because of the adsorption of sulfide or hydrosulfide ion. Such peptizations usually require freshly precipitated material, which thus is already semicolloidal, and the removal of excess electrolyte by dialysis.

(2) Condensation methods. (*a*) *The arc method.* This is one of the most important ways of obtaining *metal hydrosols.* It was

[1] The process of preparing the dried serum or plasma is due to Drs. E. W. Flosdorf and Stuart Mudd, of the Department of Bacteriology, University of Pennsylvania. See *Jour. Immunol.*, **29**, 389 (1935); *Annals of Surgery*, **111**, 623 (1940).

developed by Bredig, at Karlsrühe, in 1898. Electrodes of the proper metal are placed below the surface of the dispersion medium and a direct-current arc is formed between them as shown in Figure 223. The water darkens as the colloidal metal, the hydrosol, accumulates. The intense heat of the arc vaporizes the metal, which condenses as colloidal particles.

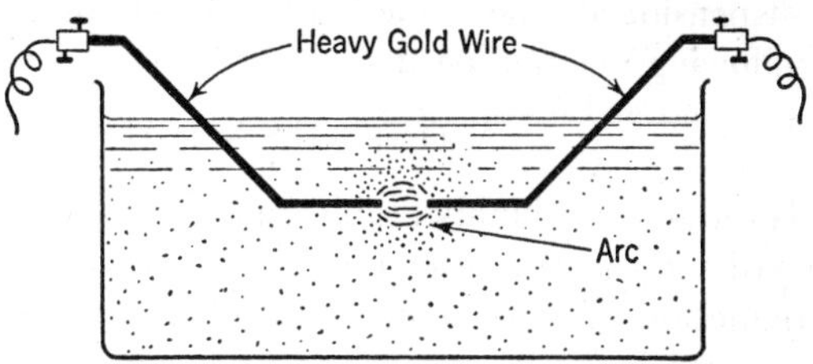

Fig. 223. Preparation of Gold Sol by the Arc Method.

Using silver, gold, and platinum electrodes, respectively, hydrosols of these metals may readily be obtained. Using more active metals, like zinc or magnesium, hydrosols of the oxides or hydroxides are produced. The metal sols, especially gold sol, are usually more permanent if dilute salt solution is used instead of pure water.

Svedberg has modified Bredig's method, employing an alternating-current arc of very high frequency in place of the direct-current arc, to prepare sols of nearly all the metals dispersed in such liquids as acetone, methanol, ethanol, ether, and chloroform, as well as in water. Probably in this case the metal comes from the electrodes in liquid droplets and the solidification of these produces the dispersion.

(*b*) *By reaction in solution.* The various types of reaction employed to produce sols may be illustrated by typical examples:

(i) *Hydrous oxide sols* may be made by hydrolysis of suitable salts, those of weak monobasic acids giving the best results. Thus an aluminum oxide sol may be made by the hydrolysis of aluminum acetate. The hydrolytic reaction is often carried out at elevated temperatures because of increased hydrolysis under those conditions. Ferric oxide sol, for example, may be prepared by adding concentrated ferric chloride solution, dropwise, to boiling water. The composition of the colloidal substance produced is given by $Fe_2O_3(H_2O)_x$. In order to stabilize the sol, excess electrolyte, *i.e.*, the Cl^- and H_3O^+, must be removed by dialysis.

(ii) *By interaction of ions.* When very dilute silver nitrate solution is added to a very dilute chloride solution, a colloidal suspension of silver chloride is obtained. Barium sulfate also is obtained in a partially colloidal condition if it is precipitated in the cold by the mixing of concentrated solutions of Ba^{++} and SO_4^{--}. *Sulfide sols* (*e.g.*, mercuric sulfide sol, arsenious sulfide sol, and antimonous sulfide sol) may be prepared by passing hydrogen sulfide into a suspension of the oxide. In the case of the arsenious oxide the following reaction occurs:

$$As_2O_3 + 3\,H_2S \longrightarrow As_2S_3 + 3\,H_2O$$

These sols are highly stable and may be kept for years.

(iii) *By oxidation or reduction.* Gold sols are produced by the reduction of auric chloride, $AuCl_3$, by such reducing agents as formaldehyde, dextrose, and hydroxylamine, NH_2OH. By varying the temperature and concentration, the color of the resulting gold sols may be gray, red, blue, or purple, depending upon the size of the sol particle. The *toning* of photographic prints may be controlled in this manner. A gold sol made by reducing auric chloride with formaldehyde finds physiological application as Formol. Colloidal sulfur may be produced by the oxidation of hydrogen sulfide with sulfurous acid in dilute solution, thus:

$$2\,H_2S + H_2SO_3 \longrightarrow 3\,\underline{S} + 3\,H_2O$$

(iv) *By addition of a liquid to a solution.* If to the solution of a substance in one liquid we add a second liquid in which the substance is not soluble, it often precipitates, but may form a sol. For example, the addition of water to a solution of sulfur in ethanol produces a sulfur sol. Likewise, the addition of ethanol to a saturated solution of calcium acetate in water produces a calcium acetate sol, the mixture setting to a fairly hard jelly, called "solid alcohol."

Purification of Sols. Since electrolytes dissolved in the dispersion medium always tend to coagulate the dispersed phase, they must be removed in order to stabilize the sol. This may be accomplished by *dialysis*, by *electrodialysis*, or by *ultrafiltration.*

(1) Dialysis. ***Dialysis*** *is the process of removing a dissolved substance from a colloidal solution by means of diffusion through a suitable membrane.* This process depends upon the facts that colloidal particles diffuse extremely slowly, and that they will not pass through certain animal membranes or sheets of Cellophane or nitrocellulose, which allow the passage of electrolyte.

A very satisfactory dialyzer described by Neidle[1] is shown

[1] *J. Am. Chem. Soc.*, **38**, 1270 (1916).

diagrammatically in Figure 224. The colloidal solution is put in a large beaker in which there is immersed the dialyzing membrane which contains distilled water. In the purification of a ferric oxide sol, the electrolyte, *i.e.*, the H_3O^+ and Cl^-, diffuses through the membrane into the water. Since the rate of diffusion is proportional to the *difference* in concentration of the diffusing substance, fresh water is run into the dialyzer bag continuously to remove the electrolyte *via* the constant-level device. Dialysis at room temperature is slow, requiring days or even weeks, but it can be hastened greatly by warming.

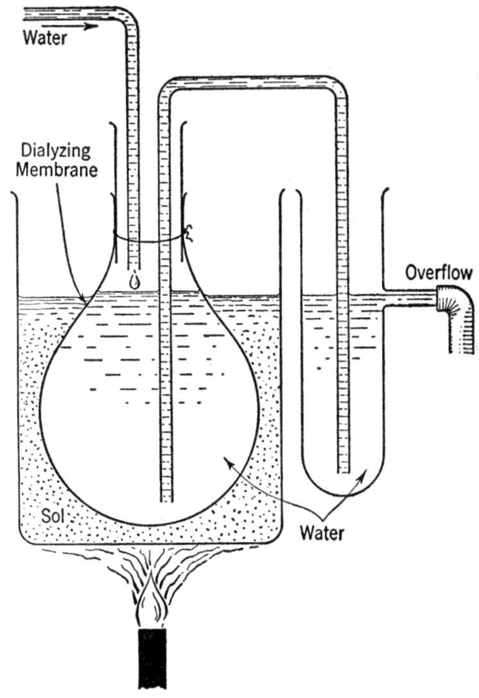

Fig. 224. Apparatus for the Purification of a Sol by Dialysis.

(2) **Electrodialysis.** The migration velocity of ions under the influence of the electric current is much greater than that due to diffusion alone. Consequently, if a colloidal solution is electrolyzed between electrodes which are placed outside the dialyzing membrane, the purification process is accelerated. An apparatus suitable for the purpose is shown in Figure 225. The middle compartment, which contains the sol, is separated from the two end compartments, which contain water, by the dialyzing membranes, M and M'. The electrodes, A and C, are placed near the membranes. When a current of 0.5 ampere or less is passed through the sol, the ions of any electrolyte pass through the membranes into the end compartments. Fresh water is added through the inlet tubes E and E', and the dilute electrolyte is removed through the outlet tubes, D and D'. The electric

current may also force some water through the membranes into the end compartments but this may be replenished through the inlet tube, *G*.

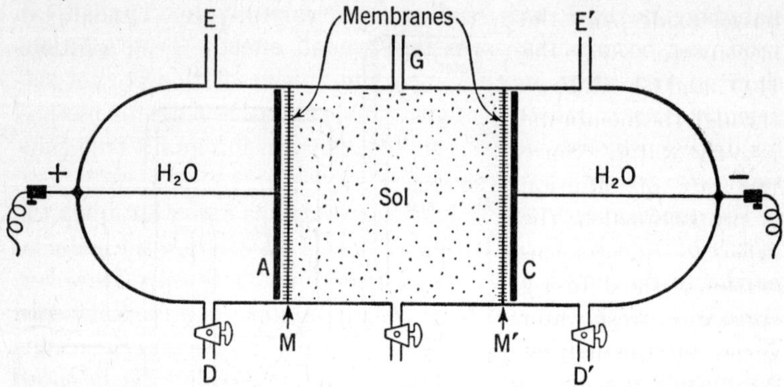

Fig. 225. Apparatus for the Purification of Sols by Electrodialysis.

(3) Ultrafiltration. ***Ultrafiltration*** *involves the use of specially prepared membranes through which solvents and solutes pass fairly readily but which is impermeable to colloid particles.* In order to speed up the process, pressure ordinarily is applied and this requires a reinforced membrane with larger pores than those in the ordinary membrane. In the *Bechhold filter,* much used in biological work, the membranes are made by impregnating cloth or filter paper with nitrocellulose. Membranes may be deposited in porcelain filters, which gives them greater strength and permits the use of strong pressure or suction. By varying the conditions, membranes of graded pore size may be made. *Pasteur filters* of fine, unglazed porcelain also serve as ultrafilters for removal of bacteria. Ultrafilters have been constructed so that the process may be accelerated by the electric current.[1]

Properties of Sols. The most fundamental characteristic of a sol is the size of the suspended particles. This determines to an important degree several other properties.

(1) Filterability. Colloidal particles pass readily through even the finer-pored filter papers. In quantitative analysis, loss of material by peptization of the precipitate must be minimized by coagulating the sol before filtering and by adding electrolytes, such as ammonium chloride in the case of ferric oxide and nitric acid in the case of stannic oxide, to the water used in washing precipitates.

[1] See, for example, H. B. Weiser, *Colloid Chemistry*, page 150.

(2) The Tyndall effect. If a strong beam of light is passed through a colloidal solution, its path is made visible by the light reflected from the particles. This phenomenon, first noted by Faraday,[1] in 1857, was studied more carefully by Tyndall,[2] in 1869, and became known as the **Tyndall effect.** True solutions show no such effect since the molecules in the solution are not sufficiently large to reflect the light. This furnishes a simple method for distinguishing between a colloidal suspension and a true solution.

The appearance of the *Tyndall beam* depends somewhat upon the nature of the sol. Other things being equal, the larger the colloidal particles, the greater will be the intensity of the beam. However, there is a marked difference between lyophobic and lyophilic sols. The latter adsorb the liquid molecules very strongly and the resulting **micelle,** *i.e., the particle of substance together with the adsorbed solvent or other material,* consists largely of the dispersing liquid. The light is not greatly scattered.

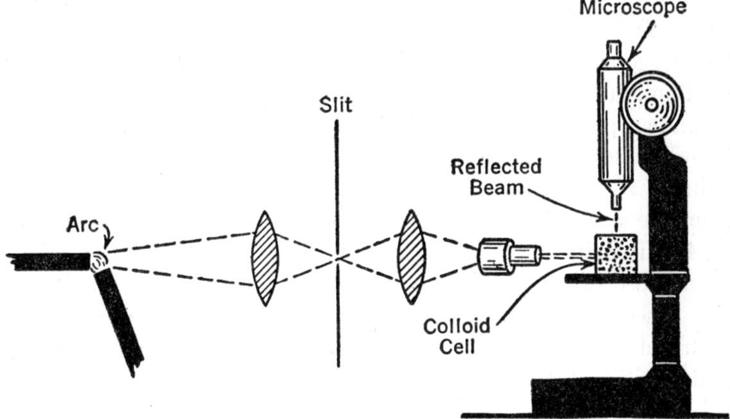

Fig. 226. Diagrammatic Representation of the Ultramicroscope.

Sol particles cannot be seen with the microscope. They may, however, be observed with the **ultramicroscope.** In this instrument the Tyndall beam through the colloidal suspension is viewed through a microscope set at right angles to the beam. The individual sol particles appear as bright spots of light against a dark background. The ultramicroscope is illustrated diagrammatically in Figure 226.

[1] *Proc. Roy. Soc.*, **6,** 356 (1857). [2] *Phil. Mag.*, (4) **37,** 384 (1869).

Another instrument based on the Tyndall effect is the **nephelometer,** designed to compare the suspended material in two sols by comparing the light they reflect. It was first employed by Richards and Wells[1] to determine the weights of silver halide lost as colloid in the washing process. It is an extremely sensitive method which has been used for the analysis of mustard gas-air mixtures and also in physiological chemistry for the determination of protein and hemoglobin and other analyses.

(3) Diffusion. The rate of diffusion of colloids, although very slow, is measurable. The separation of solutes from sols by dialysis is aided by the relatively rapid diffusion of the solute particles. The diffusion rate is proportional to the kinetic energy of the particles and inversely proportional to the viscosity of the medium and to the radius of the colloid particle. This is expressed by the equation due to Einstein:

$$D = \frac{RT}{N} \frac{1}{6\,\pi\eta r}$$

where D is the *diffusion coefficient,* N is Avogadro's number, R is the gas constant, T the absolute temperature, η the viscosity of the medium, and r the radius of the colloid particle. Using a gold sol of known particle size and measuring the rate of diffusion under known conditions, Svedberg used this equation to determine the value of N. He obtained 5.8×10^{23}, which does not differ greatly from the accepted value.

(4) Viscosity. The viscosities of colloidal solutions are greater than those of the dispersion medium under the same conditions. The viscosity of a hydrophobic sol, *e.g.,* gold or silver chloride hydrosol, is only slightly greater than that of water itself. A hydrophilic sol, however, adsorbs so many molecules of water that it becomes a comparatively large particle. These micelles occupy a considerable fraction of the total volume and increase markedly the viscosity of the colloidal solution. Viscosity is important in connection with the behavior of blood, since it determines largely the arterial pressure. The viscosity of blood serum is only about twice that of water, but that of whole blood is nearly seven times as great, probably because the blood corpuscles are hydrophilic.

(5) Colligative properties. The freezing point, boiling point, and vapor pressure of water are not measurably altered by the

[1] *Am. Chem. J.,* **31,** 238 (1904).

presence of a thoroughly dialyzed sol. The osmotic pressures of colloidal solutions are very small. Those of hydrophobic sols are difficult to determine because of the practical impossibility of removing electrolytes completely. For hydrophilic sols the results are of more significance and this property has been used as a basis for determining the molecular weights of proteins described on page 551.

(6) Sedimentation of sols. A sol will remain suspended for years, although after several months a tube containing a suspension of finely ground clay in water will show a gradation between the bottom, where the suspension is white, and the top, where it is bluish and faintly translucent. Some idea of the rate at which sol particles settle may be had from the data in Table 115, where the rates of settling are given for particles of silver of various sizes. Only the rates mentioned in the last two lines of this table apply to particles of colloidal size. Still smaller particles may never settle completely, but may form a colloidal atmosphere which is described on pages 96 to 98.

TABLE 115

RATE OF FALL OF SILVER SPHERES IN WATER

RADIUS OF PARTICLE, IN CM.	RATE OF SETTLING, IN CM. PER SEC.	TIME OF FALLING 1 CM., IN SEC.
1.0	200,000	0.000005
0.1	2,000	0.0005
0.01	20	0.05
0.001	0.2	5.0
0.0001	0.002	500
0.00001	0.00002	50,000 (14 hours)
0.000001	0.0000002	5,000,000 (58 days)

(7) Adsorption by sols. Adsorption is a surface phenomenon, hence the adsorption by a given amount of solid is increased enormously when the solid is dispersed into colloidal particles. Thus, a cube of 1 cm. edge has a total surface area on its six faces of 6 cm^2. If the cube is divided into cubes with an edge of 1×10^{-7} cm. (the lower limit for colloidal particles), the number of cubes will be 10^{21} with a total surface area of 6000 m^2. or nearly $1\frac{1}{2}$ acres.

The "purification" of a hydrophobic sol by dialysis does not mean the *complete* removal of electrolyte, which would flocculate the sol. Ions remain adsorbed on the sol particle. The adsorbed ion which renders the sol stable is known as the *stabilizing ion.*

Because of this adsorption of ions, sol particles carry either a positive or a negative charge. Neutral silver chloride sol, for example, is stabilized by a slight excess of silver ion or of chloride ion. In the former case the sol is positively charged due to the adsorbed silver ion, and in the latter case it is negatively charged due to the adsorbed chloride ion. In the surface of the sol particle, silver and chloride ions alternate, and hence the tendency to adsorb silver ion and the tendency to adsorb chloride ion are about the same, and the ion in excess will be the one adsorbed. These two cases are illustrated in Figure 227.

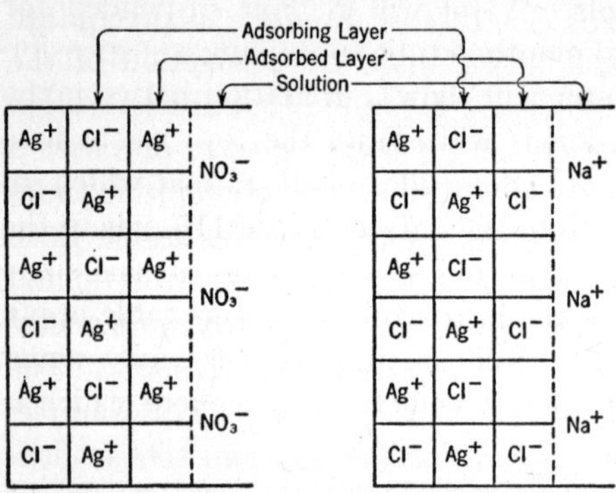

Fig. 227. Adsorption by Silver Chloride Sol Particle (Diagrammatic).

The coagulation of the sol results from the coalescence of sol particles into larger agglomerates of the substance. If the sol particles all carry the same charge, the forces of repulsion between them prevent their coalescence.

As a rule an *elementary* sol adsorbs selectively *either* positive or negative ions, but not both. Gold sol made by arcing in dilute chloride solution adsorbs $AuCl_2^-$, which renders the sol negatively charged. Silver sols may be made by arcing between silver electrodes in pure water; the sol is stabilized in this case by the adsorption of hydroxyl ion.

The micelle of stannic oxide, like other hydrophilic sols, is composed of SnO_2 plus many molecules of water. It is stabilized by a weakly basic solution because the adsorption of hydroxyl ion yields a sol particle which is negatively charged. Although the hydrous oxides, like ferric oxide and stannic oxide sols, adsorb stabilizing ions, the organic sols which consist of large molecules, such as the cellulose esters, proteins, and starch, are stabilized principally by the adsorbed dispersion medium. The adsorption of a dispersion medium by a lyophilic sol, or *solvation*, produces a micelle so sheathed with solvent molecules that the sol particles do not have a chance to come in contact with one another. Consequently, such sols do not readily coalesce and coagulate.

(8) Coagulation of sols. Although low concentrations of electrolyte are essential to stabilize most lyophobic sols, higher concentrations will almost always *coagulate* or *flocculate* them. Still higher concentrations are required to flocculate lyophilic sols, as in the salting out of proteins.

The first quantitative observation of the relative precipitating power of various electrolytes was made by Schulze, who determined the concentrations of various electrolytes required to precipitate arsenious sulfide sols, which are stabilized by adsorption of the negative sulfide or hydrosulfide ion. He found that an electrolyte with a bivalent cation had about 30 times the effect of one with a univalent cation, and that a trivalent cation was about 1650 times as effective as a univalent cation. Although the exact ratio depends upon the temperature, rate of addition of electrolyte, and other factors, the figures 1 : 30 : 1650 give an approximate measure of the effectiveness of cations in flocculating negative sols. The same holds true for the flocculating power of anions. For example, chloride, sulfate, and phosphate are increasingly effective in flocculating the positively charged ferric oxide hydrosol. A general qualitative rule, the **valence rule,** may be stated thus: *The flocculating power of electrolytes increases greatly with the increase in the valence of the ion opposite in charge to the sol being flocculated.* Flocculation of a sol can also be brought about by adding a second sol of opposite charge to the first.

The marked difference in the flocculating power of ions of different valences is illustrated by the data in Table 116. The concentrations of salts given are those which are just sufficient to effect the flocculation of the sol.

TABLE 116

FLOCCULATION OF SOLS BY IONS OF DIFFERENT VALENCES

Arsenious Sulfide Sol		Ferric Oxide Sol	
Electrolyte	Concentration Moles/Liter	Electrolyte	Concentration Moles/Liter
$NaCl$	0.051	$NaCl$	0.0093
KNO_3	0.050	KNO_3	0.0113
$CaCl_2$	0.00065	KCl	0.0090
$ZnCl_2$	0.00069	K_2SO_4	0.00020
$AlCl_3$	0.000093	$MgSO_4$	0.00022
$Al(NO_3)_3$	0.000095	$K_2Cr_2O_7$	0.00019

Protective Colloids. A lyophobic sol often can be stabilized by the addition of a lyophilic sol. The latter is then termed a **protective colloid.** An example of this is the use of gelatin to protect the silver bromide sol used in photographic films. In order to compare the protective power of various hydrophilic sols, an arbitrary standard has been set up. This is called the **gold number,** defined as *the number of milligrams of the dry hydrophilic substance which will just prevent the change from red to blue of 10 ml. of a gold sol on addition of 1 ml. of 10 per cent sodium chloride solution.* The change in color of the gold sol, from red to blue, indicates a partial flocculation, the red gold particles being much smaller than the blue. The lower the gold number, the greater the protective action. Gelatin, with a gold number of about 0.01, is one of the most effective protective colloids. Other values are egg albumin, 0.2; gum arabic, 0.2; dextrin, 9; wheat starch, 5; potato starch, 25; and sodium stearate, 10.

The Electrical Double Layer. Since the micelles in a sol are charged and the sol as a whole is electrically neutral, the dispersion medium must be oppositely charged. Each sol particle exerts an attractive influence on the oppositely charged ions remaining in the solution. Thus there is set up a system like a parallel-plate condenser which may be represented diagrammatically as in Figure 228. This is known as the **electrical double layer** or the **Helmholtz double layer.** The charges at the double layer cause a difference in potential across it which is known as the *zeta-potential* (ζ-potential), or the *electrokinetic potential.* Gortner[1] offers a general definition for the term, thus: "*The **ζ-potential** is the difference in potential across the Helmholtz double layer which exists at the boundary between two phases, or rather it is the difference in potential between the immovable liquid layer attached to the surface of the solid phase and the movable liquid layer immediately adjacent in the liquid phase.*" This can readily be pictured. For example, if a

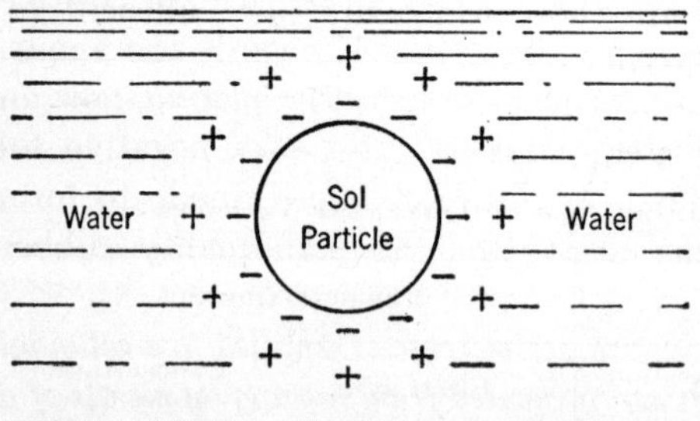

Fig. 228. Electrical Double Layer around a Sol Particle.

[1] R. A. Gortner, *Selected Topics in Colloid Chemistry*, p. 72.

glass plate is partially immersed in water as shown in Figure 229, the layer of water in immediate contact with the glass may be regarded as an "immovable layer"; furthermore, it contains

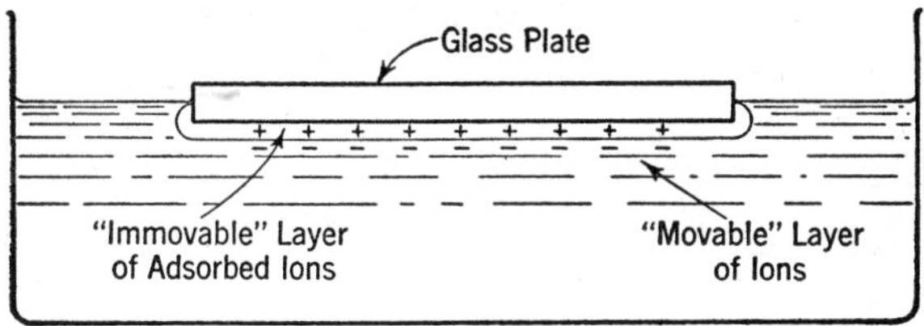

Fig. 229. **Illustrating Zeta (ζ) Potential.**

adsorbed ions. The difference in potential between this layer and the "movable" layer adjacent to it in the liquid phase would constitute the ζ-potential.

Electrophoresis (Cataphoresis). When an electromotive force is applied to a colloidal solution, the colloidal particles move towards the cathode if they carry a positive charge and towards the anode if they carry a negative charge. *This movement of colloidal particles towards an electrode is called* ***electrophoresis,*** *or* ***cataphoresis.*** The velocity of migration is much less than that of an ion under the same potential gradient, but it may be measured by direct observation of a moving boundary, by an analytical method quite similar to Hittorf's method for transference numbers, and by following the course of a large number of single particles in the ultramicroscope.

Observation of electrophoresis is the most direct and certain way of determining the sign of the charge on a sol particle; a positive sol goes towards the cathode, a negative sol towards the anode.

Electrophoresis is put to practical use in *rubber plating,* now an important commercial process. Rubber latex is a negative sol which may be deposited upon a suitably shaped anode to form rubber articles of various kinds, such as high-quality rubber gloves.[1]

Electroosmosis. *If an electromotive force is applied to a colloidal solution and the sol particles are prevented from moving by means of a suitable membrane set in porous material, the dispersion medium migrates in the direction opposite to that in which the sol particles tend to go.* This is known as **electroosmosis,** or **electroendosmosis.** The phenomenon can be illustrated experimentally very easily.

[1] Sheppard, *Trans. Am. Electrochem. Soc.*, **52,** 47 (1927).

The bottom of a U-tube is filled with porous clay, and the tube is nearly filled with some colloidal solution, *e.g.*, a ferric oxide sol. The electrodes are inserted in the arms of the U-tube and an electromotive force applied. If the colloid is positive, as in the case cited, the dispersion medium, water, will be negative; the liquid will rise in the arm containing the positive electrode. A similar effect will be observed even in the absence of colloid. Water will migrate through a capillary tube under an applied e.m.f. The wall film usually adsorbs hydroxyl ions, thus acquiring a negative charge and leaving the movable water layers positively charged. The effect may be observed more easily if there is a small air bubble in the water within the capillary tube. An apparatus, due to Briggs,[1] suitable for studying this effect is shown diagrammatically in Figure 230. Electroosmosis takes place through the porous diaphragm *D*, placed between the platinum electrodes *A* and *C*. The course of the osmosis can be followed by observing the position of the air bubble *B* on the scale *S*.

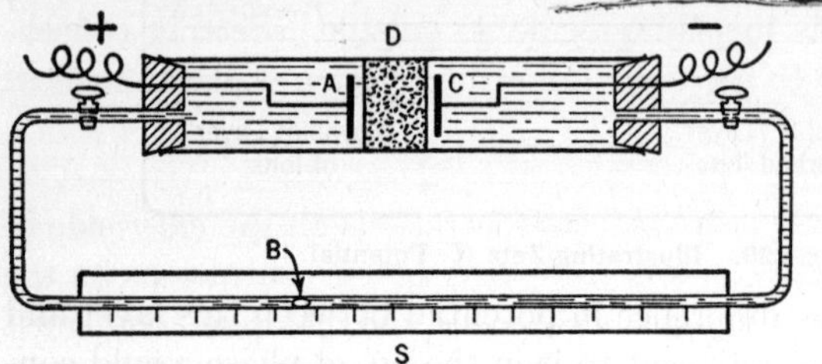

Fig. 230. Apparatus for Showing Electroosmosis.

Donnan's Membrane Equilibrium. A principle which is often applied in the interpretation of biological and physiological phenomena is that embodied in Donnan's membrane equilibrium.[2] This principle defines the state of equilibrium which exists when the solutions of two electrolytes with a common ion are separated by a membrane permeable to this common ion but impermeable to one of the other ions. Neglect of such membrane equilibrium effects may introduce considerable errors into the quantitative measurements of osmotic pressures of sols and of electrolytic effects.

Let us suppose that we separate by a suitable membrane a solution of sodium chloride and a solution of Congo red, the sodium salt of an acid with a large and complex anion, which we shall represent by X^-. The membrane is permeable to Na^+ and to Cl^-

[1] Briggs, *et al.*, *J. Phys. Chem.*, **22**, 256 (1918).
[2] Discussed in *Chem. Rev.*, **1**, 73 (1924).

but not to X^-. If the Congo red is on the *inner side* of the membrane and the sodium chloride on the *outer side,* diffusion takes place through the membrane tending to establish concentration equilibrium. Donnan showed that Na^+ and Cl^- diffused to the *inner side* of the membrane until the ionic activity product of sodium chloride was the same inside as outside. Setting concentrations equal to activities, the following relation was established:

$$[Na^+]_1 \times [Cl^-]_1 = [Na^+]_2 \times [Cl^-]_2$$

where $[Na^+]_1$ and $[Cl^-]_1$ are the concentrations on the *outer* side of the membrane and $[Na^+]_2$ and $[Cl^-]_2$ are the concentrations on the *inner* side. Equal numbers of sodium and chloride ions must diffuse through the membrane since the solution must remain neutral when equilibrium has been attained.

If then we let

$$x = [Na^+]_1 = [Cl^-]_1 \text{ on the } \textit{outer side}$$

$$y = [Cl^-]_2 \text{ on the } \textit{inner side}$$

and

$$z = [X^-] \text{ on the } \textit{inner side}$$

we find that

$$y + z = [Na^+]_2 \text{ on the } \textit{inner side}$$

Since the product of the sodium and chloride ion concentrations on the two sides are equal, it follows that:

$$x^2 = y(y + z)$$

If z is not zero, x will be greater than y, a concentration cell will be set up, and hence there will be a difference in potential across the membrane which is given by:

$$E = \frac{RT}{F} \ln \frac{x}{y}$$

In terms of activities, this expression is:

$$E = \frac{RT}{F} \ln \frac{a_1}{a_2}$$

In this expression a_1 and a_2 are the activities of the chloride ion in the *outer* and *inner* solutions, respectively; R is the gas constant; T the absolute temperature; and F the value of the faraday in coulombs.

The Isoelectric Point. The meaning of the term *isoelectric point* has already been explained in connection with *ampholytes* (see page 361). It is an important specific property of a hydrophilic sol which can adsorb, or otherwise take on, hydrogen or hydroxyl ions. In this connection it may be defined as *the* pH *of the solution when the sol moves neither to the cathode nor to the anode when an electromotive force is applied.* It is a property which is of especial interest in the colloid chemistry of proteins. Proteins retain to a considerable extent the ampholytic property of the amino acids from which they are largely constructed. The isoelectric point is thus a measure of the relative acid-base balance in the protein molecule. A few examples will illustrate the range of such values: For egg albumin the isoelectric point is at a *p*H of 4.8; for milk albumin, 4.6; for casein, 4.7; for gelatin, from 4.4 to 5.6; for hemoglobin, 4.8; for lecithin, 2.6; and for trypsin, an intestinal enzyme, about 7.5. The stability of protein sols is *least* at the isoelectric point, *i.e.*, at this *p*H the sol is most easily coagulated.

Gels. *A* ***gel*** *may be defined as a semirigid mass of lyophilic sol in which the dispersion medium has been all adsorbed by the sol particles so as to leave a sponge structure of micelles.* Under suitable conditions almost any lyophilic sol may be converted into a gel. A gel may be made, for example, by warming 1 g. of agar with 100 ml. of water and then cooling to room temperature. The agar peptizes, and upon cooling the sol sets to a firm gel. The hardness of the gel can be controlled by varying the proportions of agar to water. A gel is usually assumed to have a structure somewhat like that of a honeycomb. Each particle of the dispersed substance must adsorb a large number of molecules of the dispersion medium. Since the gel has a completely continuous structure we must assume that the micelles built up in this way are intricately interwoven.

Gels may be prepared from a very large variety of substances, both inorganic and organic. The hydrous oxides of tin, iron, chromium, and aluminum, familiar as gelatinous precipitates in the laboratory, may be obtained as compact gels. The silicic acid gel described on page 512 and the "solid alcohol" mentioned on page 536 are familiar examples. In addition to the agar mentioned above, other organic materials which form hydrophilic sols and readily form gels are gelatin, pectin, soaps of many kinds, and starch. Such gels are easily made by peptizing the solid substance with warm water and then cooling. Pectin accounts for the setting of ordinary fruit jellies. Pectin extracted commercially from apple cores is frequently added in the preparation of jellies.

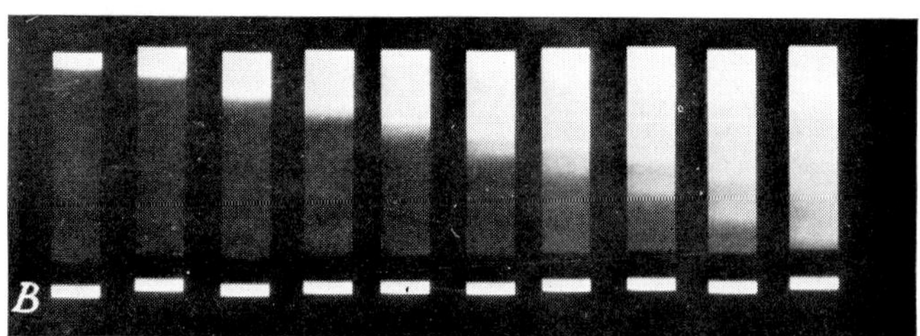

Courtesy of J. W. Williams

facing page 548

Plate XIV. (A) ULTRACENTRIFUGE WITH STEEL PROTECTING CASE OPEN (B) PHOTOGRAPHS SHOWING THE SEDIMENTATION OF A MIXTURE OF TWO PROTEIN SOLS IN THE ULTRACENTRIFUGE

On standing, an inorganic gel loses water and shrinks, at the same time showing other alterations in properties. X-ray studies indicate that changes, probably involving coalescence, take place within the sol particle itself. *The shrinking of a gel with the simultaneous exudation of solvent that is noticed on standing is called* ***syneresis.*** If water is removed by heating and at the same time air is passed into a melted gel, an *aerogel* is obtained, composed largely of air and extremely light.

Many substances, dissolved in the sol before it has set to a gel, diffuse in the gel as they would in water. The gel structure apparently offers little increased resistance to their migration. Also, in the electrolysis of a gel containing electrolyte, the ion velocity is very little different from the velocity in water.

Emulsions. *An* ***emulsion*** *is a colloidal dispersion of a liquid in a liquid.* Either liquid may be dispersed in the other, the dispersion medium usually being the one in excess. Thus, we may make an emulsion of nitrobenzene in water by shaking a little nitrobenzene with a relatively large quantity of water, while an emulsion of water in nitrobenzene often is the product when wet nitrobenzene is distilled. Obviously, as in the case of sols, an emulsion is composed of substances which are not soluble in each other. Two types of emulsions are recognized — *oil-in-water* emulsions and *water-in-oil* emulsions. Water is usually one of the components, and the other an oil or a liquid insoluble in water which takes the place of an oil.

Emulsions composed entirely of the *water* and the *oil* are not often stable. The droplets of the dispersed phase tend to come together, coalesce, and form a continuous liquid phase. A stable emulsion usually requires a third substance, called an **emulsifying agent,** which forms in the oil-water interface a film sufficiently tough to prevent the coalescence of the droplets. Soaps, gelatin, and other hydrophilic sols are useful emulsifying agents. Emulsions stabilized by emulsifying agents often contain droplets which are larger than the upper limit of colloidal dimensions. They have, however, typical colloidal properties.

Preparation of Emulsions. Methods of preparing emulsions differ only in the choice of emulsifying agents and the manner in which the dispersion is effected.

(1) The substance is mixed with the emulsifying agent and thoroughly peptized by shaking or grinding in a mortar. It is then

agitated with water to form the emulsion. A gum is often used as emulsifying agent in making pharmaceutical emulsions. The process is merely one of subdividing the oil into colloidal droplets, which retain their dispersion when mixed with water.

(2) The emulsifying agent is mixed with water and peptized; then the oil is added a very little at a time, and the mixture shaken.

(3) *Homogenizing* may be used for the preparation of an emulsion or for stabilizing an emulsion already at hand. The process consists of forcing the emulsion through capillary tubes under considerable pressure and allowing the issuing stream to break against a hard surface. Homogenized milk and cream are prepared in this way and are more stable than the natural emulsions. A similar result may be obtained by using ultrasonic waves.[1]

Properties of Emulsions. Whether a given emulsion belongs to the oil-in-water type or to the water-in-oil type may be ascertained readily by adding a little of the emulsion to each of the pure liquids. The emulsion mixes with the liquid which is acting as dispersion medium. Like sols, the droplets in an emulsion are electrically charged and migrate towards an electrode when a difference in potential is applied.

Emulsions are *broken*, or *demulsified*, by destroying the interfacial film between the colloid droplet and the dispersion medium. This may be done by adding a reagent which will react with the emulsifying agent; thus when an acid is added to an emulsion stabilized with soap, it reacts with the soap in the film, converts it to the corresponding fatty acid which has no emulsifying action, and thus permits the droplets to coalesce. It is possible also to break the emulsifying film by adding another emulsifying agent which tends to form the opposite type of emulsion. Since emulsion droplets are electrically charged, the addition of a salt with a divalent or trivalent ion of charge opposite to that on the colloid droplet (usually negative) "salts out" the colloid by dehydration of the emulsifying film. Also heating, freezing, vibration, or centrifuging, may cause coalescence of the droplets and the separation of the two liquid phases.

W. D. Bancroft,[2] of Cornell University, considers that the type of emulsion which a given emulsifying agent will stabilize depends

[1] Sollner, *J. Phys. Chem.*, **42**, 1071 (1938).

[2] W. D. Bancroft, *Applied Colloid Chemistry*, 3rd ed., McGraw-Hill Book Co., New York, 1932, p. 261.

upon the relative solubilities of the agent in water and oil. If it is more soluble in water than in oil, its adsorption will lower the surface tension of the interfacial film more on the water side than on the oil side, and the film will tend to curve around the droplets of oil, giving an *oil-in-water* emulsion. On the other hand, if the emulsifying agent is more soluble in the oil than in water, the surface tension of the film will be lessened on the side *away* from the water, and the film will tend to curve around droplets of water. In this case a *water-in-oil* emulsion will be formed. The two types of emulsions are illustrated in Figure 231.

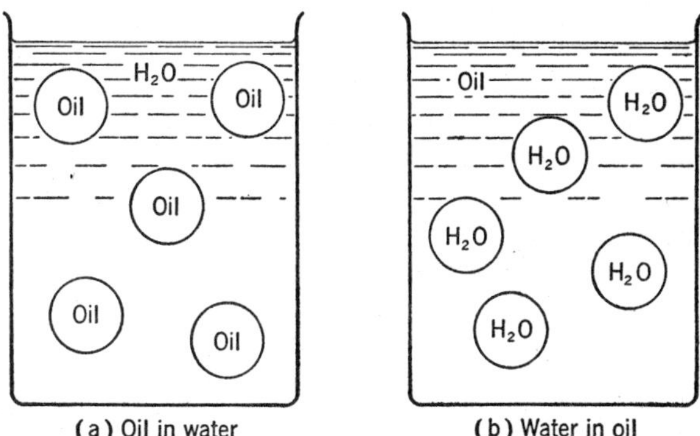

Fig. 231. Illustrating the Two Types of Emulsions.

Examples of Emulsions. Many pharmaceutical preparations are emulsions, not only such oil-in-water emulsions as those of cod-liver oil and halibut-liver oil but also salves and ointments of many kinds. *Milk* is an emulsion of butterfat in water, with the hydrophilic sol *casein* acting as emulsifying agent. The colloid droplets average about 7×10^{-4} cm. in diameter. When milk is homogenized they average about $\frac{1}{50}$th of this. *Mayonnaise* is made from oil, water, and egg, together with condiments, beaten with an egg beater to form an emulsion of oil in water with the *egg albumin* acting as emulsifying agent. It has been held that the digestion of fats in the intestines is greatly aided by emulsification. A little of the fat is saponified by the alkaline solution in the intestinal juices forming a little sodium soap. This serves to emulsify the rest of the fat, giving an emulsion of fat in water. The fine globules of the emulsion are more readily acted upon by the digestive enzymes, the *lipases*, than the fat would be in more massive form.

Methods for Determining Molecular Weights of Proteins. Proteins are substances containing carbon, hydrogen, oxygen, and nitrogen, and small amounts of other elements, especially sulfur and phosphorus. They make up most of the tissues of animals and plants and are present in the plasma of blood and in animal cells. They are compounds of very great complexity, with giant molecules of colloidal dimensions. They do not form true solutions in water or any other common solvent and cannot be vaporized or steam-distilled without decomposition, so that methods used for determining molecular weights of simpler substances are not applicable to them. However, so important is knowledge concerning proteins in physiology and related medical sciences, that some reference to the methods of determining their molecular weights seems desirable. Here we shall briefly consider methods based upon: (1) *chemical analysis;* (2) *osmotic pressure measurements;* (3) *surface tension measurements;* (4) *sedimentation data.*

(1) Chemical analysis. The per cent of an element in a compound is found from the molecular weight by the expression:

$$\text{Per cent of element} = \frac{n \times \text{At. wt. of element}}{\text{Mol. wt. of compound}} \times 100$$

where n is the number of atoms of the element in a molecule of the compound as shown by the formula. We may transpose this expression thus:

$$\text{Mol. wt. of compound} = \frac{n \times \text{At. wt. of element}}{\text{Per cent of element}} \times 100$$

The value of n may not be known, but by putting it equal to unity the *minimum* molecular weight is obtained. The minimum molecular weights of certain proteins may be found because they include in their composition a relatively small amount of some heavy metal, *e.g.*, iron in hemoglobin. In horse hemoglobin the per cent of iron is 0.335; hence the minimum molecular weight of this protein is,

$$M = 1 \times \frac{55.84}{0.335} \times 100 = 16{,}700$$

(2) Osmotic pressure measurements. Because of their high molecular weights and low solubility, proteins do not form solutions sufficiently concentrated to affect measurably any colligative property except osmotic pressure. The osmotic pressure due to 1 mole of undissociated solute per liter of solution is about 22.4 atmospheres at 0° C.; hence that of a protein of molecular weight

34,000, soluble to the extent of 0.2 per cent, would be $(2 \times 22.4)/34{,}000 = 0.0013$ atmosphere or 0.99 mm. of mercury. This would correspond to a height of 13.6 mm. of water which can be measured with sufficient accuracy.[1]

In order to eliminate the osmotic pressure of dissolved electrolyte, a membrane is used *which is permeable to electrolyte but not to protein.* Other complicating factors, however, exist. The proteins, because of their amino acid groupings, yield a small and indeterminate number of diffusible ions. Also, a Donnan membrane equilibrium will be set up. Because the membrane is impermeable to the protein molecule, there will be an unequal distribution of diffusible ions between the solutions on the two sides and consequently a difference in electrical potential which will inhibit further diffusion. This influence of ionization is practically eliminated by using the protein in *dilute* solution in a *concentrated* salt solution; the same concentrated salt solution is used also on the other side of the membrane, so that the ionic strengths on the two sides of the membrane are very nearly equal. Under these conditions the measured osmotic pressure is that due to the protein, the molecular weight of which therefore can be calculated. Since some proteins at or near their isoelectric points do not dissolve in water but are slightly soluble in such mixtures as glycerol and urea, their molecular weights often are measured in these solvents.

(3) **Surface tension measurements.** Some substances, such as soaps and proteins, tend to concentrate in the surface of a solution with a consequent lowering of the surface tension. The maximum decrease occurs when the substance has formed a monomolecular film on the surface. At certain definite concentrations the surface is assumed to contain the molecules in certain definite orientations, *i.e.*, positions in which the individual molecules lie on the surface. On this basis du Noüy devised a method of finding the molecular weights of proteins. A given protein solution is diluted stepwise. Upon each dilution the surface tension is measured with a tensiometer. The curve obtained by plotting the concentration against the surface tension shows three minima corresponding to the three different positions of the molecules possible in the monomolecular film. Below a certain concentration it is assumed that all the protein in the solution has collected in the liquid-air and the liquid-

[1] C. L. A. Schmidt, *The Chemistry of Amino Acids and Proteins*, pp. 347–348.

glass interfaces. When this condition has been reached we have the relation,

$$t = \frac{mc}{Sd}$$

where t is the thickness of the film, m is the mass of the solution, c is the concentration of protein, S the surface area, and d the density of the dry protein. It is assumed that t, at each of the surface tension minima, represents a molecular dimension. From the three values of t the volume of the protein molecule may be calculated and hence, multiplying by the density and by Avogadro's number, the molecular weight may be obtained. Although the validity of certain of the assumptions is admittedly open to question, the method has the advantages of ease and rapidity; also the protein need not be specially purified nor brought to the isoelectric point.

(4) Sedimentation methods. The most important methods for the determination of the molecular weights of proteins and other colloidal substances are based upon the study of the sedimentation of the particles under controlled conditions. The molecular weight may be calculated either from the concentrations of protein at certain levels when *sedimentation equilibrium* has been attained or from the *sedimentation rate*. *Sedimentation equilibrium* occurs when sedimentation is balanced by diffusion and no further settling takes place. Sedimentation of colloidal particles has been discussed in connection with the colloidal atmosphere on pages 96 to 98.

Protein molecules do not settle appreciably under the influence of gravity alone but may be made to settle by the application of a greater force. This has been effected by the use of the **ultracentrifuge,** developed by Svedberg, with which forces up to nearly 900,000 times that of gravity can be applied.

The construction and use of the ultracentrifuge may best be understood by reference to Figure 232, which shows diagrammatically its essential parts. The rotor R, about 6 inches in diameter and constructed of heavy chromium-nickel steel, turns about the horizontal axis CD and may be driven at high speed by an oil or air turbine, attachment to which is made at D. Since the friction with air molecules at ordinary pressure causes a rise in temperature of several degrees, the whole apparatus is enclosed in a strong steel box, $EFGH$, which either contains hydrogen at low pressure or is evacuated. The box also affords protection to the experimenter in case of the explosion of the rotor due to the very high centrifugal forces that may be developed.

Near the periphery of the rotor and on diametrically opposite sides are bore-holes into which are fitted and tightly clamped two *sedimentation cells, A* and *B*, which are provided with windows of crystalline quartz. Each cell may hold about 1 ml. When in

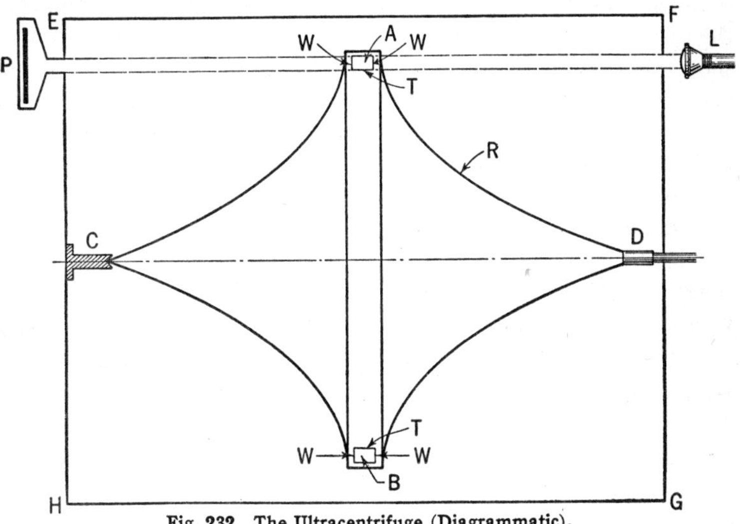

Fig. 232. The Ultracentrifuge (Diagrammatic).

operation the top of the cell is on the side marked *T*. One cell *A* contains the sol to be examined; this is at the isoelectric point and is suspended in salt solution, *e.g.*, 0.1 *N* KCl. The other cell *B* contains only the same salt solution; it has a marking which serves to align the photographic recordings of the sol in *A* and thus is called the *index cell.*

When in operation, the light from a mercury vapor lamp at *L*, adjusted by suitable slits and filters, passes through the cell and falls on a photographic plate at *P*. The plate is movable so that several recordings of the same sol may be made. If *sedimentation equilibrium* is being studied, the speed of the rotor is relatively low, corresponding to forces of 500 to 15,000 times that of gravity. The heavier the sol particle, *i.e.*, the greater the molecular weight, the lower the speed necessary to effect the desired sedimentation. At a definite speed the centrifugation is continued until the densities of the sol, as measured by the absorption of light, at various levels become constant. If *sedimentation velocities* are being measured, much higher rotational speeds are employed, giving centrifugal forces from 15,000 up to 750,000 times that of gravity. Photographs recording the condition of the sol are taken at intervals of 10 to 20 minutes. These show clearly the distance through which the sol particles have settled and hence give a measure of the sedimentation velocity. If the particles are not uniform in size, as is the case in a mixture of two or more protein sols, the recording may show the extent of sedimentation of each species. Plate XIV, facing page 548, illustrates the results obtained with representative sols.

The mathematical computation of the molecular weights is beyond the scope of this book. For this the reader is referred to Svedberg, *Chemical Reviews*, **14,** 1 (1934).

Summary of Molecular Weights of Proteins. To compare the values of the molecular weight of one protein determined by several different methods, including those discussed in the foregoing pages, we have collected in Table 117 the results for *horse hemoglobin.*

TABLE 117

Molecular Weights of Horse Hemoglobin Protein by Different Methods

Method	Mol. Wt.	Experimenters
Per cent composition, iron	16,700*	Hufner and Jacquet
Reacting weight, toward acid	50,000	Cohn, Henry, and Prentiss
Reacting weight, toward oxygen . . .	16,700*	Hufner and Jacquet
Sedimentation equilibrium	68,000	Svedberg
Sedimentation velocity	69,000	Svedberg
Surface tension	68,700	Sørensen
Osmotic pressure	67,000	Hufner and Gannser

* Minimum molecular weights. Note that they are about $\frac{1}{4}$ of the others.

READING LIST

R. A. Gortner, *Selected Topics in Colloid Chemistry.* Cornell Univ. Press, Ithaca, N. Y., 1937.

H. N. Holmes, *Introductory Colloid Chemistry.* John Wiley & Sons, New York, 1934.

H. R. Kruyt, *Colloids*, 2d ed. John Wiley & Sons, New York, 1930.

The Svedberg, *Colloid Chemistry.* Chemical Catalog Company, New York, 1924.

A. W. Thomas, *Colloidal Chemistry.* McGraw-Hill Book Company, New York, 1934. An excellent treatment of the whole subject.

H. B. Weiser, *Colloid Chemistry.* John Wiley & Sons, 1939. Also an excellent up-to-date treatment of the subject.

CHAPTER 20

CATALYSIS

The study of thermodynamics and the determination of the free energy change tell us whether or not a reaction can take place but *not how fast.* Many reactions in which there is a large decrease in free energy (for example, the combination of hydrogen and oxygen at room temperature) do not take place with measurable velocity. Where reactions which might be of economic importance are thermodynamically possible but proceed too slowly for practical use, some method of speeding up the reaction rate must be sought. A rise in temperature of 10° C. may double or triple the reaction rate; but, if the reaction is exothermic, the equilibrium yield will be lessened. The other method of speeding up a reaction is by the addition of a *catalyst.*

The first record of catalytic action dates from 1812 when G. S. C. Kirchhoff observed that the conversion of starch to sugar was hastened by adding acid. In 1818, Thénard reported that hydrogen peroxide decomposed more rapidly in the presence of platinum or gold; and in 1820, Döbereiner discovered that platinum also accelerated the reaction between hydrogen and oxygen. Berzelius, in 1836, definitely recognized what we now consider a catalytic effect but postulated the exercise of a "catalytic force." Said Berzelius: "I will call *catalysis* the decomposition of bodies by this force in the same way that one calls by the name *analysis* the decomposition of bodies by chemical affinity." [1]

Numerous cases of catalysis were recognized during the succeeding decades, but only at the end of the century, when van't Hoff's intensive studies of chemical kinetics had enhanced interest in that field, did Ostwald, in his laboratory at Leipzig, take up a really systematic study of catalytic phenomena. He showed clearly the effects of catalysis and the primary function of a catalyst in a reaction, although the details of the mechanism of catalysis remained for later chemists to work out.

We may define a ***catalyst*** *as a substance which alters the speed of a chemical reaction without undergoing permanent chemical change.*

[1] A. Findlay, *A Hundred Years of Chemistry*, page 105. The Macmillan Company, New York, 1937.

This definition does not rule out the possibility of a catalyst *slowing down* a reaction nor the possibility of its *taking part chemically* in the reaction, provided that it is the same *chemically* at the end of the reaction as at the beginning. Also, a catalyst cannot start a reaction but can only affect the rate of a reaction already in progress. For practical purposes it matters little whether or not the catalyst is completely unchanged during the reaction. Often there is a distinct alteration in physical properties. For example, in the catalysis of the decomposition of potassium chlorate by manganese dioxide, the latter will change to a fine powder at the end of the reaction even if it is crystalline to start with. In some cases the catalyst may be combined with one of the products. The essential criterion of a catalyst is that it is a *substance* that alters the speed of a reaction.

Theory of Catalysis. Although we do not yet know clearly *why* substances catalyze reactions, we know reasonably well *how* they do so. There are two general theories of catalysis which are mutually supplementary. They may be called the *activation-energy theory* and the *intermediate-compound theory.*

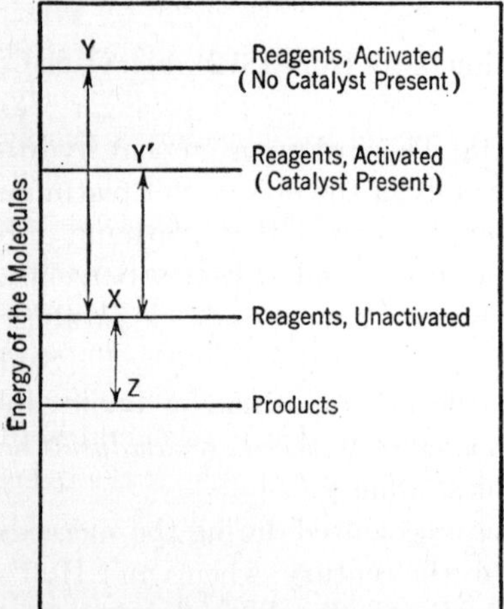

Fig. 233. Illustrating the Activation-Energy Theory of Catalysis.

The activation-energy theory. According to this theory the function of the catalyst is to lower the *energy of activation.* In consequence of this lowering, a greater proportion of the molecules of the reactants have sufficient energy to react, and the reaction proceeds more rapidly. Such a situation is presented graphically in Figure 233. In this diagram the level X represents the average energy of the molecules of the reagents and Z the average energy of the products of the reaction. The level Y denotes the minimum energy which the molecules must have in order to react, *i.e.*, the energy which the molecules must have when they are sufficiently activated to react. *The difference* $Y - X$ *is termed the* ***energy of activation.***

If the energy of activation, $Y - X$, is large so that the energy of the activated molecules is much greater than the average energy of the reagent molecules, then only a few molecules will possess this energy and the reaction will be slow. However, if $Y - X$ is small, a greater number of molecules will possess sufficient energy to react and the reaction will be rapid. It is assumed that the catalyst provides a path involving a lower energy of activation, $Y' - X$, permitting more molecules to react and thus accelerating the reaction. In the application of thermodynamics to the case, only the difference between X and Z, the initial and final energies of the molecules of the system, is considered. The catalyst cannot in any way alter the magnitudes X and Z; it can, however, alter the *path* by which the system goes from the energy state X to the energy state Z.

In the reverse reaction, the change of the system from energy level Z to energy level X, the reacting molecules must attain the same average energy Y, but the catalyst provides a path by which they can react at the lower energy level Y'. Hence the catalyst accelerates both the forward and the reverse reaction. Obviously, the catalyst cannot affect the final state of equilibrium; it merely alters the rate at which equilibrium is attained.

The intermediate-compound theory. This theory explains the mechanism by which the energy of activation is lowered. According to it, a given reaction will be accelerated if a reactant forms with the catalyst an unstable compound which either decomposes spontaneously or else reacts with another substance to yield the ultimate products. In either case, the catalyst is regenerated in the final step of the series of reactions. For example, if the overall reaction is

$$A + B \longrightarrow AB$$

and if C is the catalyst, the series of reactions may be:

$$A + C \longrightarrow AC$$
$$AC + B \longrightarrow AB + C$$

and the summation of these two reactions is

$$A + B \longrightarrow AB$$

the catalyst ending in the same chemical state as at the start of the reaction.

An example of the formation of an intermediate compound is the oxidation of sulfur dioxide to sulfur trioxide in the lead-chamber process for making sulfuric acid. The catalyst is nitric oxide. The over-all reaction is

$$2\,SO_2 + O_2 \longrightarrow 2\,SO_3$$

but the reaction probably takes place in the following steps:

$$2\,NO + O_2 \longrightarrow 2\,NO_2$$
$$2\,NO_2 + 2\,SO_2 \longrightarrow 2\,NO + 2\,SO_3$$

since sulfur dioxide is not oxidized by oxygen itself at room temperature but is readily oxidized by nitrogen dioxide in accordance with the second equation.

The scope of the *intermediate-compound theory* is greatly widened if we include as intermediate compounds the films formed by chemical adsorption on the surface of a different phase.

Types of Catalyzed Reactions. Reactions are divided broadly into two classes, *homogeneous reactions* and *heterogeneous reactions.* The former takes place in a single phase, as in the gaseous or liquid phase, so that the reacting system is homogeneous throughout. Examples of reactions in the gas phase are the decomposition of nitrogen pentoxide:

$$2\,N_2O_5 \longrightarrow 4\,NO_2 + O_2$$
$$4\,NO_2 \rightleftharpoons 2\,N_2O_4$$

the decomposition of hydrogen iodide:

$$2\,HI \rightleftharpoons H_2 + I_2$$

and the oxidation of nitric oxide:

$$2\,NO + O_2 \longrightarrow 2\,NO_2$$

An example of a homogeneous reaction in solution is the esterification of an organic acid, thus:

$$CH_3COOH + C_2H_5OH \rightleftharpoons CH_3COOC_2H_5 + H_2O$$

A heterogeneous reaction, such as the action of an acid on calcium carbonate, takes place at the boundary between two phases.

We may classify catalytic effects as **homogeneous catalysis** and **heterogeneous catalysis.** In the former *the reactants and the catalyst form a homogeneous mixture.* In the latter, almost invariably, *the system is homogeneous so far as the reactants are concerned* *but is made heterogeneous by the introduction of a catalyst in a different phase, usually solid.* Let us consider these types more in detail.

Homogeneous catalysis. In the gas phase this is rare, and the majority of known cases are chain reactions (see page 296). One well-known example of homogeneous catalysis in the gas phase is the oxidation of sulfur dioxide to sulfur trioxide with nitric oxide as catalyst. This reaction probably involves not a chain reaction but the formation of an intermediate compound, as shown on page 560.

Homogeneous catalysis in the liquid phase is more common. As a matter of fact, most reactions in solution are influenced catalytically to a greater or less extent by the solvent. This influence is especially strong when the solvent is highly polar, like water, and consequently is capable of deforming the molecule of the reacting substance and thus altering its tendency to react. Also, in aqueous solution, ions are usually present, and these frequently have a strong catalytic effect. As we shall see, hydrogen and hydroxyl ions are powerful catalysts in some reactions.

Homogeneous catalysis in solution generally is explained on the basis of intermediate compound formation. Thus, if the change of a substance A into a substance B is catalyzed by the presence in the solution of the catalyst C, we may represent the mechanism of the change by the reactions:

$$A + C \rightleftharpoons X$$
$$X \longrightarrow B + C$$

The over-all reaction is, of course:

$$A \longrightarrow B$$

The rate of the first reaction is directly proportional to the product of the concentrations of A and C. The rate of decomposition of the intermediate compound X will be proportional to its concentration. If we represent the velocity constants for the forward and reverse reactions in the first equilibrium by k_1 and k_2, respectively, and that for the second reaction by k_3, we see that the rate of the over-all reaction will depend upon the values of these three constants. *The rate of the over-all reaction, therefore, should be proportional to the concentration of the catalyst,* which is, indeed, the case.

If in the above reactions k_2 is greater than k_1, the concentration of X will be small and the rate-determining reaction is:

$$X \longrightarrow B + C$$

If k_3 is greater than k_1, the intermediate compound X decomposes into B and C as fast as it is formed, and in this case the rate-determining reaction is the formation of X, which is dependent upon A and C.

Occasionally a somewhat different mechanism, an "alternate oxidation and reduction," is encountered. An example of this is the catalysis of the decomposition of hydrogen peroxide by bromine or bromide and by iodine or iodide. Bray has suggested [1] that in the case of bromide ion, the hydrogen peroxide first oxidizes the bromide ion to hypobromite, in acid solution, and the hypobromous acid reacts with the peroxide, thus:

$$H_2O_2 + H_3O^+ + Br^- \longrightarrow 2\,H_2O + HOBr$$
$$H_2O_2 + HOBr \longrightarrow O_2 + H_3O^+ + Br^-$$

The over-all reaction is

$$2\,H_2O_2 \longrightarrow 2\,H_2O + O_2$$

For the catalysis with iodine Abel suggests the following steps:

$$H_2O_2 + I_2 \longrightarrow 2\,H^+ + 2\,I^- + O_2$$
$$H_2O_2 + 2\,H^+ + 2\,I^- \longrightarrow 2\,H_2O + I_2$$

When these are added, we obtain the over-all reaction:

$$2\,H_2O_2 \longrightarrow 2\,H_2O + O_2$$

In both these cases the catalyst, the bromide ion or the iodine, is re-formed in the reaction and hence is not permanently altered. Probably the oxidation reaction and the reduction reaction involved are not of the same velocity, but after a short interval a "steady state" is reached and the only apparent change is the decomposition of the hydrogen peroxide.

Acid-Base Catalysis. Many reactions are catalyzed by acids and by bases. The earliest recorded catalytic effect, the hydrolysis of starch, is an example. Among others, we may mention the inversion of cane sugar and the hydrolysis of other disaccharides, the mutarotation of dextrose and other simple sugars, the esterification of organic acids, and the reverse change, the hydrolysis of esters.

In 1887 when Arrhenius advanced his theory of electrolytic dissociation, Ostwald was studying the catalytic effects of acids. He

[1] Bray and Livingston, *J. Am. Chem. Soc.*, **45**, 1251 (1923).

concluded that the catalytic effects of different acids were proportional to their conductances determined under like conditions of temperature and concentration. Since Arrhenius had assumed that the conductances were proportional to the degrees of ionization, he concluded further that the catalytic effects were determined by the concentrations of hydrogen ion. Thereafter, the catalytic effects of acids were generally considered as those of the hydrogen ion.

In 1895 Goldschmidt made quantitative comparisons of the effects of various strong acids on the rates of esterification of acetic and other weak acids, with ethanol. In the presence of water, highly dissociated hydrochloric and hydrobromic acids were more effective than the slightly dissociated picric acid, which was evidence that the hydrogen ion was the effective catalytic agent. Also, the addition of a salt with an ion in common with a weak catalytic acid greatly diminished the catalytic effect. On the other hand, hydrochloric and hydrobromic acids were more effective catalysts in pure ethanol than when some water was present. Since water increases the ionization of the acids, this result indicated that the effective catalyst in this case is the *undissociated acid.* Later investigation showed quite definitely that both the hydrogen ion and the undissociated acid molecules are effective in catalyzing such reactions. Also, substances yielding the hydroxyl ion, and basic substances like aniline, $C_6H_5NH_2$, and pyridine, C_5H_5N, as well as anions, particularly those of weak acids, catalyze the esterification process.

Another reaction which has received careful study is the mutarotation of dextrose. When dextrose, $C_6H_{12}O_6$, is crystallized from boiling aqueous solution, *the specific optical rotation* (*i.e., the angle through which the plane of plane-polarized light is rotated when passed through a tube 1 dm. in length containing a solution of 1 g. of the substance dissolved in 100 ml. water*), denoted by α_D,[1] is 119.1°. If the solution is allowed to stand and the observations are continued, the angular rotation becomes progressively less until it reaches 52.4° where it remains constant. If the dextrose is crystallized from glacial acetic acid, the initial specific rotation is found to be 19°, but on standing, it increases to 52.4° where it remains constant. The modification with a specific rotation of 119.1° is

[1] The subscript $_D$ indicates that the light used in the polarimeter with which the angle of rotation is measured is *sodium light.* The *pair* of lines in the sodium spectrum often referred to as the "D line" have wave lengths of 5890 and 5896 Å; the light is thus essentially monochromatic.

called α-dextrose; the other β-dextrose; that with a specific rotation of 52.4° is the equilibrium mixture of the two. The two forms differ in the positions in space of an H atom and an OH group attached to the end carbon in the molecule.[1] The change of one form into the other is called **mutarotation.** The majority of sugars have this property.

Mutarotation in dextrose takes place slowly in neutral aqueous solution but much more rapidly if the solution is either acid or basic. It takes place fairly rapidly when the dextrose is dissolved in pyridine containing a little water, in cresol, $C_6H_4(OH)CH_3$, containing a little water, or in a mixture of cresol and pyridine. In pure, dry cresol or pyridine, either the α-dextrose or the β-dextrose remains unchanged. We may tabulate these results as follows:

Solvent	*Velocity of Mutarotation*
Water	Moderate
Water + acid	High
Water + base	High
Cresol	No change
Cresol + water	Moderate
Pyridine	No change
Pyridine + water	Moderate
Cresol + pyridine	High

Before 1923 there was no comprehensive theory which would explain these facts and the facts regarding the catalysis of esterification and other similar homogeneous solution reactions. In that year Lowry and Brønsted independently formulated a new and broader concept of acids and bases which has been found satisfactory in its application to explain the facts of acid-base catalysis. This concept has been discussed in Chapter 12, page 323.

According to this theory, the reaction is catalyzed by the transfer of a proton H^+ from the catalyst solute to the reactant X to form an intermediate compound XH^+, which thereupon reacts, giving up the proton to another substance capable of accepting it. Thus two distinct types of substance must be present in the reacting system to bring about *acid-base catalysis: an* ***acid****, defined as a substance capable of supplying a proton;* and *a* ***base****, defined as a substance capable of accepting a proton.*

[1] For further information see Lucas, *Organic Chemistry*, American Book Company, New York, 1935. Pp. 557–562.

facing page 564

Plate XV. PETER DEBYE

(*For biographical note see page 336.*)

The Lowry-Brønsted theory of acid-base catalysis serves to explain the catalysis by acids of the mutarotation of dextrose as follows:

If we begin with α-dextrose, it takes a proton from an acid, undergoes intramolecular rearrangement, then gives up the proton to a base and forms β-dextrose. This can happen only if *both* an acid and a base are present in the solution. This is the case in any aqueous solution since water is amphiprotic and can either take on or give up a proton. If a strongly acid or strongly basic substance is added to the water solution, the proton-giving or the proton-accepting ability is enhanced greatly and the reaction, in consequence, is accelerated. In cresol containing a little water, the cresol is the acid and yields one proton to the dextrose; the unstable compound of the dextrose with the proton thereupon decomposes, giving up the proton to the water forming H_3O^+. In pyridine containing water, the water gives up the proton to the dextrose, and the dextrose passes it on to the pyridine. In a mixture of cresol and pyridine, the weakly acid cresol gives up a proton to the dextrose, and the dextrose, in turn, gives it to the pyridine. In pure cresol, dextrose undergoes no change because cresol is definitely acid and has no tendency to accept protons. In solution in pure pyridine no reaction occurs because the pyridine is definitely *basic*, with no tendency to give up protons. In order to have acid catalysis, both acid and base must be present.

The catalysis of other reactions by acid or base is due, probably, to a similar mechanism. A proton donor adds a proton to the reactant, forming an intermediate compound which decomposes and gives its proton to a base. The quantitative treatment of the velocity constants for reactions catalyzed by acids and bases, and the effect of added electrolytes, which give rise to *salt effects*, are beyond the scope of this book.

Heterogeneous Catalysis. Whenever the catalyst is not in the same phase as the reactants, we have *heterogeneous catalysis*. The classification includes those reactions catalyzed by material in the colloidal state. Enzyme-catalyzed reactions, treated in the following chapter, are a borderline case. Catalysis takes place only on the surface of the catalyst where the reactants are adsorbed; hence, *heterogeneous catalysis* is commonly called **contact catalysis.**

Gas reactions. Gas reactions almost invariably involve heterogeneous catalysis, even though a catalyst is not intentionally added.

Many reactions, which at first thought appear to be homogeneous, actually are **wall reactions,** catalyzed by the walls of the containing vessel. There are several ways of distinguishing this wall effect: (1) *Increase of surface.* The effect of increased surface of wall material can be examined by adding this material in powdered form to the reacting gas mixture. If such an addition increases the velocity of the reaction, the walls of the vessel evidently are affecting the rate of reaction. Powdered glass, for example, added to a gaseous mixture reacting in a glass vessel, usually has a decided catalytic effect. (2) *Nature of the wall material.* If a reaction which takes place rapidly in a vessel made of glass takes place more slowly in a vessel made of paraffin, then we are forced to the conclusion that glass is acting as a positive catalyst or paraffin is acting as a negative catalyst. The former is more likely to be the case. A striking experiment which illustrates this effect is to take two bottles, one of glass, the other of glass coated with paraffin, fill them with ethylene, add to both some bromine solution, and shake. In the plain glass bottle the color of the bromine disappears instantly, indicating rapid reaction, thus:

$$C_2H_4 + Br_2 \longrightarrow C_2H_4Br_2$$

In the paraffin-coated bottle no reaction takes place, since this reaction proceeds only on the surface of the glass. (3) *Temperature coefficient.* The velocity of a homogeneous reaction doubles or triples for each 10° rise in temperature. In a wall reaction the slowest and therefore the rate-determining step in the process is likely to be the diffusion of the gas away from the walls. Since the diffusion rate increases only a few per cent for a rise in temperature of 10°, any gaseous reaction is likely to be a *wall reaction* if its velocity constant has a very low temperature coefficient.

Reactions in solution. Reactions between solutes likewise often are catalyzed by the introduction of a solid. The same considerations apply here as to the heterogeneously catalyzed gas reactions except that, in general, catalytic effects are less marked, due to slower diffusion and other factors. Reactions in solution that are catalyzed by colloids or by enzymes should be classed as heterogeneously catalyzed reactions. At least for the inorganic colloids the mechanism probably involves adsorption and hence is similar to that of definitely heterogeneously catalyzed reactions; but the extremely small size of the colloidal particles, and possibly of the enzyme particles, gives so nearly homogeneous distribution through the reacting mixture that the reaction often differs but slightly from a homogeneously catalyzed reaction.

Mechanism of Heterogeneous Catalysis. Adsorption plays an essential role in the catalysis of reactions by surfaces. The simplest of the various mechanisms suggested for this catalysis is as follows: In a reaction between two substances A and B, the substance A is adsorbed on the surface of the catalyst as a monomolecular layer, or both A and B may be adsorbed in different proportions. As a result of this concentration of A, or A and B, on the surface, there is greater chance of a collision between the molecules of A and the molecules of B than if both were still widely separated in the gas phase. As in the case of uncatalyzed gas reactions, the reaction requires not only that the molecules collide but that they contain sufficient *energy*. It is now thought that energy of activation is necessary for all the reactants of the particular system, and it is possible that this is supplied by the catalyst as energy of adsorption. The mechanism of this adsorption is not known in every case. In the adsorption of hydrogen on platinum black, the molecule is almost certainly split into atoms in the adsorption process, at least to some extent, and this renders the hydrogen much more reactive.

In addition to the reaction taking place at the catalyzing surface, other processes are sometimes important in determining the rate of a catalyzed reaction, *e.g.*, the diffusion of the reagents *to* the catalyst surface and the diffusion of the products *away from* the catalyst surface. If the latter is slow, the products will blanket the catalyst from the reagents. In such a case, the diffusion of the products away from the catalyst will be the slowest and hence the rate-determining step. There is also the possibility that a product will be adsorbed on the catalyst and must be desorbed before it can even begin to diffuse away.

We may outline the process of a heterogeneously catalyzed reaction as taking place by the following steps: (1) diffusion of the reagents to the catalyst surface; (2) adsorption and activation of one or more of the reagents on the surface; (3) reaction between the reagents at the surface; (4) desorption of the product, *i.e.*, decomposition of the catalyst-product compound; (5) diffusion of the products away from the catalyst surface.

Frequently the diffusion processes can be eliminated as rate-determining steps, either by stirring the reacting mixture vigorously, or in the case of a gas reaction, by passing over the surface of the catalyst a rapid stream of the reagents which will carry away the products and bring the reagents to the catalyst much more rapidly than would the process of diffusion. Generally the reaction itself is the slowest step next to the diffusion process. Not infrequently it is slower than diffusion. In this case the reaction rate will be greatly increased by rise in temperature.

In most bimolecular reactions both reagents probably are adsorbed about equally. For example, Langmuir studied the reaction between hydrogen and oxygen in contact with platinum. He found that between 400° and 1600° C. the velocity of the reaction is proportional to the partial pressure of the reagent present in *smaller* amount. He concluded that the reaction takes place when a hydrogen molecule (or atom) and an oxygen molecule (or atom) are adsorbed side by side.

Active centers. Experimental evidence indicates that all parts of a given surface are not equally effective as areas of adsorption and hence as areas of catalysis. It is assumed that atoms on an edge of a crystal or on a corner have more free valences than atoms in a plane surface. If there are irregularities in the surface of a catalyst, there will be more edges and corners than if the surface is a perfect plane, and hence there will be more free valences available to exert chemical adsorption. Such irregularities, which increase the adsorption and hence increase the catalytic effect, are called *active centers.*

There are various lines of experimental evidence pointing to the existence of such *active centers.* Among these may be mentioned the following: (1) The heat evolved when a portion of the surface has been covered by the adsorbed substance is not proportional to the extent of surface. (2) The method by which the surface is prepared has a marked influence upon its catalytic effect and upon its adsorptive capacity. (3) Small traces of impurities have an abnormal effect upon the adsorptive capacity of a surface. The last point will be discussed in more detail in connection with *catalyst poisons* on page 571.

If some atoms on the surface, particularly those at corners and at peaks of irregularities, are most capable of binding molecules or atoms from another phase, those peaks will be covered first, and the combination will take place with greater vigor than at less active parts. The heat of adsorption per unit surface therefore will decrease as adsorption proceeds. On an iron surface H. S. Taylor found the following data for heats of adsorption of successive quantities of ammonia adsorbed on the same surface:

Ml. ammonia adsorbed.	**2**	**4**	**6**	**8**	**10**	**12**	**14**
Heat of adsorption, kcal. per mole.	18	16	14	12.5	11.3	10.5	9.9

Catalysis by inorganic colloids. Colloids usually are more effective as catalysts than solids in the macroscopic state because the same weight of material presents enormously greater surface and hence has an increased power for adsorption of gas or solute. Furthermore, a catalyst in the colloidal state is distributed nearly uniformly throughout the reacting system and its particles are in vigorous Brownian motion. This nearly eliminates the slow diffusion of reagents to the catalyst and of products away from the catalyst as a rate-determining influence. With colloidal catalysts, therefore, the actual chemical process is one of the main rate-determining factors. A second important rate-determining factor would be the concentration of the colloidal solution. So completely dispersed is the material in the colloidal state that the rate of the reaction will be nearly proportional to the concentration of the colloid, as in the case of homogeneous catalysis.

One of the most illuminating examples of the difference between macro and colloidal catalysis is in the behavior of hydrogen peroxide studied by Bredig and Teletow. In one case the catalyst used was roughened sheet platinum; in the other it was colloidal platinum prepared by the arc method. The decomposition, as pointed out on page 285, is a first-order reaction. In the macro process the temperature coefficient was low and the rate was considerably increased by stirring, showing that the diffusion process is an important rate-determining influence. The colloidal process, on the other hand, was not influenced by stirring and had a high temperature coefficient. The decomposition of hydrogen peroxide by the enzyme *catalase* is similar in these respects to the colloidally catalyzed decomposition.

Selectivity of catalysts. The fact that catalysts are *selective* in their action has long been recognized. Of all the possible reactions which any given set of reagents might undergo, only one as a rule is accelerated by a given catalyst. The speeds of other possible reactions remain unchanged. At a sufficiently high temperature, at which all reactions are fairly rapid, the state of equilibrium calculated thermodynamically may be reached quickly; but at lower temperatures one of the reactions may be accelerated more than any of the others, so that the desired product may be obtained by altering conditions or by removing it from the neighborhood of the catalyst. This is often effected in practice by passing the gas rapidly over the catalyst.

There are two principal types of competing reaction:

(1) *Successive reactions* may occur, thus:

$$A \longrightarrow B \longrightarrow C$$

If the substance B is the desired product, a catalyst which accelerates the first step in the process is desirable. For example, in the oxidation of ammonia, the thermodynamic equilibrium mixture contains predominating amounts of nitrogen and water. But at suitable temperatures and with the proper catalyst, such as platinum, nitric oxide is obtained as the product. This is the basis for making nitric acid from ammonia by the Ostwald process. In the case of this oxidation there are two successive reactions:

$$4\,NH_3 + 5\,O_2 \longrightarrow 4\,NO + 6\,H_2O \qquad \text{(i)}$$

$$4\,NO \longrightarrow 2\,N_2 + 2\,O_2 \qquad \text{(ii)}$$

The over-all reaction, obtained by adding these two, is:

$$4\,NH_3 + 3\,O_2 \longrightarrow 2\,N_2 + 6\,H_2O$$

If the reacting mixture is allowed too protracted contact with the catalyst, reaction (ii) occurs and decreases the yield of nitric oxide. By passing the gas mixture rapidly over the catalyst a good yield is obtained.[1]

(2) The second type of competing reaction may be called the *alternative reaction*. Here we have the possibilities:

$$A \longrightarrow B \quad \text{and} \quad A \longrightarrow C$$

A specific example of alternative reactions is the decomposition of ethanol, which may take place in either of two ways, thus:

$$C_2H_5OH \longrightarrow C_2H_4 + H_2O \qquad (\textit{dehydration})$$

and

$$C_2H_5OH \longrightarrow CH_3CHO + H_2 \qquad (\textit{dehydrogenation})$$

[1] For a more complete discussion of the process see Schwab, Taylor, and Spence, *Catalysis*, page 266.

These two reactions may occur simultaneously, but fortunately there are specific catalysts for one or the other. For example, with copper as catalyst the yield is mostly acetaldehyde, whereas with aluminum oxide it is mostly ethylene. The basic reason for this specificity is not understood.

Catalyst Poisons. Foreign substances, sometimes in extremely small amount, when added to a catalyzed reaction, frequently have the effect of slowing it down or completely stopping it. A substance which has this effect is called a **catalyst poison.** In some cases the poisoning effect is temporary, and the catalyst recovers its former activity when the poisoning substance has been removed. In other cases it is permanent, and the catalyst does not recover its activity upon the removal of the poisoning substance.

Catalyst poisoning, like contact catalysis itself, is an adsorption phenomenon. The surface of the catalyst adsorbs the poison, leaving a diminished surface or no surface at all available for the adsorption of the reagents, thus stopping the catalysis. When the products of the reaction are not desorbed with sufficient rapidity, they also may act as catalyst poisons. If one of the reagents is so strongly adsorbed that no room is left for the adsorption of the other reagent, the catalysis is not so effective as when both are adsorbed in more nearly equal proportions. For example, in the case of the reaction,

$$CO + 3\,H_2 \longrightarrow CH_4 + H_2O$$

the reaction velocity is greater with a nickel catalyst, which adsorbs carbon monoxide and hydrogen about equally, than it is with a copper catalyst, which adsorbs carbon monoxide much more strongly than it does hydrogen.

Two particularly powerful catalyst poisons are arsenic, which forms arsenides on the surface of the platinum in the contact process, and sulfur, which forms sulfides and thus poisons most metallic catalysts. In a number of cases the quantity of a catalyst poison required to stop a reaction is less than the quantity required to form a complete monomolecular layer. This has been taken as further evidence of the existence of *active centers* on the catalyst surface. Obviously, if catalysis occurs only when the reactants are adsorbed on the few active centers of the catalyst, reaction will stop when these active centers have been covered by the adsorbed catalyst poison.

Catalyst Promoters. Frequently the activity of a catalyst is enhanced by the addition of a small amount of a second substance which by itself may be quite lacking in catalytic activity. Generally, the catalytic effect of mixed substances is greater than the sum of the catalytic effects of the individual components. In some cases, the mixing of two inactive substances yields an active mixture; *e.g.*, aluminum and magnesium separately exert no catalytic influence on the reaction of nitrogen with hydrogen to form ammonia, but a mixture of the two gives good yields.

Any substance which, added to another substance, increases its catalytic activity is called a ***promoter.*** Among the *promoted catalysts* in general use might be cited (1) *mixed metals, e.g.*, aluminum and magnesium in the ammonia synthesis; (2) *metal-oxide, e.g.*, the *oxides* of aluminum, chromium, and vanadium, with the *metals* iron, tungsten, and so forth, in the synthesis of ammonia, and *aluminum oxide* added to *nickel* in hydrogenation reactions; (3) *metal-alkali, e.g.*, the mixture of *lime* or *sodium carbonate* with *iron* in the synthesis of methanol from carbon monoxide and hydrogen; (4) *mixed oxides, e.g.*, the mixture of *chromic oxide* with *zinc oxide* in the methanol synthesis.

The mechanism of promoter action is not yet understood. In some cases the promoter prevents poisoning of the catalyst by itself adsorbing the poison substance. Possibly the interface between the promoter and the catalyst may be a place of especially high activity. In the case of mixed catalysts, one may adsorb one reagent strongly, the other the other reagent, and migration on the surfaces may bring the adsorbed reagents into contact at the boundary between the catalyst and the promoter, where they react.

There are cases of promoter action in homogeneous catalysis. For example, cupric chloride alone has no catalytic effect on the decomposition of hydrogen peroxide, but it accelerates the decomposition taking place under the influence of ferric chloride as catalyst. Thus it acts as a *promoter* towards the ferric chloride catalyst.

Some reactions begin slowly, then speed up as they proceed, before finally slowing down at the approach to equilibrium. In such cases products of the reaction itself act as catalysts; this phenomenon is called **autocatalysis.** An example is the reaction between potassium permanganate and oxalic acid in the presence of dilute sulfuric acid,

$$5\,C_2O_4^{--} + 2\,MnO_4^- + 16\,H_3O^+ \longrightarrow 10\,CO_2 + 2\,Mn^{++} + 24\,H_2O$$

which is catalyzed by manganous ion. Manganous sulfate added at the beginning of the reaction greatly accelerates it.

Inhibitors (Negative Catalysts). *Substances which retard reactions are known as* ***inhibitors*** *or* ***negative catalysts.*** A positive catalyst is effective because it provides a new, easier path, *i.e.*, a path requiring a lower energy of activation, for the reaction to follow. Negative catalysis cannot be merely the reverse of positive catalysis, *i.e.*, finding a more difficult path.

There are various possible mechanisms by which inhibition may be effected, such as the following: (1) The inhibitor may remove a positive catalyst, a process similar to catalyst poisoning. (2) The inhibitor may react with one of the reagents or with an intermediate compound. (3) The inhibitor may deactivate molecules which have been activated. (4) A chain reaction may be stopped (see page 297).

An inhibitor which finds extensive practical application is lead tetraethyl, $Pb(C_2H_5)_4$, which is used as an antiknock in gasoline for automobile engines. The knock in an internal combustion engine is caused by the too rapid combustion of the fuel-air mixture. The lead tetraethyl slows down the explosion rate and thus renders engine operation smoother.

Applications of Catalysis in Industry. Catalysts find so many important applications in the manufacture of chemical products that they are quite indispensable in modern chemical industry. We may recall a few of the most outstanding of these applications.

Two processes of great economic importance are the *Haber process* for the synthesis of ammonia, utilizing mixed-metal catalysts such as iron and molybdenum, and the *Ostwald process* for the oxidation of ammonia to nitric oxide, which uses a platinum gauze catalyst. These processes are so well known that they need no further discussion here.

The *lead chamber process* for making sulfuric acid involves the oxidation of sulfur dioxide to sulfur trioxide with nitric oxide as a catalyst in the gas phase.

The *contact process* for sulfuric acid was discovered over a century ago. Platinum was first used in 1831 to catalyze the oxidation of sulfur dioxide to sulfur trioxide; but the attempt to utilize the method on the commercial scale met with failure. The platinum rapidly lost its catalytic activity, and the method was abandoned. Later the loss in activity was found to be due to catalyst poisons, especially arsenic oxides. If the sulfur dioxide was carefully purified to remove these, the catalyst maintained its activity. In recent years other catalysts have been developed which are nearly as efficient as platinum and are much less susceptible to catalyst poisons.

In recent years *hydrogenation* and *dehydrogenation* processes have become important. In the vapor phase, catalytic dehydrogenation of alcohols yields aldehydes or ketones, and catalytic hydrogenation of aldehydes and ketones yields alcohols. In the liquid phase, vegetable oils, which contain unsaturated esters of glycerol, are hydrogenated to hard fats. For this the catalyst is specially prepared colloidal nickel.

Methanol, so long supplied from the distillation of wood, now is made mainly by the synthetic process. When carbon monoxide and hydrogen are brought together at a temperature of about 500° C. and under pressure in the presence of a mixed-oxide catalyst, such as zinc oxide mixed with chromic oxide, a good yield of methanol is obtained, according to the reaction,

$$CO + 2\,H_2 \rightleftharpoons CH_3OH$$

The *vulcanization of rubber* is carried out by heating the raw rubber with sulfur. But the rate of combination is vastly increased by the addition of small quantities of organic substances, such as piperidine and thiourea, which are known as *rubber accelerators*.

READING LIST

K. G. Falk, *Catalytic Action.* Chemical Catalog Company, New York, 1922. A general discussion.

N. F. Hall, "Systems of Acids and Bases," *J. Chem. Ed.*, **17**, 124 (1940). A discussion of the various acid-base concepts.

T. P. Hilditch, *Catalytic Processes in Applied Chemistry.* D. Van Nostrand Company, New York, 1929.

P. Sebatier, *Catalysis in Organic Chemistry*, trans. by E. Reid. D. Van Nostrand Company, New York, 1922.

G. M. Schwab, *Catalysis*, trans. by H. S. Taylor and R. Spence. D. Van Nostrand Company, New York, 1937. An excellent summary and discussion of modern work in catalysis. The proton mechanism of acid-base catalysis is discussed on pp. 121–132.

CHAPTER 21

ENZYMES

The term *enzyme* comes from the Greek ἐν ζύμῃ, meaning *in yeast.* Yeast contains some of the most interesting of the enzymes and much intensive study has been centered on this material.

Enzymes are among the most important requisites for any living organism. They play a dominant role in the life processes of the higher animals and probably of *all* animals and plants. For example, they are indispensable to the digestive process in man. They are responsible for the various fermentations, such as that of dextrose to alcohol and carbon dioxide. One enzyme brings about the hydrolysis of indican in the production of indigo blue; another promotes the change of dextrose to carbon dioxide, hydrogen, acetone, and butanol. Numerous other examples might be cited. The study of enzymes, their behavior and composition, is of interest not only to future students of medicine but also to those who will apply chemistry to industry.

What Are Enzymes? Various definitions have been suggested which throw some light upon their peculiar mode of functioning. According to Waldschmidt-Leitz:[1] ***Enzymes** are definite material catalyzers of organic nature with specific powers of reaction, formed indeed by living cells, but independent of the presence of the latter in their operation.* To this definition Gortner[2] has added: *and when in the moist state, readily destroyed by heat.* J. B. S. Haldane, the noted biochemist at Oxford University, prefers: ***Enzymes** are soluble, colloidal, organic catalysts produced by the living organism.* In the light of recent work and for the purposes of this discussion we may consider an ***enzyme** as an organic compound, produced or secreted by the living cell, which acts as a catalyst.*

Historical Sketch. The first recorded observations concerning enzyme-catalyzed reactions date from the early decades of the nineteenth century. But the field of biochemistry, as we know it today, in which enzyme-catalyzed reactions naturally lie, is notably

[1] E. Waldschmidt-Leitz, *Enzyme Actions and Properties*, trans. by R. P. Walton, John Wiley & Sons, New York, 1929, p. 3.

[2] R. A. Gortner, *Outlines of Biochemistry*, John Wiley & Sons, New York, 1929, p. 713.

complex. This fact, coupled with the vagueness of the concepts concerning life processes, held back the study of such reactions. In 1814 G. S. C. Kirchhoff showed that wheat meal contained something which brought about the change of starch to dextrose. In 1833 Payen and Persoz found that malted grain had the same effect. In 1837 Wöhler and von Liebig studied the hydrolysis of the glucoside *amygdalin*, obtained from the stone of the bitter almond, and ascribed the change to the catalytic action of *emulsin*. In the preceding year Berzelius had advanced the idea of inorganic catalysis and suggested that something of a closely similar nature was involved in reactions such as those cited. In 1838 Schwann assumed the presence of a catalyzing agent in the gastric juice which promoted protein digestion and called it *pepsin*.

Louis Pasteur studied the fermentation of dextrose to produce alcohol and carbon dioxide, a reaction promoted by yeast, and showed that yeast killed by boiling was inactive. Hence he concluded that the living cell was an essential and that fermentation was a result of the life process of the microorganisms present in yeast. This vitalistic concept of enzyme action persisted for twenty-five years. In 1897 Büchner completely disproved it. He showed that when yeast is thoroughly ground with sand to destroy the cell structure, and the aqueous extract filtered to get rid of cell material, the extract is just as powerful in promoting the fermentation of glucose as are the living yeast cells. This discovery was extremely important. It threw open the field to the application of purely chemical methods and led to a more thorough examination of the properties of enzymes and to attempts to isolate and purify them. These attempts have met with notable success although a great deal yet remains to be done.

Examples of Enzyme Catalysis. Numerous cases of enzyme-catalyzed reactions have been studied. We list in Table 118 only some of these, which will serve as examples to illustrate the discussion of the properties of enzymes. According to the generally accepted system of nomenclature, the name of an enzyme is derived by adding the suffix *-ase* to that of the ***substrate**, as the substance changed under the influence of the enzyme is called.* Thus, the enzyme that acts on the substrate *lactose* is called *lactase* and that promoting the hydrolysis of *urea* is called *urease*. Certain of the first-discovered enzymes retain the names originally given them.

TABLE 118

Enzymes and Reactions Which They Catalyze

Enzyme	Substrate	Reaction
Catalase	Hydrogen peroxide	Decomposition to water and oxygen
Diastase	Starch	Hydrolysis to maltose
Emulsin	Amygdalin	Hydrolysis to dextrose, benzaldehyde and hydrocyanic acid
Invertase	Sucrose	Hydrolysis to dextrose and levulose
Lactase	Lactose	Hydrolysis to dextrose and galactose
Maltase	Maltose	Hydrolysis to dextrose
Pepsin	Protein	Hydrolysis to simpler proteins
Steapsin	Fat	Hydrolysis to glycerol and fatty acid
Trypsin	Protein	Hydrolysis to amino acids
Urease	Urea	Hydrolysis to ammonia and carbonic acid
Zymase	Dextrose	Fermentation to ethanol and carbon dioxide

Occurrence and Extraction of Enzymes. All of the enzymes listed in Table 118 are found in growing plants or in animal secretions. *Diastase* and *maltase,* for example, are produced in the sprouting of grain; *invertase* and *zymase* are among the enzymes found in yeast; *lactase, steapsin, trypsin,* and *invertase* are among the many enzymes promoting digestion in the animal body and occur in the intestinal juices; *pepsin* occurs in the gastric juice in the stomach. *Urease* occurs in the soy bean, in the jack bean, and in other plants. *Catalase* is present in the red blood cells and is widely distributed in all living matter, both animal and vegetable. Probably the number of enzymes is very great, although relatively few have been sufficiently isolated for individual study and some of these actually may be mixtures of several different enzymes.

Early attempts to isolate and analyze enzymes met with little success, although some were concentrated enough for the study of their activities and related properties. This was because the original concentration of the enzymes is very low; they occur in the presence of other complex substances; being colloidal, they adsorb other solutes strongly; and finally they are sensitive to heat, acidity, and other influences. Willstäter, at Munich, carried out extensive experiments, attempting to concentrate enzymes by treating them with various materials such as china clay, silica, and alumina, which adsorb the colloidal enzymes strongly and to some extent selectively, and so separated them from the other materials with which they were associated. Still better results have been obtained by adding a suitable precipitant, usually a precipitant for proteins, which would yield the enzyme combined with the precipitant as a colloid and then dialyzing the mixture.[1] In 1926 Sumner isolated *urease* from jack beans as octahedral crystals, which were about 800 times as active as the original crude material. In 1930 Northrop, at the Rockefeller Institute in Princeton, isolated *pepsin* from the gastric juice. By precipitation with magnesium sulfate and treatment with dilute sulfuric acid, he obtained it in crystalline form with high catalytic activity. A crystalline *amylase* has been obtained by H. C. Sherman, at Columbia University. *Catalase* and *trypsin* have also been obtained in highly concentrated form.

Composition of Enzymes. Although several enzymes have been obtained in crystalline form and have been analyzed, there is still doubt as to their structure. Analysis of the crystalline material indicates that they contain mainly carbon, hydrogen, oxygen, and nitrogen. They are probably *protein* in nature, since they yield amino acids upon hydrolysis and often are precipitated by reagents used to precipitate proteins. However, the crystalline material obtained may not in all cases represent the enzyme itself but may consist of some *carrier* combined with the enzyme, which may be an active atomic grouping, as suggested by Willstäter. N. K. Adam[2] suggests that enzymes are colloidal protein particles on the surface of which there is a "patch" of atoms, *i.e.*, an atomic grouping which has high adsorptive power and composes an *active center* which is particularly active catalytically.

Catalytic Properties of Enzymes. We may consider that enzymes are protein in nature, with molecular weights of 50,000 or higher, and molecules of colloidal magnitude. In body fluids and in the living cell they catalyze such reactions as those involved in the digestion of foods. This consists merely of the hydrolysis of complex carbohydrates to form simple sugars, of fats to glycerol and fatty acids, and of proteins to amino acids and other simple substances. Enzymes probably catalyze nearly all reactions that take place in the growth and decay of both animals and plants. They catalyze fermentations such as those of dextrose to ethanol and carbon dioxide, to butanol and acetone, or to glycerol. Their physiological function generally is to promote reactions that are attended by only slight changes in heat content, and presumably also in free energy. Without the influence of such extremely

[1] For a discussion of methods which have been applied see Northrop, *Crystalline Enzymes*.

[2] *Nature*, **136**, 499 (1935).

active catalysts these reactions in the animal body would be impossibly slow.

As examples of reactions which are catalyzed by enzymes and which can be carried out readily in the test tube, we may cite the following:

(1) The hydrolysis of urea:

$$CO(NH_2)_2 + 3\ H_2O \longrightarrow 2\ NH_4^+ + HCO_3^- + OH^-$$

This reaction, carried out with the aid of *urease* (from the soy bean), is used in the quantitative determination of urea in urine.

(2) The decomposition of hydrogen peroxide by *catalase* (from blood):

$$2\ H_2O_2 \longrightarrow 2\ H_2O + O_2$$

(3) The inversion of sucrose by *invertase* (from malted grain):

$$\underset{\text{sucrose}}{C_{12}H_{22}O_{11}} + H_2O \longrightarrow \underset{\text{dextrose}}{C_6H_{12}O_6} + \underset{\text{levulose}}{C_6H_{12}O_6}$$

(4) The fermentation of dextrose by *zymase* (from yeast):

$$C_6H_{12}O_6 \longrightarrow 2\ C_2H_5OH + 2\ CO_2$$

When an enzyme is compared with an inorganic catalyst which promotes the same reaction *the enzyme is found to be the more effective catalyst.* For example, the enzyme *catalase* is more active, weight for weight, than colloidal platinum in the decomposition of hydrogen peroxide. A single drop of saliva, which contains the starch-splitting enzyme *ptyalin,* is much more effective than the same weight of concentrated hydrochloric acid added to the same volume of starch emulsion. Also, in the reaction of water with lactose to form the two simple sugars, dextrose and galactose, the enzyme *lactase* has been found to be several thousand times as effective as hydrochloric acid. Carbohydrate, like starch, is but slightly changed in the distinctly acid medium in the stomach but hydrolyzes rapidly in the intestines under the influence of the enzyme *diastase.*

An enzyme, like any other catalyst, cannot affect the proportions of reactants present when a system is in equilibrium. In a reversible reaction a catalyst accelerates both the forward and the reverse reactions, hence we should expect to find that an enzyme not only accelerates the change in the substrate but also effects its synthesis from the products. In certain cases this has been verified experimentally. Fats have been synthesized from glycerol and fatty acids under the influence of fat-splitting *lipases.* Using *maltase* from yeast, a sugar which at least has the same empirical formula as maltose has been obtained from dextrose. The fact that *pepsin* added to the products of hydrolysis of protein brings about synthesis of protein has been well substantiated.[1] The enzyme *carbonic anhydrase,* which catalyzes the dehydration of the carbonic acid of the blood to allow rapid release of the carbon dioxide in the lungs also accelerates the reverse change. The action of enzymes in promoting the synthesis of plant and animal substances is probably essential to growth. Although the equilibrium may lie strongly to the decomposition side, the reaction nevertheless can take place due to removal of the product as solid or by combination with other substances.

The effect of an enzyme on the forward and reverse reactions has been studied quantitatively by Bayliss. He has demonstrated that a glucoside formed by the interaction of glycerol and glucose is hydrolyzed under the influence of *emulsin* and that glycerol and glucose react under the influence of the same enzyme to form the glucoside. This may be represented by the reversible reaction:

$$\underset{\text{glucoside}}{C_6H_{11}O_6 \cdot C_3H_5(OH)_2} + H_2O \rightleftharpoons \underset{\text{glucose}}{C_6H_{12}O_6} + \underset{\text{glycerol}}{C_3H_5(OH)_3}$$

Since the glucoside and the glucose are optically active, the approach to equilibrium from either side can be followed by the change in optical activity. The measurements obtained are plotted in Figure 234.

Specificity of Enzymes. We know that *platinum* catalyzes the oxidation of sulfur dioxide to sulfur trioxide and of ammonia to oxides of nitrogen, the decomposition of hydrogen peroxide, and other reactions; that *nickel* is useful in various hydrogenation processes; and that *hydrogen ion* catalyzes hydrolysis of esters, of proteins, and of carbohydrates, and also affects the rates of various other reactions. Enzymes, on the contrary, are generally more *specific* than are such inorganic catalysts. Some examples may be cited.

Catalase, found in red blood cells but very widely distributed in living matter, is highly specific. Apparently, it catalyzes only the decomposition, and possibly the synthesis, of hydrogen per-

[1] Wasteneys and Borsook, *J. Gen. Physiol.*, **13**, 295 (1930).

oxide. *Invertase*, found in the pancreatic juice and elsewhere, hydrolyzes sucrose but has no effect on lactose or maltose which have the same empirical formula, $C_{12}H_{22}O_{11}$. Likewise, *lactase*, which promotes the hydrolysis of lactose to dextrose and galactose, has no effect on sucrose. Of somewhat more general catalytic

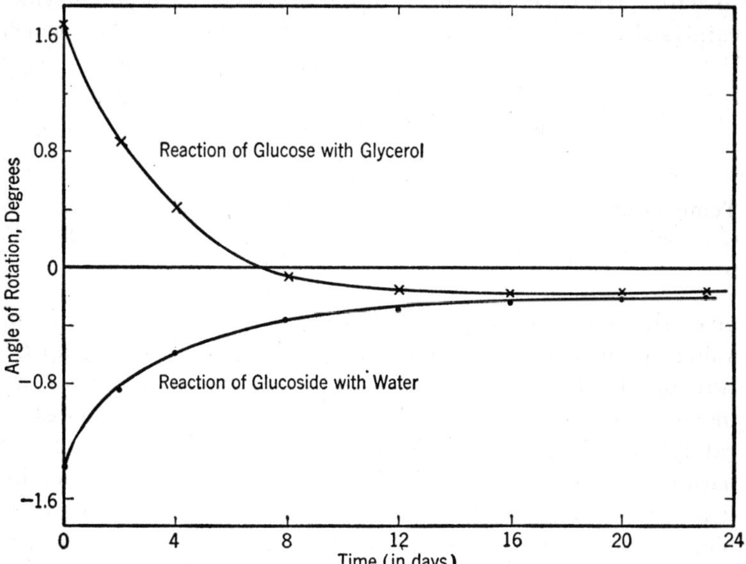

Fig. 234. Attainment of Equilibrium in an Enzyme-Catalyzed System.

effect are *steapsin*, in the pancreatic juice, which seems to promote the hydrolysis of various fats; *emulsin*, which catalyzes the hydrolysis of various glucosides; and *trypsin*, in the pancreatic juice, which probably catalyzes the hydrolysis of proteins in general.

In the case of inorganic catalysis the same substance may take part in different reactions depending upon the catalyst used; *e.g.*, the oxidation of ammonia with platinum as catalyst yields nitric oxide, while its oxidation using copper as catalyst gives nitrogen. Similarly, in enzyme-catalyzed reactions the same substrate may give rise to different products under the influence of different enzymes. Thus, dextrose ferments under the influence of *zymase*, from yeast, to give ethanol and carbon dioxide; with Weizmann's bacteria, the main products are acetone and butanol, with some carbon dioxide and hydrogen; still a third fermentation, carried out in the presence of bisulfite, yields glycerol.

Effect of Temperature upon Enzyme Activity. The effect of temperature on the rate of an enzyme-catalyzed reaction is usually inappreciable at or near 0° C. With rise in temperature the activity of the enzyme increases, but at a characteristic temperature it reaches a maximum, and eventually the catalytic effect decreases to zero. The effect of temperature on the velocity of an enzyme-catalyzed reaction is illustrated by the data in Table 119, which

TABLE 119

EFFECT OF TEMPERATURE ON ENZYME ACTIVITY
(Time for coagulation of milk by rennin)

Temperature, ° C.	**25**	**30**	**33**	**36**	**39**	**42**	**45**
Coagulation time, sec.	100	60	40	30	25	35	45

gives the times required for the coagulation of milk by *rennin*, of animal origin, at various temperatures. An optimum temperature of about 39° C. is indicated in this case. Enzymes are much more sensitive to external conditions than are inorganic catalysts, as might be expected from their organic and colloidal nature. The catalytic activity is destroyed by heat and generally it is not recovered when the material cools. Most enzymes have temperatures of optimum activity lying between 40° and 50° C., but some have optimum temperatures higher than this. An enzyme may lose its activity due to prolonged heating even at the optimum temperature. In some cases, the activity is recovered upon standing. Concentrated solutions of enzymes are more sensitive to heat than are more dilute preparations. The dry material, however, is much less sensitive.

Hydrogen-Ion Concentration and Enzyme Activity. The catalytic activity of enzymes is markedly affected by the *p*H. Most enzymes are active only within a definite *p*H range. Sørensen and Michaelis have studied this effect exhaustively. Since acids are often formed or destroyed during the reaction, their solutions were buffered. Thus, with the *p*H maintained constant at successive levels, the effects upon reaction velocity could be studied.

Within the activity range of each enzyme there is always an increase to a maximum, followed by a decrease, as the *p*H increases. Typical results are shown in Figure 235. In (*a*) are plotted data obtained by Michaelis and Davidsohn on the velocity of inversion of sucrose by *invertase;* the velocities are represented as the per cents of sucrose hydrolyzed in a given time at different acidities. In (*b*) are plotted data obtained by Northrop on the velocity of

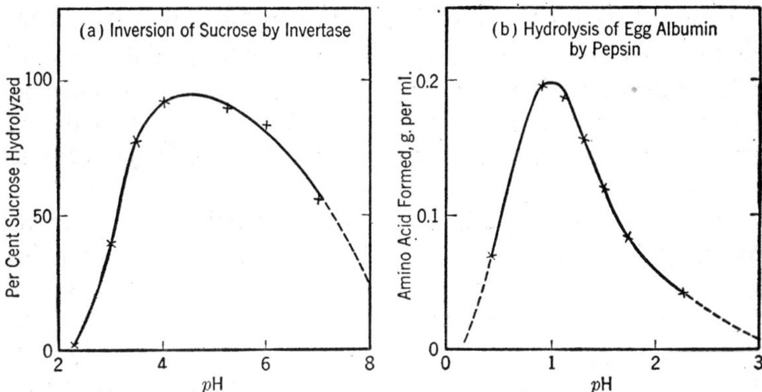

Fig. 235. Effect of Hydrogen Ion Concentration on Enzyme Activity.

hydrolysis of egg albumin by *pepsin,* resulting in the production of amino acids. These two examples show that different enzymes have maximum activities at different *p*H values. **Some such optimum *p*H values** are given in Table 120.

TABLE 120

*p*H Values for Optimum Enzyme Activity

Enzyme	Substrate	Optimum *p*H	Enzyme	Substrate	Optimum *p*H
Pepsin	Protein	1.6	Maltase	Maltose	6.6
Invertase	Sucrose	4.5	Catalase	Water	7.0
Amylase	Starch	6.0	Erepsin	Protein	7.7
Rennin	Casein	6.1	Lipase	Ethyl butyrate	8.3

The *p*H of the gastric juice, in which *pepsin* promotes protein digestion, or hydrolysis, is very nearly 1.6, the optimum for this enzyme. The *p*H of the pancreatic juice and other fluids that form the aqueous medium in the intestines, where most of the digestion takes place, is slightly on the alkaline side, which corresponds with the optimum *p*H values of their enzymes which promote the further digestive hydrolyses. Too high a hydrogen-ion concentration not only may render the enzyme temporarily inactive; it may completely destroy its activity.

Influence of Other Factors on Enzyme Activity. In addition to temperature and hydrogen-ion concentration, the activity of enzymes is influenced by other factors to which we can make only a brief reference.

One such factor is the presence of *electrolytes* other than acids or bases. Certain salts may increase and others decrease or completely arrest the catalytic activity of a particular enzyme. No general rule can be stated except that the effect of the electrolyte generally is greater the greater the electrolyte concentration.

Just as some inorganic catalysts are inactivated by certain *catalyst poisons*, so most enzymes are sensitive to substances which act as "poisons," or *inhibitors*. Since enzymes appear to be protein in nature, they are naturally inactivated by protein precipitants, *e.g.*, picric acid and phosphotungstic acid, and by substances, like nitrites, which may react with the amino group, $—NH_2$. Enzymes are also inactivated by oxidizing agents, such as permanganate and the halogens, and by mercuric chloride, hydrocyanic acid, and other toxic substances. Other inhibitors are *selective*, affecting one enzyme but not another. In some cases the activity can be regenerated; in others the "poisoning" completely destroys the enzyme.

In order to act as catalysts, enzymes apparently require *promoters* called *coenzymes*. The coenzymes often are inorganic ions. For example, if *amylase* extracted from the pancreatic juice is purified by dialysis, it is quite inactive towards starch; the addition of sodium chloride or potassium chloride restores the activity. Likewise, if *zymase* from yeast is dialyzed, it fails to promote the fermentation of dextrose. The solution passing through the dialyzing membrane also is inactive towards dextrose. However, the mixture of the two promotes fermentation. Other cases have been examined with like results. In some cases the activity may be restored to the enzyme by some solute other than that present in the original solution.

Rate of Reaction and Substrate Concentration. In an uncatalyzed reaction and in a reaction catalyzed by a homogeneous catalyst in constant concentration, the velocity of change of a substance is proportional to its concentration. This does not hold for an enzyme-catalyzed reaction even though the reacting system appears to be homogeneous. Thus, for the inversion of sucrose catalyzed by a constant concentration of hydrochloric acid:

$$C_{12}H_{22}O_{11} + H_2O \longrightarrow C_6H_{12}O_6 + C_6H_{12}O_6$$

the rate is given by the expression for a first order reaction:

$$-\frac{d[C_{12}H_{22}O_{11}]}{dt} = k_1[C_{12}H_{22}O_{11}]$$

In the case of the inversion of sucrose catalyzed by a constant concentration of *invertase*, the rate of inversion is directly proportional to the sucrose concentration when this concentration is fairly low but does not obey the expression for a first-order reaction when the concentration becomes higher. This is illustrated by the data given in Table 121.

TABLE 121

INVERSION OF SUCROSE WITH INVERTASE

SUCROSE CONCENTRATION (G. PER LITER)	SUCROSE INVERTED (G. PER LITER PER HR.)	SUCROSE INVERTED (PER CENT PER HR.)
2.5	0.60	24
5.0	1.25	26
10.0	2.49	25
48.9	12.30	25
98.5	13.55	14
199.1	13.55	7
299.6	12.35	4

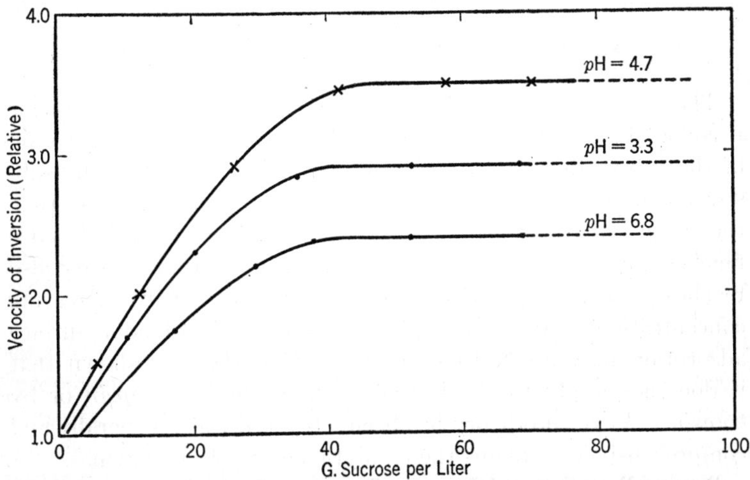

Fig. 236. Rate of Inversion of Sucrose at Different Sucrose Concentrations and *p*H Values.

The rate of inversion at first increases proportionally to the increase in concentration of the substrate but ultimately reaches a constant value, as the data in the second column of Table 121 show. Other data which show the change of velocity of inversion with increasing concentration of sucrose are shown in Figure 236, in which the effect of hydrogen-ion concentration is also illustrated. Similar results were obtained by Northrop for the hydrolysis of egg albumin by *pepsin*.

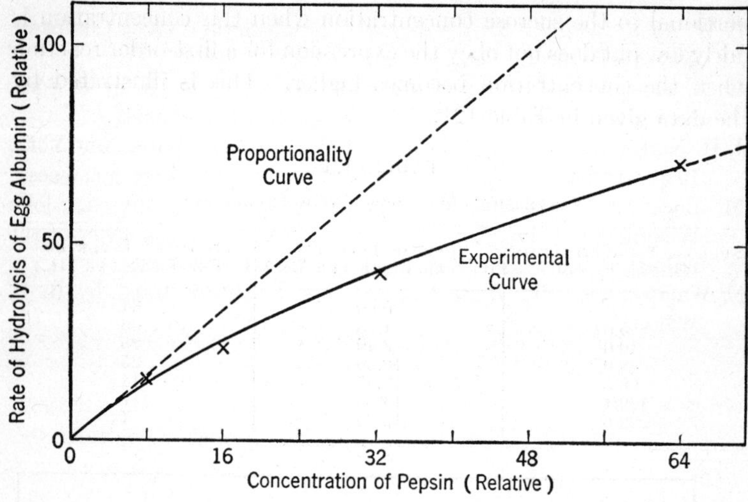

Fig. 237. Reaction Velocity and Enzyme Concentration.

These results are quite in line with the theory that the enzyme is colloidal and that it is exercising *surface catalysis* by adsorption of the substrate on the surface of the particles. When the substrate concentration becomes high relative to that of the enzyme, the surface of the enzyme particles becomes saturated and hence reaches a maximum catalyst activity. The reaction velocity also reaches a maximum and can no longer increase with increasing concentration. However well this theory of colloidal surface adsorption may apply to some cases, Northrop has shown that it does not apply to the hydrolysis of protein by *pepsin* or by *trypsin*. As yet no theory has been advanced which generally and comprehensively explains the catalytic effects of all enzymes.

Rate of Reaction and Enzyme Concentration. In most enzyme-catalyzed reactions the reacting medium is nearly homogeneous, with practically uniform distribution of the enzyme throughout the acting system. Accordingly, the rate of reaction increases with increasing enzyme concentration, although not proportionally. This is shown by Figure 237, in which the relative rates of hydrolysis of a given quantity of egg albumin are plotted against the relative concentrations of the enzyme *pepsin*.

READING LIST

P. W. Allen, *Industrial Fermentations.* The Chemical Catalog Company, New York, 1926.

R. A. Gortner, *Outlines of Biochemistry,* 2d ed. John Wiley & Sons, New York, 1938. Pp. 707–734. A good brief treatment.

J. H. Northrop, *Crystalline Enzymes.* Columbia Univ. Press, New York, 1939. Discusses isolation and properties of a few specific enzymes.

M. Bodansky, *Introduction to Physiological Chemistry,* 4th ed. John Wiley & Sons, New York, 1938. Pp. 123–146. A summary of the properties of enzymes with special reference to digestion.

E. Waldschmidt-Leitz, *Enzyme Actions and Properties,* trans. by R. P. Walton. John Wiley & Sons, New York, 1929.

CHAPTER 22

THE PHASE RULE

The *phase rule* defines the conditions which determine the equilibrium in a physical or chemical system. It was enunciated by J. Willard Gibbs in 1876.[1] He derived it by purely mathematical reasoning from the principles of thermodynamics. It attracted little attention at the time, and its importance was not realized until 1888 when Roozeboom[2] demonstrated its applicability to chemical systems.

The derivation of the phase rule is beyond the scope of this book,[3] but its application to specific systems of common interest and the explanation of the relations within such systems will concern us particularly. Many facts familiar from the study of inorganic chemistry are clarified by the *phase rule*.

Definitions and Statement of the Phase Rule. Before stating the phase rule in mathematical form, we shall define the terms used in describing systems in equilibrium.

Any system is made up of one or more chemically distinct substances which we call the **components** of the system. We may define *the* ***number of components*** *of a system as the smallest number of chemical individuals that will serve to define the system chemically.* Its meaning may be understood from the consideration of examples. In the system,

$$H_2 + I_2 \rightleftharpoons 2\,HI$$

when the H_2 and I_2 are not present in stoichiometric proportions, the smallest number of substances that can define the system is *two, i.e.*, hydrogen and iodine, hydrogen and hydrogen iodide, or iodine and hydrogen iodide. If any two of these are present, then the third must also be present. Similarly, in the system,

$$\underline{CaCO_3} \rightleftharpoons \underline{CaO} + CO_2$$

[1] Josiah Willard Gibbs was professor of mathematical physics at Yale University, his alma mater, from 1871 until his death in 1903. His paper on the phase rule entitled "On the Equilibrium in Heterogeneous Systems" was published in two parts in 1876 and 1878 in the *Transactions of the Connecticut Academy*. The limited circulation of this journal doubtless was mainly responsible for the belated application of the rule.

[2] Hendrik W. B. Roozeboom, Professor of Chemistry, University of Amsterdam, *Zeit. physik. Chem.*, **2**, 449 (1888).

[3] For a brief derivation see Findlay, *Phase Rule*, 8th ed., p. 13.

at 500° C., the number of components is *two,* since under the conditions indicated, *in a closed system,* if any two of the three substances are present, the third one must be also, and the system, therefore, is defined. Both of these are *two-component systems.* Water and a salt also would form a two-component system.

In a system at equilibrium we may have a gas phase, one or more liquid phases, and one or more solid phases. *The* ***phases*** *of a system are those parts of a system which are separated by definite physical boundaries.* A mixture of gases, or of gas and vapor,[1] is homogeneous and cannot have parts separated by physical boundaries, and so there can be only one *gas phase,* or *vapor phase,* as it is often called. Similarly, the solution of a liquid in another liquid, or a solid in a liquid, or a solid in a solid, is homogeneous and constitutes only one phase. Two liquids which are not completely miscible may form two liquid phases. For example, when water and ether are shaken together in suitable proportions, the system separates into two layers, the upper being a solution of water in ether and the lower a solution of ether in water. Substances present in a system in several different crystalline forms constitute an equal number of different solid phases. Thus *rhombic* and *monoclinic sulfur* may be present as two solid phases; and in the case of the one-component system, *water,* we shall see that three different crystalline forms, representing three solid phases, may be present in equilibrium.

The equilibrium in any system may be shifted by changing one or more external conditions, usually *temperature, pressure,* or *composition.* Any change in any of these conditions will alter the *proportions* of the various phases initially present in accordance with the principle of Le Chatelier discussed on page 307. However, one or more of these conditions may be varied without changing the *number* of phases. *The number of conditions which the experimenter may alter without causing the appearance or disappearance of a phase is called the* **number of degrees of freedom** *of the given system.*

The **phase rule** may be stated thus: *The number of degrees of freedom possessed by a system in equilibrium is equal to two more than the number of components minus the number of phases.* Stated in mathematical form, this is:

$$F = (C + 2) - P$$

[1] By *vapor* is meant a substance in gaseous form at a temperature below its normal boiling point.

where F is the *number of degrees of freedom,* C is the *number of components,* and P is the *number of phases* in equilibrium. The three symbols, C, P, and F, represent numbers only. They have no reference to the kind of substances present, the nature of the several phases, or the way in which a condition may be altered. The term *2* in the rule is a consequence of the fact that in most systems there are two variables, temperature and pressure, in addition to the composition variable, which influence the equilibrium. If, in addition, variation in gravitational field or in some other factor influenced the equilibrium, the number *2* would be increased, or if the pressure had no influence on the equilibrium, the number would be reduced to *1*. The rule might then be stated in a more general form, thus,

$$F = C + n - P$$

where n is the number of variables, in addition to composition, which influence the equilibrium.

Phase Diagrams. A *phase diagram* is a graphical representation of a chemical system as it exists under various conditions. It is constructed from experimental data and is useful because it shows at a glance what phases can exist under any given conditions and how conditions must be altered in order to bring about changes in the system. Although each phase diagram applies to only one system, phase diagrams may be classified into a few general types.

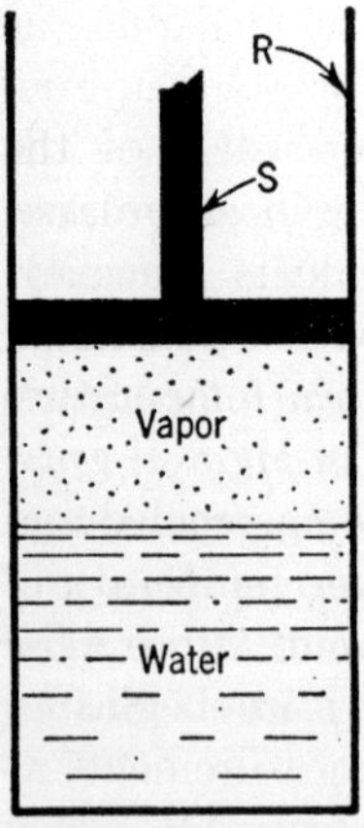

In order to understand more clearly the meaning and terminology of the phase rule and the way in which phase diagrams are interpreted, we shall consider a number of chemical systems, most of them familiar to us from the study of inorganic chemistry. We shall confine ourselves chiefly to systems of one or two components, with only a brief reference to those of greater complexity.

Fig. 238. Illustrating Phase Equilibrium in the System, *Water.*

One-Component Systems

The System, *Water*. The phase diagram of this one-component system is constructed from measurements which are obtained in a closed system, which is represented diagrammatically in Figure 238.

The liquid water and water vapor alone are contained in the cylinder *R*, fitted with the piston *S*, which serves in measuring or applying pressure. The vapor pressure of the water is measured at suitable intervals above and below room temperature T_1. By plotting the temperatures as abscissas and the vapor pressures as ordinates, we obtain the curve *ABD* in Figure 239. The upper

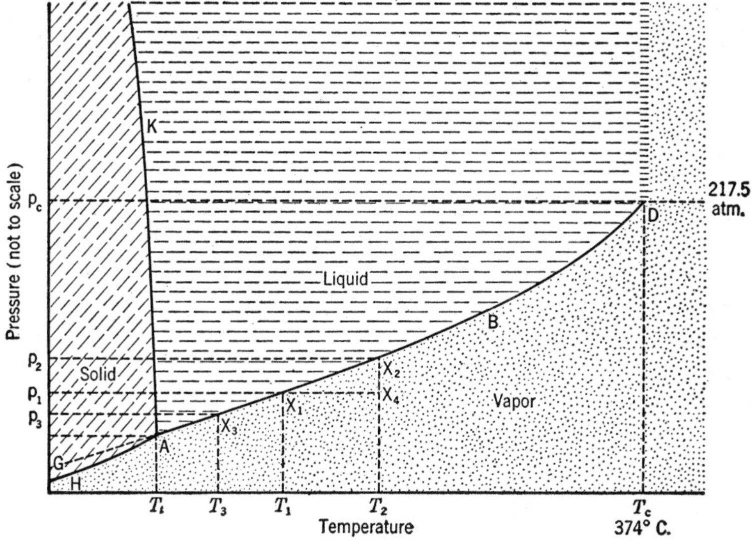

Fig. 239. Phase Diagram in the System, *Water*.

limit to these measurements is the *critical temperature* of the water, T_c, which is 374° C., corresponding to the *critical pressure*, 217.5 atmospheres. As vapor pressure measurements are made at temperatures lower than T_1, a point *A* is reached at which liquid water changes to ice. This point corresponds to a temperature of 0.0075° C. and to a vapor pressure of 4.57 mm. of Hg. If great care is taken not to agitate the water, it may be supercooled and the vapor pressure measurements carried to lower temperatures than this point *A*. Thus we obtain the vapor pressure curve *ABD* which extends as *AG* for supercooled water. If ice begins to separate at *A*, we may continue vapor pressure measurements at successively lower temperatures and obtain the curve *AH*, which is the vapor-pressure curve for ice.

The curve *ABD* then represents the vapor pressures and the

temperatures at which liquid water is in equilibrium with water vapor, and the curve AH, the vapor pressures and the temperatures at which ice is in equilibrium with water vapor. The point A represents the temperature and the vapor pressure at which the liquid and the solid have the same vapor pressure and therefore are in equilibrium with each other as well as with the vapor. The point A is a ***triple point*** *at which three phases are in equilibrium.*

Let us now apply the phase rule to the system. On the curve ABD at a point X_1 corresponding to the temperature T_1 and the vapor pressure p_1, there is equilibrium between liquid and vapor. Applying the phase rule, we have:

$$F = (C + 2) - P = (1 + 2) - 2 = 1$$

One condition may be altered arbitrarily without causing a change of phase. If, for example, the temperature is raised from T_1 to T_2, some of the water vaporizes to raise the vapor pressure to p_2 and thus re-establish equilibrium at the point X_2. If the temperature is lowered from T_1 to T_3, vapor condenses until the vapor pressure has the value p_3, *i.e.*, equilibrium is established as represented by the point X_3 on the curve.

If now the temperature is raised from T_1 to T_2 and the vapor is pumped off so that the pressure is held at p_1, the liquid passes completely into vapor as represented by the point X_4. If the temperature is lowered from T_1 to T_3 and at the same time the pressure on the piston is maintained at p_1, then the vapor condenses completely and only the liquid phase remains. The piston now is in contact with the liquid itself. In both of these cases we have arbitrarily fixed *two* conditions, instead of one, and according to the phase rule, only one phase can be present in a one-component system, *i.e.*,

$$2 = (1 + 2) - P \quad \text{or} \quad P = 1$$

The above considerations show why the area below the curves ABD and AH is labeled "vapor" and that above the curve ABD is labeled "liquid"; within those areas of pressure and temperature only vapor and liquid, respectively, are stable. Similarly, the area above the curve AH is labeled "solid."

At the triple point, A, the three phases, solid, liquid, and vapor, are in equilibrium. We have then,

$$F = (1 + 2) - 3 = 0$$

No condition can be changed without causing the disappearance of one phase. If the temperature is raised slightly, the vapor pressure of the system is raised and the solid phase, ice, disappears. If the pressure is lowered, by expansion, the liquid and solid phases will disappear. If the pressure is raised by applying greater pressure to the piston (Fig. 238), the vapor phase disappears, and only solid and liquid remain; the temperature drops to that required for equilibrium at the arbitrarily fixed pressure, as given by points on the curve *AK*.

The *triple point, A*, corresponds to a temperature of 0.0075° C. and to a vapor pressure of 4.57 mm. of Hg. This temperature is slightly higher than the *freezing point* of water, 0° C., which is the temperature at which ice and water are in equilibrium under a *total atmospheric pressure* of 760 mm. Since ice has a lower density than water, an increase of pressure will shift the equilibrium toward the formation of the liquid phase; in other words, ice melts at a lower temperature when the pressure is increased. This is in accord with the principle of Le Chatelier.

When a system has no degrees of freedom it is termed *invarient;* if it has one degree of freedom it is *univarient;* if it has two degrees of freedom it is *bivarient.* The invarient system is denoted on a phase diagram by a *point* which is a triple point in the case of a one-component system; the univarient system is denoted by a *line;* and the bivarient system by an *area.*

In constructing the phase diagram for the system, *water*, the curves *ABD* and *AH* are merely the plots of vapor pressure measurements of water and ice at various temperatures. But how is the direction of the curve *AK* ascertained? Points on such a curve may be determined either from *time-temperature curves* at constant pressure or from *time-pressure* or *time-volume* curves at constant temperature. The first is most commonly employed.

The *time-temperature curve* is drawn from readings of time and temperature taken as the material cools, or is heated, past the temperature of change. This has been discussed on page 249. The rapid rise in temperature of the supercooled liquid, as shown in Figure 125, page 249, is due, of course, to the evolution of latent heat of fusion of the substance, 79.76 cal. per gram in the case of water. But why does the temperature rise just to the transition point and there remain constant? To answer this we may again apply the phase rule. There are in the system two phases, ice and water, so that we have:

$$F = (C + 2) - P = (1 + 2) - 2 = 1$$

But since the pressure is arbitrarily fixed, there is no degree of freedom and so the temperature must remain constant.

The change of a substance from one physical state into another, that is, from one phase into another, almost always is accompanied by a change in energy and either the evolution or absorption of heat. This means that a time-temperature curve, run either as a cooling curve or as a heating curve, will show a break at the temperature at which the change of phase occurs. The time-temperature curve, therefore, serves as the most general method for determining temperatures of change of phase, generally called *transition temperatures*. *The* ***transition temperature*** *is the temperature at which any change of phase takes place.* It may be the melting point or freezing point of a substance, the temperature of transition of one solid phase into another, or the temperature at which a hydrated salt loses its water of crystallization.

Extension of the System, *Water*. Much more is known concerning the system, *water*, than is indicated in the diagram in Figure 239. The investigation of the behavior of water under high pressures by Tammann [1] and by Bridgman [2] has yielded very interesting results.

By running a series of cooling curves at various constant pressures higher than the vapor pressure of water at the triple point A on the diagram in Figure 239, the curve AK may be drawn, representing the equilibrium temperatures and pressures for liquid water and ordinary ice, which we shall now call *ice I*. When these transition temperatures are determined at pressures higher than 2047 atmospheres, they do not lie on the curve AK. The temperature of transition *rises* instead of *falling* with increasing pressure. A new set of points is obtained and the curve KL drawn through them intersects AK sharply at K as shown in Figure 240. Since the solid phase appearing here has different properties from *ice I*, as evidenced by this change in transition temperature with pressure, it must be a different phase. This new phase is called *ice III*. At pressures higher than 3436 atmospheres the curve along

[1] Gustav Tammann, Director, Institute for Physical Chemistry, University of Göttingen.

[2] P. W. Bridgman, Professor of Physics, Harvard University.

which liquid water and ice are in equilibrium again alters its direction, intersecting the *ice III-water* curve at *L* and indicating another crystalline form of ice called *ice V*. At pressures higher

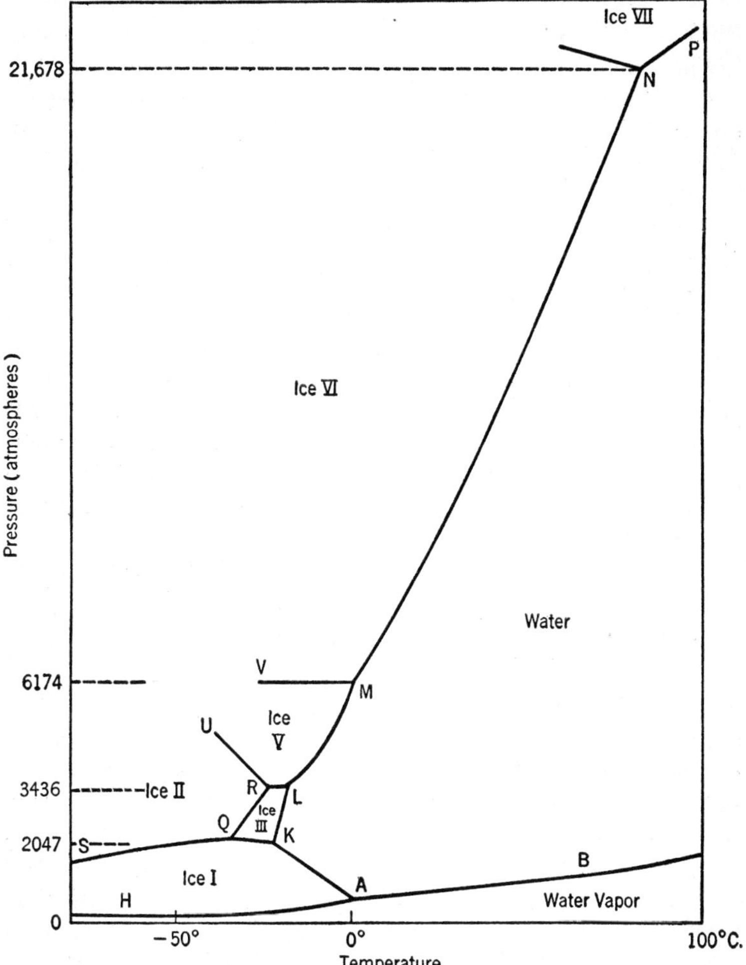

Fig. 240. Phase Diagram for the System, *Water*.

than 6174 atmospheres another form of ice is obtained, called *ice VI*, which is in equilibrium with liquid water at pressures and temperatures indicated by the curve *MN*. A break in this curve at a temperature of 81.6° C. and a pressure of 21,678 atmospheres indicates the existence of still another form of ice, *ice VII*, which has been shown to exist up to about 100° C. The equilibrium between this form of ice and liquid water is shown as the curve *NP*. This form of ice would, of course, be hot to the touch but actually when the pressure is released the ice would change rapidly to *ice I* or to *water*. The points *K*, *L*, *M*, and *N* are triple points. The point *K*, for example, indicates the temperature and pressure at which *ice I*, *ice III*, and *liquid water* are in equilibrium; it is also the temperature at which *ice I* undergoes transition into *ice III* when in contact with liquid water.

If transition points are determined by varying the pressure at various fixed temperatures below that at *K*, which is − 22.0° C., the curve *KQ* can be traced. This is the curve which indicates temperatures and pressures at which *ice I* and *ice III* are in equilibrium. At temperatures below − 34.7° C., it changes its direction, indicating the existence of another solid phase, which is called *ice II*. Similarly, the curves *LR*, *QR*, *QS*, *RU*, and *MV* are established. The area of stability of *ice III* has been completely circumscribed; the conditions under which this phase of ice can exist are definitely known. This is true for none of the other solid phases.

The phases which co-exist at the various triple points in the system, together with the temperatures and corresponding pressures, are shown in Table 122.

TABLE 122

Triple Points in the System, *Water*

Triple Points (Fig. 240)	Phases in Equilibrium	Temperature ° C.	Pressure	
			Kg./cm.²	Atm.
A	Water–Vapor–Ice I	0.0075	0.0062	0.0060
K	Water–Ice I–Ice III	− 22.0	2,115	2,047
L	Water–Ice III–Ice V	− 17.0	3,550	3,436
M	Water–Ice V–Ice VI	0.16	6,380	6,174
N	Water–Ice VI–Ice VII	81.6	22,400	21,678
Q	Ice I–Ice II–Ice III	− 34.7	2,170	2,100
R	Ice II–Ice III–Ice V	− 24.3	3,510	3,397

The System, *Deuterium Oxide*. Bridgman [1] has examined the behavior of deuterium oxide, *heavy water*, under high pressures. The results, so far as stable phases are concerned, are shown in

[1] *J. Chem. Phys.*, **3**, 601 (1935).

Figure 241, which includes the phase diagram for ordinary water for purposes of comparison. Note that the diagram for D_2O is shifted nearly uniformly to the right of that for H_2O.

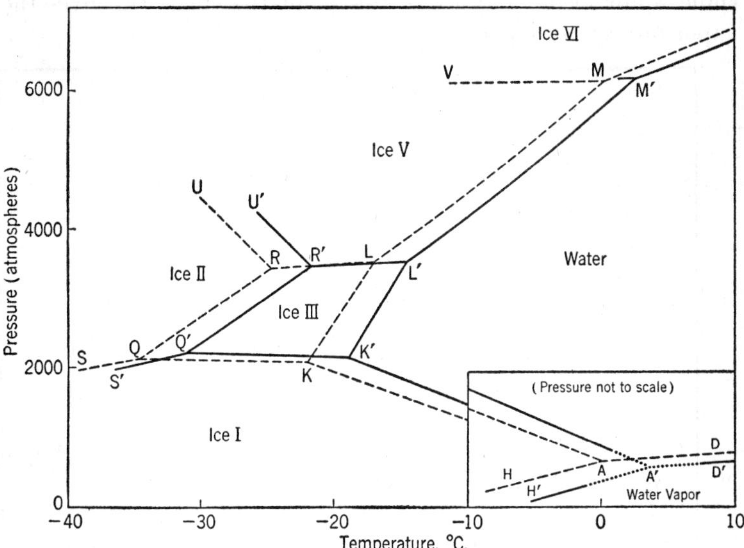

Fig. 241. Comparison of Phase Diagrams of Ordinary Water (dashed lines) and Heavy Water (solid lines).

The System, *Sulfur*. The system, *sulfur*, is another one-component system the behavior of which is understood more clearly from the standpoint of the phase rule. In elementary chemistry we learned that *rhombic sulfur* is the modification stable at room temperature, while *monoclinic sulfur* results when melted sulfur is cooled and solidifies slowly. Upon standing, monoclinic sulfur loses its form as clear yellow crystals and goes over into the rhombic variety. When sulfur is heated almost to boiling and is then cooled quickly by pouring into water, it yields a dark brown, rubbery mass which gradually hardens and becomes opaque and yellow, going over into the rhombic form.

The phase diagram for *sulfur*, shown in Figure 242, aids in realizing the meaning of these effects. If one begins with rhombic sulfur and determines the vapor pressures at various temperatures, as in the study of the system, *water*, the curve AB may be drawn. At the point B, corresponding to a temperature of 95.6° C., there is a break in the curve, and the sulfur undergoes a transition from the rhombic form into the monoclinic form. As the temperature rises, the vapor pressure of the sulfur increases along the curve *BD*. At 119° C., represented by the point *D*, the monoclinic sulfur melts, and above this point the curve *DG* gives the vapor pressure of liquid sulfur.

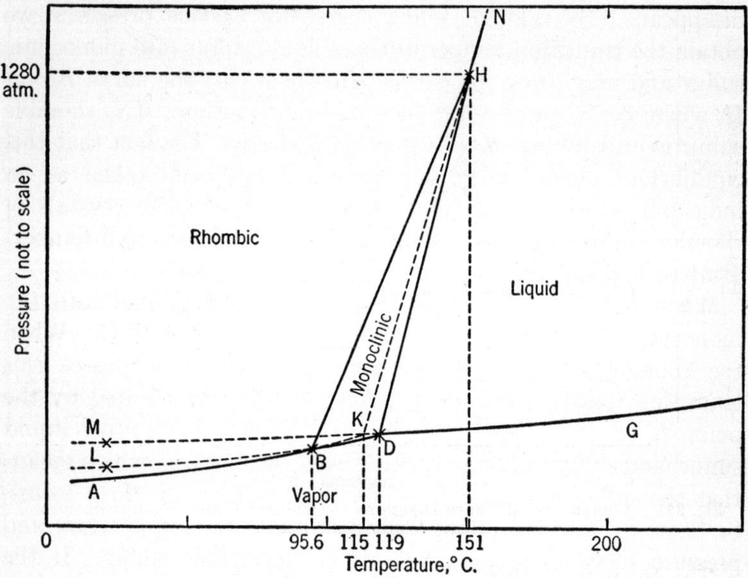

Fig. 242. Phase Diagram for Sulfur.

From *A* to *B* there is equilibrium between rhombic sulfur, S_r, and sulfur vapor, S_v; from *B* to *D* there is equilibrium between monoclinic sulfur, S_m, and sulfur vapor; and above *D*, the liquid, S_l, is in equilibrium with the vapor. The points *B* and *D* are triple points; at *B* the three phases, $S_r - S_m - S_v$, are in equilibrium; at *D*, the three phases, $S_m - S_l - S_v$.

If, as we have assumed, the sulfur is in the cylinder provided with a piston as represented in Figure 238, we may determine the effect of applying external pressure. Let us suppose that the system is in equilibrium at the point *B*, *i.e.*, $S_r - S_m - S_v$, and that we raise the pressure. The vapor phase disappears and the piston will be in contact with the two solid sulfur phases. By plotting cooling, or heating, curves at various pressures higher than that represented by *B*, we obtain transition temperatures of S_m into S_r. These temperatures plotted against the applied pressures enable us to draw the curve *BH*, which gives the equilibrium pressures and temperatures for coexistence of rhombic and monoclinic sulfur, S_r and S_m.

Similarly, if the system is in equilibrium at the point *D*, *i.e.*, $S_m - S_l - S_v$, and external pressure is applied, the vapor phase disappears. By taking cooling curves for various pressures, we obtain the transition temperatures of liquid sulfur into monoclinic sulfur and may draw the curve *DH*, which cuts the curve *BH* at *H*, where S_r, S_m, and S_l are in equilibrium. Along *HN*, rhombic sulfur is in equilibrium with the liquid phase. The fact that this equilibrium exists under high pressures has been taken as an indication of the reason for the occurrence of large crystals of rhombic sulfur in nature. The point *H* corresponds to a temperature of 151° C. and a pressure of 1280 atmospheres.

When rhombic sulfur is heated *slowly*, it goes over into the monoclinic sulfur at 95.6° C. and this melts at 119° C. When the rhombic sulfur is heated *rapidly*, however, it passes this transition temperature and melts at 115° C., represented by the point *K* in the phase diagram. At *K*, rhombic sulfur, liquid sulfur, and sulfur vapor are in *metastable* equilibrium, which means that the sulfur will go over slowly from any of the three forms, S_r, S_l, or S_v, into the phase that is stable at the temperature and pressure represented by *K*, *i.e.*, into monoclinic sulfur. If the change took place *rapidly*, the condition would be described as *unstable*.

Applying external pressure to the system at *K* causes the vapor phase to disappear and the transition temperatures from liquid sulfur to rhombic sulfur may be determined at various pressures, thus enabling us to draw the curve *KH*, which represents metastable equilibrium between rhombic sulfur and liquid sulfur, until the point *H* is passed, after which the equilibrium becomes stable, since monoclinic sulfur no longer exists under the conditions represented by the curve *HN*. The curve *HN* is the continuation of the curve *KH*.

Sulfur heated just above its melting point, *i.e.*, just above 119° C., and then slowly cooled, solidifies as long, shining crystals of monoclinic sulfur, which remain when the sulfur cools to room temperature. The vapor pressure follows the curve *DBL*. On standing the crystals crumble and become opaque, going over from the metastable monoclinic phase into the stable rhombic phase. This is easily understood. At the point L we have the equilibrium,

$$S_m \rightleftharpoons S_v$$

the sulfur exerting a definite vapor pressure represented by the ordinate at L. This vapor pressure is higher than that of rhombic sulfur at the same temperature, so that the vapor which is *saturated* with respect to monoclinic sulfur is *supersaturated* with respect to rhombic sulfur. Accordingly, sulfur vapor would condense as rhombic sulfur and a slow *sublimation* of sulfur will take place from the monoclinic to the rhombic form. The same change may take place by other mechanisms.

Sulfur heated nearly to the boiling point and then cooled quickly by pouring into water forms a rubbery mass. During this cooling, its vapor pressure has changed along the curve GD for liquid sulfur, and then since no separation of the solid phase has taken place, along the curve DKM, which is GD produced to lower temperatures. At M, therefore, we have metastable *supercooled liquid* sulfur. Since the vapor pressure of the liquid is higher than the vapor pressure of the rhombic sulfur at the same temperature, the liquid would alter into the rhombic again by a slow distillation process. Thus we see that the phase diagram is a comprehensive summary of the relations among the various phases in which sulfur may exist.

Other One-Component Systems. It has been shown that *water* and *sulfur* can exist in several modifications, *i.e.*, as several solid phases differing from one another in crystalline form and that each phase, whether stable or metastable, exists only within certain limits of temperature and pressure. These systems are not exceptional. Many other substances, both elements and compounds, likewise can exist in several different solid phases and change from one phase to another at definite transition temperatures. Some of these are of common interest. *Phosphorus*, for example, exists at room temperature as the stable *red* modification or the metastable *α-white* modification. Study of the phase diagram shown in Fig. 243 readily explains several facts concerning the behavior of phosphorus learned in our elementary chemistry. The cooling curve for *iron* shows breaks at 1535° C., 1400° C., and 930° C. The first of these is the freezing point, when the liquid iron changes into the solid phase, δ-ferrite; the second is the transition temperature of δ-ferrite into γ-ferrite; and the third is the transition temperature of γ-ferrite into α-ferrite, which is the solid phase stable at ordinary temperatures. The element *tin* exists as three solid phases, ordinary *white tin*, or *β-tin*, stable between 18° and 161° C.; *brittle tin*, or *γ-tin*, stable from 161° C. to the melting point, 232° C.; and *gray tin*, or *α-tin*, which is the stable form below 18° C. Fortunately for the modern

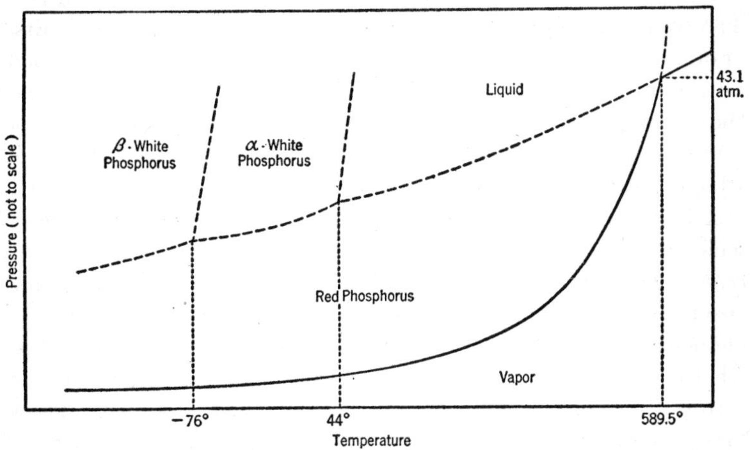

Fig. 243. Phase Diagram of the System, *Phosphorus* (not drawn to scale).

food-packing industry *white tin* is metastable below 18° C. and changes only very slowly into the *gray* modification. At very low temperatures the *white tin* becomes less stable and may change over quite rapidly into the *gray* form, especially if inoculation with the *gray tin* occurs. This change often is called the *tin disease*. The fact that gray tin exists was discovered in dramatic fashion in 1867. In the exceptionally cold winter of that year blocks of tin stored by the Russian government in St. Petersburg (Leningrad) were found to be completely disintegrated into a gray powder. However, upon heating, this *gray tin* fused and the liquid on cooling yielded the familiar white metal. Cases were recorded at still earlier dates of tin organ pipes being destroyed by disintegration into a gray powder.

Among other examples of substances which may exist as different solid phases might be mentioned *ammonium nitrate*, which changes from β-rhombic to α-rhombic at 35° C., from α-rhombic to rhombohedral at 83° C., and from rhombohedral to regular at 125° C.; *mercuric iodide*, which shows a transition at 126° C.; *silver nitrate*, with a transition at 160° C.; and *sodium sulfate*, which changes from rhombic to monoclinic crystals at 234° C.

Two-Component Systems

The two-component systems to which the methods of the phase rule apply with greatest profit are those which involve solid phases. The components of such systems may be metals, nonmetals, salts, or organic compounds. Although the vapor phase may be assumed to be present under all ordinary experimental conditions and the vapor pressure changes with temperature, the graphical representation of this would necessitate a three-dimensional diagram, which is awkward to construct and to interpret.

A two-component system usually is represented by a diagram in which *composition*, or *concentration*, either as *per cent* or as *mole per cent*, is plotted against *temperature*. The temperatures appearing specifically on a phase diagram are usually those representing a change of phase. Regardless of the nature of the components, whether they are metals, salts, organic compounds, or salt and water, the phase diagrams are of three principal types. These types are (1) systems involving a *eutectic mixture*, (2) systems involving *compound formation*, (3) systems involving *solid solutions*. We shall discuss two-component systems of metals in order to illustrate these three types and to indicate the relationships in two-component systems in general.

A Two-Component System Involving a Eutectic Mixture, Pb–Sb. As an example we may take the system, *lead–antimony*. The data upon which its phase diagram may be constructed are obtained from cooling curves. If we melt pure antimony in a crucible surrounded with insulation to cut down the cooling rate, insert a suitable thermometer and take time and temperature readings as the substance cools, we obtain a cooling curve similar in form to that of pure water except that it shows less supercooling. The result is shown as curve *ABDG* in Figure 244. Along *AB* we have liquid under atmospheric pressure; along *BD* the temperature stays constant because the two phases, solid and liquid, are present under a fixed pressure, *i.e.*, the pressure of the atmosphere; along *DG* we have the cooling curve of the solid. When lead is added to the antimony, the whole liquefied, and the liquid then cooled, a time-temperature curve like $A'B'HIG'$ is obtained. This is similar in form to the curve obtained for the cooling of the solution of a salt in water. As the liquid cools, the solid phase, which is pure antimony, begins to separate; as it freezes out, the remaining solution becomes increasingly richer in lead and consequently the freezing temperature drops continuously; when the

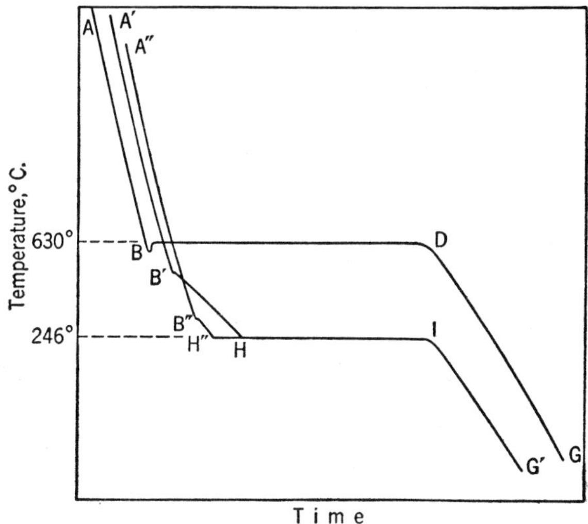

Fig. 244. Typical Cooling Curves for a Two-Component System Involving Formation of a Eutectic Mixture.

residual solution has reached a certain concentration of lead, antimony and lead crystals form simultaneously, a *mixture* of the two kinds of crystals separating. The composition of the liquid phase is now the same as that of the solid material separating and so the temperature remains constant along HI until solidification is complete at I. The section IG' is the cooling curve of the solid mixture. Note that the point B' is lower than B; this means that the addition of lead lowers the freezing point of the antimony.

With a melt containing a still higher proportion of lead, a cooling curve like $A''B''H''IG'$ is obtained, the interpretation of which is precisely the same as that of the preceding one. The first break in the curve, however, is still lower than B', the section $B''H''$ is shorter than $B'H'$, and the horizontal section $H''I$ is longer but occurs at the same temperature, called the *eutectic temperature.*

The mixture of lead and antimony crystals separating at the eutectic temperature is termed a *eutectic mixture.*

The phase diagram for the system *lead–antimony* constructed on the basis of cooling curve data is shown in Figure 245, which we may now interpret.

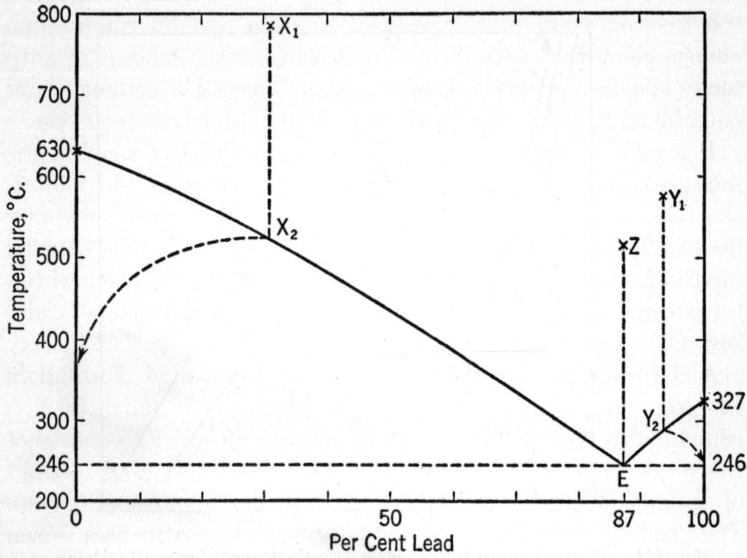

Fig. 245. Phase Diagram for a Two-Component System Forming a Single Eutectic: Pb–Sb.

When two metals are fused together, they become completely miscible, thus the area above the freezing point curves for the system represents liquid solutions of all possible concentrations of lead and antimony. When a liquid solution of antimony and lead of the composition and at the temperature indicated by X_1 is cooled, there is a break in the time-temperature curve at the temperature corresponding to X_2. This break indicates the separation of a solid phase, which is pure antimony. As the cooling proceeds, antimony continues to separate, and the temperature of freezing becomes further lowered. At the temperature indicated by E, the remaining liquid solidifies as a heterogeneous mixture of antimony and lead crystals, the eutectic mixture. As the cooling from X_2 to E takes place, the composition of the residual liquid changes also from that represented by the abscissa at X_2 to that at E. Thus the point E represents the composition and the freezing point of the eutectic mixture.

Similarly, when we cool a fused mixture of the two metals represented in composition and temperature by the point Y_1, separation of the solid phase, pure lead, takes place at the temperature represented by the point Y_2. As the separation continues, the freezing point of the residual solution and its composition change along the curve Y_2E. At E, once more, crystals of antimony and lead separate simultaneously, forming a heterogeneous eutectic mixture identical with that obtained in the former case.

If a melt of the two metals of the composition of the eutectic mixture is cooled from the temperature represented by the point Z, the time-temperature curve is the same as for a pure substance because the composition of the solid separating, *i.e.*, the eutectic mixture, is the same as that of the residual solution. The horizontal portion of the curve corresponds to the eutectic temperature, 246° C.

A Two-Component System Involving Compound Formation, Pb–Mg. A system of two metallic components which form a compound is that of *lead* and *magnesium*. In order to construct the phase diagram for this system, one would carry out a series of cooling experiments as in the case of the *lead–antimony* system. The phase diagram is shown in Figure 246. The entire area shown in the phase diagram above the curves AE_1, E_1DE_2, and E_2B represents the solution phase, *i.e.*, any point within this area represents a liquid solution of lead and magnesium.

If we take a melt of the composition and at a temperature represented by the point X_1 and cool it, a break in the time-temperature curve gives us the point X_2, at which magnesium begins to separate as the solid phase. As separation proceeds, the residual melt becomes richer in lead, and the freezing temperature and the composition change to those represented by the point E_1. Magnesium crystals and some other solid phase separate at this point as a eutectic mixture. The second solid phase is not, however, pure lead, as microscopic examination of the fractured solid would show. It is instead a *compound* of magnesium and lead with a melting point and the composition corresponding to the topmost point of the curve E_1DE_2. This composition corresponds to the formula Mg_2Pb.

A melt with the composition and at the temperature represented by Y_1 begins to freeze at the temperature Y_2. The solid phase separating is the compound Mg_2Pb; and as it separates, the melt becomes richer in magnesium and the freezing point drops and comes finally to E_1. As before, the compound and pure magnesium crystallize simultaneously.

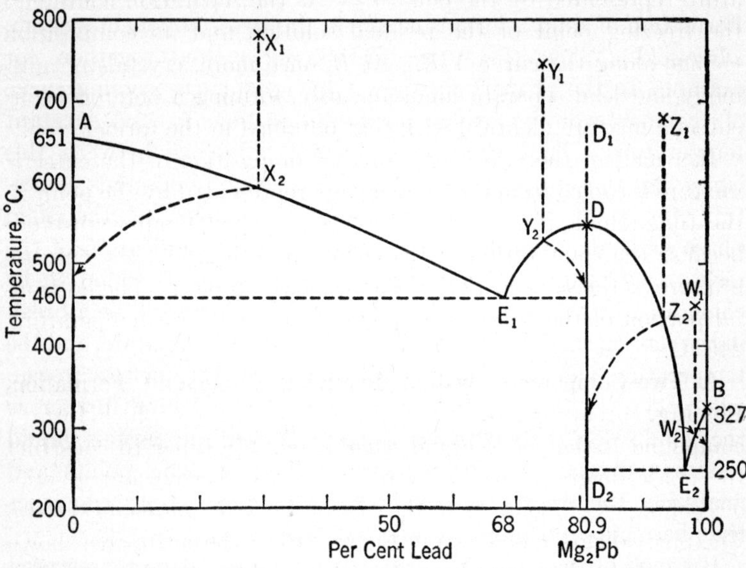

Fig. 246. Phase Diagram for a System Involving Compound Formation: Pb–Mg.

If we cool a melt of the composition and at the temperature represented by Z_1, the solid phase (which is again the compound Mg_2Pb) begins to separate at Z_2. As it separates, the melt becomes richer in lead, and the composition and freezing point change to those at the point E_2, and there the residual melt solidifies as a mixture of crystals of lead and the compound Mg_2Pb. A melt of composition and temperature represented by the point W_1 begins to freeze at W_2, lead separating as the solid phase. As lead separates, the melt becomes richer in magnesium and at the eutectic point E_2 lead and the compound Mg_2Pb again separate simultaneously.

A melt of composition represented by the point D_1 freezes at the temperature represented by D; it shows the same form of cooling curve that water or any other pure substance would show.

This system involves the formation of the compound Mg_2Pb

and its phase diagram shows two eutectic points; E_1 corresponds to a temperature of 460° C.; E_2 to a temperature of 250° C. Such a diagram could be divided by a line like D_1DD_2 to form *two* phase diagrams, each involving a single eutectic, in which the compound is taken as one of the components.

A Two-Component System Involving Solid Solutions, Ag–Au. Formation of solid solutions occurs in the two-component system, *silver-gold.* When these two metals are melted together, for example, in the proportion of 1 : 1 by weight, the cooling curve of the melt would show no horizontal section, *i.e.*, no constant temperature. Thus there is a definite difference between this curve and those in which eutectic mixtures or compounds constitute the solid phase. Furthermore, if samples of the solid phase are removed from time to time as the solidification of the melt proceeds and are analyzed, the solid phase is found to be changing in composition. As the melt cools, there will be a break in the cooling curve when the solid phase begins to separate, and the temperature will continue to fall until all of the melt is frozen, when there is another break, the temperature falling further as the solid cools. By running cooling curves on various liquid mixtures of the two metals, noting their freezing points and analyzing the solid phase first separating, one could construct the phase diagram shown in Figure 247.

If a melt of the composition and at the temperature represented by the point X_1 is cooled, a break in the time-temperature curve at X_2 indicates the separation of a solid phase. If the solid phase first separating is removed and analyzed, it is found to have the composition represented by the point X_3; that is, the solid phase is richer in the higher melting component, gold, than is the initial melt. If another melt of the composition and at the temperature represented by Y_1 is cooled and a similar examination made, the point Y_2 is found as the freezing point and the point Y_3 as the composition of the solid phase first separating. Thus we are enabled to draw the two curves which are necessary to describe the system; one of them, AY_2X_2B, gives the freezing points of melts of compositions indicated by points like Y_2 and X_2; the other, AY_3X_3B, gives the compositions of the solid solutions which would be in equilibrium with those melts at the temperatures indicated by points like Y_2 or Y_3 and X_2 or X_3. As any of these melts solidify, the compositions of the solid solutions separating are changing as represented by the curve AX_3B, while the temperature of the melt is changing as represented by the curve AX_2B.

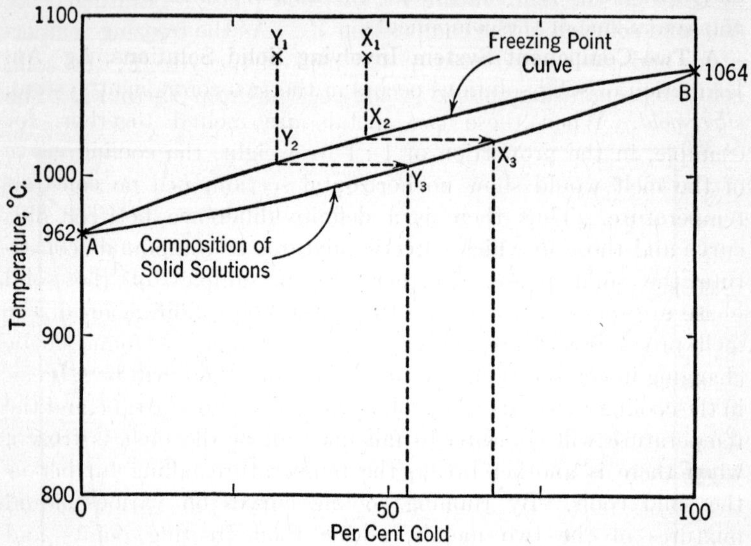

Fig. 247. Phase Diagram for a System Involving Solid Solutions: Ag–Au.

Other Two-Component Systems. We shall now discuss some two-component systems which are of special interest or importance. Some of these conform less closely to the fundamental types than the systems we have already treated and involve combinations or modifications of these types to which it is worth while drawing attention.

Potassium Nitrate–Sodium Nitrate. The melting point of sodium nitrate is 308° C.; that of potassium nitrate is 339° C. The two salts form a eutectic mixture, containing about 50 per cent of each salt, which melts at 218° C. The eutectic mixture is often used as a bath when heating at temperatures a little above 218° C. is desirable. As indicated in Figure 248, when a melt of the composition and at the temperature represented by the point X_1 is cooled, the solid phase begins to separate at the temperature represented by X_2. The solid phase, however, is not pure sodium nitrate but a *solid solution* of the composition represented by X_3. As the melt changes in composition and freezing point to the eutectic point E, the solid phase separating changes in composition along the curve X_3X_4. Similarly, a melt of the composition and at the temperature represented by the point Y_1 begins to freeze at the temperature Y_2, the solid phase separating being the solid solution of the composition Y_3. As the freezing temperature and the composition of the melt changes to E, the solid solutions separating change in composition from Y_3 to Y_4. The

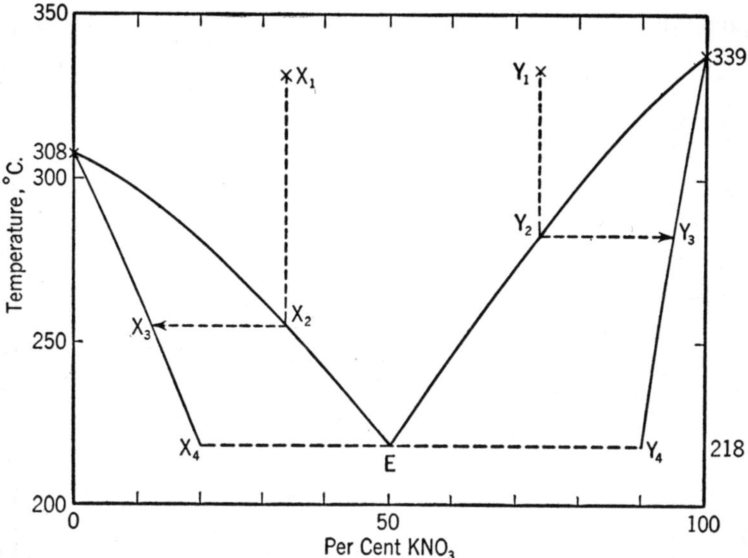

Fig. 248. Phase Diagram for a System Involving a Eutectic and Solid Solution Formation: KNO_3-NaNO_3.

eutectic mixture separating at E, corresponding to 218° C., is a heterogeneous mixture of the two solid solutions, the compositions of which are represented by the points X_4 and Y_4.

Sodium Chloride–Water. This system is used for so many purposes, such as salt solutions and freezing mixtures, that a brief reference to its phase diagram is worth while. The curve OE in Figure 249 represents the freezing point depression of water by sodium chloride. It also represents the temperatures at which salt solutions of various concentrations up to the per cent of sodium chloride indicated by E are in equilibrium with ice. If a solution of the composition and at the temperature X_1 is cooled, a break in the time-temperature curve at the temperature X_2 indicates the separation of the solid phase, ice. As ice separates, the solution becomes richer in salt, the freezing point drops to E, and at the same time the composition changes from X_2 to E. At E, which is a eutectic point, formerly called a *cryohydric point*, the solution completely solidifies, the solid phases being *ice* and a salt hydrate of the composition $NaCl \cdot 2\,H_2O$. The point E, which corresponds to $-\ 21.13°$ C. and 23.3 per cent sodium chloride, is the lowest temperature attainable with a freezing mixture of ice and salt.

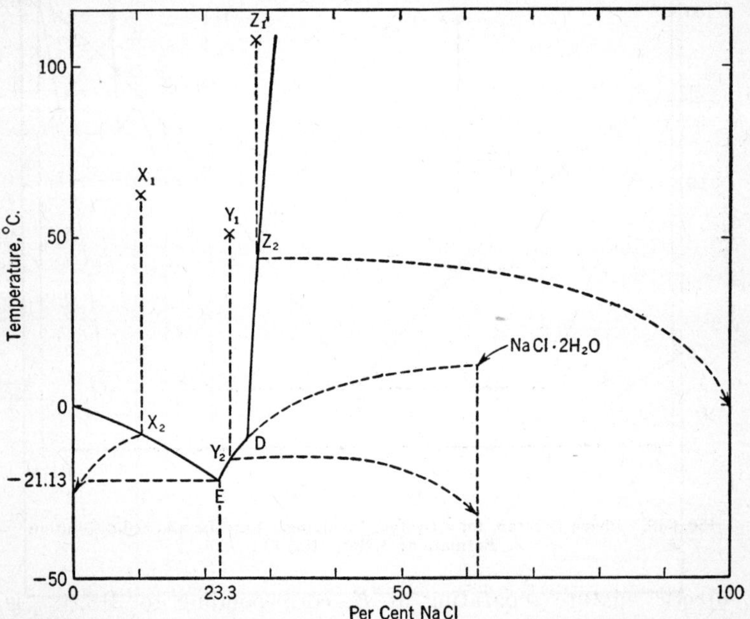

Fig. 249. Phase Diagram for the Two-Component System: NaCl–H₂O.

Although, as the diagram in Figure 249 indicates, the hydrate $NaCl \cdot 2\,H_2O$ separates as the solid phase when a solution of the composition represented by the point Y_1 is cooled, the phase diagram does not show the form of curve typical of compound formation. Thus a solution of the composition and at the temperature represented by the point Z_1, which contains considerably less sodium chloride than does the compound $NaCl \cdot 2\,H_2O$, does not yield $NaCl \cdot 2\,H_2O$ as the solid phase on cooling but instead deposits NaCl. This is because the salt hydrate, $NaCl \cdot 2\,H_2O$, is unstable and cannot exist above the temperature represented by the point D, the highest temperature at which it is deposited by cooling salt solutions. The point D, *at which the solid phase becomes unstable and forms a liquid phase,* is termed an **incongruent melting point.** The curve DE is the solubility curve of $NaCl \cdot 2\,H_2O$; the curve Z_2D is the solubility curve for NaCl.

Ferric Chloride-Water. The phase diagram shown in Figure 250 indicates the phase relations in this rather complex system. The curve OE is the freezing point depression curve of water by ferric

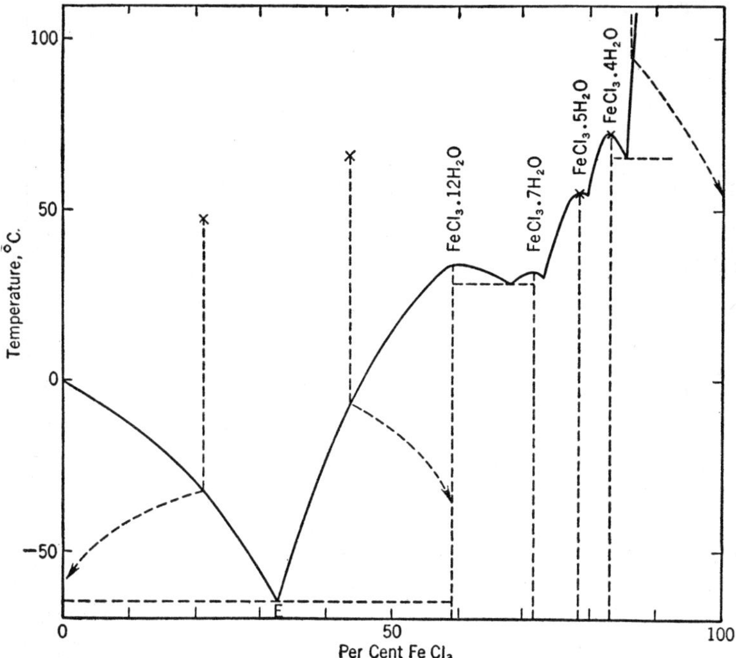

Fig. 250. Phase Diagram for a Salt-Water System Involving Several Eutectics: $FeCl_3-H_2O$.

chloride, extending to the eutectic point E, corresponding to $-65°$ C. and 33 per cent ferric chloride; this curve also could be termed the curve of solubility of ice in ferric chloride solutions of various compositions from 0 to E per cent. Various hydrates are formed, each of which appears as a *compound* on the phase diagram. Between each pair of compounds is a eutectic point. From the standpoint of the phase rule water is "just another substance."

Sodium Amalgams. Amalgams are often referred to as solutions of other metals in mercury. This is not precisely true. From the standpoint of the phase rule, mercury is in no way different from any other metal. It forms alloys just like other metals and shows the same types of phase diagrams. One of these systems is that of *sodium* and *mercury*. As the phase diagram given in Figure 251 indicates, the actual substances present in the amalgam depend upon the proportions of the two components. As the

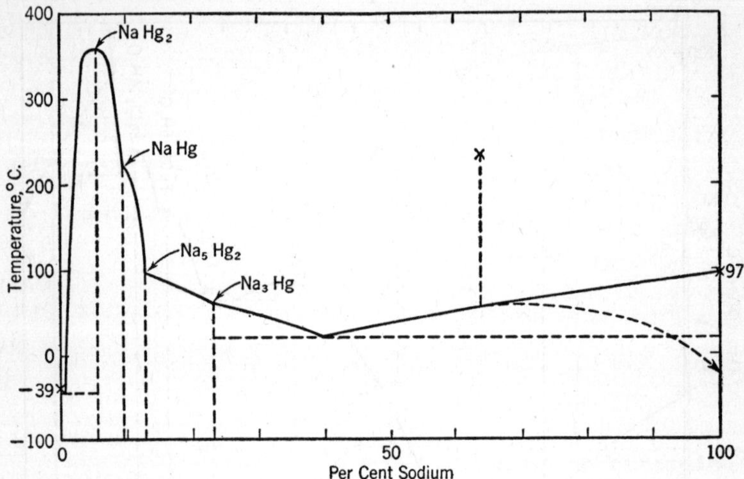

Fig. 251. Phase Diagram for the System: Na – Hg (Sodium Amalgams).

per cent of sodium increases, we have first the formation of a eutectic, with a slight lowering of the freezing point from that of pure mercury, then the formation of the compound $NaHg_2$, then a succession of other less stable compounds as indicated by the several incongruent melting points, then a eutectic point corresponding to about 40 per cent sodium and a temperature of 20° C., after which the liquid system on cooling would yield only sodium as the solid phase.

The System, *Iron–Carbon.* This is a two-component system of much importance and interest, especially in the steel industry. The phase diagram shown in Figure 252 serves to explain various properties of iron and steel with which metallurgists and steel fabricators must be familiar. It shows the application of some of the fundamental phase rule principles which we have been studying and some of the facts regarding iron metallurgy learned in elementary chemistry. We cannot discuss the whole diagram in detail but only certain features of special interest.

Carbon dissolves readily in liquid iron to form liquid solutions. The conditions under which these solutions exist correspond to points in the area ABE_1G in the diagram.

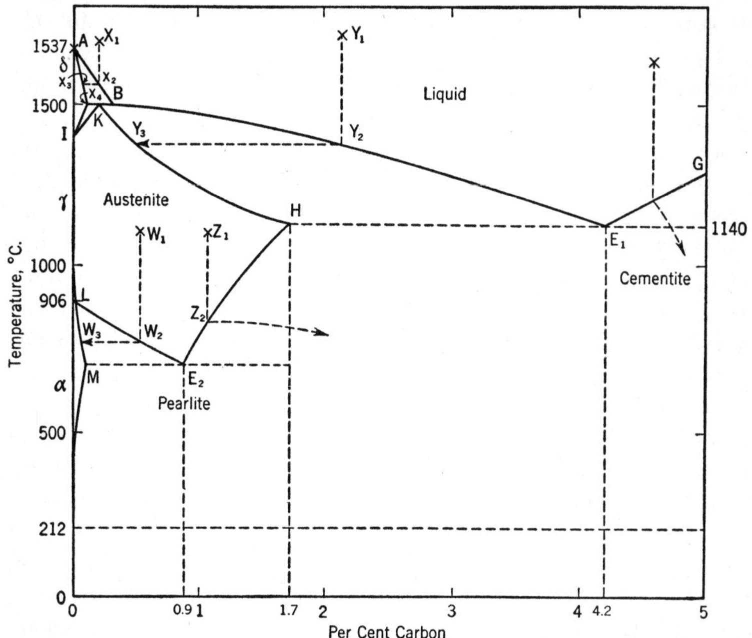

Fig. 252. Phase Diagram for the Two-Component System, *Iron-Carbon.*

Such a solution, containing, for example, 0.3 per cent of carbon, if cooled from the temperature represented by the point X_1, freezes at the temperature X_2. The solid phase separating is not iron but a solid solution of carbon in δ-ferrite of the composition X_3. As cooling proceeds, the solid phase which separates is composed of solid solutions corresponding to points along the curve X_3X_4.

If a liquid solution of the composition and at the temperature represented by Y_1 is cooled, freezing begins at the temperature Y_2. The solid phase separating is a solid solution of iron in γ-ferrite of the composition Y_3. As cooling proceeds, the temperature and the composition of the melt change along the curve Y_2E_1; the solid phase separating is a solid solution of carbon in γ-ferrite of compositions represented by the points on the curve Y_3H. At the eutectic point E_1, the residual liquid solidifies completely without further change in temperature; the eutectic mixture which separates is a heterogeneous mixture of the solid solution of carbon in γ-ferrite of the composition H and a compound of iron and carbon, iron carbide or *cementite*, Fe_3C. A liquid solution of composition greater than that corresponding to the point E_1, 4.2 per cent carbon, gives cementite as the solid phase when it begins to freeze and the same eutectic as the solution of the composition Y_1.

Let us transfer our attention now to the point Z_1. This represents a solid solution of carbon in γ-ferrite containing about 1.03 per cent carbon. On cooling very slowly, change of phase occurs at the point Z_2, where the solid solution begins to change into cementite. As cooling proceeds, cementite continues to form until the composition of the solid solution and its temperature reach the point E_2. Here the homogeneous solid solution changes completely without further change of temperature, yielding the heterogeneous mixture known as *pearlite*, which consists of cementite and a solid solution of carbon in α-ferrite of the composition represented by the point M. Similarly, a solid solution of the composition and at the temperature represented by W_1, when cooled, gives the solid solution of the composition W_2 as transition product and on further cooling the same mixture as above forming at E_2. The point E_2 is called a **eutectoid point**; the mixture forming from the solid solution is called a *eutectoid mixture.* The term refers to *the production of a heterogeneous mixture of two solid phases by the cooling of a solid solution.*

The area in the phase diagram, $IKHE_2L$, indicates the limits of composition and temperature at which solid solutions of carbon in γ-ferrite can exist as stable phases. Any such solid solution is known as *austenite.* Most steels fall within this area in composition.

One way in which this phase diagram is of use may be indicated briefly. If a steel of, say, 0.3 per cent of carbon is heated at a temperature within the austenite area, the result will be a solid solution of carbon in γ-ferrite. If this is cooled slowly a solid solution of carbon in α-ferrite mixed with cementite is obtained; the result is a *soft steel.* If, on the contrary, it is cooled quickly by quenching in oil or water, the transition into the eutectoid mixture does not take place; instead we obtain a supercooled solid solution of carbon in γ-ferrite, which is an *extremely hard steel.* To render this steel less hard and brittle it is further *heat-treated* or *tempered,* which is the process of "letting down" the hardness as much as may be desired. The hard steel is reheated to a temperature between 230° C. and 320° C. This allows a partial separation of the solid phases that would normally separate at the temperature E_2. The higher the temperature of reheating, the greater the extent to which this separation takes place and the softer the steel. As might be deduced from a study of the phase diagram neither *wrought iron,* containing practically no carbon, nor *pig iron,* containing several per cent of carbon, can be tempered.

Three-Component Systems. Since a three-component system involves three composition variables, any two of which may be considered independent, the construction of its phase diagram requires the use of triangular co-ordinate paper. Furthermore, for each series of measurements the pressure and temperature must remain constant. One such diagram, that for the system $(NH_4)_2SO_4-H_2O-Li_2SO_4$, at 30° C., is shown in Figure 253.

This diagram indicates that solutions of the compositions represented by points on the curve AB are in equilibrium with the solid phase, Li_2SO_4; those of compositions represented by points on the curve BD are in equilibrium with the solid phase, $Li_2SO_4 \cdot (NH_4)_2SO_4$; and those of compositions represented by the curve DG are in equilibrium with the solid phase, $(NH_4)_2SO_4$.

The solid phase may be dried and analyzed directly, or it may be analyzed while still wet with the saturated solution. In the latter case the line joining the point, such as X_1, representing the composition of the saturated solution and the point corresponding to the composition of the wet solid phase, X_2, passes through a point on the axis which represents the composition of the solid phase. Such *tie lines* are much used in practice. The compositions of the wet solid phase obtained in the construction of the diagram shown in Figure 253 are given by the points represented as circles in the diagram. In other cases these tie lines converge at points within the diagram corresponding to compounds of the three components.

By obtaining phase diagrams like that for the system discussed in the foregoing at different temperatures and superimposing these along a temperature axis perpendicular to their planes, a three-dimensional diagram is constructed which represents the

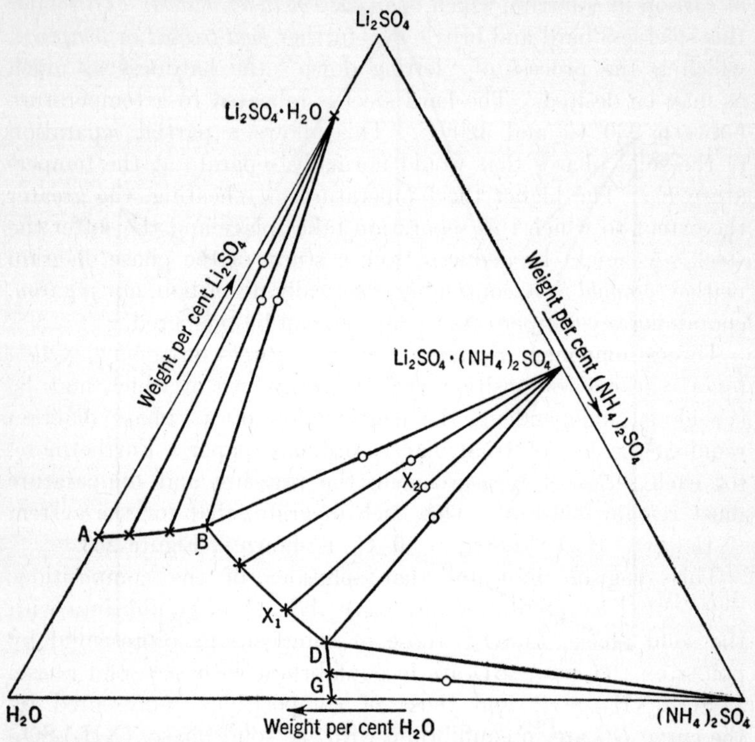

Fig. 253. Phase Diagram for the Three-Component System, $Li_2SO_4-(NH_4)_2SO_4-H_2O$ at 30° C.

phase relations in the system not only with variable composition but also at different temperatures. Such a diagram is shown in Figure 254 for the three-component system Bi–Sn–Pb. This shows the three eutectics E_1, E_2, and E_3 for the binary systems Bi–Sn, Sn–Pb, and Pb–Bi, respectively, and also a eutectic point E_4 for the ternary eutectic mixture. This eutectic point corresponds to a temperature of 96° C., or 4° below the boiling point of water, which is the lowest temperature at which a liquid phase consisting of any of these metals can exist. Many more complex three-component systems have been studied as well as systems containing four and more components. Classic among such studies was the working out of the phase relations among the salts composing the Stassfurt deposits by van't Hoff. The discussion of such complex systems is beyond the scope of this book.[1]

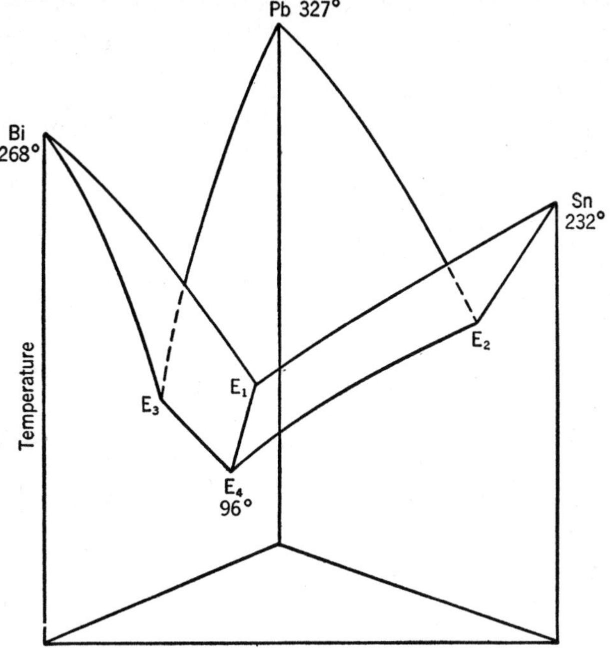

Fig. 254. Phase Diagram for the System Bi–Sn–Pb.

PROBLEMS AND EXERCISES

1. Explain why *rhombic sulfur* is the stable phase at room temperature. (See phase diagram, p. 598.)

2. From the following data construct the phase diagram for the system, Al–Mg:

Per cent Mg	**0**	**10**	**20**	**30**	**40**	**50**	**60**	**70**	**80**	**90**	**100**
Freezing point, ° C.	657	598	580	460	453	469	461	451	570	587	651
Melting point, ° C.	657	452	452	452	452	452	440	440	440	440	651

3. Draw cooling curves of the forms which would be obtained when liquid mixtures of aluminum and magnesium of the following compositions are cooled to a temperature below their melting points: Per cent Mg: (i) 27; (ii) 47; (iii) 87; (iv) 55.

4. Explain, with reference to the phase diagram for Al and Mg, the changes that occur on cooling from 600° C. to 400° C. a mixture of the two metals containing (*a*) 36 per cent Mg; (*b*) 85 per cent Mg.

[1] For references to such systems see page 618.

5. By reference to the phase diagram shown in Figure 243, on page 610, explain (*a*) how you would prepare red phosphorus from white phosphorus, (*b*) how you would convert red phosphorus to white phosphorus, (*c*) why red phosphorus is the stable form at room temperature.

6. On the basis of the phase rule explain why (*a*) salt added to ice, both dry at − 2° C., melts the ice; (*b*) dry camphor mixed with dry phenol, both solid, gives a liquid solution; (*c*) steel heated to 1000° C. and quickly cooled is very hard and brittle but is softened when heated to 250° C.

7. Construct the phase diagram for each of the following systems from the data given:

(*a*) System, $CaCl_2-KCl$

Mole per cent KCl	**0**	**10**	**20**	**30**	**40**	**50**	**60**	**70**	**80**	**100**
Freezing point, ° C. . .	777	741	686	687	735	754	729	660	683	776
Melting point, ° C. . .	777	640	640	640	640	754	600	600	600	776

(*b*) System, SO_3-H_2O

Per cent SO_3	**0**	**10**	**20**	**30**	**40**	**50**	**60**	**70**	**80**	**90**	**95**
Freezing point, ° C.	0	− 7	− 22	− 71	− 37	− 32	− 39	8	9	35	10
Melting point, ° C.	0	− 74	− 74	− 74	− 74	− 50	− 40	− 37	− 37	35	10

8. Selecting liquid solutions of several compositions in each of the systems in Problem 7, describe what occurs when each is cooled to complete solidification.

READING LIST

S. T. Bowden, *The Phase Rule and Phase Reactions.* The Macmillan Company, New York, 1938. An excellent elementary treatment.

A. Findlay and A. N. Campbell, *The Phase Rule and Its Applications,* 8th ed. Longmans, Green & Company, New York, 1938. This excellent treatise has long been regarded as a standard for reference.

H. G. Deming, "An Introduction to the Phase Rule," *J. Chem. Ed.,* **16,** 215, 260 (1939).

Data on alloys, salt pairs, systems of salts and water, and systems involving organic substances, will be found in Landolt-Börnstein, *Physikalisch-Chemische Tabellen,* 5th ed., vol. 1, pp. 500–586; supp. 1, pp. 239–301; supp. 2, pp. 334–460; supp. 3, pp. 409–681. Many other data are given in the *International Critical Tables,* published by McGraw-Hill Book Company, New York, 1928; alloys, vol. 2, pp. 358–455; liquid pairs, vol. 3, pp. 386–435; elements and salts, vol. 4, pp. 1–97; organic compounds, vol. 4, pp. 1–215; salts and water, vol. 4, pp. 216–395; others, vol. 4, pp. 396–429. Many phase diagrams are included in both books.

CHAPTER 23

THERMODYNAMICS AND MATHEMATICAL DERIVATIONS

The Scope and Methods of Thermodynamics. ***Thermodynamics*** *covers the study of the transformation of different forms of energy, the natural limitations upon these transformations, and their practical applications.* Many of these applications are in the fields of physics and engineering, and most of the early developments of the subject during the past two centuries were made by workers in these fields. The development of the steam engine was stimulated by the theoretical work of Sadi Carnot, and the development of other types of engines and of refrigerating machines has also been based upon thermodynamic laws. Within the last fifty years, the applications of thermodynamics to chemistry have achieved greater and greater importance, until thermodynamic principles now are considered fundamental to most fields. The relationships between the lowering of the vapor pressure of a solution, the depression of its freezing point, the elevation of its boiling point, and the osmotic pressure were derived by van't Hoff by thermodynamic reasoning. The *free energy change* during chemical reactions is another thermodynamic concept of fundamental importance, with which the study of equilibria in chemical systems is connected closely. The change of equilibrium constant, vapor pressure, and heat of reaction with temperature, and the change of electrode potentials with concentration all may be correlated with other physical properties by the methods of thermodynamics. Chemical thermodynamics finds constant application in industry and in all branches of science and technology. A thorough understanding of its theory and practice is indispensable to any competent chemist.

One of the most remarkable things about the field of thermodynamics is the wide variety of conclusions which can be deduced from a very few fundamental postulates. Although specific applications require experimental data in addition, the general equations of what we may call *classical thermodynamics* all are derived from two fundamental postulates or laws. A third such law, deduced more recently, finds wide application in chemical thermodynamics and allows the calculation of free energy changes and equilibria from thermal data alone. In the present chapter we shall state these laws and illustrate a few of their many applications to chemical problems.

The First Law of Thermodynamics. This sometimes is called the **law of conservation of energy,** and is a generalization based upon experiment, like the law of conservation of mass. ***The first law of thermodynamics*** *states that energy may be transformed from one kind to another within an isolated system but that its total amount does not change.* ***Mechanical energy*** *usually is defined as the ability to do work.* ***Kinetic energy*** *is the energy which depends upon the motion of a body, while* ***potential energy*** *depends upon its position.* Thus when the weight of a pile-driver is lifted, its potential energy increases because it is farther above the surface of the earth and can do work in falling back to its original position. If it is allowed to fall freely, it moves more and more rapidly and, neglecting small frictional losses, acquires an amount of kinetic energy which, at the moment of impact, is exactly equal to the potential energy it possessed initially. The energy of the ideal monatomic gas is all kinetic, while that of a wound spring is potential.

In addition to the *mechanical energy* considered above, there are also **electrical energy, chemical energy,** and **thermal energy.** In a generator, mechanical energy is transformed into electrical energy, while the reverse change takes place in an electric motor. A galvanic cell illustrates the transformation of chemical energy into electrical energy, and an electrolytic cell shows the reverse change. The equality of mechanical energy and thermal energy was first demonstrated by Count Rumford,[1] at the end of the eighteenth century. While superintending the boring of cannon in the Munich arsenal, he showed that the mechanical energy of the boring machine was converted into enough thermal energy to boil water without fire. Although the conversion of heat into other forms of energy is limited by the second law of thermodynamics (see page 623), any other form of energy can be converted into heat. Hence we may give a second definition of energy: ***Energy*** *is heat or anything which can be converted into heat.*

[1] Benjamin Thompson (1753–1814), born and educated in this country, later went to England, where he was one of the founders of the Royal Institution. Afterwards he lived in Germany and became Count Rumford. Still later he moved to Paris and married the widow of Lavoisier.

Any form of energy can be resolved into two components — an **intensity factor** and a **capacity factor,** which often can be measured separately. Thus electrical energy is the product of the potential difference (intensity factor) and the quantity of electricity (capacity factor). Other kinds of energy can be resolved into two factors in exactly the same way, as shown in Table 123, which includes the common energy units and conversion factors.

TABLE 123

INTENSITY AND CAPACITY FACTORS, UNITS, AND CONVERSION FACTORS FOR DIFFERENT FORMS OF ENERGY

Form of Energy	Intensity Factor	Capacity Factor	Product	Equivalent in Joules
Mechanical	force (dynes)	distance (cm.)	ergs	10^{-7}
Mechanical	pressure (atm.)	volume (liters)	l. × atm.	101.33
	(g./cm.^{2})	(cm.^{3})	g. × cm.	9.807×10^{-5}
Surface	surface tension (dynes/cm.)	surface area (cm.^{2})	ergs	10^{-7}
Electrical	potential difference or e.m.f. (volts)	quantity of electricity (coulombs)	joules	1
Thermal	temperature difference (degrees)	heat capacity (cal./degree)	calories	4.1833

It is often convenient to distinguish between the different kinds of energy which can be converted into each other freely and thermal energy, which can be formed from any of the others but can only be converted into the others to an extent limited by the second law of thermodynamics. The latter is usually called "heat" and the former "work," since any of these forms of energy can be converted into an equal amount of useful work outside the system, by means of a suitable machine. Thus the chemical energy in a galvanic cell can be converted into electrical energy and made to do useful work outside of the cell. When a system loses energy to the surroundings by thermal conduction or radiation, it is said to lose heat; and when it gives up energy in any other form, it is said to be doing work upon the surroundings.

Energy Content and Heat Content. The ***internal energy content,*** *E, of a system is the sum total of the energy which the system contains, in whatever form it is found.* It cannot be measured in the same way that the mass of the system can, but ***changes in internal energy content*** *during physical or chemical changes can be measured in a constant-volume calorimeter.* In studying heats of combustion in a bomb calorimeter, the value measured directly is the change in *energy content*, ΔE, as was mentioned on page 208. If the same process is carried out in a calorimeter at constant pressure, the heat absorbed will measure the change in *heat content*, ΔH. The relation between the two changes can be determined as a consequence of the first law of thermodynamics.

If the increase in volume during the reaction is ΔV, then at constant pressure the system will do an amount of work upon the surroundings equal to $\Delta W = P\Delta V$, and the heat absorbed by the system will be *greater* by this amount than it would have been at constant volume. In other words:

$$\Delta H = \Delta E + P\Delta V$$

In every case, the change in each property is the value in the *final* state minus that in the *initial* state, *e.g.*:

$$\Delta V = V'' - V'$$

By definition, the general relationship between the heat content and the energy content of a system is:

$$H = E + PV$$

To give a numerical illustration of the difference between change in energy content and change in heat content, let us consider the combustion of methanol according to the equation:

$$CH_3OH\ (l) + \tfrac{3}{2}\, O_2\ (g) = CO_2\ (g) + 2\, H_2O\ (l)$$

After applying corrections for the small amount of methanol vapor at the beginning of a bomb combustion and the small amount of water vapor at the end, the isothermal increase in energy content in the reaction as determined in the bomb calorimeter is:

$$\Delta E = -\ 173.45 \text{ kcal. (at } 18° \text{ C.)}$$

The relationship connecting the changes in E, H, and PV is:

$$\Delta H = \Delta E + \Delta(PV)$$

Assuming that oxygen and carbon dioxide behave as perfect gases, the gas law equation $PV = nRT$ shows that the isothermal *change* in PV is:

$$\Delta(PV) = \Delta nRT$$

In this case the products contain $\frac{1}{2}$ mole of gas less than the reactants, so that $\Delta n = -\frac{1}{2}$. Substituting the numerical factor for R in calorie units, and the absolute temperature gives:

$$\begin{aligned}\Delta H &= \Delta E + \Delta(PV) = \Delta E + \Delta nRT \\ &= -173.45 - \left(\frac{1.99}{2} \times 291\right) \times 10^{-3} \\ &= -173.45 - 0.29 = -173.74 \text{ kcal.}\end{aligned}$$

In the case of gases, the change in heat content differs from that in energy content by about 600 calories for each mole of gas formed or consumed during the reaction. ΔH and ΔE are the same for ideal gases, if there is no change in the number of moles.

The Change of Energy and Heat Content with Temperature. The temperature coefficients of the energy content and heat content of a system, called respectively the *heat capacities at constant volume and at constant pressure,* are defined by the equations:

$$\left(\frac{\partial E}{\partial T}\right)_V = C_V \qquad \text{and} \qquad \left(\frac{\partial H}{\partial T}\right)_P = C_P$$

Since the change in heat content during a reaction is given by the equation:

$$\Delta H = H'' - H'$$

differentiation of both sides with respect to temperature, at constant pressure gives at once the Person-Kirchhoff relationship which was derived in a different way on pages 215–217:

$$\left(\frac{\partial \Delta H}{\partial T}\right)_P = \left(\frac{\partial H''}{\partial T}\right)_P - \left(\frac{\partial H'}{\partial T}\right)_P = C_P'' - C_P'$$

or

$$\left(\frac{\partial \Delta H}{\partial T}\right)_P = \Delta C_P$$

Similar reasoning leads to an analogous relationship between the temperature coefficient of the change in energy content and the difference in heat capacities at constant volume:

$$\left(\frac{\partial \Delta E}{\partial T}\right)_V = \Delta C_V$$

The Second Law of Thermodynamics. It is a familiar fact that heat will flow spontaneously, by conduction or radiation, from a body with a higher temperature to one with a lower, while the transfer of heat from a lower to a higher temperature takes place only at the expense of work done upon the system from outside. This is one statement of the second law of thermodynamics, but a comparison of the heat change and the work done on the system will give it a more quantitative significance. Sadi Carnot, in 1824, first calculated the maximum work which could be derived from the conversion of heat in a suitable engine. In order to obtain the maximum work, the machine must operate under conditions of balance, so that the force of the system is opposed by an almost identical force. Thus if the system consisted of a cylinder of gas, confined at one end by a piston, the expansion of the gas would do work upon the surroundings. The *maximum* work would be done when the force of the gas is so nearly balanced by the force upon the piston that each step of the process is reversible. Carnot studied the cyclical process shown in Figure 255. (1) The gas was allowed to expand at a constant temperature T_1 from A to B, doing work upon the outside and absorbing a quantity of heat Q_1 from the surroundings. (2) The gas was insulated thermally and allowed to expand *adiabatically* from B to C, doing work upon the outside at the expense of its own energy, so that its temperature fell to T_2 in the process. (3) The gas was compressed *isothermally* at T_2 from C to D, giving up a quantity of heat Q_2 to the surroundings as work is done *upon it* from outside. (4) The gas was compressed *adiabatically* to the original temperature T_1 from D to A by means of additional work from the outside. Carnot showed that the work done in the two adiabatic steps was equal, so that these terms canceled each other. The process was cyclical, since the gas was returned to the same state at the end of the cycle of changes, and the work obtained in the process was the difference between that done *by* the system in (1) and that done *on* the system in (3). Carnot calculated this maximum work to be:

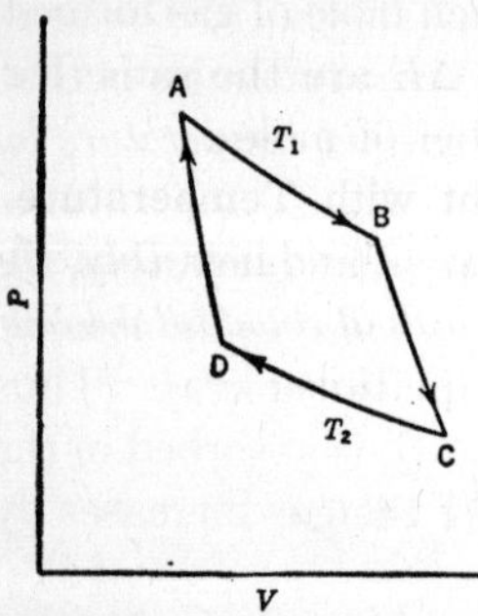

Fig. 255. The Carnot Cycle.

$$W_{\text{max.}} = Q_1 \left(\frac{T_1 - T_2}{T_1} \right)$$

This represents the maximum work which can be done by the flow of heat from a higher temperature T_1 to a lower temperature T_2, and shows the limited possibility of converting thermal energy into any other form of energy. Instead of yielding an amount of mechanical or electrical energy equal to the quantity of heat absorbed at the higher temperature, it yields this amount multiplied by the ratio of the difference in temperature to the absolute temperature at which the heat is absorbed. In differential form, for a very small difference in temperature, the equation becomes:

$$dW_{\text{max.}} = Q\frac{dT}{T}$$

Another statement of the second law of thermodynamics is that *heat cannot be changed directly into work at constant temperature by any cyclical process.*

Entropy. *When a change in a system takes place* **reversibly,** *the quantity of heat absorbed from the surroundings, divided by the absolute temperature, is called the* **entropy change** *ΔS in the process.* Thus in the Carnot cycle, when the quantity of heat Q_1 is absorbed in the first step, at a temperature T_1, the entropy of the gas increases by an amount:

$$\Delta S_1 = \frac{Q_1}{T_1} \qquad (1)$$

There is no entropy change during the adiabatic steps in the Carnot cycle, since no heat is gained or lost. During the isothermal compression in step (3), Q_2 is negative and there is a decrease in the entropy of the gas:

$$-\Delta S_2 = \frac{Q_2}{T_2} \qquad (3)$$

Now entropy, like mass, heat content, etc., is a **property** of a system; that is, it depends upon the temperature, pressure, and quantity of material. Hence for a fixed quantity of gas it is the same at the beginning and the end of a cyclical process, when the conditions are the same. In this case, the increase in entropy in (1) must be exactly equal to the decrease in (3):

$$\Delta S_1 = -\Delta S_2 \qquad \text{or} \qquad \frac{Q_1}{T_1} = \frac{Q_2}{T_2}$$

From the first law of thermodynamics, the work done by the system must be the difference between the heat absorbed and that given up:

$$W_{\text{max.}} = Q_1 - Q_2$$

Combining these two equations gives the expression for the maximum work from the reversible cycle, which we have already stated.

We can determine the entropy change in the free expansion of one mole of a perfect gas, by allowing the expansion to take place reversibly, in a cylinder fitted with a piston. In this case, the work of expansion for an infinitesimal change in pressure is given by the expression:

$$dW = PdV$$

For a finite change, the work of expansion is obtained by integration:

$$W = \int_{V_1}^{V_2} PdV$$

Substituting the value of dV from the perfect gas law, changing the limits to correspond to the pressures, and integrating, gives:

$$W = -RT\int_{P_1}^{P_2} \frac{dP}{P} = RT \ln \frac{P_1}{P_2}$$

since the temperature is constant. By the first law, the work done by the system is equal to the heat absorbed, hence:

$$\Delta S = \frac{Q}{T} = \frac{W}{T} = R \ln \frac{P_1}{P_2}$$

The entropy change in the expansion of a real gas could be determined from a more suitable equation of state, but the principles are the same.

In the isothermal expansion of the ideal gas which we have considered above, the internal energy does not change, since it depends upon the temperature alone. However, the entropy *increases* as the gas expands, and at the same time the gas loses in ability to do further work. The entropy increase in any process is a quantitative measure of the degradation of the energy of the system, *i.e.*, the extent to which its energy becomes less available for doing external work. If the gas under pressure is connected to an evacuated space, without the intervention of a piston, the gas will diffuse rapidly until the pressures are equalized. This is an *irreversible* process, since the flow of the gas is not balanced by any external force. During such free expansion the flow of the gas cannot be reversed any more than the free diffusion of a concentrated solution into a dilute one can be reversed. *Natural processes like those mentioned above are always irreversible, and always occur with an* ***increase*** *in the entropy of the system.* This is another way of stating the second law of thermodynamics. This entropy change cannot be measured in an irreversible change, but it can be measured by carrying out the same process in a reversible manner.

Entropy Changes in Changes of State. Whenever there is a change in state of a substance, this change takes place reversibly at a fixed temperature and pressure. In this case the entropy change is simply the latent heat absorbed in the process, divided by the temperature at which the change occurs. Thus the *entropy of fusion* per mole of ice at 0° C. is:

$$\Delta S = \frac{1437}{273.2} = 5.260 \text{ cal.} \times \text{deg.}^{-1} \times \text{mole}^{-1} \quad \text{or} \quad 5.260 \text{ entropy units}$$

The ***entropy unit*** *(**E.U.**) is 1 calorie per degree per mole.* **Trouton's rule** may be stated in terms of entropy thus: *The entropy of vaporization per mole of any substance at its boiling point is a constant, equal to 21 E.U.*

The determination of entropy changes in other physical and chemical processes is less simple than in the case of change of state. Unless the process is reversible, the entropy cannot be calculated as the quotient of the heat absorbed divided by the temperature. Thus the entropy of solution and dilution and the entropy changes in chemical reactions must usually be determined less directly.

The Change of Entropy with Temperature. When the difference in temperature between two systems becomes smaller and smaller, the flow of heat between them becomes more and more nearly reversible, since a small change in temperature will cause the heat to flow in the opposite direction. If a system with heat capacity C is heated by contact with another system at a temperature dT higher, so that its temperature rises by dT, the heat absorbed will be:

$$Q = CdT$$

Since this process may be regarded as reversible, the increase in entropy will be:

$$dS = C\frac{dT}{T}$$

or

$$dS = Cd \ln T$$

Over short temperature intervals, where the heat capacity can be considered constant, integration gives for the change in entropy when the system is heated at constant pressure:

$$S_2 - S_1 = C_p \ln \frac{T_2}{T_1}$$

Thus entropy in any system increases with increasing temperature. If the heat capacity is known as a function of temperature, its value can be inserted in the differential equation above, and the integration will give the change in entropy as before. If values of the heat capacity are known over a range of temperature, the change in entropy between any two temperatures on the experimental range can be determined graphically, by making a plot of C against $\ln T$ and measuring the area between the curve and the $\ln T$ axis. In actual calculations, the abscissa usually is made the logarithm to the base 10, and the measured area is multiplied by 2.303. Figure 256 illustrates such a plot of the molal heat capacity of glycine against the logarithm of the temperature, between 93.2 and 299.5° A. In order to calculate the change in entropy between 90° and 298° A., we extrapolate the curve a short distance to the left and measure the area under the curve, between the ordinates log 90 and log 298. This area, multiplied by 2.303, gives a value of 18.57 cal. × deg.$^{-1}$ × mole^{-1}, or entropy units, E.U. Since C_p is plotted, the result is the difference in entropy under a constant atmospheric pressure. The entropy at 298° A. is 18.57 units higher than at 90° A.

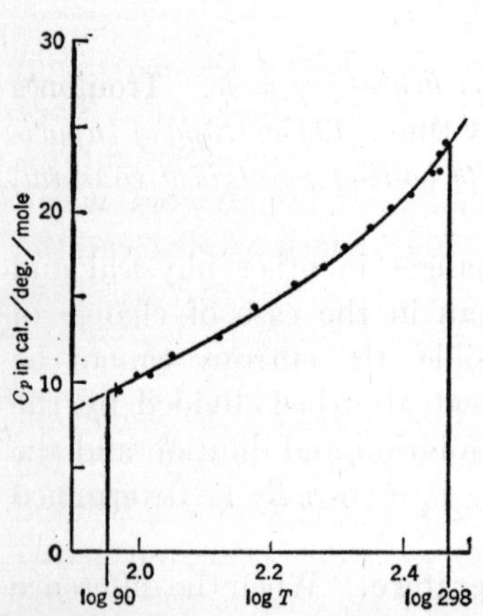

Fig. 256. Graphical Calculation of Change of Entropy of Glycine with Temperature.

Free Energy. For many purposes, a more convenient function than the entropy is the free energy F, which may be defined by the equation:

$$F = H - TS$$

The free energy is not measurable directly, although *changes in free energy* are measurable. The free energy decrease in a chemical reaction is a measure of the *driving force* of the reaction, and the free energy decrease in any process represents the maximum work which can be obtained from the system undergoing such a change. For any isothermal process, T is constant, and the free energy change is:

$$\Delta F = \Delta H - T\Delta S$$

By the first law of thermodynamics, the change in the internal energy of the system during the process is equal to the heat absorbed from the surroundings, minus the work done upon the outside:

$$\Delta E = \Delta Q - \Delta W$$

Since at constant pressure the change in internal energy is equal also to $\Delta H - P\Delta V$, we can write:

$$\Delta W - P\Delta V = \Delta Q - \Delta H$$

If the process is *reversible*, the system will deliver the maximum work to the outside, and the heat absorbed, $\Delta Q = T\Delta S$. Since the work $P\Delta V$ is the work of expansion against the external pressure, it is not *useful* work. The maximum useful work which the system can deliver is ($\Delta W_{max.} - P\Delta V$), which we shall call the maximum *net work*, $\Delta W'_{max.}$

$$\Delta W'_{max.} = (\Delta W_{max.} - P\Delta V) = -(\Delta H - T\Delta S) = -\Delta F$$

The free energy decrease, $-\Delta F$, therefore represents the maximum net work which the system can deliver in a given change. If the change is not carried out reversibly, some of the work will be used up in frictional losses and dissipated as heat; hence no actual process can extract the maximum work from such a system, and no imagined process can extract *more* than the amount of work, $-\Delta F$.

Whenever a change takes place *irreversibly* in a system at constant pressure, without doing any useful work, $\Delta W' = 0$, and $-\Delta F > 0$, or $\Delta F < 0$. This must be true of *any* process which occurs spontaneously, subject to no force except a constant external pressure. Thus the free energy change in a reaction measures the driving force of the reaction, or its tendency to proceed. The possibilities are:

$\Delta F < 0$ Reaction will proceed as written: natural process.
$\Delta F = 0$ Reaction will not proceed: equilibrium.
$\Delta F > 0$ Reaction will proceed not as written but in the reverse direction: unnatural process.

The Measurement of Free Energy Changes. A study of reversible galvanic cells furnishes the most direct way to measure free energy changes in many chemical reactions. In this case, the maximum net work is the electrical work which can be produced by the cell. A measurement of the e.m.f. of the cell operating reversibly at a constant temperature gives at once the *intensity factor* of the free energy change. The *capacity factor* is the quantity of electricity which flows when the cell operates according to the chemical equation describing the reaction. Thus the decrease in free energy is given by the formula which we introduced before, on page 416:

$$-\Delta F = nFE$$

Another important method of determining free energy changes is based upon a study of chemical equilibria, as outlined in a succeeding section. A third method, based upon thermal data alone, is based upon the third law of thermodynamics and is taken up after a discussion of that subject.

The Change of Free Energy with Pressure and Temperature. For any reversible process in a system under a pressure equal to that of its surroundings, the change in internal energy is equal, as before, to the heat absorbed, minus the work done. In differential form:

$$dE = dQ - dW$$

Under these reversible conditions, the last two terms are equal to TdS and PdV respectively, so that:

$$dE + PdV = TdS$$

Taking the equation defining the heat content:

$$H = E + PV$$

and differentiating this gives:

$$dH = dE + PdV + VdP = TdS + VdP$$

For any *isothermal* process this equation can be rewritten in the form:

$$V = \left(\frac{\partial H}{\partial P}\right)_T - T\left(\frac{\partial S}{\partial P}\right)_T$$

Starting with the equation defining the free energy:

$$F = H - TS$$

and differentiating it with respect to P at constant temperature gives:

$$\left(\frac{\partial F}{\partial P}\right)_T = \left(\frac{\partial H}{\partial P}\right)_T - T\left(\frac{\partial S}{\partial P}\right)_T = V$$

Thus for any isothermal process the change in free energy between two different pressures is given by the equation:

$$\int dF = \int V dP$$

The change in free energy with temperature is derived even more simply. Differentiating the equation defining the free energy, with respect to temperature at constant pressure gives:

$$\left(\frac{\partial F}{\partial T}\right)_P = \left(\frac{\partial H}{\partial T}\right)_P - T\left(\frac{\partial S}{\partial T}\right)_P - S$$

Since the partial derivative of the heat content with respect to the temperature at constant pressure is equal to the heat capacity at constant pressure, and the change of entropy with temperature at constant pressure is equal to the heat capacity at constant pressure, divided by the temperature, the first two terms on the right side of the equation cancel, leaving:

$$\left(\frac{\partial F}{\partial T}\right)_P = - S = \frac{F - H}{T}$$

Having defined the free energy and determined its change with pressure and with temperature, we shall show in the next few sections how the free energy function can be applied to the derivation of a number of important thermodynamic equations.

The Change of Equilibrium Pressure with Temperature. In any system consisting of the same substance in two or more phases in equilibrium, the free energy of the substance is the same in all of the phases. This is true, for example, of ice and water at the freezing point. As long as equilibrium is maintained, the free energy of the liquid and solid are the same. As soon as conditions are altered so that the free energy of the two phases becomes different, the phase with the greater free energy will disappear to form the more stable phase. In general, if we represent the equilibrium by the equation:

$$\mathrm{A} \rightleftharpoons \mathrm{B}$$

then

$$F_{\mathrm{A}} = F_{\mathrm{B}} \qquad \text{and} \qquad dF_{\mathrm{A}} = dF_{\mathrm{B}}$$

If the temperature of the system changes, the pressure must change in such a way as to keep the free energy the same in the two different phases if they are to remain at equilibrium. Since the free energy in each phase is a function of temperature and pressure alone, the total differentials are:

$$dF_A = \left(\frac{\partial F_A}{\partial T}\right)_P dT + \left(\frac{\partial F_A}{\partial P}\right)_T dP$$

$$dF_B = \left(\frac{\partial F_B}{\partial T}\right)_P dT + \left(\frac{\partial F_B}{\partial P}\right)_T dP$$

Equating the total differentials of the free energy of the two phases:

$$\left(\frac{\partial F_B}{\partial P}\right)_T dP - \left(\frac{\partial F_A}{\partial P}\right)_T dP = \left(\frac{\partial F_A}{\partial T}\right)_P dT - \left(\frac{\partial F_B}{\partial T}\right)_P dT$$

Substituting the values of the partial derivatives which we determined on page 631, we find:

$$(V_B - V_A)dP = (S_B - S_A)dT$$

or

$$\frac{dP}{dT} = \frac{\Delta S}{\Delta V} = \frac{\Delta H}{T\Delta V}$$

This equation shows the change in pressure necessary to maintain equilibrium for any given change in the temperature of the two-phase system. Here ΔH is the latent heat when phase A changes to phase B.

The Change of Melting Point with Pressure. If the two phases are solid and liquid, ΔH is the latent heat of fusion, and the equation shows the effect of pressure upon the melting point. As an application of this equation we can calculate the change of the melting point of ice with pressure by means of the equation:

$$\frac{dT_m}{dP} = \frac{T_m \Delta V}{L_f} = \frac{T_m(V_l - V_s)}{L_f}$$

In the case of water the numerical values are:

$$\begin{aligned} \Delta V &= V_l - V_s = 18.018 - 19.651 = -1.633 \text{ ml./mole} \\ L_f &= 1437 \text{ cal./mole} \\ &= 1437 \times 4.1833 = 6011 \text{ joules/mole} \\ &= 6011 \times \frac{1000}{101.33} = 59{,}330 \text{ ml. atm./mole} \end{aligned}$$

Hence

$$\frac{dT_m}{dP} = \frac{273.16 \times (-1.633)}{59{,}330} = -0.007519 \text{ degree/atmosphere}$$

In this case and in a few others, the solid is less dense than the liquid, so that pressure lowers the melting point exactly as we would predict from Le Chatelier's principle. The melting point of ice, at 1 atmosphere pressure, defines 0° C. The *triple point*, at which ice, water, and vapor are in equilibrium under the vapor pressure of the system, is *higher*. Since the pressure at the triple point is 4.6 mm. or 0.0061 atm., the temperature of the triple point is + 0.00747° C. Since most substances expand on melting, the usual effect of pressure is to increase the melting point. In any case, the magnitude of the change can be calculated from the equation above.

The Clapeyron Equation. Returning to the general equation for the change of equilibrium pressure with temperature in a two-phase system:

$$\frac{dP}{dT} = \frac{\Delta S}{\Delta V} = \frac{\Delta H}{T\Delta V}$$

if the phases are liquid and vapor, ΔH is the heat of vaporization L_v, P becomes the vapor pressure of the liquid, which we shall designate by p, and $\Delta V = V_g - V_l$. Thus we obtain the **Clapeyron equation:**

$$\frac{dp}{dT} = \frac{\Delta H}{(V_g - V_l)T}$$

This equation was derived by Clapeyron in 1834 — the first application of the principle of the second law of thermodynamics to a physicochemical system.

The Clausius-Clapeyron Equation. Clausius later showed how the Clapeyron equation is modified when the vapor may be considered a perfect gas. Then we can put $V = \frac{RT}{p}$. For a system at ordinary temperatures and at pressures not much greater than atmospheric, the molal volume of the liquid may be neglected in comparison with that of the vapor, and we obtain the **Clausius-Clapeyron equation:**

$$\frac{dp}{dT} = \frac{pL_v}{RT^2} \quad \text{or} \quad \frac{d \ln p}{dT} = \frac{L_v}{RT^2}$$

If the latent heat of vaporization is independent of temperature, this equation may be integrated to give:

$$\log \frac{p_2}{p_1} = -\ 0.4343\, \frac{L_v}{R} \left[\frac{1}{T_2} - \frac{1}{T_1}\right]$$

For numerical calculations L_v and R obviously must be expressed in corresponding units.

In most cases L_v is sufficiently constant, at least over short temperature intervals, so that this integrated form of the equation holds fairly satisfactorily. As shown in Figure 52 on page 151, the logarithm of the vapor pressure is nearly a linear function of the reciprocal of the temperature. Even if the relationship is less simple, it is easy to show that in any case the heat of vaporization can be calculated by plotting the logarithm of the vapor pressure against the reciprocal of the temperature, determining the slope s at any point, and multiplying it by $-\ 2.303\ R$.

$$L_v = -\ 2.303\ Rs$$

Since the equation applies to a system under its own vapor pressure, the heat of vaporization which it yields is the heat absorbed when a mole of the liquid evaporates *under its own vapor pressure.* A slight correction must be applied before comparing this value with the heat absorbed when the liquid vaporizes *under*

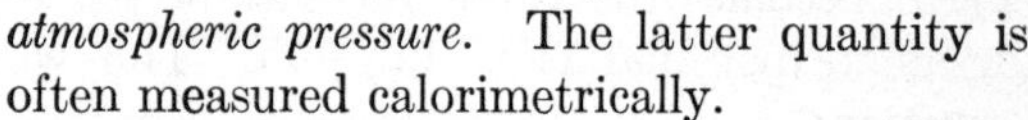

atmospheric pressure. The latter quantity is often measured calorimetrically.

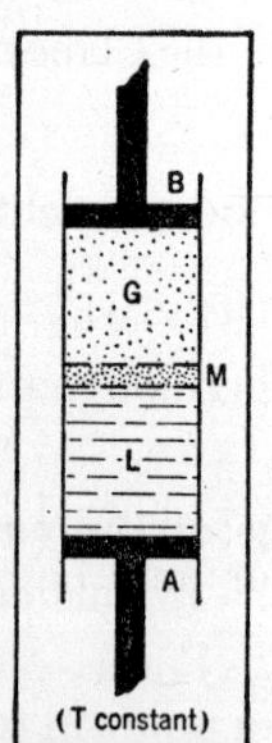

Fig. 257. Isothermal Equilibrium between Vapor and Liquid under Different Pressures.

The same principles apply to the equilibrium between a solid and its vapor. The vapor pressure curve of a solid (the **sublimation curve**) is determined by the magnitude of the latent heat of sublimation L_s instead of the latent heat of vaporization of the liquid.

The Change of Vapor Pressure with Total Pressure. The Clausius-Clapeyron equation shows how the vapor pressure of a liquid changes with changing temperature. We shall now show how the vapor pressure changes with changing total pressure upon the liquid, at constant temperature. An apparatus in which such a system could be studied is shown in Figure 257. The liquid L is separated from the vapor G by the membrane M, which is permeable only to the vapor. If the liquid were mercury, the membrane might be a disk of sintered glass or porcelain, the pores of which would allow passage of the vapor, while they were too small to allow the passage of the liquid, with its high surface tension. In such a system the piston A can be used to apply pressure to the liquid, while the piston B exerts a different pressure upon the vapor. Our problem is to calculate the relationship between these two pressures at equilibrium. Since the change in the free energy is the same in both phases at equilibrium, and the system is isothermal:

$$dF_l = V_l dP_l = dF_g = V_g dP_g \qquad (T \text{ constant})$$

or

$$\left(\frac{\partial P_g}{\partial P_l}\right)_T = \frac{V_l}{V_g}$$

Since the gas is in equilibrium with the liquid, its pressure P_g is equal to the vapor pressure p of the liquid. Similarly P_l is the total pressure upon the liquid, which we can designate by P. Hence we can write:

$$\left(\frac{\partial p}{\partial P}\right)_T = \frac{V_l}{V_g}$$

If the vapor may be considered a perfect gas, we may set $V_g = RT/p$ and the equation above becomes:

$$\left(\frac{\partial \ln p}{\partial P}\right)_T = \frac{V_l}{RT}$$

When the volume of the liquid may be considered independent of pressure, this equation can be integrated to give:

$$\ln \frac{p_2}{p_1} = \frac{V_l}{RT}(P_2 - P_1)$$

Similar equations hold for the isothermal change of the vapor pressure of a solid with the total pressure upon it. In this case, of course, the molal volume is that of the solid.

The Law of Atmospheres. In a column of gas at a uniform temperature T, in a uniform gravitational field, the molal free energy will be a function of the pressure of the gas and the height in the gravitational field. If we raise 1 mole of the gas an infinitesimal distance dh, the total change in free energy is given by the equation:

$$dF = \left(\frac{\partial F}{\partial P}\right)_h dP + \left(\frac{\partial F}{\partial h}\right)_P dh \qquad (T \text{ constant})$$

If the column of gas is in equilibrium, the molal free energy must be the same at every point, hence $dF = 0$, and the change in free energy due to the change in pressure is exactly balanced by the change due to the difference in height. As we have seen before, $\left(\frac{\partial F}{\partial P}\right)_h = V$ for any isothermal change. When a weight is lifted in a uniform gravitational field, the increase in free energy is equal to the increase in potential energy, since all of this is available for doing work:

$$dF = Mgdh$$

where M is the molecular weight, and g the force of gravity per gram. Hence $\left(\frac{\partial F}{\partial h}\right)_P = Mg$, and the equation connecting pressure and height is:

$$VdP + Mgdh = 0 \qquad \text{or} \qquad \left(\frac{\partial P}{\partial h}\right)_T = -\frac{Mg}{V}$$

For an ideal gas, we may substitute $\frac{P}{RT}$ for $\frac{1}{V}$, so that:

$$\left(\frac{\partial P}{\partial h}\right)_T = -\frac{MgP}{RT} \qquad \text{or} \qquad \left(\frac{\partial \ln P}{\partial h}\right)_T = -\frac{Mg}{RT} \quad (T \text{ constant})$$

Integrating this equation between corresponding limits of height and pressure gives the **equation for the law of atmospheres:**

$$\log \frac{P_1}{P_2} = 0.4343 \frac{Mg}{RT} (h_2 - h_1)$$

The Colligative Properties of Dilute Solutions. In 1887 van't Hoff first derived the thermodynamic relationships between the concentration of a dilute solution, the depression of the vapor pressure and of the freezing point, the elevation of the boiling point, and the osmotic pressure. A translation of his memoir [1] subsequently has appeared in the *Alembic Club Reprints.* Van't Hoff's equations will be derived in this section.

(1) As a starting point in the treatment of the properties of dilute solutions we shall take ***Raoult's law,*** *that the relative lowering of the vapor pressure of a dilute solution, at constant temperature, is equal to the mole fraction of the solute:*

$$\frac{\Delta p}{p^0} = x_2 \ (T \text{ constant})$$

[1] "The Role of Osmotic Pressure in the Analogy between Solutions and Gases" in *Alembic Club Reprint* No. 19, Gurney and Jackson, London, 1929.

Since the depression of the vapor pressure is the pressure of the pure solvent p^0 minus that of the solution p, this equation may be written in the form:

$$\frac{p}{p^0} = 1 - x_2$$

Differentiating this equation with respect to mole fraction of solute, x_2, at constant temperature gives a relationship which is very useful, namely:

$$\left(\frac{\partial p}{\partial x_2}\right)_T = -p^0$$

Also, from the preceding equation, since the sum of the two mole fractions in a binary mixture is unity, we find:

$$p = p^0 x_1$$

which states that the vapor pressure of the solvent from a solution is equal to the product of the mole fraction of the solvent in the solution, and the vapor pressure of the pure solvent. This is an alternative method of stating Raoult's law.

(2) The change in the **freezing point** with concentration may be derived from Raoult's law and the Clausius-Clapeyron equation. Referring to Figure 258, which illustrates the vapor pressure curves of pure solid and liquid solvent, and solution in the immediate neighborhood of the freezing point, we see that the vapor pressure of the solid depends upon the temperature alone, while that of the solution depends upon the temperature and also upon the concentration of the solution. *The* ***freezing point*** *of the solution is the temperature at which the vapor pressure of the solvent is equal to the vapor pressure of the pure solid.* Taking a very dilute solution, its change in vapor pressure below the freezing point of the pure solvent will be given by the usual expression for a total differential:

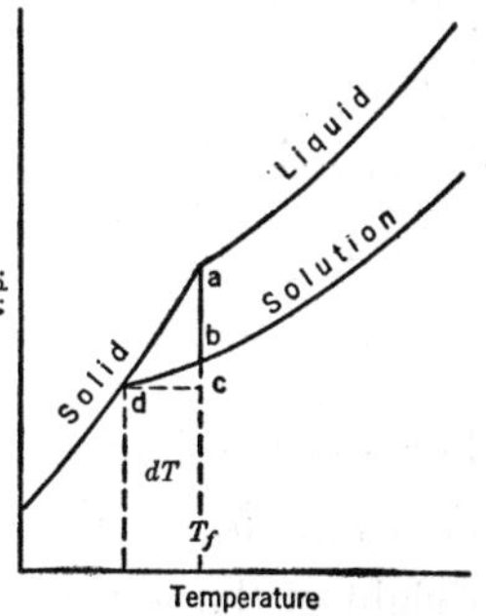

Fig. 258. The Depression of the Freezing Point.

$$dp_{\text{soln.}} = \left(\frac{\partial p}{\partial x_2}\right)_T dx_2 + \left(\frac{\partial p}{\partial T}\right)_{x_2} dT$$

The two terms on the right-hand side of the equation correspond to the lines *ab* and *bc* respectively in Figure 258. The first partial derivative, evaluated in the preceding paragraph, is $-p^0$, while the second is given by the Clausius-Clapeyron equation. The total change in the vapor pressure of the solution therefore is:

$$dp_{\text{soln.}} = -p^0 dx_2 + \frac{p^0 L_v}{RT^2} dT$$

The corresponding change in the vapor pressure of the solid, *ac* in Figure 258, is given by the Clausius-Clapeyron equation:

$$dp_s = \frac{p^0 L_s}{RT^2} dT$$

Since the two depressions of the vapor pressure are equal at the freezing point of the solution, the two preceding equations may be set equal to each other. Canceling the common term p^0 and rearranging the others, we find:

$$\frac{(L_s - L_v)dT}{RT^2} = -dx_2$$

The difference between the molal heats of sublimation and of vaporization is the molal heat of fusion, L_f, so that the preceding equation becomes:

$$\frac{dT}{dx_2} = -\frac{RT^2}{L_f}$$

In terms of the molality, the mole fraction is given by the equation:

$$x_2 = \frac{m}{\dfrac{1000}{M_1} + m}$$

For a very dilute solution, the m in the denominator is negligible in comparison with the term $\dfrac{1000}{M_1}$, where M_1 is the molecular weight of the solvent, hence:

$$x_2 \approx \frac{mM_1}{1000} \qquad \text{and} \qquad \frac{dx_2}{dm} = \frac{M_1}{1000}$$

Multiplying this equation by the one which shows the change of temperature with the mole fraction of the solute, the differential dx_2 cancels out and we find:

$$-\frac{dT}{dm} = \frac{M_1 RT^2}{1000\ L_f} = \frac{RT^2}{1000\ l_f} = K_f$$

This equation gives the thermodynamic method for evaluating the **molecular depression constant,** or **molecular freezing point constant** for any solvent. It is the rate of change of the freezing point, per unit change in the molality of a very dilute solution. If the solution is ideal, the linear relationship between freezing point and molality will extend to more concentrated solutions, and this is true of many real solutions of nonelectrolytes. Often, however, even these solutions show deviations at fairly low concentrations, but all nonelectrolytic solutions obey this limiting law at great enough dilution.

As an example of the use of this equation, we may calculate the molecular depression constant for water, using the values of the different terms which we have tabulated elsewhere in this text. The value is:

$$K_f = \frac{18.016 \times 1.9873 \times (273.16)^2}{1000 \times 1437} = 1.859$$

This value is corroborated by careful studies of the freezing points of dilute solutions of nonelectrolytes.

(3) The **elevation of the boiling point** by a nonvolatile solute may be calculated even more simply than the depression of the freezing point. As Figure 259 shows, at the boiling point of the solvent, its vapor pressure from the solution is less than that from the pure solvent, and the temperature must be raised in order to compensate for the presence of the solute and bring the vapor pressure back to that of the atmosphere. This may be stated in terms of the calculus by setting equal to zero the total differential of the vapor pressure of the solution, which is a function of mole fraction and temperature:

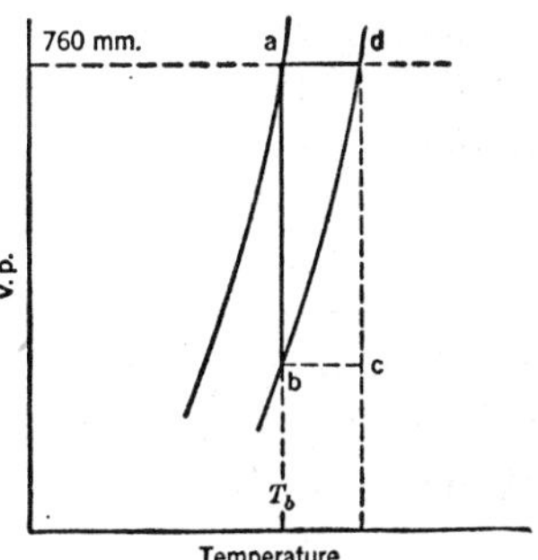

Fig. 259. The Elevation of the Boiling Point.

$$dp_{\text{soln.}} = \left(\frac{\partial p}{\partial x_2}\right)_T dx_2 + \left(\frac{\partial p}{\partial T}\right)_{x_2} dT = 0$$

In Figure 259 the first term of the equation represents the line *ab*, and the second the line *cd*. Substituting the values of the coefficients as before, and rearranging terms we find:

$$\frac{dT}{dx_2} = \frac{RT^2}{L_v}$$

Changing to terms of the molality as in the case of the depression of the freezing point gives:

$$\frac{dT}{dm} = \frac{M_1RT^2}{1000\,L_v} = \frac{RT^2}{1000\,l_v} = K_b$$

This equation may be used to calculate the boiling-point constant when the latent heat of vaporization at the boiling point is known.

(4) The **osmotic pressure** of a dilute solution also may be calculated. When a solution and pure solvent are separated by a semipermeable membrane, the pure solvent passes through the membrane into the solution and builds up an osmotic pressure, because the vapor pressure of the pure solvent is greater than that of the solution. However, as the pressure upon the solution is increased, its vapor pressure also is increased until it is equal to that of the pure solvent and equilibrium is reached. *The excess pressure, in addition to that upon the solvent, required to bring about this equilibrium is equal to* π, *the osmotic pressure of the solution.* Under isothermal conditions, the vapor pressure is a function of the mole fraction and the pressure, and the condition of equilibrium is that the total differential of the vapor pressure is zero:

$$dp_{\text{soln.}} = \left(\frac{\partial p}{\partial x_2}\right)_{T,\,P} dx_2 + \left(\frac{\partial p}{\partial P}\right)_{T,\,x_2} dP = 0$$

The first partial derivative is now familiar. The second can be evaluated from the relationship derived on page 635. For a pure substance the vapor of which obeys the ideal gas law, the change of vapor pressure with total pressure is given by the equation:

$$\left(\frac{\partial p}{\partial P}\right)_T = \frac{V_l p}{RT}$$

In an infinitely dilute solution, $p = p^0$ and, assuming that the molal volume, V_l, of the solvent in the solution is the same as that in the pure solvent, V_1, we can write:

$$\left(\frac{\partial p}{\partial P}\right)_{T,\,x_2} = \frac{V_1 p^0}{RT}$$

Substituting the values of the derivatives in the original equation and simplifying, we find:

$$dP = \frac{RT}{V_1}\,dx_2 \qquad (T \text{ constant})$$

Integrating this isothermal equation between mole fractions of 0 and x_2, and between corresponding pressures of P^0 and P, upon the pure solvent and the solution respectively, we find:

$$P - P^0 = \frac{RT}{V_1} x_2 = \frac{RTn_2}{V_1(n_1 + n_2)}$$

This is the equation for the osmotic pressure. Since n_2 may be neglected in comparison with n_1 in a very dilute solution, this may be written:

$$\pi = \frac{n_2 RT}{n_1 V_1}$$

Since $n_1 V_1$ is V the volume of solvent for n_2 moles of solute, the fraction $\frac{n_2}{n_1 V_1}$ is equal to c the concentration of the solute. If V_1 is expressed in liters, the equation for the osmotic pressure reduces to that of van't Hoff for 1 mole of solute:

$$\pi = cRT \qquad \text{or} \qquad \pi V = RT$$

The Gibbs-Helmholtz Equation. This important equation, relating the temperature coefficient of the e.m.f. of a reversible cell with the change in heat content in the reaction, has been introduced and used already on page 432. It is derived from the free energy function. For a reaction in a reversible cell, the decrease in free energy is given by the equation:

$$-\Delta F = nFE$$

Differentiating this equation with respect to temperature at constant pressure, and substituting the value of the temperature coefficient of the free energy which we derived on page 631, we obtain **the Gibbs-Helmholtz equation:**

$$nF\left(\frac{\partial E}{\partial T}\right)_P = \Delta S = \frac{nFE + \Delta H}{T}$$

This equation often is written in the form:

$$E = -\frac{\Delta H}{nF} + T\left(\frac{\partial E}{\partial T}\right)_P$$

A consideration of this equation applied to a particular reaction (*e.g.*, that in the Daniell cell) will illustrate the principles given above. If the cell is made up with the zinc and cupric ions at unit activity, it could be represented thus:

$$(-)\ \ Zn\ \ |\ \ Zn^{++}(a = 1)\ \ \|\ \ Cu^{++}(a = 1)\ \ |\ \ Cu\ \ (+)$$

The cell reaction is:

$$Zn + Cu^{++}(a = 1) \longrightarrow Cu + Zn^{++}(a = 1)$$

The free energy decrease in this reaction, ***nFE***, therefore represents the decrease in free energy when 1 mole of zinc ions goes into a solution in which the activity of zinc ion is 1, and when cupric ion is deposited from a solution of unit activity. Both of these solutions would have to be present in such large quantities that they did not change appreciably in concentration during this process.

Similarly, the decrease in heat content corresponds to the same process described above, where the ions are formed or used up in solutions of the concentrations indicated. It is not the same as the change in heat content measured calorimetrically when a bar of zinc is immersed in a solution of copper sulfate at unit activity, since the reaction in the latter case involves a zinc ion activity which *increases* from 0 to 1 as the cupric ion activity *decreases* from 1 nearly to 0.

The entropy change in the cell process can be determined from a measurement of the e.m.f. at different temperatures. It corresponds to $\frac{Q}{T}$, where Q is the amount of heat which the cell absorbs from the surroundings when it operates reversibly at the absolute temperature T. In theory, it can be measured by allowing the reaction to proceed infinitely slowly and measuring the absorption of heat per mole of cupric ion displaced.

The Free Energy of Expansion: Fugacity. We have derived the general equation for the change of the free energy with pressure in any *isothermal* process:

$$dF = VdP \qquad (T \text{ constant})$$

For n moles of the ideal gas, the equation of state is:

$$PV = nRT$$

Solving this equation for V and substituting in the preceding one gives:

$$dF = nRTd\ln P$$

which can be integrated to give the isothermal free energy of expansion of the ideal gas:

$$F - F' = nRT\ln\frac{P}{P'}$$

This equation does not apply exactly to *real* gases, which do not obey the ideal gas law. In order to study the properties of real gases, G. N. Lewis has defined an idealized pressure, the **fugacity, *f*,** by means of the isothermal equations:

$$dF = nRTd\ln f \qquad \text{or} \qquad F - F' = nRT\ln\frac{f}{f'}$$

and the further condition that the fugacity becomes equal to the pressure for all substances at very low pressure, where they behave ideally. The fugacity of real gases at higher pressures can be determined from the equation of state of the gas, or by graphical methods.[1] A discussion of these details is beyond the scope of this book.

Since the free energy of a liquid or a solid is the same as that of the vapor in equilibrium with it, the fugacity of the two phases also must be the same. The vapor pressure of a solid or liquid often is taken as a qualitative measure of its escaping tendency. The fugacity, which is the idealized or corrected vapor pressure, is a quantitative measure of the escaping tendency of the liquid or solid.

The Activity. In many cases a more convenient property than the fugacity of a substance is the *relative fugacity* or **activity,** also introduced by Lewis and used with great skill in his studies of the properties of solutions. The activity is taken as unity in the **standard state** of the substance, which may be chosen arbitrarily as a matter of convenience. If the fugacity and free energy in the standard state are designated by f^0 and F^0 respectively, the activity is defined by the equation:

$$F - F^0 = RT\ln\frac{f}{f^0} = RT\ln a$$

*The **standard state** for gases usually is taken as a state of **unit fugacity.*** For the ideal gas, this would correspond to unit pressure, or a pressure of 1 atmosphere. For other gases, it would correspond to a corrected pressure or fugacity of 1 atmosphere.

The standard state for a solid, liquid, or solvent is taken as the pure substance under atmospheric pressure at each temperature.

[1] *Cf.* Lewis and Randall, *Thermodynamics*, Chapter XVII, "The Fugacity."

The standard state for a solute in aqueous solution is taken as a state of unit activity. *The* ***activity*** *is defined as equal to the molality in the infinitely dilute solution:*

$$a_2 = m \ (m \doteq 0)$$

The ***activity coefficient*** γ *is defined as the ratio of the activity to the concentration:*

$$\gamma = \frac{a}{m}$$

Free Energy and Equilibrium. The relationships between free energy and equilibrium are derived most conveniently in terms of activities. To take a concrete example, consider the formation of ammonia in the gas phase, according to the reaction:

$$N_2 + 3\,H_2 \rightleftharpoons 2\,NH_3$$

Following the method of van't Hoff, we can assume that the nitrogen and hydrogen are contained in large vessels, from which they can be transferred reversibly to an **equilibrium box,** as shown in Figure 260. Here they reach equilibrium with the resulting ammonia, which is transferred reversibly to its containing vessel. If the whole system is kept at a constant temperature, the free energy changes accompanying the transference of the gases will be given by equations involving the ratio of the pressures in the reservoirs and in the equilibrium box. *In defining the* ***standard free energy change*** *of the process, we will take the activities of the factors and product each as unity.* Under these circumstances, the three free energy changes will be:

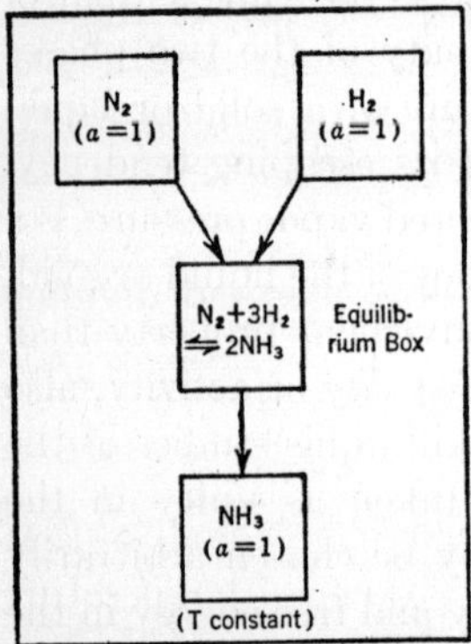

Fig. 260. The van't Hoff Equilibrium Box.

$$\Delta F_1 = RT \ln \frac{a_{N_2}}{1} = RT \ln a_{N_2}$$

$$\Delta F_2 = 3\,RT \ln \frac{a_{H_2}}{1} = RT \ln a^3_{H_2}$$

$$\Delta F_3 = 2\,RT \ln \frac{1}{a_{NH_3}} = -\,RT \ln a^2_{NH_3}$$

$$\Delta F^0 = \Delta F_1 + \Delta F_2 + \Delta F_3 = RT \ln \frac{a_{N_2} \times a^3_{H_2}}{a^2_{NH_3}}$$

The symbol ΔF^0 is used to indicate the standard free energy change of the process. The equilibrium constant is defined by the equation:

$$K = \frac{a^2_{NH_3}}{a_{N_2} \times a^3_{H_2}}$$

This is simply the reciprocal of the logarithmic term in the equation above, hence we find:

$$\Delta F^0 = - RT \ln K$$

The van't Hoff equation relating the change in equilibrium constant with the standard heat content change of the reaction now can be derived. The differentiation of the preceding equation with respect to temperature, at constant pressure, gives:

$$\left(\frac{\partial \Delta F^0}{\partial T}\right)_P = - R \ln K - RT\left(\frac{\partial \ln K}{\partial T}\right)_P$$

The equation which we derived for the temperature coefficient of the free energy may be applied equally well to that of the free energy change in a reaction:

$$\left(\frac{\partial \Delta F^0}{\partial T}\right)_P = \frac{\Delta F^0 - \Delta H^0}{T} = - R \ln K - \frac{\Delta H^0}{T}$$

Subtracting this equation from the preceding one and dividing through by RT gives:

$$\left(\frac{\partial \ln K}{\partial T}\right)_P = \frac{\Delta H^0}{RT^2}$$

If the heat capacities of factors and products are equal, so that ΔH^0 is independent of temperature, or if the range of temperature is so short that this change may be neglected, the van't Hoff equation may be integrated to yield:

$$2.303 \log \frac{K_2}{K_1} = \frac{\Delta H^0}{R}\left[\frac{T_2 - T_1}{T_1 T_2}\right]$$

where the subscripts indicate equilibrium constants at corresponding values of the absolute temperature. This equation may be used to calculate the standard heat content change in the reaction, from measurements of the equilibrium constant at two or more temperatures. It also may be used to calculate the equilibrium constant at any temperature, from a knowledge of the standard heat content change and the equilibrium constant determined at some one temperature. It does *not* enable us to calculate equilibrium constants from thermal data alone.

For reactions between ideal gases, pressures and activities are equal, and we can use K_p, the equilibrium constant expressed in terms of the partial pressures instead of the activities. Van't Hoff originally derived the equations in terms of partial pressures, but they hold rigorously only for perfect gases. When we are dealing with such imperfect gases as ammonia under considerable pressure, the deviations of the value of K_p may become large. This does not invalidate the thermodynamic equations but merely shows that the simplifying assumption of perfect gaseous behavior is not justified.

For the general reaction,

$$a\mathrm{A} + b\mathrm{B} + \cdots \rightleftharpoons c\mathrm{C} + d\mathrm{D} + \cdots$$

involving ideal gases, van't Hoff showed that:

$$-\Delta F^0 = RT \ln K_p \qquad \text{where} \qquad K_p = \frac{p^c_{\mathrm{C}} \times p^d_{\mathrm{D}} \times \cdots}{p^a_{\mathrm{A}} \times p^b_{\mathrm{B}} \times \cdots}$$

Integration of the Free Energy Equation. The general equation for the temperature coefficient of the free energy change is:

$$\left(\frac{\partial \Delta F}{\partial T}\right)_P = -\Delta S = \frac{\Delta F - \Delta H}{T}$$

This may be put into a form more suitable for our purposes by calculating the temperature coefficient of the function $\frac{\Delta F}{T}$, given by the equation:

$$\left(\frac{\partial(\Delta F/T)}{\partial T}\right)_P = \frac{1}{T}\left(\frac{\partial \Delta F}{\partial T}\right)_P - \frac{\Delta F}{T^2} = \frac{\Delta F}{T^2} - \frac{\Delta H}{T^2} - \frac{\Delta F}{T^2}$$

or

$$\left(\frac{\partial(\Delta F/T)}{\partial T}\right)_P = -\frac{\Delta H}{T^2}$$

If we know the change in heat capacity during the reaction, *e.g.*, as a power series in the temperature, we can apply the Person-Kirchhoff equation (page 623) to obtain the heat content change as a function of temperature:

$$\Delta C_p = \left(\frac{\partial \Delta H}{\partial T}\right)_P = \Delta\Gamma_0 + \Delta\Gamma_1 T + \Delta\Gamma_2 T^2 + \cdots$$

On integration, this equation becomes:

$$\Delta H = \Delta H_0 + \Delta\Gamma_0 T + \tfrac{1}{2}\,\Delta\Gamma_1 T^2 + \tfrac{1}{3}\,\Delta\Gamma_2 T^3 + \cdots$$

where ΔH_0 is a constant of integration, which can be evaluated by determining the change in heat content in the reaction, at any one temperature. Substituting this value of ΔH into the equation for the change of $\frac{\Delta F}{T}$ with temperature and integrating, we find:

$$\frac{\Delta F}{T} = \frac{\Delta H_0}{T} - \Delta\Gamma_0 \ln T - \tfrac{1}{2}\Delta\Gamma_1 T - \tfrac{1}{6}\Delta\Gamma_2 T^2 - \cdots + I$$

or

$$\Delta F = \Delta H_0 - \Delta\Gamma_0 T \ln T - \tfrac{1}{2}\Delta\Gamma_1 T^2 - \tfrac{1}{6}\Delta\Gamma_2 T^3 - \cdots + IT$$

In this case, the integration constant I can be evaluated by determining the value of the free energy change at any one temperature, *e.g.*, from a study of the equilibrium constant at that temperature. Then the free energy change can be calculated at any other temperature.

The Third Law of Thermodynamics. Le Chatelier integrated the free energy equation in 1888, and pointed out that, if there were some way to determine the integration constant I, free energy changes could be calculated from thermal data alone. "It would permit us to determine *a priori*, independently of any new experimental data, the full conditions corresponding to a given chemical reaction."

In 1899 G. N. Lewis investigated the free energy equation and found that in some cases the value of I was nearly zero, as far as the available data showed. In 1902 T. W. Richards carried out a study of galvanic cells over a wide range of temperature. He found that in every case the values of ΔF and ΔH for the reactions rapidly approach each other at low temperatures, as indicated in a schematic way in Figure 261. His work indicated that the values of $(\partial\Delta F/\partial T)_P$ and $(\partial\Delta H/\partial T)_P$ are opposite in sign and both approached zero at the absolute zero. Since these coefficients are equal respectively to $-\Delta S$ and ΔC_p, both of these quantities also must approach zero at the absolute zero. This work, and later work of van't Hoff

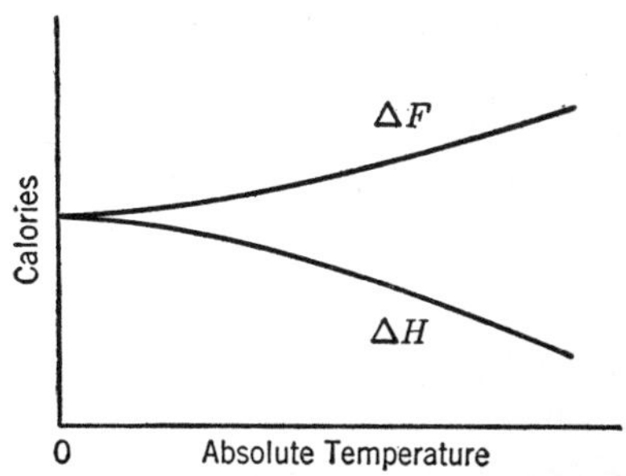

Fig. 261. Change of ΔF and ΔH with Temperature.

and of Haber, was brought together by W. Nernst, in 1906, into the **Nernst heat theorem,** which as modified by later work is now known as the third law of thermodynamics. *The* ***third law of thermodynamics*** *states that the heat capacity and entropy of every crystalline solid become zero at the absolute zero of temperature.*

On the basis of the third law of thermodynamics, supplementing the results of the other two, it is possible to calculate free energy changes and equilibrium constants from thermal data alone. The general method is to study, down to the lowest possible temperature, the heat capacities of elements and compounds which are crystalline solids. Debye's theory of the heat capacities of crystalline solids, discussed on page 163, predicts that, near the absolute zero of temperature, the heat capacity increases from zero in proportion to the *cube* of the absolute temperature. Below the lowest experimental temperature, heat capacity data are extrapolated to 0 by means of this T^3 law. A plot of C_p against log T, or of C_p/T against T is then made, to allow a graphical evaluation of the entropy at any temperature, from the relationship:

$$\int dS = \int C_p \frac{dT}{T} = \int C_p d \ln T$$

An illustration of such a graphical evaluation of entropy is given in Figure 262. The data of Kelley[1] for the heat capacity of toluene from 14 to 298° A. are used to calculate C_p/T at each experimental temperature. These values are plotted against the absolute temperature, and extrapolated to zero by means of the Debye equation. The total area under the curve from 0 to 177.95° gives 26.02 E.U. for the entropy of the solid at the melting point. Only 0.52 of this value depends upon the extrapolation. The value of the heat of fusion was found to be 1582 cal./mole;

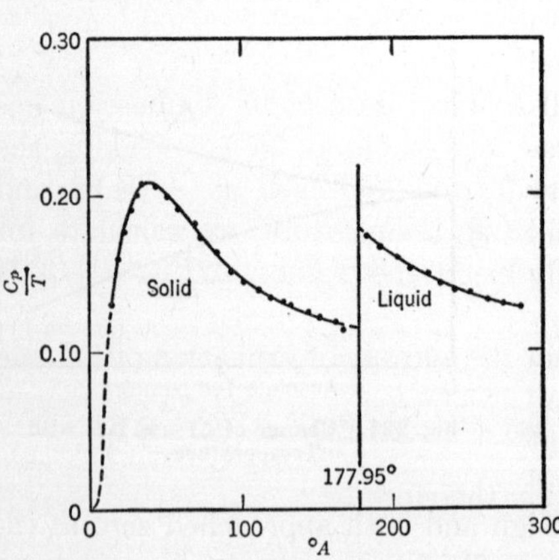

Fig. 262. Plot of $\frac{C_p}{T}$ vs. T for Toluene.

[1] Kenneth K. Kelley, *J. Am. Chem. Soc.*, **51**, 2738 (1929).

hence the entropy of fusion is $\frac{1582}{177.95} = 8.89$ E.U. The area under the liquid curve from the melting point to 298.2° A. is 17.46 E.U., making the entropy of 1 mole of liquid toluene 52.4 E.U. at 298° A. The estimated uncertainty in this value is ± 0.3 E.U.

In Table 124 we have collected values for the standard entropies of a few representative elements and compounds. Those of the solids and liquids are determined by a study of heat capacities down to low temperatures, as we have illustrated above. The entropies of the gases are obtained most accurately from a spectroscopic determination of their energy states, an explanation of which is beyond the scope of this book.

TABLE 124

SOME ATOMIC AND MOLECULAR ENTROPIES AT 25° C.

ELEMENT	S^0_{298}	COMPOUND	S^0_{298}
C (graphite)	1.365 E.U.	CO (g)	47.321
H_2 (g)	31.230	CO_2 (g)	51.091
N_2 (g)	45.78	CH_4 (g)	43.95
O_2 (g)	49.026	C_2H_6 (g)	53.51
S (rhombic)	7.6	C_6H_6 (l)	41.9
Cl_2 (g)	53.24	$C_6H_5 \cdot CH_3$ (l)	52.4
Br_2 (l)	32.6	CH_3OH (l)	30.3
I_2 (s)	26.6	C_2H_5OH (l)	38.4

Values chiefly from Parks and Huffman, *Free Energies of Some Organic Compounds*, supplemented by more recent values of Rossini, *B. Standards J. Research*, **22**, 407 (1939).

Returning to the study of toluene, its heat of combustion has been determined as − 935.10 kcal./mole at 25° C. Taking the heats of combustion of carbon and hydrogen as − 94.03 and − 68.313 kcal./mole at the same temperature, we calculate for the heat of formation of toluene the value: $\Delta H^0_{298} = + 3.64$ kcal./mole.

From Table 124 we find that the entropy of formation of toluene is:

$$\Delta S^0_{298} = 52.4 - (7 \times 1.365 + 4 \times 31.230) = - 82.1 \text{ E.U.}$$

The free energy of formation therefore is:

$$\Delta F^0 = \Delta H^0 - T\Delta S^0$$
$$= 3.64 + \frac{298.2 \times 82.1}{1000} = 28.12 \text{ kcal./mole}$$

It is interesting to notice the large difference between the free energy and heat of formation of toluene. The latter is small and positive, indicating that the substance probably is not stable, according to Berthelot's **law of maximum work (heat).** The free energy of formation is an even larger positive quantity, showing that toluene is unstable with respect to its elements at 25° C. The equilibrium constant for its formation from its elements is given by:

$$RT \ln K = -\ 28{,}120 \text{ cal.}$$

$$\log K = -\frac{28{,}120 \times 0.4343}{1.9873 \times 298.16} = -\ 20.61$$

$$\therefore\ K = 2.5 \times 10^{-21}\ (25°\text{ C.})$$

PROBLEMS AND EXERCISES

1. When 1 mole of zinc reacts with excess hydrochloric acid at 25° C., calculate the work done by the expansion of the dry gas against the constant atmospheric pressure. What is the difference, in calories per mole, between the change in energy content (ΔE) and in heat content (ΔH) in this reaction?

2. From the tabulated values of the changes in heat content (ΔH) in combustion (Table 37, page 209) calculate the heat changes per mole in the combustion of ethylene, sucrose, and glycine in the constant volume combustion bomb.

3. One mole of a gas obeying the van der Waals' equation of state expands reversibly from a volume V_1 to a larger volume V_2, at a constant temperature T. Calculate the maximum work done by the gas and the change in free energy of the gas.

4. Prove that the molal heat of vaporization of a liquid at any temperature can be calculated by plotting the logarithm of the vapor pressure against the reciprocal of the absolute temperature, determining the slope at the desired temperature and multiplying it by $-\ 2.303\ R$.

5. From the data of Table 14, page 80, make a suitable plot and determine the heat of vaporization of water at 0, 25, and 100° C.

6. Make use of the Clausius-Clapeyron equation to show that at the freezing point of any substance the slope of the sublimation curve is steeper than that of the vaporization curve.

7. From the data of Table 34, page 200, assuming a constant heat of vaporization, calculate the vapor pressure of oxygen at 80.0 and at 100.0° A.

8. From the data of Table 35, page 201, calculate the molecular depression constant K_f for oxygen, ammonia, mercury, carbon tetrachloride, and benzene. Wherever possible, compare these values with those given in Table 53, page 251.

9. From the data of Table 34, page 200, calculate the boiling point constants for ammonia, ethanol, benzene, aniline, and naphthalene. Whenever possible, compare these values with those given in Table 54, page 254.

10. From the data of Table 53, page 251, calculate the heat of fusion of acetamide and camphor.

11. From the data of Table 54, page 254, calculate the heat of vaporization of carbon tetrachloride and of diphenyl.

12. Taking the vapor pressure of carbon tetrachloride at 20° C. as 91 mm. of mercury, its surface tension as 26.8 dynes per cm., and its density as 1.595 g./ml., calculate the vapor pressure of a drop of carbon tetrachloride 0.0001 mm. in diameter.

13. Find the relationship between the relative vapor pressure, p/p^0, and the *weight* of a drop of liquid of known surface tension and density.

14. Parks, Huffman, and Barmore found the following values for the molal heat capacity of glycine, $CH_2(NH_2)COOH$, at different absolute temperatures.

T	C_p	T	C_p	T	C_p
93.2	9.68	173.1	15.62	260.3	21.01
104.6	10.67	192.1	16.83	278.9	22.32
112.8	11.34	207.3	17.80	282.8	22.45
131.7	12.68	225.7	18.92	290.9	23.25
150.5	14.03	243.6	20.03	299.5	24.03

Plot these values against log T, as in Figure 262, extrapolate to 90° A. and evaluate the change in entropy between this temperature and 298.2° A. Taking the entropy at 90° A. as 7.55 E.U., calculate that at 298.2° A. Combining this with the standard entropies of the elements given in Table 124, calculate the standard entropy of formation of glycine, ΔS^0_{298}.

Taking $\Delta H_{298} = -$ 232.57, $-$ 68.31, and $-$ 94.25 kcal./mole as the heats of combustion of glycine, hydrogen, and diamond, respectively, calculate the standard heat of formation of glycine, ΔH^0_{298}. Next calculate the free energy of formation of glycine, ΔF^0_{298}. Finally, write down the equilibrium constant for the reaction, evaluate it, and show what conclusions you can draw from these calculations as to the thermodynamic stability of glycine.

READING LIST

Gilbert N. Lewis and Merle Randall, *Thermodynamics and the Free Energy of Chemical Substances.* McGraw-Hill Book Company, New York, 1923. This excellent book is a classic in the field of chemical thermodynamics. The nomenclature and methods developed in it have been adopted widely not only in this country but also in Europe. The thermodynamic treatment requires hardly any revision at the present time, although the numerical illustrations are largely outdated by more recent experimental results. The treatment in this text is chiefly based upon this book.

F. H. MacDougall, *Thermodynamics and Chemistry*, 3d ed. John Wiley & Sons, New York, 1939. This book is much more up to date in its experimental data, and contains more adequate treatment of some of the more recent developments, such as the Debye-Hückel theory of interionic attraction, and the applications of statistical mechanics to the third law of thermodynamics.

George S. Parks and Hugh M. Huffman, *The Free Energies of Some Organic Compounds.* Reinhold Publishing Corporation, New York, 1932. After a brief review of fundamental thermodynamic relationships, this book deals in a systematic way with the free energies of hydrocarbons, alcohols, acids, and compounds containing nitrogen and sulfur. It contains useful tables of thermodynamic data and discusses their application to various problems.

APPENDIX

LOGARITHMS

ATOMIC WEIGHTS

SYMBOLS

LOGARITHMS

N	0	1	2	3	4	5	6	7	8	9	Proportional Parts								
											1	2	3	4	5	6	7	8	9
10	0000	0043	0086	0128	0170	0212	0253	0294	0334	0374	4	8	12	17	21	25	29	33	37
11	0414	0453	0492	0531	0569	0607	0645	0682	0719	0755	4	8	11	15	19	23	26	30	34
12	0792	0828	0864	0899	0934	0969	1004	1038	1072	1106	3	7	10	14	17	21	24	28	31
13	1139	1173	1206	1239	1271	1303	1335	1367	1399	1430	3	6	10	13	16	19	23	26	29
14	1461	1492	1523	1553	1584	1614	1644	1673	1703	1732	3	6	9	12	15	18	21	24	27
15	1761	1790	1818	1847	1875	1903	1931	1959	1987	2014	3	6	8	11	14	17	20	22	25
16	2041	2068	2095	2122	2148	2175	2201	2227	2253	2279	3	5	8	11	13	16	18	21	24
17	2304	2330	2355	2380	2405	2430	2455	2480	2504	2529	2	5	7	10	12	15	17	20	22
18	2553	2577	2601	2625	2648	2672	2695	2718	2742	2765	2	5	7	9	12	14	16	19	21
19	2788	2810	2833	2856	2878	2900	2923	2945	2967	2989	2	4	7	9	11	13	16	18	20
20	3010	3032	3054	3075	3096	3118	3139	3160	3181	3201	2	4	6	8	11	13	15	17	19
21	3222	3243	3263	3284	3304	3324	3345	3365	3385	3404	2	4	6	8	10	12	14	16	18
22	3424	3444	3464	3483	3502	3522	3541	3560	3579	3598	2	4	6	8	10	12	14	15	17
23	3617	3636	3655	3674	3692	3711	3729	3747	3766	3784	2	4	6	7	9	11	13	15	17
24	3802	3820	3838	3856	3874	3892	3909	3927	3945	3962	2	4	5	7	9	11	12	14	16
25	3979	3997	4014	4031	4048	4065	4082	4099	4116	4133	2	3	5	7	9	10	12	14	15
26	4150	4166	4183	4200	4216	4232	4249	4265	4281	4298	2	3	5	7	8	10	11	13	15
27	4314	4330	4346	4362	4378	4393	4409	4425	4440	4456	2	3	5	6	8	9	11	13	14
28	4472	4487	4502	4518	4533	4548	4564	4579	4594	4609	2	3	5	6	8	9	11	12	14
29	4624	4639	4654	4669	4683	4698	4713	4728	4742	4757	1	3	4	6	7	9	10	12	13
30	4771	4786	4800	4814	4829	4843	4857	4871	4886	4900	1	3	4	6	7	9	10	11	13
31	4914	4928	4942	4955	4969	4983	4997	5011	5024	5038	1	3	4	6	7	8	10	11	12
32	5051	5065	5079	5092	5105	5119	5132	5145	5159	5172	1	3	4	5	7	8	9	11	12
33	5185	5198	5211	5224	5237	5250	5263	5276	5289	5302	1	3	4	5	6	8	9	10	12
34	5315	5328	5340	5353	5366	5378	5391	5403	5416	5428	1	3	4	5	6	8	9	10	11
35	5441	5453	5465	5478	5490	5502	5514	5527	5539	5551	1	2	4	5	6	7	9	10	11
36	5563	5575	5587	5599	5611	5623	5635	5647	5658	5670	1	2	4	5	6	7	8	10	11
37	5682	5694	5705	5717	5729	5740	5752	5763	5775	5786	1	2	3	5	6	7	8	9	10
38	5798	5809	5821	5832	5843	5855	5866	5877	5888	5899	1	2	3	5	6	7	8	9	10
39	5911	5922	5933	5944	5955	5966	5977	5988	5999	6010	1	2	3	4	5	7	8	9	10
40	6021	6031	6042	6053	6064	6075	6085	6096	6107	6117	1	2	3	4	5	6	8	9	10
41	6128	6138	6149	6160	6170	6180	6191	6201	6212	6222	1	2	3	4	5	6	7	8	9
42	6232	6243	6253	6263	6274	6284	6294	6304	6314	6325	1	2	3	4	5	6	7	8	9
43	6335	6345	6355	6365	6375	6385	6395	6405	6415	6425	1	2	3	4	5	6	7	8	9
44	6435	6444	6454	6464	6474	6484	6493	6503	6513	6522	1	2	3	4	5	6	7	8	9
45	6532	6542	6551	6561	6571	6580	6590	6599	6609	6618	1	2	3	4	5	6	7	8	9
46	6628	6637	6646	6656	6665	6675	6684	6693	6702	6712	1	2	3	4	5	6	7	7	8
47	6721	6730	6739	6749	6758	6767	6776	6785	6794	6803	1	2	3	4	5	5	6	7	8
48	6812	6821	6830	6839	6848	6857	6866	6875	6884	6893	1	2	3	4	4	5	6	7	8
49	6902	6911	6920	6928	6937	6946	6955	6964	6972	6981	1	2	3	4	4	5	6	7	8
50	6990	6998	7007	7016	7024	7033	7042	7050	7059	7067	1	2	3	3	4	5	6	7	8
51	7076	7084	7093	7101	7110	7118	7126	7135	7143	7152	1	2	3	3	4	5	6	7	8
52	7160	7168	7177	7185	7193	7202	7210	7218	7226	7235	1	2	2	3	4	5	6	7	7
53	7243	7251	7259	7267	7275	7284	7292	7300	7308	7316	1	2	2	3	4	5	6	6	7
54	7324	7332	7340	7348	7356	7364	7372	7380	7388	7396	1	2	2	3	4	5	6	6	7

LOGARITHMS

N	0	1	2	3	4	5	6	7	8	9	Proportional Parts								
											1	**2**	**3**	**4**	**5**	**6**	**7**	**8**	**9**
55	7404	7412	7419	7427	7435	7443	7451	7459	7466	7474	1	2	2	3	4	5	5	6	7
56	7482	7490	7497	7505	7513	7520	7528	7536	7543	7551	1	2	2	3	4	5	5	6	7
57	7559	7566	7574	7582	7589	7597	7604	7612	7619	7627	1	2	2	3	4	5	5	6	7
58	7634	7642	7649	7657	7664	7672	7679	7686	7694	7701	1	1	2	3	4	4	5	6	7
59	7709	7716	7723	7731	7738	7745	7752	7760	7767	7774	1	1	2	3	4	4	5	6	7
60	7782	7789	7796	7803	7810	7818	7825	7832	7839	7846	1	1	2	3	4	4	5	6	6
61	7853	7860	7868	7875	7882	7889	7896	7903	7910	7917	1	1	2	3	4	4	5	6	6
62	7924	7931	7938	7945	7952	7959	7966	7973	7980	7987	1	1	2	3	3	4	5	6	6
63	7993	8000	8007	8014	8021	8028	8035	8041	8048	8055	1	1	2	3	3	4	5	5	6
64	8062	8069	8075	8082	8089	8096	8102	8109	8116	8122	1	1	2	3	3	4	5	5	6
65	8129	8136	8142	8149	8156	8162	8169	8176	8182	8189	1	1	2	3	3	4	5	5	6
66	8195	8202	8209	8215	8222	8228	8235	8241	8248	8254	1	1	2	3	3	4	5	5	6
67	8261	8267	8274	8280	8287	8293	8299	8306	8312	8319	1	1	2	3	3	4	5	5	6
68	8325	8331	8338	8344	8351	8357	8363	8370	8376	8382	1	1	2	3	3	4	4	5	6
69	8388	8395	8401	8407	8414	8420	8426	8432	8439	8445	1	1	2	2	3	4	4	5	6
70	8451	8457	8463	8470	8476	8482	8488	8494	8500	8506	1	1	2	2	3	4	4	5	6
71	8513	8519	8525	8531	8537	8543	8549	8555	8561	8567	1	1	2	2	3	4	4	5	5
72	8573	8579	8585	8591	8597	8603	8609	8615	8621	8627	1	1	2	2	3	4	4	5	5
73	8633	8639	8645	8651	8657	8663	8669	8675	8681	8686	1	1	2	2	3	4	4	5	5
74	8692	8698	8704	8710	8716	8722	8727	8733	8739	8745	1	1	2	2	3	4	4	5	5
75	8751	8756	8762	8768	8774	8779	8785	8791	8797	8802	1	1	2	2	3	3	4	5	5
76	8808	8814	8820	8825	8831	8837	8842	8848	8854	8859	1	1	2	2	3	3	4	5	5
77	8865	8871	8876	8882	8887	8893	8899	8904	8910	8915	1	1	2	2	3	3	4	4	5
78	8921	8927	8932	8938	8943	8949	8954	8960	8965	8971	1	1	2	2	3	3	4	4	5
79	8976	8982	8987	8993	8998	9004	9009	9015	9020	9025	1	1	2	2	3	3	4	4	5
80	9031	9036	9042	9047	9053	9058	9063	9069	9074	9079	1	1	2	2	3	3	4	4	5
81	9085	9090	9096	9101	9106	9112	9117	9122	9128	9133	1	1	2	2	3	3	4	4	5
82	9138	9143	9149	9154	9159	9165	9170	9175	9180	9186	1	1	2	2	3	3	4	4	5
83	9191	9196	9201	9206	9212	9217	9222	9227	9232	9238	1	1	2	2	3	3	4	4	5
84	9243	9248	9253	9258	9263	9269	9274	9279	9284	9289	1	1	2	2	3	3	4	4	5
85	9294	9299	9304	9309	9315	9320	9325	9330	9335	9340	1	1	2	2	3	3	4	4	5
86	9345	9350	9355	9360	9365	9370	9375	9380	9385	9390	1	1	2	2	3	3	4	4	5
87	9395	9400	9405	9410	9415	9420	9425	9430	9435	9440	0	1	1	2	2	3	3	4	4
88	9445	9450	9455	9460	9465	9469	9474	9479	9484	9489	0	1	1	2	2	3	3	4	4
89	9494	9499	9504	9509	9513	9518	9523	9528	9533	9538	0	1	1	2	2	3	3	4	4
90	9542	9547	9552	9557	9562	9566	9571	9576	9581	9586	0	1	1	2	2	3	3	4	4
91	9590	9595	9600	9605	9609	9614	9619	9624	9628	9633	0	1	1	2	2	3	3	4	4
92	9638	9643	9647	9652	9657	9661	9666	9671	9675	9680	0	1	1	2	2	3	3	4	4
93	9685	9689	9694	9699	9703	9708	9713	9717	9722	9727	0	1	1	2	2	3	3	4	4
94	9731	9736	9741	9745	9750	9754	9759	9763	9768	9773	0	1	1	2	2	3	3	4	4
95	9777	9782	9786	9791	9795	9800	9805	9809	9814	9818	0	1	1	2	2	3	3	4	4
96	9823	9827	9832	9836	9841	9845	9850	9854	9859	9863	0	1	1	2	2	3	3	4	4
97	9868	9872	9877	9881	9886	9890	9894	9899	9903	9908	0	1	1	2	2	3	3	4	4
98	9912	9917	9921	9926	9930	9934	9939	9943	9948	9952	0	1	1	2	2	3	3	4	4
99	9956	9961	9965	9969	9974	9978	9983	9987	9991	9996	0	1	1	2	2	3	3	3	4

INTERNATIONAL ATOMIC WEIGHTS

1941

	Symbol	Atomic Number	Atomic Weight		Symbol	Atomic Number	Atomic Weight
Aluminum	Al	13	26.97	Molybdenum	Mo	42	95.95
Antimony	Sb	51	121.76	Neodymium	Nd	60	144.27
Argon	A	18	39.944	Neon	Ne	10	20.183
Arsenic	As	33	74.91	Nickel	Ni	28	58.69
Barium	Ba	56	137.36	Nitrogen	N	7	14.008
Beryllium	Be	4	9.02	Osmium	Os	76	190.2
Bismuth	Bi	83	209.00	Oxygen	O	8	16.0000
Boron	B	5	10.82	Palladium	Pd	46	106.7
Bromine	Br	35	79.916	Phosphorus	P	15	30.98
Cadmium	Cd	48	112.41	Platinum	Pt	78	195.23
Calcium	Ca	20	40.08	Potassium	K	19	39.096
Carbon	C	6	12.010	Praseodymium	Pr	59	140.92
Cerium	Ce	58	140.13	Protactinium	Pa	91	231
Cesium	Cs	55	132.91	Radium	Ra	88	226.05
Chlorine	Cl	17	35.457	Radon	Rn	86	222
Chromium	Cr	24	52.01	Rhenium	Re	75	186.31
Cobalt	Co	27	58.94	Rhodium	Rh	45	102.91
Columbium	Cb	41	92.91	Rubidium	Rb	37	85.48
Copper	Cu	29	63.57	Ruthenium	Ru	44	101.7
Dysprosium	Dy	66	162.46	Samarium	Sm	62	150.43
Erbium	Er	68	167.2	Scandium	Sc	21	45.10
Europium	Eu	63	152.0	Selenium	Se	34	78.96
Fluorine	F	9	19.00	Silicon	Si	14	28.06
Gadolinium	Gd	64	156.9	Silver	Ag	47	107.880
Gallium	Ga	31	69.72	Sodium	Na	11	22.997
Germanium	Ge	32	72.60	Strontium	Sr	38	87.63
Gold	Au	79	197.2	Sulfur	S	16	32.06
Hafnium	Hf	72	178.6	Tantalum	Ta	73	180.88
Helium	He	2	4.003	Tellurium	Te	52	127.61
Holmium	Ho	67	164.94	Terbium	Tb	65	159.2
Hydrogen	H	1	1.0080	Thallium	Tl	81	204.39
Indium	In	49	114.76	Thorium	Th	90	232.12
Iodine	I	53	126.92	Thulium	Tm	69	169.4
Iridium	Ir	77	193.1	Tin	Sn	50	118.70
Iron	Fe	26	55.85	Titanium	Ti	22	47.90
Krypton	Kr	36	83.7	Tungsten	W	74	183.92
Lanthanum	La	57	138.92	Uranium	U	92	238.07
Lead	Pb	82	207.21	Vanadium	V	23	50.95
Lithium	Li	3	6.940	Xenon	Xe	54	131.3
Lutecium	Lu	71	174.99	Ytterbium	Yb	70	173.04
Magnesium	Mg	12	24.32	Yttrium	Y	39	88.92
Manganese	Mn	25	54.93	Zinc	Zn	30	65.38
Mercury	Hg	80	200.61	Zirconium	Zr	40	91.22

SYMBOLS

[A list of symbols used in the text, and the page on which each is introduced or defined.]

A Absolute temperature, 76.
Å Angstrom unit, 190.
[A] Concentration of A, 282.
[A] Original acid concentration in equation for buffer index, 464.
A Atomic weight, 34; constant in various equations; energy of activation, 293.
a Acceleration, 84; activity, 324; area, 78; constant in various equations; ionic diameter, 328; vapor pressure of water, 80.

B Barometric pressure, 80; constant in Arrhenius equation, 292.
[B] Concentration of base in equation for buffer index, 464.
b Constant in various equations.

C Circumference, 132; concentration, 97; number of components, 590.
C_P Molar heat capacity at constant pressure, 91.
C_V Molar heat capacity at constant volume, 91.
c Concentration, 343.

D Deuterium, 36.
D Density of liquid, 130; dielectric constant, 326; diffusion coefficient, 540.
d Deuteron, 61.
d Density, 81; distance, 78.
d_m Average of orthobaric densities, 129.

E Energy content, 621.
$\boldsymbol{E}$ E.m.f. in volts, 370.
$\boldsymbol{E}^\circ$ Standard electrode potential on hydrogen scale, 410.
$\boldsymbol{E}^{\circ\prime} = \boldsymbol{E} + 0.1183 \log m$ Function used to determine $\boldsymbol{E}^\circ$, 426.
$\boldsymbol{E}^\circ_{\text{cal.}}$ Standard potential of calomel half-cell system, 443.
E.U. Entropy unit, 627.
e Base of natural logarithms, 8.

F Drop-weight function, 135; free energy, 628; force, 326; number of degrees of freedom, 590.
$\boldsymbol{F}$ Faraday, 372.
f Force, 84; fugacity, 643.
f° Fugacity in standard state, 643.

g Gravitational attraction, 94.
(g) Gas, 209.

H Heat content, 201.
H_i Molal heat content of ice, 201.
H_w Molal heat content of water, 201.
$[H_3O^+]_i$ Isoelectric hydrogen ion concentration, 361.
H_2Q Hydroquinone, 445.
h Height, 94.

I Current, in amperes, 370; integration constant in free energy equation, 647; intensity of radioactivity, 285.
i Van't Hoff factor, 330.

K Cell constant, 385; equilibrium constant, 645; constant in various equations.
K_a', K_a'', etc. Primary, secondary, etc., acid ionization constants, 341, 345.
K_b', etc. Same for basic ionization constants, 342.
K_b Boiling-point constant, 251.
K_c Concentration equilibrium constant, 299.
K_d Distribution constant, 255.
K_f Freezing-point constant, 251.
K_h Hydrolysis constant, 356.
K_p Pressure equilibrium constant, 299.
K_s Solubility product, 362.
K_w Ion product for water, 349.
k Boltzmann's constant, 86; constant in various other equations.
k_a, k_b Ionization constants of ampholytes on "neutral molecule" theory, 353.
k_0, k_1, etc. Rate constants for reactions of order indicated by subscript, 288 *et seq.*

L_f Molar heat of fusion, 201.
L_s Molar heat of sublimation, 158.
L_v Molar heat of vaporization, 199.
(l) Liquid, 209.
l_f Heat of fusion per gram, 201.
l_s Heat of sublimation per gram.
l_v Heat of vaporization per gram, 200.

M Molarity, 225; molecular weight, 88.
m Mass, 84; molality, 225.

N Normality, 225.
$\mathbf{N}$ Avogadro's number, 27.
n Neutron, 55.
n Number, in various equations.
n_a Transference number of anion, 374.
n_c Transference number of cation, 374.

P Pressure, 11; number of phases, 590.
[P] Parachor, 143.
p Proton, 61.
P_c Critical pressure, 124.
p_A Partial pressure of constituent A, 79.
pH Hydrogen exponent, 351.
$p\mathrm{H}_i$ Isoelectric exponent, 361.
pK_{in} Indicator exponent, 474.
pK_w Ionization exponent of water, 438.
pOH Hydroxyl exponent, 351.

Q Quinone, 445.
Q Quantity of electricity, in coulombs, 370.
q Charge, 326.

R Gas constant, 77; resistance, in ohms, 370.
r Radius, in various equations; rate in various equations.

S Entropy, 625; slope of line, 150; surface area, 554.
(s) Solid, 205.

T Absolute temperature, 75.
T_c Critical temperature, 124.
t Centigrade temperature, 75; thickness of film, 554; time, 9.

u Velocity, 84.

V Volume of gas, 11.
V_c Critical volume, 123.
v Volume of liquid, 227.

w Weight, 134.

x Variable quantity in numerous equations.
x_A Mole fraction of A, 226.

y Variable quantity in numerous equations.

Z Atomic number, 59.
z_i Valence of ith ion, 338.

α Degree of dissociation (ionization), 331.
α_Λ Conductance ratio, 332.
α_v Van't Hoff coefficient, 332.

β Buffer index, 464.

γ Activity coefficient, 334; ratio of heat capacities, 92; surface tension, 132.

ΔE Change in energy content, 622.
ΔF Change in free energy, 629.
ΔF° Standard change in free energy, 303.
ΔH Change in heat content, 201.
ΔH° Standard change in heat content, 302.
ΔH_0 Constant in heat content equation, 647.
ΔS Change in entropy, 625.
ΔS° Standard change in entropy, 649.
ΔT_b Boiling point depression, 253.
ΔT_f Freezing point depression.
$\Delta\Gamma_0$, $\Delta\Gamma_i$, etc. Constants in heat capacity equation, 646.

ϵ Electron, 46.
ϵ^+ Positron, 55.

η Coefficient of viscosity, 145.

θ Angle, 175; characteristic temperature, 163.

κ Specific conductance, 384.

Λ Equivalent conductance of salt, 385.
Λ_c Equivalent conductance of salt at concentration c, 386.
Λ_0 Equivalent conductance of salt at zero concentration, 387.
Λ_ϵ Equivalent conductance of salt corrected for interionic attraction, 393.
λ Wave length, 175.
λ_a Equivalent conductance of anion, 388.
λ_c Equivalent conductance of cation, 388.

μ Joule-Thomson coefficient, 116.

ν Frequency, 59.

π Osmotic pressure, 267; ratio of circumference to diameter of circle, 134.

ρ Specific resistance, 385.

Σ Summation sign, 338.

INDEX

[Names of persons are set in SMALL CAPITALS, and names of publications in *italics*. Page references to definitions, full discussions, and biographical notes are indicated by **boldface** numbers.]

B

C

G

V

W